PEARSON

Linear Algebra and Differential Calculus of Several Variables

Custom Edition for Stanford University

Taken from:
Vector Calculus, Fourth Edition
by Susan Jane Colley

Linear Algebra
by Steven Levandosky

Cover Art: Courtesy of Photodisc/Getty Images.

Taken from:

Vector Calculus, Fourth Edition
by Susan Jane Colley
Copyright © 2012, 2006, 2002 by Pearson Education, Inc.
New York, NY 10013

Linear Algebra
by Steven Levandosky
Copyright © 2002 by Pearson Education, Inc.
New York, NY 10013

This special edition published in cooperation with Pearson Learning Solutions.

All trademarks, service marks, registered trademarks, and registered service marks are the property of their respective owners and are used herein for identification purposes only.

Pearson Learning Solutions, 501 Boylston Street, Suite 900, Boston, MA 02116
A Pearson Education Company
www.pearsoned.com

Printed in the United States of America

3   16

000200010272000847

RD

 ISBN 10: 1-323-28716-7
ISBN 13: 978-1-323-28716-3

Contents

PART 1

LINEAR ALGEBRA

by Steven Levandosky

1 Vectors in $\mathbf{R}^n$

The set of all real numbers is denoted by $\mathbf{R}$. The set of all ordered n-tuples of real numbers is denoted by $\mathbf{R}^n$. That is

$$\mathbf{R}^n = \{(x_1, x_2, \ldots, x_n) \mid x_i \in \mathbf{R} \text{ for } 1 \le i \le n\}.$$

We usually represent $\mathbf{R}$ by points on the number line, $\mathbf{R}^2$ by points in the plane, and $\mathbf{R}^3$ by points in space.

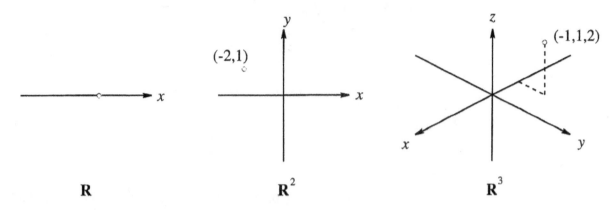

A **vector** in $\mathbf{R}^n$ is an ordered list of n real numbers

$$\mathbf{v} = \begin{bmatrix} v_1 \\ v_2 \\ \vdots \\ v_n \end{bmatrix},$$

where the numbers $v_1, v_2, \ldots, v_n$ are called the **components** of $\mathbf{v}$.

Example 1.1.

$$\mathbf{v} = \begin{bmatrix} 2 \\ -1 \end{bmatrix} \quad \text{and} \quad \mathbf{w} = \begin{bmatrix} 0 \\ 5 \end{bmatrix}$$

are vectors in $\mathbf{R}^2$ and

$$\mathbf{a} = \begin{bmatrix} \pi \\ 16 \\ -8 \\ 1 \end{bmatrix} \quad \text{and} \quad \mathbf{b} = \begin{bmatrix} 0 \\ 0 \\ 0 \\ 0 \end{bmatrix}$$

are vectors in $\mathbf{R}^4$. $\diamondsuit$

The vector in $\mathbf{R}^n$ whose components are all zero is called the **zero vector** and is denoted by $\mathbf{0}$. There are two basic vector operations in $\mathbf{R}^n$, addition and scalar multiplication, both of which are performed *component-wise*. If $\mathbf{v}$ and $\mathbf{w}$ are vectors in $\mathbf{R}^n$ and c is a scalar (a real number), we define the sum of $\mathbf{v}$ and $\mathbf{w}$ by

$$\mathbf{v} + \mathbf{w} = \begin{bmatrix} v_1 \\ v_2 \\ \vdots \\ v_n \end{bmatrix} + \begin{bmatrix} w_1 \\ w_2 \\ \vdots \\ w_n \end{bmatrix} = \begin{bmatrix} v_1 + w_1 \\ v_2 + w_2 \\ \vdots \\ v_n + w_n \end{bmatrix},$$

and the scalar multiple c of $\mathbf{v}$ by

$$c\mathbf{v} = c \begin{bmatrix} v_1 \\ v_2 \\ \vdots \\ v_n \end{bmatrix} = \begin{bmatrix} cv_1 \\ cv_2 \\ \vdots \\ cv_n \end{bmatrix}.$$

Example 1.2.

$$2 \begin{bmatrix} 3 \\ 2 \\ -1 \end{bmatrix} + 3 \begin{bmatrix} 2 \\ 0 \\ 4 \end{bmatrix} = \begin{bmatrix} 6 \\ 4 \\ -2 \end{bmatrix} + \begin{bmatrix} 6 \\ 0 \\ 12 \end{bmatrix} = \begin{bmatrix} 12 \\ 4 \\ 10 \end{bmatrix}$$

$\diamond$

We denote by $-\mathbf{v}$ the vector $(-1)\mathbf{v}$. The following properties of addition and scalar multiplication follow from the analogous properties of real numbers and are left as exercises.

Proposition 1.1. Let $\mathbf{u}$, $\mathbf{v}$ and $\mathbf{w}$ be vectors in $\mathbf{R}^n$ and let c and d be real numbers. Then

1. $\mathbf{u} + \mathbf{v} = \mathbf{v} + \mathbf{u}$
2. $\mathbf{u} + (\mathbf{v} + \mathbf{w}) = (\mathbf{u} + \mathbf{v}) + \mathbf{w}$
3. $\mathbf{v} + \mathbf{0} = \mathbf{v}$
4. $\mathbf{v} + (-\mathbf{v}) = \mathbf{0}$
5. $c(d\mathbf{v}) = (cd)\mathbf{v}$
6. $(c + d)\mathbf{v} = c\mathbf{v} + d\mathbf{v}$
7. $c(\mathbf{v} + \mathbf{w}) = c\mathbf{v} + c\mathbf{w}$
8. $1\mathbf{v} = \mathbf{v}$.

We represent vectors in $\mathbf{R}^2$ graphically by directed line segments. A nonzero vector

$$\mathbf{v} = \begin{bmatrix} v_1 \\ v_2 \end{bmatrix}$$

can be represented by a line segment starting at any point (x_1, x_2) in the plane and ending at the point $(x_1 + v_1, x_2 + v_2)$. The starting point is called the tail of $\mathbf{v}$ and the ending point is called the head of $\mathbf{v}$ and is denoted by an arrow.

Example 1.3. The vectors

$$\mathbf{u} = \begin{bmatrix} 1 \\ 2 \end{bmatrix} \qquad \mathbf{v} = \begin{bmatrix} 1 \\ -2 \end{bmatrix}$$

are shown below.

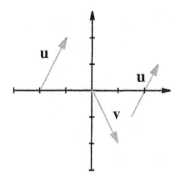

The vector **u** is shown in two different positions. A vector whose tail is at the origin is said to be in **standard position**. The vector **v** is shown in standard position. Notice that the point at the head of **v** is $(1, -2)$, whose coordinates are just the components of **v**. For this reason, it is common to identify a vector in standard position with the point at the head of the vector.   ◇

Multiplication of a vector by a scalar $c \neq 1$ either lengthens or shortens the vector, and if the scalar is negative the direction of the vector is reversed.

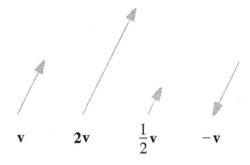

The sum of two vectors is represented geometrically by placing the vectors head to tail. The sum is the vector from the tail of the first vector to the head of the second vector.

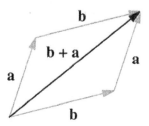

When the tails of **a** and **b** are at the same point, the difference vector **b** − **a** is represented by the vector whose tail is at the head of **a** and whose head is at the head of **b**. This is because **b** − **a** is the vector that, when added to **a**, equals **b**. Equivalently, **b** − **a** is the sum of **b** and −**a**.

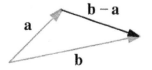   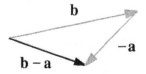

Vectors in $\mathbf{R}^3$ are also represented by directed line segments.

Example 1.4. The vector

$$\mathbf{v} = \begin{bmatrix} 2 \\ -1 \\ 3 \end{bmatrix}$$

is represented below in standard position.

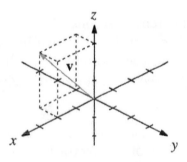

$\diamond$

Exercises

1.1. Compute the following.

(a) $2 \begin{bmatrix} 1 \\ 2 \end{bmatrix} - \begin{bmatrix} 3 \\ 1 \end{bmatrix}$

(b) $2 \left(\begin{bmatrix} 1 \\ 2 \end{bmatrix} - \begin{bmatrix} 3 \\ 1 \end{bmatrix} \right)$

1.2. Compute the following.

(a) $\begin{bmatrix} 1 \\ 3 \\ 2 \end{bmatrix} - 2 \begin{bmatrix} -1 \\ 1 \\ 1 \end{bmatrix}$

(b) $3 \begin{bmatrix} 4 \\ 0 \\ -1 \end{bmatrix} + 2 \begin{bmatrix} 0 \\ 1 \\ 4 \end{bmatrix} - 3 \begin{bmatrix} 1 \\ 1 \\ 0 \end{bmatrix}$

1.3. Let

$$\mathbf{v} = \begin{bmatrix} 3 \\ -2 \\ 3 \end{bmatrix} \qquad \mathbf{w} = \begin{bmatrix} 2 \\ 1 \\ -1 \end{bmatrix} \qquad \mathbf{x} = \begin{bmatrix} 1 \\ 4 \\ -5 \end{bmatrix}$$

Compute the following.

(a) $\mathbf{v} - 2\mathbf{w} + \mathbf{x}$

(b) $\mathbf{v} + \mathbf{w} + \mathbf{x}$

1.4. Let

$$\mathbf{a} = \begin{bmatrix} 1 \\ 2 \\ 3 \\ 4 \end{bmatrix} \qquad \mathbf{b} = \begin{bmatrix} 2 \\ 0 \\ 4 \\ 2 \end{bmatrix} \qquad \mathbf{c} = \begin{bmatrix} -1 \\ 3 \\ -2 \\ 4 \end{bmatrix}$$

Compute the following.

(a) $2\mathbf{a} + \mathbf{b} + \mathbf{c}$

(b) $2(\mathbf{a} + \mathbf{b}) - 3\mathbf{c}$

1.5. Sketch the following vectors in standard position.

(a) $\begin{bmatrix} 3 \\ 1 \end{bmatrix}$ (b) $\begin{bmatrix} -3 \\ -1 \end{bmatrix}$ (c) $\begin{bmatrix} -1 \\ 3 \end{bmatrix}$ (d) $\begin{bmatrix} 2 \\ 0 \end{bmatrix}$

1.6. Sketch the following vectors in standard position.

(a) $\begin{bmatrix} 2 \\ 1 \end{bmatrix}$ (b) $\begin{bmatrix} -2 \\ 1 \end{bmatrix}$ (c) $\begin{bmatrix} 0 \\ 0 \end{bmatrix}$ (d) $\begin{bmatrix} 0 \\ -2 \end{bmatrix}$

1.7. Let

$$\mathbf{a} = \begin{bmatrix} 2 \\ 1 \\ 1 \end{bmatrix} \qquad \mathbf{b} = \begin{bmatrix} 1 \\ -2 \\ 0 \end{bmatrix} \qquad \mathbf{c} = \begin{bmatrix} 4 \\ 2 \\ -2 \end{bmatrix} \qquad \mathbf{x} = \begin{bmatrix} 2 \\ 3 \end{bmatrix} \qquad \mathbf{y} = \begin{bmatrix} -3 \\ 2 \end{bmatrix}$$

Calculate the following.

(a) $\mathbf{a} + 2\mathbf{b} - \mathbf{c}$ (b) $\mathbf{a} + 2(\mathbf{b} - \mathbf{c})$ (c) $2\mathbf{x} - 3\mathbf{y}$ (d) $3\mathbf{x} + 2\mathbf{y}$

1.8. Consider the vectors shown below.

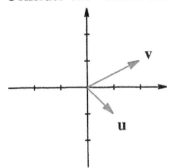

Sketch the following vectors in standard position.

(a) $-2\mathbf{u} + \mathbf{v}$

(b) $3\mathbf{u} + 2\mathbf{v}$

(c) $\mathbf{v} - \mathbf{u}$

(d) $\mathbf{u} - \mathbf{v}$.

1.9. Consider the vectors shown below.

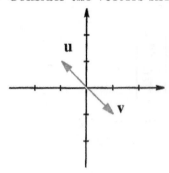

Sketch the following vectors in standard position.

(a) $-2\mathbf{u} + \mathbf{v}$

(b) $3\mathbf{u} + 2\mathbf{v}$

(c) $\mathbf{v} - \mathbf{u}$

(d) $\mathbf{u} - \mathbf{v}$.

1.10. Verify Properties 1-4 of Proposition 1.1.

1.11. Verify Properties 5-8 of Proposition 1.1.

2 Linear Combinations and Spans

Using the operations of addition and scalar multiplication, we can combine vectors to form new vectors. A **linear combination** of a set of vectors $\{\mathbf{v}_1, \mathbf{v}_2, \dots, \mathbf{v}_k\}$ in $\mathbf{R}^n$ is a vector of the form

$$\mathbf{v} = c_1\mathbf{v}_1 + c_2\mathbf{v}_2 + \cdots + c_k\mathbf{v}_k$$

where the coefficients $c_1, \cdots, c_k$ are real numbers. Any or all of the coefficients could be zero.

Example 2.1. Let

$$\mathbf{v}_1 = \begin{bmatrix} 1 \\ 2 \\ 3 \end{bmatrix} \quad \text{and} \quad \mathbf{v}_2 = \begin{bmatrix} 2 \\ 0 \\ -1 \end{bmatrix}$$

Then

$$2\mathbf{v}_1 + 3\mathbf{v}_2 = \begin{bmatrix} 8 \\ 4 \\ 3 \end{bmatrix}$$

is a linear combination of $\mathbf{v}_1$ and $\mathbf{v}_2$. Both $\mathbf{v}_1$ and $\mathbf{v}_2$ are linear combinations of $\mathbf{v}_1$ and $\mathbf{v}_2$ since

$$\mathbf{v}_1 = 1\mathbf{v}_1 + 0\mathbf{v}_2$$
$$\mathbf{v}_2 = 0\mathbf{v}_1 + 1\mathbf{v}_2.$$

The zero vector in $\mathbf{R}^3$ is also a linear combination of $\mathbf{v}_1$ and $\mathbf{v}_2$ since $\mathbf{0} = 0\mathbf{v}_1 + 0\mathbf{v}_2$. $\diamond$

The **span** of a nonempty set of vectors is the set of all linear combinations of those vectors. That is,

$$\text{span}(\mathbf{v}_1, \mathbf{v}_2, \dots, \mathbf{v}_k) = \{c_1\mathbf{v}_1 + c_2\mathbf{v}_2 + \cdots + c_k\mathbf{v}_k \mid c_i \in \mathbf{R} \text{ for } 1 \leq i \leq k\}.$$

Example 2.2. Since $c\mathbf{0} = \mathbf{0}$ for any $c \in \mathbf{R}$, the span of the zero vector is itself. That is,

$$\text{span}(\mathbf{0}) = \{\mathbf{0}\}.$$

$\diamond$

Example 2.3. Let

$$\mathbf{v} = \begin{bmatrix} 1 \\ 2 \end{bmatrix}.$$

Then $\text{span}(\mathbf{v}) = \{c\mathbf{v} \mid c \in \mathbf{R}\}$ is the set of all scalar multiples of $\mathbf{v}$. When all of these vectors are placed in standard position, this set is represented by the line shown below.

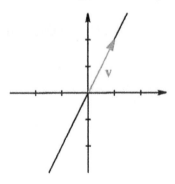

$\diamond$

The span of any nonzero vector is represented by a line passing through the origin, and conversely, any line which passes through the origin represents the span of some nonzero vector. By adding a fixed vector $\mathbf{x}_0$ to each vector in the span of some nonzero vector $\mathbf{v}$, we obtain the set $\{\mathbf{x}_0 + c\mathbf{v} \mid c \in \mathbf{R}\}$. When all of these vectors are placed in standard position, their heads represent points on the line which passes through $\mathbf{x}_0$ and is parallel to the line spanned by the vector $\mathbf{v}$.

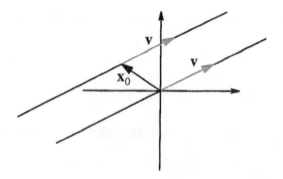

Thus we say that the set

$$L = \{\mathbf{x}_0 + t\mathbf{v} \mid t \in \mathbf{R}\}$$

is a **parametric** representation of the line in $\mathbf{R}^n$ which passes through $\mathbf{x}_0$ with direction $\mathbf{v}$. The variable t is called the **parameter**. Any given line may be parametrized in many ways. The point $\mathbf{x}_0$ can be any point on the line, and the direction vector $\mathbf{v}$ can be any nonzero vector whose head and tail are points in the line.

Example 2.4. Find a parametric representation of the line in $\mathbf{R}^3$ which passes through the points $(1, 1, 1)$ and $(2, -3, 6)$.
Solution. We may let

$$\mathbf{x}_0 = \begin{bmatrix} 1 \\ 1 \\ 1 \end{bmatrix}.$$

To obtain the direction of the line, we subtract the coordinates of the two points. So

$$\mathbf{v} = \begin{bmatrix} 2 \\ -3 \\ 6 \end{bmatrix} - \begin{bmatrix} 1 \\ 1 \\ 1 \end{bmatrix} = \begin{bmatrix} 1 \\ -4 \\ 5 \end{bmatrix}$$

and the line is given by

$$\left\{ \begin{bmatrix} 1 \\ 1 \\ 1 \end{bmatrix} + t \begin{bmatrix} 1 \\ -4 \\ 5 \end{bmatrix} \,\middle|\, t \in \mathbf{R} \right\}.$$

The components x, y and z of a point $\mathbf{x}$ on the line satisfy

$$x = 1 + t$$
$$y = 1 - 4t$$
$$z = 1 + 5t.$$

Each choice of t determines a point (x, y, z) on the line. $\diamond$

A **line segment** may be described by restricting the values of the parameter t in the parametric representation of the line containing the segment. The line segment which passes through the points $\mathbf{x}_0$ and $\mathbf{x}_1$ is contained in the line $\{\mathbf{x}_0 + t(\mathbf{x}_1 - \mathbf{x}_0) \mid t \in \mathbf{R}\}$. This parametrization yields $\mathbf{x}_0$ when $t = 0$, and $\mathbf{x}_1$ when $t = 1$. Thus the line segment between $\mathbf{x}_0$ and $\mathbf{x}_1$ is given by

$$S = \{\mathbf{x}_0 + t(\mathbf{x}_1 - \mathbf{x}_0) \mid 0 \le t \le 1\} = \{(1-t)\mathbf{x}_0 + t\mathbf{x}_1 \mid 0 \le t \le 1\}.$$

Next we consider the span of sets consisting of two vectors.

Example 2.5. Let

$$\mathbf{v}_1 = \begin{bmatrix} 1 \\ 2 \end{bmatrix} \quad \text{and} \quad \mathbf{v}_2 = \begin{bmatrix} 2 \\ 1 \end{bmatrix}.$$

Then $\operatorname{span}(\mathbf{v}_1, \mathbf{v}_2) = \{c_1\mathbf{v}_1 + c_2\mathbf{v}_2 \mid c_1, c_2 \in \mathbf{R}\}$. It turns out that $\operatorname{span}(\mathbf{v}_1, \mathbf{v}_2) = \mathbf{R}^2$. That is, *every* vector $\mathbf{x}$ in $\mathbf{R}^2$ can be expressed as a linear combination of $\mathbf{v}_1$ and $\mathbf{v}_2$. We will justify this assertion in two ways.

Geometrically. Consider some particular values of c_1 and c_2. First, fix $c_2 = 0$ and let c_1 vary over all of $\mathbf{R}$ to see that $\operatorname{span}(\mathbf{v}_1, \mathbf{v}_2)$ contains the line spanned by $\mathbf{v}_1$. Next fix $c_2 = 1$ and let c_1 vary over $\mathbf{R}$ to see that $\operatorname{span}(\mathbf{v}_1, \mathbf{v}_2)$ contains the line which passes through the head of $\mathbf{v}_2$ and is parallel to the line spanned by $\mathbf{v}_1$. By continuing to fix c_2 and let c_1 vary over $\mathbf{R}$ we see that $\operatorname{span}(\mathbf{v}_1, \mathbf{v}_2)$ contains every line which passes through the line spanned by $\mathbf{v}_2$ and is parallel to the line spanned by $\mathbf{v}_1$.

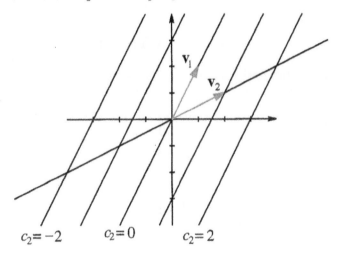

The union of all these lines is all of $\mathbf{R}^2$, so $\operatorname{span}(\mathbf{v}_1, \mathbf{v}_2) = \mathbf{R}^2$.

Algebraically. Consider an arbitrary vector

$$\mathbf{x} = \begin{bmatrix} x_1 \\ x_2 \end{bmatrix}$$

in $\mathbf{R}^2$. We want to find scalars c_1 and c_2 such that $\mathbf{x} = c_1\mathbf{v}_1 + c_2\mathbf{v}_2$. That is,

$$\begin{bmatrix} x_1 \\ x_2 \end{bmatrix} = c_1 \begin{bmatrix} 1 \\ 2 \end{bmatrix} + c_2 \begin{bmatrix} 2 \\ 1 \end{bmatrix} = \begin{bmatrix} c_1 + 2c_2 \\ 2c_1 + c_2 \end{bmatrix}.$$

11

Equating the components of these vectors, we get

$$\begin{aligned} c_1 + 2c_2 &= x_1 \\ 2c_1 + c_2 &= x_2, \end{aligned}$$

a system of two linear equations in the two unknowns c_1 and c_2. Such a system can be solved easily. If we subtract twice the first equation from the second equation, we get

$$\begin{aligned} c_1 + 2c_2 &= x_1 \\ -3c_2 &= x_2 - 2x_1. \end{aligned}$$

Solving the second equation for c_2 gives $c_2 = \frac{2}{3}x_1 - \frac{1}{3}x_2$. Substituting this into the first equation gives $c_1 = -\frac{1}{3}x_1 + \frac{2}{3}x_2$, and thus

$$\mathbf{x} = \left(-\frac{1}{3}x_1 + \frac{2}{3}x_2\right)\mathbf{v}_1 + \left(\frac{2}{3}x_1 - \frac{1}{3}x_2\right)\mathbf{v}_2.$$

This final expression gives an explicit formula for $\mathbf{x}$ as a linear combination of $\mathbf{v}_1$ and $\mathbf{v}_2$, so $\text{span}(\mathbf{v}_1, \mathbf{v}_2) = \mathbf{R}^2$. ◇

Example 2.6. Let

$$\mathbf{v}_1 = \begin{bmatrix} 2 \\ 1 \end{bmatrix} \quad \text{and} \quad \mathbf{v}_2 = \begin{bmatrix} -4 \\ -2 \end{bmatrix},$$

and notice that $\mathbf{v}_2 = -2\mathbf{v}_1$. Thus

$$\text{span}(\mathbf{v}_1, \mathbf{v}_2) = \{c_1\mathbf{v}_1 + c_2\mathbf{v}_2 \mid c_1, c_2 \in \mathbf{R}\} = \{(c_1 - 2c_2)\mathbf{v}_1 \mid c_1, c_2 \in \mathbf{R}\}.$$

This set consists of all scalar multiples of $\mathbf{v}_1$ and is therefore a line, not all of $\mathbf{R}^2$.

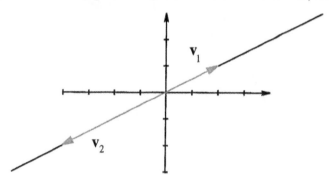

The fact that $\mathbf{v}_2$ is a scalar multiple of $\mathbf{v}_1$ means that $\mathbf{v}_2$ is in $\text{span}(\mathbf{v}_1)$. In this sense, $\mathbf{v}_2$ is *redundant*, since adding multiples of $\mathbf{v}_2$ does not contribute anything new to the span. We could likewise regard $\mathbf{v}_1$ as redundant, since multiples of $\mathbf{v}_2$ alone are also sufficient to span the line. Thus, in this case $\text{span}(\mathbf{v}_1, \mathbf{v}_2) = \text{span}(\mathbf{v}_1) = \text{span}(\mathbf{v}_2)$. ◇

Two nonzero vectors are called **collinear** if one vector is a scalar multiple of the other. Notice that, if this is the case, then actually both vectors are scalar multiples of each other. For if $\mathbf{v} = c\mathbf{w}$, then the scalar c must be nonzero, so $\mathbf{w} = \frac{1}{c}\mathbf{v}$. It follows as in Example 2.6 that the span of any two collinear vectors is a line.

Example 2.7. Let

$$\mathbf{v}_1 = \begin{bmatrix} 1 \\ 2 \\ -1 \end{bmatrix} \qquad \text{and} \qquad \mathbf{v}_2 = \begin{bmatrix} 0 \\ 2 \\ 1 \end{bmatrix}.$$

Then

$$\operatorname{span}(\mathbf{v}_1, \mathbf{v}_2) = \{c_1\mathbf{v}_1 + c_2\mathbf{v}_2 \mid c_1, c_2 \in \mathbf{R}\}.$$

As in Example 2.5, $\operatorname{span}(\mathbf{v}_1, \mathbf{v}_2)$ contains every line which passes through $\operatorname{span}(\mathbf{v}_2)$ and is parallel to $\operatorname{span}(\mathbf{v}_1)$.

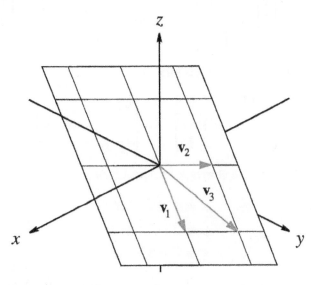

The union of all such lines forms a plane in $\mathbf{R}^3$ which passes through the origin and contains both $\mathbf{v}_1$ and $\mathbf{v}_2$. $\diamond$

Generally, the span of any two nonzero, non-collinear vectors $\mathbf{v}_1$ and $\mathbf{v}_2$ in $\mathbf{R}^n$ ($n \geq 2$) is a plane which passes through the origin and contains the two spanning vectors. As we did with lines, we can represent arbitrary planes in $\mathbf{R}^n$ by adding a fixed vector $\mathbf{x}_0$ to vectors in this span. Thus we say that the set

$$P = \{\mathbf{x}_0 + s\mathbf{v}_1 + t\mathbf{v}_2 \mid s, t \in \mathbf{R}\}$$

is a parametric representation of the plane in $\mathbf{R}^n$ which passes through $\mathbf{x}_0$ and is parallel to $\operatorname{span}(\mathbf{v}_1, \mathbf{v}_2)$. The variables s and t are the parameters.

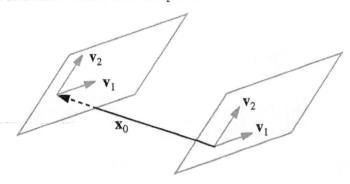

13

Example 2.8. Find a parametrization of the plane in $\mathbf{R}^3$ which contains the points $(1, 2, 3)$, $(2, -5, 4)$ and $(6, 4, 7)$.

Solution. We can first let

$$\mathbf{x}_0 = \begin{bmatrix} 1 \\ 2 \\ 3 \end{bmatrix}.$$

To obtain two direction vectors, we may use the vectors whose tails are at $(1, 2, 3)$ and whose heads are at $(2, -5, 4)$ and $(6, 4, 7)$ to get

$$\mathbf{v}_1 = \begin{bmatrix} 2 \\ -5 \\ 4 \end{bmatrix} - \begin{bmatrix} 1 \\ 2 \\ 3 \end{bmatrix} = \begin{bmatrix} 1 \\ -7 \\ 1 \end{bmatrix} \quad \text{and} \quad \mathbf{v}_2 = \begin{bmatrix} 6 \\ 4 \\ 7 \end{bmatrix} - \begin{bmatrix} 1 \\ 2 \\ 3 \end{bmatrix} = \begin{bmatrix} 5 \\ 2 \\ 4 \end{bmatrix}.$$

Thus the plane can be written parametrically as

$$\left\{ \begin{bmatrix} 1 \\ 2 \\ 3 \end{bmatrix} + s \begin{bmatrix} 1 \\ -7 \\ 1 \end{bmatrix} + t \begin{bmatrix} 5 \\ 2 \\ 4 \end{bmatrix} \;\middle|\; s, t \in \mathbf{R} \right\}$$

or in terms of the components of a point $\mathbf{x}$ in the plane,

$$x = 1 + s + 5t$$
$$y = 2 - 7s + 2t$$
$$z = 3 + s + 4t.$$

Each choice of the parameters s and t determines a point (x, y, z) on the plane. $\diamond$

Now we consider spans of three vectors.

Example 2.9. The vectors

$$\mathbf{e}_1 = \begin{bmatrix} 1 \\ 0 \\ 0 \end{bmatrix}, \qquad \mathbf{e}_2 = \begin{bmatrix} 0 \\ 1 \\ 0 \end{bmatrix}, \qquad \text{and} \qquad \mathbf{e}_3 = \begin{bmatrix} 0 \\ 0 \\ 1 \end{bmatrix}$$

span all of $\mathbf{R}^3$. To see this, let

$$\mathbf{v} = \begin{bmatrix} v_1 \\ v_2 \\ v_3 \end{bmatrix}$$

be an arbitrary vector in $\mathbf{R}^3$. Then

$$\mathbf{v} = v_1 \begin{bmatrix} 1 \\ 0 \\ 0 \end{bmatrix} + v_2 \begin{bmatrix} 0 \\ 1 \\ 0 \end{bmatrix} + v_3 \begin{bmatrix} 0 \\ 0 \\ 1 \end{bmatrix} = v_1 \mathbf{e}_1 + v_2 \mathbf{e}_2 + v_3 \mathbf{e}_3,$$

so $\mathbf{v}$ is a linear combination of $\mathbf{e}_1$, $\mathbf{e}_2$ and $\mathbf{e}_3$. Hence $\operatorname{span}(\mathbf{e}_1, \mathbf{e}_2, \mathbf{e}_3) = \mathbf{R}^3$. $\diamond$

Remark 2.1. The previous example can be extended naturally to $\mathbf{R}^n$ if we define $\mathbf{e}_j$ to be the vector in $\mathbf{R}^n$ whose components are all zero except for the jth component, which equals one. Then by the same reasoning as above it follows that $\mathbf{R}^n = \text{span}(\mathbf{e}_1, \mathbf{e}_2, \dots, \mathbf{e}_n)$. In $\mathbf{R}^3$, the vectors $\mathbf{e}_1$, $\mathbf{e}_2$ and $\mathbf{e}_3$ are often denoted $\mathbf{i}$, $\mathbf{j}$ and $\mathbf{k}$, respectively, and vectors in $\mathbf{R}^3$ are commonly written as linear combinations of $\mathbf{i}$, $\mathbf{j}$ and $\mathbf{k}$. For instance, the vector

$$\begin{bmatrix} 2 \\ -4 \\ 7 \end{bmatrix}$$

is written $2\mathbf{i} - 4\mathbf{j} + 7\mathbf{k}$.

The next example shows that not every set of three vectors in $\mathbf{R}^3$ spans all of $\mathbf{R}^3$.

Example 2.10. Let

$$\mathbf{v}_1 = \begin{bmatrix} 1 \\ 2 \\ -1 \end{bmatrix}, \qquad \mathbf{v}_2 = \begin{bmatrix} 0 \\ 2 \\ 1 \end{bmatrix}, \qquad \text{and} \qquad \mathbf{v}_3 = \begin{bmatrix} 1 \\ 4 \\ 0 \end{bmatrix}.$$

Notice that $\mathbf{v}_3 = \mathbf{v}_1 + \mathbf{v}_2$. Therefore

$$\begin{aligned}
\text{span}(\mathbf{v}_1, \mathbf{v}_2, \mathbf{v}_3) &= \{ c_1\mathbf{v}_1 + c_2\mathbf{v}_2 + c_3\mathbf{v}_3 \mid c_1, c_2, c_3 \in \mathbf{R} \} \\
&= \{ c_1\mathbf{v}_1 + c_2\mathbf{v}_2 + c_3(\mathbf{v}_1 + \mathbf{v}_2) \mid c_1, c_2, c_3 \in \mathbf{R} \} \\
&= \{ (c_1 + c_3)\mathbf{v}_1 + (c_2 + c_3)\mathbf{v}_2 \mid c_1, c_2, c_3 \in \mathbf{R} \} \\
&= \text{span}(\mathbf{v}_1, \mathbf{v}_2).
\end{aligned}$$

That is, since $\mathbf{v}_3$ is in the plane spanned by $\mathbf{v}_1$ and $\mathbf{v}_2$, adding multiples of $\mathbf{v}_3$ does not contribute anything new to the span, so $\text{span}(\mathbf{v}_1, \mathbf{v}_2, \mathbf{v}_3)$ is the same plane as in Example 2.7. For this reason we can regard $\mathbf{v}_3$ as redundant in the same sense that $\mathbf{v}_2$ was redundant in Example 2.6. Notice also that $\text{span}(\mathbf{v}_1, \mathbf{v}_2, \mathbf{v}_3) = \text{span}(\mathbf{v}_1, \mathbf{v}_3) = \text{span}(\mathbf{v}_2, \mathbf{v}_3)$. (Why?) $\diamond$

Exercises

2.1. Let

$$\mathbf{v} = \begin{bmatrix} 1 \\ 2 \end{bmatrix} \qquad \text{and} \qquad \mathbf{w} = \begin{bmatrix} 2 \\ 1 \end{bmatrix}.$$

(a) Write $\begin{bmatrix} 1 \\ 0 \end{bmatrix}$ as a linear combination of $\mathbf{v}$ and $\mathbf{w}$.

(b) Write $\begin{bmatrix} 0 \\ 1 \end{bmatrix}$ as a linear combination of $\mathbf{v}$ and $\mathbf{w}$.

(c) Write $\mathbf{x} = \begin{bmatrix} x_1 \\ x_2 \end{bmatrix}$ as a linear combination of $\begin{bmatrix} 1 \\ 0 \end{bmatrix}$ and $\begin{bmatrix} 0 \\ 1 \end{bmatrix}$.

(d) Write $\mathbf{x} = \begin{bmatrix} x_1 \\ x_2 \end{bmatrix}$ as a linear combination of $\mathbf{v}$ and $\mathbf{w}$.

2.2. Let

$$\mathbf{v} = \begin{bmatrix} 2 \\ 0 \\ 1 \end{bmatrix} \qquad \mathbf{w} = \begin{bmatrix} -1 \\ 2 \\ -2 \end{bmatrix}.$$

For each of the following vectors, either express it as a linear combination of $\mathbf{v}$ and $\mathbf{w}$, or explain why it is not a linear combination of $\mathbf{v}$ and $\mathbf{w}$.

(a) $\begin{bmatrix} 1 \\ 2 \\ 1 \end{bmatrix}$ (b) $\begin{bmatrix} 1 \\ 2 \\ -1 \end{bmatrix}$ (c) $\begin{bmatrix} 1 \\ 0 \\ 0 \end{bmatrix}$ (d) $\begin{bmatrix} 0 \\ 0 \\ 0 \end{bmatrix}$

For each set of vectors in Exercises 3 through 10 determine whether its span is a line, a plane or all of $\mathbf{R}^3$.

2.3. $\left\{ \begin{bmatrix} 2 \\ 1 \\ 1 \end{bmatrix}, \begin{bmatrix} 5 \\ 8 \\ 0 \end{bmatrix}, \begin{bmatrix} 1 \\ 6 \\ -2 \end{bmatrix} \right\}$

2.4. $\left\{ \begin{bmatrix} 2 \\ 1 \\ 1 \end{bmatrix}, \begin{bmatrix} 5 \\ 8 \\ 0 \end{bmatrix}, \begin{bmatrix} 2 \\ 6 \\ -2 \end{bmatrix} \right\}$

2.5. $\left\{ \begin{bmatrix} 1 \\ 0 \\ 1 \end{bmatrix}, \begin{bmatrix} 0 \\ 8 \\ 0 \end{bmatrix}, \begin{bmatrix} 2 \\ 2 \\ 2 \end{bmatrix} \right\}$

2.6. $\left\{ \begin{bmatrix} 1 \\ 2 \\ 3 \end{bmatrix}, \begin{bmatrix} 4 \\ 8 \\ 12 \end{bmatrix} \right\}$

2.7. $\left\{ \begin{bmatrix} 2 \\ 0 \\ 1 \end{bmatrix}, \begin{bmatrix} 6 \\ 3 \\ -3 \end{bmatrix}, \begin{bmatrix} 2 \\ 3 \\ -5 \end{bmatrix} \right\}$

2.8. $\left\{ \begin{bmatrix} 1 \\ 3 \\ -1 \end{bmatrix}, \begin{bmatrix} 2 \\ 6 \\ 2 \end{bmatrix} \right\}$

2.9. $\left\{ \begin{bmatrix} -2 \\ 3 \\ 1 \end{bmatrix}, \begin{bmatrix} 6 \\ -9 \\ -3 \end{bmatrix}, \begin{bmatrix} -4 \\ 6 \\ 2 \end{bmatrix} \right\}$

2.10. $\left\{ \begin{bmatrix} 1 \\ 2 \\ -3 \end{bmatrix}, \begin{bmatrix} 0 \\ 1 \\ 4 \end{bmatrix}, \begin{bmatrix} 0 \\ 0 \\ 1 \end{bmatrix} \right\}$

In Exercises 11 through 14 find a parametric representation of the line containing the given points.

2.11. $(3, 1)$ and $(2, -3)$

2.12. $(-4, 5)$ and $(0, 2)$

2.13. $(1, 2, 3)$ and $(-2, 1, 2)$

2.14. $(0, 4, 1)$ and $(2, -2, 4)$

In Exercises 15 and 16 find a parametric representation of the plane containing the given points.

2.15. $(1, 2, 3)$, $(2, 3, 4)$ and $(2, 1, 5)$

2.16. $(1, 1, 1)$, $(2, -3, 1)$ and $(4, 5, 2)$

2.17. Find a parametric form of the "hyperplane" in $\mathbf{R}^4$ which contains the points $(2, 3, 4, 5)$, $(1, 1, 1, 1)$, $(0, 1, 0, 1)$ and $(-1, -2, 3, 1)$. Hint: There are three direction vectors.

3   Linear Independence

We now give a precise meaning to the concept of redundancy of vectors illustrated in Examples 2.6 and 2.10. A set of vectors $\{\mathbf{v}_1, \mathbf{v}_2, \ldots, \mathbf{v}_k\}$ is called **linearly dependent** if at least one of the vectors is a linear combination of the others. Otherwise the set is called **linearly independent**. This definition applies to sets of two or more vectors. We say that a set consisting of a single vector $\mathbf{v}$ is linearly independent if $\mathbf{v} \neq \mathbf{0}$ and linearly dependent if $\mathbf{v} = \mathbf{0}$. For sets consisting of two vectors linear dependence simply means that one vector is a scalar multiple of the other. Any two nonzero, non-collinear vectors are linearly independent.

Example 3.1. In the figures below, $\mathbf{v}$ and $\mathbf{w}$ are linearly dependent, while $\mathbf{x}$ and $\mathbf{y}$ are linearly independent.

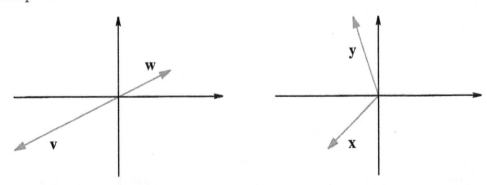

$\diamond$

Example 3.2. Let

$$\mathbf{u} = \begin{bmatrix} 1 \\ 2 \end{bmatrix}, \qquad \mathbf{v} = \begin{bmatrix} 3 \\ 2 \end{bmatrix}, \qquad \text{and} \qquad \mathbf{w} = \begin{bmatrix} 3 \\ -2 \end{bmatrix}.$$

The sets $\{\mathbf{u}, \mathbf{v}\}$, $\{\mathbf{u}, \mathbf{w}\}$ and $\{\mathbf{v}, \mathbf{w}\}$ are each linearly independent since no two of the vectors are collinear. The set $\{\mathbf{u}, \mathbf{v}, \mathbf{w}\}$, however, is linearly dependent since $\mathbf{w} = 2\mathbf{v} - 3\mathbf{u}$. We will see later that any set of three or more vectors in $\mathbf{R}^2$ is linearly dependent. $\diamond$

Note that the linear dependence in Example 3.2 is not entirely the fault of $\mathbf{w}$. We could also observe that $\mathbf{v} = \frac{1}{2}\mathbf{w} + \frac{3}{2}\mathbf{u}$, so $\mathbf{v}$ is dependent on $\mathbf{u}$ and $\mathbf{w}$, or $\mathbf{u} = \frac{2}{3}\mathbf{v} - \frac{1}{3}\mathbf{w}$ so $\mathbf{u}$ is dependent on $\mathbf{v}$ and $\mathbf{w}$. It is the fact that there are linear relations among the three vectors that makes $\{\mathbf{u}, \mathbf{v}, \mathbf{w}\}$ a linearly dependent set. An equivalent formulation of linear dependence is the following symmetric condition.

Proposition 3.1. A set of vectors $\{\mathbf{v}_1, \mathbf{v}_2, \dots, \mathbf{v}_k\}$ is linearly dependent if and only if

$$c_1\mathbf{v}_1 + c_2\mathbf{v}_2 + \cdots + c_k\mathbf{v}_k = \mathbf{0} \tag{3.1}$$

for some scalars $c_1, c_2, \dots c_k$, not all of which are zero.

In other words, a set $\{\mathbf{v}_1, \mathbf{v}_2, \dots, \mathbf{v}_k\}$ is linearly independent if the *only* linear combination of $\mathbf{v}_1$ through $\mathbf{v}_k$ which equals $\mathbf{0}$ is the combination with all the coefficients equal to zero, called the **trivial** combination.

Proof. First suppose a set of vectors is linearly dependent. Then one of the vectors (say $\mathbf{v}_1$) equals a linear combination of the others. So

$$\mathbf{v}_1 = d_2\mathbf{v}_2 + \cdots + d_k\mathbf{v}_k.$$

Subtracting $\mathbf{v}_1$ from both sides results in

$$(-1)\mathbf{v}_1 + d_2\mathbf{v}_2 + \cdots + d_k\mathbf{v}_k = \mathbf{0}$$

which is an equation of the form (3.1) with not all the coefficients equal to zero. On the other hand, suppose (3.1) holds with at least one nonzero coefficient. Suppose $c_1 \neq 0$. Then solving for $\mathbf{v}_1$ gives

$$\mathbf{v}_1 = -\frac{c_2}{c_1}\mathbf{v}_2 - \cdots - \frac{c_k}{c_1}\mathbf{v}_k$$

18

so $\mathbf{v}_1$ is a linear combination of the other vectors, and the set $\{\mathbf{v}_1, \mathbf{v}_2, \ldots, \mathbf{v}_k\}$ is linearly dependent. $\qquad \square$

Example 3.3. Let

$$\mathbf{v}_1 = \begin{bmatrix} 1 \\ 2 \\ 2 \end{bmatrix}, \qquad \mathbf{v}_2 = \begin{bmatrix} 1 \\ 3 \\ 1 \end{bmatrix}, \qquad \text{and} \qquad \mathbf{v}_3 = \begin{bmatrix} -1 \\ -5 \\ 1 \end{bmatrix}.$$

Is $\{\mathbf{v}_1, \mathbf{v}_2, \mathbf{v}_3\}$ a linearly independent set?

Solution. To answer this question we need to determine if there exist real numbers c_1, c_2 and c_3 (not all zero) such that $c_1 \mathbf{v}_1 + c_2 \mathbf{v}_2 + c_3 \mathbf{v}_3 = \mathbf{0}$. Equating the components of this vector equation we get the equations

$$\begin{array}{rcrcrcl} c_1 & + & c_2 & - & c_3 & = & 0 \\ 2c_1 & + & 3c_2 & - & 5c_3 & = & 0 \\ 2c_1 & + & c_2 & + & c_3 & = & 0. \end{array}$$

This is called a **system of linear equations**. To solve this system we use the method of **elimination**. The idea is to use one of the equations to eliminate one of the variables from the other equations. If we subtract twice the first equation from both the second and third equations, we get the new (but equivalent) system

$$\begin{array}{rcrcrcl} c_1 & + & c_2 & - & c_3 & = & 0 \\ & & c_2 & - & 3c_3 & = & 0 \\ & & -c_2 & + & 3c_3 & = & 0. \end{array}$$

Adding the second equation to the third gives

$$\begin{array}{rcrcrcl} c_1 & + & c_2 & - & c_3 & = & 0 \\ & & c_2 & - & 3c_3 & = & 0 \\ & & & & 0 & = & 0. \end{array}$$

Thus the third equation reduces to the trivially true statement $0 = 0$, so we can ignore it. To find a solution of the first two equations, notice that, given any choice of c_3, we can solve for c_1 and c_2. Thus we are free to choose c_3 however we desire. A simple choice is $c_3 = 1$ which leads to $c_2 = 3$ from the second equation, and then $c_1 = -2$ from the first equation. It is easy to check that these values satisfy all three of the original equations. Thus

$$-2\mathbf{v}_1 + 3\mathbf{v}_2 + \mathbf{v}_3 = \mathbf{0}$$

which means that $\{\mathbf{v}_1, \mathbf{v}_2, \mathbf{v}_3\}$ is a linearly dependent set. $\qquad \diamond$

Example 3.4. The vectors $\mathbf{e}_1, \ldots, \mathbf{e}_n$ defined in Remark 2.1 are linearly independent. To see this, suppose

$$c_1 \mathbf{e}_1 + c_2 \mathbf{e}_2 + \cdots + c_n \mathbf{e}_n = \mathbf{0}.$$

Writing out the components, this equation becomes

$$\begin{bmatrix} c_1 \\ c_2 \\ \vdots \\ c_n \end{bmatrix} = \begin{bmatrix} 0 \\ 0 \\ \vdots \\ 0 \end{bmatrix}$$

so all of the coefficients must equal zero, and thus the vectors are linearly independent. ◇

Exercises

For each set in Exercises 1 through 6 show that the set is linearly independent or express one of the vectors in the set as a linear combination of the others.

3.1. $\left\{ \begin{bmatrix} 2 \\ 1 \end{bmatrix}, \begin{bmatrix} 3 \\ 2 \end{bmatrix} \right\}$

3.2. $\left\{ \begin{bmatrix} 2 \\ 1 \end{bmatrix}, \begin{bmatrix} 3 \\ 2 \end{bmatrix}, \begin{bmatrix} 1 \\ 2 \end{bmatrix} \right\}$

3.3. $\left\{ \begin{bmatrix} 2 \\ 1 \\ 1 \end{bmatrix}, \begin{bmatrix} 1 \\ 1 \\ 0 \end{bmatrix}, \begin{bmatrix} 1 \\ 0 \\ 1 \end{bmatrix}, \begin{bmatrix} 0 \\ 0 \\ 1 \end{bmatrix} \right\}$

3.4. $\left\{ \begin{bmatrix} 1 \\ -1 \\ 2 \end{bmatrix}, \begin{bmatrix} 2 \\ 1 \\ 3 \end{bmatrix}, \begin{bmatrix} -1 \\ 0 \\ 2 \end{bmatrix} \right\}$

3.5. $\left\{ \begin{bmatrix} 2 \\ 0 \end{bmatrix}, \begin{bmatrix} 0 \\ 3 \end{bmatrix}, \begin{bmatrix} 5 \\ 7 \end{bmatrix} \right\}$

3.6. $\left\{ \begin{bmatrix} 1 \\ -1 \\ 3 \end{bmatrix}, \begin{bmatrix} 2 \\ 1 \\ 3 \end{bmatrix}, \begin{bmatrix} 3 \\ 3 \\ 3 \end{bmatrix} \right\}$

3.7. Let $\{\mathbf{u}, \mathbf{v}, \mathbf{w}\}$ be a linearly independent set. Show that $\{\mathbf{u} + \mathbf{v}, \mathbf{u} + \mathbf{w}, \mathbf{v} + \mathbf{w}\}$ is a linearly independent set.

3.8. Let $\{\mathbf{u}, \mathbf{v}, \mathbf{w}\}$ be a linearly independent set. Is $\{\mathbf{u} - \mathbf{v}, \mathbf{v} - \mathbf{w}, \mathbf{u} - \mathbf{w}\}$ a linearly independent set? Show that it is or show why it is not.

3.9. Let $\{\mathbf{u}, \mathbf{v}, \mathbf{w}\}$ be a linearly independent set. Is $\{2\mathbf{u} + \mathbf{v}, \mathbf{u} + \mathbf{v} + \mathbf{w}, 2\mathbf{v} + 3\mathbf{w}\}$ a linearly independent set? Show that it is or show why it is not.

True/False. For Exercises 10 through 13, determine whether the given statement is true or false. If true, show why. If false, provide a counterexample.

3.10. If $S = \{\mathbf{v}_1, \ldots, \mathbf{v}_k\}$ is a set of linearly independent vectors in $\mathbf{R}^n$, then any subset of S must be linearly independent.

3.11. If $S = \{\mathbf{v}_1, \ldots, \mathbf{v}_k\}$ is a set of linearly dependent vectors in $\mathbf{R}^n$, then any subset of S must be linearly dependent.

3.12. If $\text{span}(\mathbf{v}_1, \mathbf{v}_2, \mathbf{v}_3) = \mathbf{R}^3$, then $\{\mathbf{v}_1, \mathbf{v}_2, \mathbf{v}_3\}$ must be a linearly independent set.

3.13. If $S = \{\mathbf{v}_1, \mathbf{v}_2, \mathbf{v}_3\}$ is a linearly dependent set, then every vector in S can be written as a linear combination of the other 2 vectors.

4   Dot Products and Cross Products

The **dot product** of two vectors $\mathbf{v}$ and $\mathbf{w}$ in $\mathbf{R}^n$ is defined to be

$$\mathbf{v} \cdot \mathbf{w} = \begin{bmatrix} v_1 \\ v_2 \\ \vdots \\ v_n \end{bmatrix} \cdot \begin{bmatrix} w_1 \\ w_2 \\ \vdots \\ w_n \end{bmatrix} = v_1 w_1 + v_2 w_2 + \cdots + v_n w_n.$$

Notice that the dot product of two vectors is a scalar (real number), not a vector.

Example 4.1. Let

$$\mathbf{v} = \begin{bmatrix} 2 \\ 1 \end{bmatrix} \quad \mathbf{w} = \begin{bmatrix} -1 \\ 3 \end{bmatrix} \quad \mathbf{a} = \begin{bmatrix} 4 \\ 2 \\ 1 \end{bmatrix} \quad \mathbf{b} = \begin{bmatrix} 0 \\ -1 \\ 2 \end{bmatrix}.$$

Then $\mathbf{v} \cdot \mathbf{w} = 2(-1) + 1(3) = 1$ and $\mathbf{a} \cdot \mathbf{b} = 4(0) + 2(-1) + 1(2) = 0$. $\diamond$

The following properties of the dot product are easy to check.

Proposition 4.1. For any vectors $\mathbf{v}$, $\mathbf{w}$ and $\mathbf{x}$ in $\mathbf{R}^n$ and any scalar c,

1. $\mathbf{v} \cdot \mathbf{w} = \mathbf{w} \cdot \mathbf{v}$

2. $(\mathbf{v} + \mathbf{w}) \cdot \mathbf{x} = \mathbf{v} \cdot \mathbf{x} + \mathbf{w} \cdot \mathbf{x}$

3. $(c\mathbf{v}) \cdot \mathbf{w} = c(\mathbf{v} \cdot \mathbf{w})$.

There is a very close relationship between dot products and the notions of lengths and angles in $\mathbf{R}^n$. We define the **length** of a vector $\mathbf{v}$ in $\mathbf{R}^n$ to be

$$\|\mathbf{v}\| = \sqrt{v_1^2 + v_2^2 + \cdots + v_n^2}.$$

The expression under the square root is the dot product of $\mathbf{v}$ with itself, so

$$\boxed{\mathbf{v} \cdot \mathbf{v} = \|\mathbf{v}\|^2.}$$

The length of $\mathbf{v}$ is also commonly called the **magnitude** or **norm** of $\mathbf{v}$. The zero vector has length zero, and by the Pythagorean Theorem, the length of any nonzero vector $\mathbf{v} = (v_1, v_2)$ in $\mathbf{R}^2$ is just the length of the line segment which represents $\mathbf{v}$.

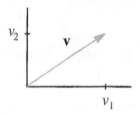

The same holds for vectors in $\mathbf{R}^3$. The segment which represents the nonzero vector $\mathbf{v} = (v_1, v_2, v_3)$ shown below is the hypotenuse of a right triangle.

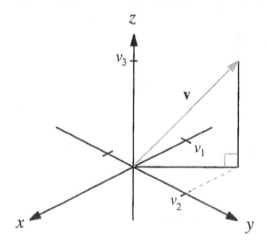

The leg in the xy-plane has length $\sqrt{v_1^2 + v_2^2}$, so the length of the hypotenuse is

$$\sqrt{\left(\sqrt{v_1^2 + v_2^2}\right)^2 + v_3^2} = \sqrt{v_1^2 + v_2^2 + v_3^2},$$

the length of $\mathbf{v}$. The following properties are left as exercises.

Proposition 4.2.

1. $\|\mathbf{v}\| \geq 0$ for any $\mathbf{v}$ in $\mathbf{R}^n$.

2. $\|\mathbf{v}\| = 0$ if and only if $\mathbf{v} = \mathbf{0}$.

3. $\|c\mathbf{v}\| = |c|\|\mathbf{v}\|$ for any $\mathbf{v}$ in $\mathbf{R}^n$ and any scalar c.

A vector with length 1 is called a **unit vector**. Given any nonzero vector $\mathbf{v}$, if we apply the third property above with $c = 1/\|\mathbf{v}\|$, it follows that the vector

$$\mathbf{u} = \frac{\mathbf{v}}{\|\mathbf{v}\|}$$

is a unit vector in the same direction as $\mathbf{v}$.

The following result, known as the Cauchy-Schwarz inequality, provides an upper bound on the size of $\mathbf{v} \cdot \mathbf{w}$ in terms of the lengths of $\mathbf{v}$ and $\mathbf{w}$.

Proposition 4.3. (Cauchy-Schwarz Inequality) For any nonzero vectors $\mathbf{v}, \mathbf{w}$ in $\mathbf{R}^n$,

$$|\mathbf{v} \cdot \mathbf{w}| \leq \|\mathbf{v}\|\|\mathbf{w}\| = \sqrt{\mathbf{v} \cdot \mathbf{v}}\sqrt{\mathbf{w} \cdot \mathbf{w}}$$

Furthermore, we have the equality $|\mathbf{v} \cdot \mathbf{w}| = \|\mathbf{v}\|\|\mathbf{w}\|$ if and only if $\mathbf{v} = c\mathbf{w}$ for some nonzero scalar c.

Proof. Let $\mathbf{v}$ and $\mathbf{w}$ be any nonzero vectors in $\mathbf{R}^n$ and define $p(t) = \|t\mathbf{w} - \mathbf{v}\|^2$ for any real number t. Using the properties listed above, we have

$$\begin{aligned}
p(t) &= \|t\mathbf{w} - \mathbf{v}\|^2 \\
&= (t\mathbf{w} - \mathbf{v}) \cdot (t\mathbf{w} - \mathbf{v}) \\
&= t\mathbf{w} \cdot (t\mathbf{w} - \mathbf{v}) - \mathbf{v} \cdot (t\mathbf{w} - \mathbf{v}) \\
&= t^2\mathbf{w} \cdot \mathbf{w} - 2t\mathbf{v} \cdot \mathbf{w} + \mathbf{v} \cdot \mathbf{v} \\
&= \|\mathbf{w}\|^2 t^2 - 2(\mathbf{v} \cdot \mathbf{w})t + \|\mathbf{v}\|^2 \\
&= at^2 - bt + c
\end{aligned}$$

where $a = \|\mathbf{w}\|^2$, $b = 2(\mathbf{v} \cdot \mathbf{w})$ and $c = \|\mathbf{v}\|^2$. Since $\|\mathbf{v} - t\mathbf{w}\|^2$ is nonnegative, it follows that $p(t)$ is nonnegative for all t. In particular, $p(b/2a) \geq 0$ (the quantity $b/2a$ is defined since a is positive). This gives

$$a\left(\frac{b}{2a}\right)^2 - b\left(\frac{b}{2a}\right) + c = -\frac{b^2}{4a} + c \geq 0.$$

Since a is positive, this implies $b^2 \leq 4ac$, so

$$4(\mathbf{v} \cdot \mathbf{w})^2 \leq 4\|\mathbf{v}\|^2\|\mathbf{w}\|^2.$$

Dividing by 4 and taking the square root of both sides proves the inequality.

Next suppose $\mathbf{v} = c\mathbf{w}$ for some nonzero scalar c. Then

$$|\mathbf{v} \cdot \mathbf{w}| = |c\mathbf{w} \cdot \mathbf{w}| = |c|\|\mathbf{w}\|^2 = |c|\|\mathbf{w}\|\|\mathbf{w}\| = \|c\mathbf{w}\|\|\mathbf{w}\| = \|\mathbf{v}\|\|\mathbf{w}\|.$$

Conversely, suppose that we have the equality $|\mathbf{v} \cdot \mathbf{w}| = \|\mathbf{v}\|\|\mathbf{w}\|$. Then $b^2 = 4ac$, so

$$p(b/2a) = -\frac{b^2}{4a} + c = 0$$

which implies that

$$\left\| \mathbf{v} - \frac{b}{2a}\mathbf{w} \right\| = 0.$$

Since the only vector with norm zero is the zero vector, it follows that

$$\mathbf{v} = \frac{b}{2a}\mathbf{w}.$$

Since $\mathbf{v}$ and $\mathbf{w}$ are nonzero, $\mathbf{v}$ is a nonzero scalar multiple of $\mathbf{w}$. $\quad\square$

An immediate consequence of the Cauchy-Schwarz inequality is the triangle inequality.

Proposition 4.4. (Triangle Inequality) Let $\mathbf{v}$ and $\mathbf{w}$ be nonzero vectors in $\mathbf{R}^n$. Then

$$\|\mathbf{v} + \mathbf{w}\| \le \|\mathbf{v}\| + \|\mathbf{w}\|,$$

and we have the equality $\|\mathbf{v} + \mathbf{w}\| = \|\mathbf{v}\| + \|\mathbf{w}\|$ if and only if $\mathbf{v} = c\mathbf{w}$ for some positive scalar c.

Geometrically this is equivalent to the statement that the length of any side of a triangle is no larger than the sum of the lengths of the other two sides.

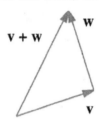

Proof. Using the properties of dot products, we have

$$\begin{aligned}
\|\mathbf{v} + \mathbf{w}\|^2 &= (\mathbf{v} + \mathbf{w}) \cdot (\mathbf{v} + \mathbf{w}) \\
&= \mathbf{v} \cdot \mathbf{v} + 2\mathbf{v} \cdot \mathbf{w} + \mathbf{w} \cdot \mathbf{w} \\
&\le \mathbf{v} \cdot \mathbf{v} + 2\|\mathbf{v}\|\|\mathbf{w}\| + \mathbf{w} \cdot \mathbf{w} \\
&= \|\mathbf{v}\|^2 + 2\|\mathbf{v}\|\|\mathbf{w}\| + \|\mathbf{w}\|^2 \\
&= (\|\mathbf{v}\| + \|\mathbf{w}\|)^2
\end{aligned}$$

where the Cauchy-Schwarz inequality was applied in the third line. Taking the square root of both sides proves the inequality.

Observe that we have equality if and only if $\mathbf{v} \cdot \mathbf{w} = \|\mathbf{v}\|\|\mathbf{w}\|$. By the second statement in the Cauchy-Schwarz inequality, this means that $\mathbf{v} = c\mathbf{w}$ for some $c \ne 0$. Then

$$c\|\mathbf{w}\|^2 = c\mathbf{w} \cdot \mathbf{w} = \mathbf{v} \cdot \mathbf{w} = \|\mathbf{v}\|\|\mathbf{w}\|$$

so c is positive. On the other hand, if $\mathbf{v} = c\mathbf{w}$ for some positive scalar c, then

$$\mathbf{v} \cdot \mathbf{w} = c\mathbf{w} \cdot \mathbf{w} = c\|\mathbf{w}\|^2 = c\|\mathbf{w}\|\|\mathbf{w}\| = \|c\mathbf{w}\|\|\mathbf{w}\| = \|\mathbf{v}\|\|\mathbf{w}\|$$

and therefore we have equality. $\quad\square$

Using the triangle inequality it is possible to make sense of the angle between two vectors in $\mathbf{R}^n$. Let $\mathbf{v}$ and $\mathbf{w}$ be nonzero vectors in $\mathbf{R}^n$ and assume that $\mathbf{v}$ is not a scalar multiple of $\mathbf{w}$. We can associate to this pair of vectors a triangle in the plane with side lengths $A = \|\mathbf{v}\|$, $B = \|\mathbf{w}\|$ and $C = \|\mathbf{v} - \mathbf{w}\|$.

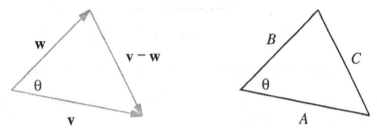

To see that there exists such a triangle we apply the triangle inequality three times. First

$$\|\mathbf{v} - \mathbf{w}\| = \|\mathbf{v} + (-\mathbf{w})\| < \|\mathbf{v}\| + \|-\mathbf{w}\| = \|\mathbf{v}\| + \|\mathbf{w}\|$$

so $C < A + B$. Next

$$\|\mathbf{v}\| = \|\mathbf{w} + (\mathbf{v} - \mathbf{w})\| < \|\mathbf{w}\| + \|\mathbf{v} - \mathbf{w}\|$$

so $A < B + C$. Finally

$$\|\mathbf{w}\| = \|\mathbf{v} + (\mathbf{w} - \mathbf{v})\| < \|\mathbf{v}\| + \|\mathbf{w} - \mathbf{v}\| = \|\mathbf{v}\| + \|\mathbf{v} - \mathbf{w}\|$$

so $B < A + C$. By the SSS Theorem of plane geometry, all such triangles are congruent. We can therefore *define* the angle θ between $\mathbf{v}$ and $\mathbf{w}$ to be the corresponding angle in any plane triangle with sides of length $\|\mathbf{v}\|$, $\|\mathbf{w}\|$ and $\|\mathbf{v} - \mathbf{w}\|$. If $\mathbf{v} = c\mathbf{w}$ then we define $\theta = 0$ if c is positive and $\theta = \pi$ if c is negative. Dot products provide us with an easy way to determine the angle between two vectors.

Proposition 4.5. Let $\mathbf{v}, \mathbf{w}$ be nonzero vectors in $\mathbf{R}^n$. Then

$$\mathbf{v} \cdot \mathbf{w} = \|\mathbf{v}\|\|\mathbf{w}\| \cos \theta$$

where θ is the angle between $\mathbf{v}$ and $\mathbf{w}$.

Proof. Consider the plane triangle with side lengths $A = \|\mathbf{v}\|$, $B = \|\mathbf{w}\|$ and $C = \|\mathbf{v} - \mathbf{w}\|$. The Law of Cosines states that

$$C^2 = A^2 + B^2 - 2AB \cos \theta.$$

That is,

$$\|\mathbf{v} - \mathbf{w}\|^2 = \|\mathbf{v}\|^2 + \|\mathbf{w}\|^2 - 2\|\mathbf{v}\|\|\mathbf{w}\| \cos \theta. \tag{4.1}$$

Using the properties of dot products, the left side of equation (4.1) may be rewritten

$$\|\mathbf{v} - \mathbf{w}\|^2 = (\mathbf{v} - \mathbf{w}) \cdot (\mathbf{v} - \mathbf{w})$$
$$= \mathbf{v} \cdot (\mathbf{v} - \mathbf{w}) - \mathbf{w} \cdot (\mathbf{v} - \mathbf{w})$$
$$= \mathbf{v} \cdot \mathbf{v} - \mathbf{v} \cdot \mathbf{w} - \mathbf{w} \cdot \mathbf{v} + \mathbf{w} \cdot \mathbf{w}$$
$$= \|\mathbf{v}\|^2 + \|\mathbf{w}\|^2 - 2(\mathbf{v} \cdot \mathbf{w}).$$

Comparing this with the right side of equation (4.1) proves the identity. $\square$

We say two nonzero vectors are **perpendicular** if the angle between them is a right angle. In this case $\cos\theta = 0$. Thus Proposition 4.5 implies the following test for perpendicularity.

Proposition 4.6. Two nonzero vectors $\mathbf{v}$ and $\mathbf{w}$ in $\mathbf{R}^n$ are perpendicular if and only if $\mathbf{v} \cdot \mathbf{w} = 0$.

We say that two vectors $\mathbf{v}$ and $\mathbf{w}$ are **orthogonal** if $\mathbf{v} \cdot \mathbf{w} = 0$. The distinction between the terms perpendicular and orthogonal arises only with regard to the zero vector. Perpendicularity does not make sense when one of the vectors is the zero vector, since angles are only defined between nonzero vectors. Thus we never say that the zero vector is perpendicular to another vector. However, the dot product of the zero vector in $\mathbf{R}^n$ with any other vector in $\mathbf{R}^n$ makes sense, and is always zero, so the zero vector is orthogonal to every vector in $\mathbf{R}^n$. The following is the vector form of the Pythagorean Theorem. Its proof is left as an exercise.

Proposition 4.7. Suppose $\mathbf{v}$ and $\mathbf{w}$ are orthogonal. Then

$$\|\mathbf{v} + \mathbf{w}\|^2 = \|\mathbf{v}\|^2 + \|\mathbf{w}\|^2.$$

$(v+w) \cdot (v+w) = \ldots$

$v \cdot (v+w) + w \cdot (v+w) =$

$\|v\|^2 + 2(v \cdot w) + \|w\|^2 = \ldots$

Dot products may be used to describe planes in $\mathbf{R}^3$. Given a plane, any vector perpendicular to the plane is called a **normal vector** to the plane. For instance, the vector $\mathbf{k}$ is a normal vector to the xy-plane.

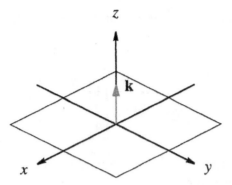

Suppose we know that a plane has a normal vector $\mathbf{n}$ and contains the point $\mathbf{x}_0$. If $\mathbf{x}$ is any other point in the plane then the difference $\mathbf{x} - \mathbf{x}_0$ is a vector parallel to the plane, and therefore perpendicular to $\mathbf{n}$.

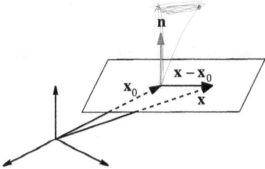

Thus by Proposition 4.6, $\mathbf{n} \cdot (\mathbf{x} - \mathbf{x}_0) = 0$. Using the notation

$$\mathbf{x} = \begin{bmatrix} x \\ y \\ z \end{bmatrix} \qquad \mathbf{x}_0 = \begin{bmatrix} x_0 \\ y_0 \\ z_0 \end{bmatrix} \qquad \mathbf{n} = \begin{bmatrix} n_1 \\ n_2 \\ n_3 \end{bmatrix}$$

the relation $\mathbf{n} \cdot (\mathbf{x} - \mathbf{x}_0) = 0$ takes the form

$$n_1(x - x_0) + n_2(y - y_0) + n_3(z - z_0) = 0.$$

This is the equation of the plane passing through $\mathbf{x}_0$ with normal vector $\mathbf{n}$.

Example 4.2. If a plane passes through the point $(1, 2, 3)$ and has normal vector

$$\mathbf{n} = \begin{bmatrix} 1 \\ 3 \\ -2 \end{bmatrix},$$

then its equation is $1(x - 1) + 3(y - 2) - 2(z - 3) = 0$, or equivalently $x + 3y - 2z = 1$. $\diamond$

Often the difficult part is finding a normal vector.

Example 4.3. Find the equation of the plane containing the points $(1, 2, 3)$, $(2, -5, 4)$ and $(6, 4, 7)$.

Solution. We may choose

$$\mathbf{x}_0 = \begin{bmatrix} 1 \\ 2 \\ 3 \end{bmatrix}.$$

To obtain two vectors parallel to the plane, we may use the vectors between $(1, 2, 3)$ and the other two points. Computing the difference vectors, we find

$$\mathbf{v} = \begin{bmatrix} 1 \\ -7 \\ 1 \end{bmatrix} \qquad \mathbf{w} = \begin{bmatrix} 5 \\ 2 \\ 4 \end{bmatrix}$$

are parallel to the plane. Thus any normal vector $\mathbf{n} = \begin{bmatrix} n_1 \\ n_2 \\ n_3 \end{bmatrix}$ must be perpendicular to both $\mathbf{v}$ and $\mathbf{w}$. So

$$\mathbf{v} \cdot \mathbf{n} = 0 \quad \text{and} \quad \mathbf{w} \cdot \mathbf{n} = 0.$$

This leads to the system of equations

$$\begin{array}{rcrcrcl} 1n_1 & - & 7n_2 & + & 1n_3 & = & 0 \\ 5n_1 & + & 2n_2 & + & 4n_3 & = & 0. \end{array}$$

Subtracting 5 times the first equation from the second equation we get

$$\begin{array}{rcrcrcl} n_1 & - & 7n_2 & + & 1n_3 & = & 0 \\ & & 37n_2 & - & n_3 & = & 0. \end{array}$$

Any choice of n_3 will allow us to solve the second equation for n_2 and then the first equation for n_1. In view of the second equation it makes sense to choose $n_3 = 37$, so that from the second equation we get $n_2 = 1$, and then from the third equation $n_1 = -30$. So

$$\mathbf{n} = \begin{bmatrix} -30 \\ 1 \\ 37 \end{bmatrix}$$

is a normal vector and thus the equation of the plane is

$$-30(x - 1) + 1(y - 2) + 37(z - 3) = 0.$$

$\diamond$

A quick way to find a normal vector is to use cross products. The **cross product** of two vectors $\mathbf{v}$ and $\mathbf{w}$ in $\mathbf{R}^3$ is the vector

$$\mathbf{v} \times \mathbf{w} = \begin{bmatrix} v_2 w_3 - v_3 w_2 \\ v_3 w_1 - v_1 w_3 \\ v_1 w_2 - v_2 w_1 \end{bmatrix}.$$

The following properties are left as exercises.

Proposition 4.8. For any $\mathbf{u}$, $\mathbf{v}$ and $\mathbf{w}$ in $\mathbf{R}^3$

1. $\mathbf{v} \times \mathbf{w} = -\mathbf{w} \times \mathbf{v}$,

2. $(\mathbf{u} + \mathbf{v}) \times \mathbf{w} = \mathbf{u} \times \mathbf{w} + \mathbf{v} \times \mathbf{w}$,

3. $(c\mathbf{v}) \times \mathbf{w} = c(\mathbf{v} \times \mathbf{w})$,

4. $\mathbf{v} \cdot (\mathbf{v} \times \mathbf{w}) = 0$,

5. $\mathbf{w} \cdot (\mathbf{v} \times \mathbf{w}) = 0$.

The final two properties imply that the cross product of $\mathbf{v}$ and $\mathbf{w}$ is orthogonal to both $\mathbf{v}$ and $\mathbf{w}$. The direction of $\mathbf{v} \times \mathbf{w}$ is determined by the **right hand rule**. With the right hand positioned so that the fingers point in the direction of $\mathbf{v}$ and the palm faces toward $\mathbf{w}$, the thumb points in the direction of $\mathbf{v} \times \mathbf{w}$.

Example 4.4. Consider the plane from Example 4.3, with direction vectors

$$\mathbf{v} = \begin{bmatrix} 1 \\ -7 \\ 1 \end{bmatrix} \quad \text{and} \quad \mathbf{w} = \begin{bmatrix} 5 \\ 2 \\ 4 \end{bmatrix}.$$

Their cross product

$$\mathbf{v} \times \mathbf{w} = \begin{bmatrix} (-7)(4) - (1)(2) \\ (1)(5) - (1)(4) \\ (1)(2) - (-7)(5) \end{bmatrix} = \begin{bmatrix} -30 \\ 1 \\ 37 \end{bmatrix}$$

is precisely the normal vector we found earlier. $\diamond$

The length of $\mathbf{v} \times \mathbf{w}$ also depends on the lengths of $\mathbf{v}$ and $\mathbf{w}$ and the angle between $\mathbf{v}$ and $\mathbf{w}$.

Proposition 4.9. Let $\mathbf{v}$ and $\mathbf{w}$ be nonzero vectors in $\mathbf{R}^3$. Then

$$\|\mathbf{v} \times \mathbf{w}\| = \|\mathbf{v}\| \|\mathbf{w}\| \sin \theta$$

where θ is the angle between $\mathbf{v}$ and $\mathbf{w}$.

Proof. First,

$$\|\mathbf{v} \times \mathbf{w}\|^2 = (v_2 w_3 - v_3 w_2)^2 + (v_3 w_1 - v_1 w_3)^2 + (v_1 w_2 - v_2 w_1)^2$$
$$= v_1^2(w_2^2 + w_3^2) + v_2^2(w_1^2 + w_3^2) + v_3^2(w_1^2 + w_2^2)$$
$$- 2(v_1 w_1 v_2 w_2 + v_1 w_1 v_3 w_3 + v_2 v_2 v_3 w_3).$$

Next, squaring both sides of the relation $\mathbf{v} \cdot \mathbf{w} = \|\mathbf{v}\|\|\mathbf{w}\| \cos \theta$ gives

$$\|\mathbf{v}\|^2 \|\mathbf{w}\|^2 \cos^2 \theta = (v_1 w_1 + v_2 w_2 + v_3 w_3)^2$$
$$= v_1^2 w_1^2 + v_2^2 w_2^2 + v_3^2 w_3^2 + 2(v_1 w_1 v_2 w_2 + v_1 w_1 v_3 w_3 + v_2 v_2 v_3 w_3).$$

Adding these equations gives

$$\|\mathbf{v} \times \mathbf{w}\|^2 + \|\mathbf{v}\|^2 \|\mathbf{w}\|^2 \cos^2 \theta = (v_1^2 + v_2^2 + v_3^2)(w_1^2 + w_2^2 + w_3^2) = \|\mathbf{v}\|^2 \|\mathbf{w}\|^2$$

so

$$\|\mathbf{v} \times \mathbf{w}\|^2 = \|\mathbf{v}\|^2 \|\mathbf{w}\|^2 (1 - \cos^2 \theta) = \|\mathbf{v}\|^2 \|\mathbf{w}\|^2 \sin^2 \theta.$$

Taking the square root of both sides proves the identity. $\square$

This identity can be interpreted as a statement about area. Consider the parallelogram formed by $\mathbf{v}$ and $\mathbf{w}$.

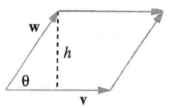

The width of the parallelogram is $\|\mathbf{v}\|$ and the height is $h = \|\mathbf{w}\| \sin \theta$, so the area is $\|\mathbf{v}\|\|\mathbf{w}\| \sin \theta$. Thus by Proposition 4.9, we have the following result.

> **Proposition 4.10.** The area of the parallelogram formed by $\mathbf{v}$ and $\mathbf{w}$ is $\|\mathbf{v} \times \mathbf{w}\|$.

Example 4.5. Find the area of the triangle in $\mathbf{R}^3$ with vertices $(1, 1, 1)$, $(2, -1, 3)$ and $(0, 4, 1)$.

Solution. The sides adjacent to the vertex $(1, 1, 1)$ are described by the vectors

$$\mathbf{v} = \begin{bmatrix} 1 \\ -2 \\ 2 \end{bmatrix} \quad \text{and} \quad \mathbf{w} = \begin{bmatrix} -1 \\ 3 \\ 0 \end{bmatrix}.$$

The triangle is therefore half of the parallelogram generated by $\mathbf{v}$ and $\mathbf{w}$. Since

$$\mathbf{v} \times \mathbf{w} = \begin{bmatrix} -6 \\ -2 \\ 1 \end{bmatrix}$$

the area of the triangle is $\frac{1}{2}\|\mathbf{v} \times \mathbf{w}\| = \frac{1}{2}\sqrt{41}$. $\diamond$

Exercises

4.1. Let

$$\mathbf{a} = \begin{bmatrix} 2 \\ 1 \\ 1 \end{bmatrix} \qquad \mathbf{b} = \begin{bmatrix} 1 \\ -2 \\ 0 \end{bmatrix} \qquad \mathbf{c} = \begin{bmatrix} 4 \\ 2 \\ -2 \end{bmatrix} \qquad \mathbf{x} = \begin{bmatrix} 2 \\ 3 \end{bmatrix} \qquad \mathbf{y} = \begin{bmatrix} -3 \\ 2 \end{bmatrix}$$

Calculate the following.

(a) $\mathbf{a} \cdot \mathbf{b}$ (b) $\mathbf{a} \cdot (\mathbf{b} + \mathbf{c})$ (c) $\mathbf{x} \cdot \mathbf{y}$ (d) $\|\mathbf{x} - \mathbf{y}\|$

4.2. Let

$$\mathbf{u} = \begin{bmatrix} 1 \\ 2 \\ -1 \\ -2 \end{bmatrix} \qquad \mathbf{v} = \begin{bmatrix} -2 \\ 0 \\ 4 \\ 3 \end{bmatrix} \qquad \mathbf{w} = \begin{bmatrix} 1 \\ 6 \\ 1 \\ -3 \end{bmatrix}$$

Calculate the following.

(a) $\mathbf{u} \cdot (\mathbf{w} - \mathbf{v})$ (b) $\mathbf{u} \cdot \mathbf{w} - \mathbf{u} \cdot \mathbf{v}$ (c) $\|\mathbf{u} + \mathbf{v}\|$
(d) $\|\mathbf{u}\| + \|\mathbf{v}\|$ (e) $\mathbf{v} \cdot \mathbf{w}$ (f) $(2\mathbf{v}) \cdot \mathbf{w}$ (g) $\mathbf{v} \cdot (2\mathbf{w})$

4.3. Find the length of each of the following vectors.

(a) $\begin{bmatrix} 1 \\ -1 \end{bmatrix}$ (b) $\begin{bmatrix} 4 \\ 3 \end{bmatrix}$ (c) $\begin{bmatrix} 2 \\ 1 \\ -2 \end{bmatrix}$ (d) $\begin{bmatrix} 1 \\ 1 \\ 1 \\ 1 \end{bmatrix}$

4.4. Find a vector in $\mathbf{R}^2$ with length 3 which points in the same direction as $\begin{bmatrix} 1 \\ -3 \end{bmatrix}$.

4.5. Find a vector in $\mathbf{R}^3$ which points in the opposite direction as $\begin{bmatrix} 2 \\ -7 \\ 1 \end{bmatrix}$, but is three times as long.

4.6. A force $\mathbf{F}_1$ of magnitude 3N is applied in the direction $\begin{bmatrix} -1 \\ 2 \end{bmatrix}$. In what direction should a force $\mathbf{F}_2$ of magnitude 2N be applied in order for the net force to have first component zero?

4.7. Suppose an airplane is pointing due west and flying with an airspeed of 500 mph, and that there is a 20 mph wind out of the southwest. Find the velocity vector of the plane relative to the ground. What is the speed of the plane relative to the ground?

4.8. Simplify the following expressions.

(a) $(\mathbf{a} + \mathbf{b}) \cdot (\mathbf{c} + \mathbf{d})$

31

(b) $(\mathbf{a} + \mathbf{b}) \cdot (\mathbf{a} - \mathbf{b})$

4.9. (a) Simplify $\|\mathbf{x} + \mathbf{y}\|^2 - \|\mathbf{x}\|^2 - \|\mathbf{y}\|^2$ using dot products.

(b) Suppose $\|\mathbf{w}\| = \|\mathbf{z}\|$. Use dot products to show that $\mathbf{w} + \mathbf{z}$ and $\mathbf{w} - \mathbf{z}$ are orthogonal.

4.10. Suppose $\mathbf{u}$, $\mathbf{v}$ and $\mathbf{w}$ are nonzero vectors in $\mathbf{R}^n$ which are mutually orthogonal. That is, $\mathbf{u} \cdot \mathbf{v} = 0$, $\mathbf{u} \cdot \mathbf{w} = 0$ and $\mathbf{v} \cdot \mathbf{w} = 0$. Show that $\{\mathbf{u}, \mathbf{v}, \mathbf{w}\}$ is a linearly independent set.

4.11. Suppose that

$$
\begin{array}{lll}
\mathbf{u} \cdot \mathbf{x} = 1 & \mathbf{u} \cdot \mathbf{y} = 2 & \mathbf{u} \cdot \mathbf{z} = 0 \\
\mathbf{v} \cdot \mathbf{x} = -1 & \mathbf{v} \cdot \mathbf{y} = 2 & \mathbf{v} \cdot \mathbf{z} = 3 \\
\mathbf{w} \cdot \mathbf{x} = 1. & \mathbf{w} \cdot \mathbf{y} = -2 & \mathbf{w} \cdot \mathbf{z} = -1
\end{array}
$$

Compute $(\mathbf{u} - \mathbf{v} + 2\mathbf{w}) \cdot (\mathbf{x} + \mathbf{y} - \mathbf{z})$.

4.12. Suppose that

$$
\begin{array}{lll}
\mathbf{x} \cdot \mathbf{y} = 3 & \mathbf{x} \cdot \mathbf{z} = -1 & \mathbf{y} \cdot \mathbf{z} = 2 \\
\|\mathbf{x}\| = 2 & \|\mathbf{y}\| = 3 & \|\mathbf{z}\| = 4
\end{array}
$$

Compute the following.

(a) $(\mathbf{x} + \mathbf{y}) \cdot (\mathbf{x} + \mathbf{z})$
(b) $\|\mathbf{x} + \mathbf{y} + \mathbf{z}\|$

4.13. Let

$$
\mathbf{u} = \begin{bmatrix} 1 \\ -2 \\ 0 \end{bmatrix} \qquad \mathbf{v} = \begin{bmatrix} 1 \\ 2 \\ 3 \end{bmatrix} \qquad \mathbf{w} = \begin{bmatrix} 2 \\ 1 \\ -1 \end{bmatrix}
$$

Compute

(a) $\mathbf{u} \times \mathbf{v}$
(b) $\mathbf{v} \times \mathbf{u}$
(c) $\mathbf{v} \times \mathbf{w}$
(d) $(\mathbf{u} \times \mathbf{v}) \times \mathbf{w}$
(e) $\mathbf{u} \times (\mathbf{u} \times \mathbf{w})$
(f) $\mathbf{u} \times \mathbf{u}$

In Exercises 14 and 15, find the angle between the two vectors.

4.14. $\mathbf{u} = (1, 2)$ and $\mathbf{v} = (3, 4)$.

4.15. $\mathbf{u} = (-2, 1)$ and $\mathbf{v} = (4, 2)$.

4.16. Find a vector perpendicular to $\mathbf{v} = (1, 3)$.

4.17. Find two linearly independent vectors perpendicular to $\mathbf{v} = (1, 2, 3)$.

In Exercises 18 and 19 find (a) a normal vector to the plane containing the given points, and (b) an equation for the plane in terms of x, y and z.

4.18. $(1, 2, 3)$, $(2, 3, 4)$ and $(2, 1, 5)$.

4.19. $(1, 1, 1)$, $(2, -3, 1)$ and $(4, 5, 2)$.

4.20. (a) Show that $\mathbf{v} \cdot \mathbf{w} = \mathbf{w} \cdot \mathbf{v}$ for any vectors $\mathbf{v}$ and $\mathbf{w}$ in $\mathbf{R}^n$.

   (b) Show that $(\mathbf{v} + \mathbf{w}) \cdot \mathbf{x} = \mathbf{v} \cdot \mathbf{x} + \mathbf{w} \cdot \mathbf{x}$ for any vectors $\mathbf{v}$, $\mathbf{w}$ and $\mathbf{x}$ in $\mathbf{R}^n$.

   (c) Show that $(c\mathbf{v}) \cdot \mathbf{w} = c(\mathbf{v} \cdot \mathbf{w})$ for any vectors $\mathbf{v}$ and $\mathbf{w}$ in $\mathbf{R}^n$ and any scalar c in $\mathbf{R}$.

4.21. (a) Show that $\|\mathbf{v}\| \geq 0$ for any $\mathbf{v}$ in $\mathbf{R}^n$.

   (b) Show that $\|\mathbf{v}\| = 0$ if and only if $\mathbf{v} = \mathbf{0}$.

   (c) Show that $\|c\mathbf{v}\| = |c|\|\mathbf{v}\|$ for any $\mathbf{v}$ in $\mathbf{R}^n$ and any scalar c in $\mathbf{R}$.

4.22. Prove the following properties of cross products.

   (a) $\mathbf{v} \times \mathbf{w} = -\mathbf{w} \times \mathbf{v}$

   (b) $(\mathbf{u} + \mathbf{v}) \times \mathbf{w} = \mathbf{u} \times \mathbf{w} + \mathbf{v} \times \mathbf{w}$

   (c) $(c\mathbf{v}) \times \mathbf{w} = c(\mathbf{v} \times \mathbf{w})$

   (d) $\mathbf{v} \cdot (\mathbf{v} \times \mathbf{w}) = 0$

   (e) $\mathbf{w} \cdot (\mathbf{v} \times \mathbf{w}) = 0$

4.23. Find the area of the parallelogram in $\mathbf{R}^2$ with vertices $(1, 1)$, $(3, 2)$, $(4, 3)$ and $(2, 2)$.

4.24. Find the area of the triangle in $\mathbf{R}^3$ with vertices $(-2, 1, 2)$, $(3, 4, 1)$ and $(2, -1, 0)$.

4.25. Prove the Pythagorean Theorem for vectors. That is, show that if $\mathbf{v}$ and $\mathbf{w}$ are orthogonal then $\|v + w\|^2 = \|v\|^2 + \|w\|^2$.

4.26. Let P be the **parallelopiped** generated by vectors $\mathbf{u}$, $\mathbf{v}$ and $\mathbf{w}$. Show that the volume of P is $|\mathbf{u} \cdot (\mathbf{v} \times \mathbf{w})|$. *Hint: The volume of a region with uniform cross sectional area is its base area times its height.*

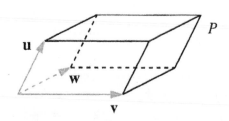

5   Systems of Linear Equations

We have encountered systems of linear equations when trying to answer the following questions.

- Is a given vector in the span of some collection of vectors?

- Given a collection of vectors, are they linearly independent?

- What vectors are perpendicular to a given collection of vectors?

The general form of a linear system of m equations in n unknowns is

$$
\begin{array}{ccccccccc}
a_{11}x_1 & + & a_{12}x_2 & + & \cdots & + & a_{1n}x_n & = & b_1 \\
a_{21}x_1 & + & a_{22}x_2 & + & \cdots & + & a_{2n}x_n & = & b_2 \\
\vdots & & \vdots & & & & \vdots & & \vdots \\
a_{m1}x_1 & + & a_{m2}x_2 & + & \cdots & + & a_{mn}x_n & = & b_m
\end{array}
$$

where the coefficients a_{ij} and the right hand sides b_i are given and we wish to solve for the unknowns x_1 through x_n.

The standard technique for solving systems of linear equations is called **Gaussian elimination**. The idea is to use one equation to eliminate one of the variables from the other equations. We illustrate the process in the following examples.

Example 5.1. Find all solutions of the system

$$
\begin{array}{ccccccc}
x_1 & - & x_2 & + & x_3 & = & -2 \\
3x_1 & - & x_2 & - & x_3 & = & 8 \\
2x_1 & + & x_2 & - & 2x_3 & = & 11.
\end{array}
$$

Solution. First, we use the top equation to eliminate x_1 from the other equations. Subtracting 3 times the first equation from the second equation and subtracting 2 times the first equation from the third equation gives

$$
\begin{array}{ccccccc}
x_1 & - & x_2 & + & x_3 & = & -2 \\
& & 2x_2 & - & 4x_3 & = & 14 \\
& & 3x_2 & - & 4x_3 & = & 15.
\end{array}
$$

Next use the new middle equation to eliminate x_2 from the other equations. First divide by 2 to make the calculations simpler.

$$
\begin{array}{ccccccc}
x_1 & - & x_2 & + & x_3 & = & -2 \\
& & x_2 & - & 2x_3 & = & 7 \\
& & 3x_2 & - & 4x_3 & = & 15.
\end{array}
$$

Adding the second equation to the first and subtracting 3 times the second equation from the third gives

$$
\begin{array}{ccccc}
x_1 & & - & x_3 & = & 5 \\
& x_2 & - & 2x_3 & = & 7 \\
& & & 2x_3 & = & -6.
\end{array}
$$

34

Dividing the new third equation by 2 gives

$$
\begin{aligned}
x_1 \qquad\quad -\quad x_3 &= 5 \\
x_2 \;-\; 2x_3 &= 7 \\
x_3 &= -3.
\end{aligned}
$$

Finally, adding the third equation to the first and adding 2 times the third equation to the second gives

$$
\begin{aligned}
x_1 \qquad\qquad\quad &= 2 \\
x_2 \qquad\quad &= 1 \\
x_3 &= -3.
\end{aligned}
$$

Thus the solution is

$$
\begin{bmatrix} x_1 \\ x_2 \\ x_3 \end{bmatrix} = \begin{bmatrix} 2 \\ 1 \\ -3 \end{bmatrix}.
$$

Geometrically this solution is the point of intersection of the three planes described by the original equations.

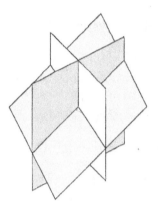

$\Diamond$

Example 5.2. Find all solutions of the system

$$
\begin{aligned}
x_1 \;-\; x_2 \;+\; x_3 &= 2 \\
4x_1 \;-\; 3x_2 \;+\; x_3 &= 3.
\end{aligned}
$$

Solution. Proceeding as in Example 5.1, we use the first equation to eliminate x_1 from the second equation to get

$$
\begin{aligned}
x_1 \;-\; x_2 \;+\; x_3 &= 2 \\
x_2 \;-\; 3x_3 &= -5.
\end{aligned}
$$

Adding the second equation to the first then yields

$$
\begin{aligned}
x_1 \qquad\quad -\; 2x_3 &= -3 \\
x_2 \;-\; 3x_3 &= -5.
\end{aligned}
$$

35

Since there is no third equation with which to eliminate x_3 from these two equations, the process terminates here. For each choice of x_3 these equations can be solved separately for x_1 and x_2. Thus, by letting x_3 vary over $\mathbf{R}$ we obtain an infinite set of solutions. Solving for x_1 and x_2 we get $x_1 = -3 + 2x_3$ and $x_2 = -5 + 3x_3$. So the solutions take the form

$$\begin{bmatrix} x_1 \\ x_2 \\ x_3 \end{bmatrix} = \begin{bmatrix} -3 + 2x_3 \\ -5 + 3x_3 \\ x_3 \end{bmatrix} = \begin{bmatrix} -3 \\ -5 \\ 0 \end{bmatrix} + x_3 \begin{bmatrix} 2 \\ 3 \\ 1 \end{bmatrix}.$$

This is precisely the parametric representation of a line in $\mathbf{R}^3$, the intersection of the planes described by the two equations.

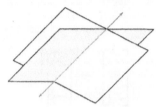

The set of solutions is infinite since the two equations do not provide enough information to uniquely determine a solution. $\diamond$

Example 5.3. Find all solutions of the system

$$\begin{array}{rcrcrcl} x_1 & + & x_2 & + & 2x_3 & = & 1 \\ x_1 & + & 2x_2 & + & x_3 & = & 2 \\ 2x_1 & + & 4x_2 & + & x_3 & = & 3 \\ 3x_1 & - & 2x_2 & + & 4x_3 & = & 4. \end{array}$$

Using the first equation to eliminate x_1 from the other three gives

$$\begin{array}{rcrcrcl} x_1 & + & x_2 & + & 2x_3 & = & 1 \\ & & x_2 & - & x_3 & = & 1 \\ & & 2x_2 & - & 3x_3 & = & 1 \\ & & -5x_2 & - & 2x_3 & = & 1. \end{array}$$

Using the second equation to eliminate x_2 from the other three gives

$$\begin{array}{rcrcrcl} x_1 & & & + & 3x_3 & = & 0 \\ & & x_2 & - & x_3 & = & 1 \\ & & & & -x_3 & = & -1 \\ & & & & -7x_3 & = & 6. \end{array}$$

Finally, dividing the third equation by -1 and using it to eliminate x_3 from the other equations, we arrive at

$$\begin{array}{rcr} x_1 & = & -3 \\ x_2 & = & 2 \\ x_3 & = & 1 \\ 0 & = & 13. \end{array}$$

36

The last equation is obviously impossible, so the system has no solution. In this case the system is said to be **inconsistent**. The four equations provide too many conditions to be satisfied by the three unknowns. Geometrically, there is no point which lies on all four of the planes described by the four equations. $\diamond$

Based on these examples it is tempting to say that a system has no solution if there are more equations than unknowns, and infinitely many solutions if there are fewer equations than unknowns. However, this is *not* always the case.

Example 5.4. Consider the system

$$
\begin{aligned}
x_1 &+& x_2 &-& x_3 &=& 3 \\
2x_1 &+& 3x_2 &+& 2x_3 &=& 4 \\
2x_1 &+& x_2 &-& 6x_3 &=& 8 \\
3x_1 &+& 5x_2 &+& 5x_3 &=& 5.
\end{aligned}
$$

Using the first equation to eliminate x_1 results in

$$
\begin{aligned}
x_1 &+& x_2 &-& x_3 &=& 3 \\
&& x_2 &+& 4x_3 &=& -2 \\
&& -x_2 &-& 4x_3 &=& 2 \\
&& 2x_2 &+& 8x_3 &=& -4.
\end{aligned}
$$

Notice that the last three equations are multiples of one another. So when the second equation is used to eliminate x_2 we get

$$
\begin{aligned}
x_1 && -& 5x_3 &=& 5 \\
&x_2 &+& 4x_3 &=& -2 \\
&& & 0 &=& 0 \\
&& & 0 &=& 0.
\end{aligned}
$$

The final two equations are trivial, and solving for x_1 and x_2 in terms of x_3, we find

$$
\begin{bmatrix} x_1 \\ x_2 \\ x_3 \end{bmatrix} = \begin{bmatrix} 5 + 5x_3 \\ -2 - 4x_3 \\ x_3 \end{bmatrix} = \begin{bmatrix} 5 \\ -2 \\ 0 \end{bmatrix} + x_3 \begin{bmatrix} 5 \\ -4 \\ 1 \end{bmatrix}.
$$

Geometrically, the set of solutions is the line of intersection of the four planes described by the four equations.

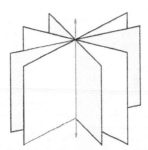

Thus the set of solution is infinite, even though there are more equations than unknowns. $\diamond$

Example 5.5. The system

$$x_1 + 3x_2 - 4x_3 = 3$$
$$2x_1 + 6x_2 - 8x_3 = 2$$

reduces to

$$x_1 + 3x_2 - 4x_3 = 3$$
$$0 = -4$$

so there are no solutions even though there are fewer equations than unknowns. Geometrically, the two planes described by these equations are parallel, and therefore do not intersect.

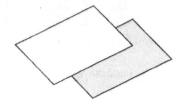

$\diamond$

Exercises

In Exercises 1 through 8 find all solutions to each system. Describe the intersection of the planes geometrically.

5.1.
$$3x_1 + 2x_2 - 2x_3 = -8$$
$$-3x_1 \qquad + 2x_3 = 10$$
$$3x_1 + 4x_2 - 4x_3 = 10.$$

5.2.
$$7x_1 + x_2 - 5x_3 = 10$$
$$4x_1 + x_2 - 2x_3 = 7$$
$$6x_1 + x_2 - 4x_3 = 9.$$

5.3.
$$2x_1 + 3x_2 + 9x_3 = 3$$
$$-2x_1 + x_2 + 3x_3 = -5$$
$$3x_1 + 2x_2 + 6x_3 = 6.$$

5.4.
$$-3x_1 + x_2 + 4x_3 = 2$$
$$6x_1 - 2x_2 - 8x_3 = 1.$$

5.5.
$$2x_1 + 3x_2 - x_3 = 0$$
$$-x_1 + 4x_2 + 6x_3 = 2.$$

5.6.
$$-4x_1 + 4x_2 + x_3 = -1$$
$$2x_1 - 2x_2 - x_3 = 3$$
$$8x_1 + 6x_2 + 2x_3 = -5.$$

$$
\begin{array}{llll}
\text{5.7.} & \begin{array}{rrrrr}
2x_1 & - & x_2 & + & 3x_3 & = & -15 \\
-3x_1 & - & 4x_2 & + & 2x_3 & = & -7 \\
x_1 & + & 4x_2 & + & 2x_3 & = & -3 \\
-2x_1 & + & x_2 & + & x_3 & = & 4.
\end{array}
\end{array}
$$

$$
\begin{array}{llll}
\text{5.8.} & \begin{array}{rrrrr}
x_1 & & & + & x_3 & = & -1 \\
x_1 & + & x_2 & + & 3x_3 & = & -1 \\
& & x_2 & + & 2x_3 & = & 0 \\
-2x_1 & + & x_2 & & & = & 4.
\end{array}
\end{array}
$$

In Exercises 9 through 16 write the vector $\mathbf{v}$ as a linear combination of vectors in the given set, or show that $\mathbf{v}$ is not in the span of the set.

5.9. $\left\{ \begin{bmatrix} 2 \\ 1 \end{bmatrix}, \begin{bmatrix} 3 \\ 2 \end{bmatrix} \right\}$ $\quad \mathbf{v} = \begin{bmatrix} 1 \\ 2 \end{bmatrix}$

5.10. $\left\{ \begin{bmatrix} 2 \\ 1 \\ 1 \end{bmatrix}, \begin{bmatrix} 5 \\ 8 \\ 0 \end{bmatrix}, \begin{bmatrix} 1 \\ 6 \\ -2 \end{bmatrix} \right\}$ $\quad \mathbf{v} = \begin{bmatrix} 8 \\ -5 \\ -11 \end{bmatrix}$

5.11. $\left\{ \begin{bmatrix} 2 \\ 1 \\ 1 \end{bmatrix}, \begin{bmatrix} 5 \\ 8 \\ 0 \end{bmatrix}, \begin{bmatrix} 11 \\ 2 \\ -12 \end{bmatrix} \right\}$ $\quad \mathbf{v} = \begin{bmatrix} 8 \\ -5 \\ -11 \end{bmatrix}$

5.12. $\left\{ \begin{bmatrix} 1 \\ 1 \\ 1 \\ 1 \end{bmatrix}, \begin{bmatrix} 1 \\ 2 \\ 3 \\ 4 \end{bmatrix}, \begin{bmatrix} 4 \\ 3 \\ 2 \\ 1 \end{bmatrix} \right\}$ $\quad \mathbf{v} = \begin{bmatrix} 1 \\ 5 \\ 9 \\ 13 \end{bmatrix}$

5.13. $\left\{ \begin{bmatrix} 2 \\ -1 \\ 1 \end{bmatrix}, \begin{bmatrix} 5 \\ 3 \\ -1 \end{bmatrix}, \begin{bmatrix} 1 \\ 5 \\ 3 \end{bmatrix} \right\}$ $\quad \mathbf{v} = \begin{bmatrix} -2 \\ 1 \\ -3 \end{bmatrix}$

5.14. $\left\{ \begin{bmatrix} 1 \\ 2 \\ 3 \\ 4 \end{bmatrix}, \begin{bmatrix} -2 \\ 1 \\ -1 \\ 3 \end{bmatrix} \right\}$ $\quad \mathbf{v} = \begin{bmatrix} -1 \\ 8 \\ 7 \\ 16 \end{bmatrix}$

5.15. $\left\{ \begin{bmatrix} 1 \\ 1 \end{bmatrix}, \begin{bmatrix} 1 \\ 3 \end{bmatrix} \right\}$ $\quad \mathbf{v} = \begin{bmatrix} 0 \\ 0 \end{bmatrix}$

5.16. $\left\{ \begin{bmatrix} 3 \\ 2 \\ -2 \end{bmatrix}, \begin{bmatrix} -1 \\ -1 \\ 2 \end{bmatrix} \right\}$ $\quad \mathbf{v} = \begin{bmatrix} 1 \\ -1 \\ 6 \end{bmatrix}$

In Exercises 17 through 25, find all vectors which are orthogonal to all of the given vectors.

5.17. $\left\{ \begin{bmatrix} 1 \\ 1 \\ 1 \end{bmatrix}, \begin{bmatrix} 3 \\ 2 \\ 4 \end{bmatrix} \right\}$

5.18. $\left\{ \begin{bmatrix} 2 \\ -1 \\ 5 \end{bmatrix}, \begin{bmatrix} -1 \\ 0 \\ 3 \end{bmatrix} \right\}$

5.19. $\left\{ \begin{bmatrix} 1 \\ -1 \\ 1 \end{bmatrix}, \begin{bmatrix} -1 \\ 0 \\ 3 \end{bmatrix}, \begin{bmatrix} -3 \\ 2 \\ 3 \end{bmatrix} \right\}$

5.20. $\left\{ \begin{bmatrix} 1 \\ -1 \\ 1 \end{bmatrix}, \begin{bmatrix} -1 \\ 0 \\ 3 \end{bmatrix}, \begin{bmatrix} -3 \\ 2 \\ 1 \end{bmatrix} \right\}$

5.21. $\left\{ \begin{bmatrix} 2 \\ 3 \\ 5 \end{bmatrix} \right\}$

5.22. $\left\{ \begin{bmatrix} 0 \\ 0 \\ 0 \end{bmatrix} \right\}$

5.23. $\left\{ \begin{bmatrix} 1 \\ 1 \\ 1 \\ 1 \end{bmatrix}, \begin{bmatrix} 1 \\ 2 \\ 3 \\ 4 \end{bmatrix}, \begin{bmatrix} 1 \\ -1 \\ 1 \\ -1 \end{bmatrix} \right\}$

5.24. $\left\{ \begin{bmatrix} 1 \\ -1 \\ -1 \\ 1 \end{bmatrix} \right\}$

5.25. $\left\{ \begin{bmatrix} 1 \\ 0 \\ 1 \\ 0 \end{bmatrix}, \begin{bmatrix} 0 \\ 1 \\ 0 \\ 1 \end{bmatrix} \right\}$

6 Matrices

Each step in Gaussian elimination simply modifies the coefficients a_{ij} and the right hand sides b_i of the system. To save time and space it is convenient to work only with these numbers. An $m \times n$ **matrix** is a rectangular array of numbers with m rows and n columns. Given a linear system

$$
\begin{array}{ccccccccc}
a_{11}x_1 & + & a_{12}x_2 & + & \cdots & + & a_{1n}x_n & = & b_1 \\
a_{21}x_1 & + & a_{22}x_2 & + & \cdots & + & a_{2n}x_n & = & b_2 \\
& & & & \vdots & & & & \\
a_{m1}x_1 & + & a_{m2}x_2 & + & \cdots & + & a_{mn}x_n & = & b_m
\end{array}
$$

the **coefficient matrix** of the system is the $m \times n$ matrix

$$
A = \begin{bmatrix}
a_{11} & a_{12} & \cdots & a_{1n} \\
a_{21} & a_{22} & \cdots & a_{2n} \\
\vdots & \vdots & \ddots & \vdots \\
a_{m1} & a_{m2} & \cdots & a_{mn}
\end{bmatrix}
$$

whose entries are the coefficients of the system. The **augmented matrix** for the system is the $m \times (n+1)$ matrix

$$
\left[\begin{array}{cccc|c}
a_{11} & a_{12} & \cdots & a_{1n} & b_1 \\
a_{21} & a_{22} & \cdots & a_{2n} & b_2 \\
\vdots & \vdots & \ddots & \vdots & \vdots \\
a_{m1} & a_{m2} & \cdots & a_{mn} & b_m
\end{array}\right]
$$

obtained by augmenting the coefficient matrix with the entries on the right hand side of the equations. The vertical line distinguishes an augmented matrix from a coefficient matrix.

Example 6.1. The system

$$
\begin{array}{ccccccc}
3x_1 & - & 2x_2 & + & x_3 & = & 9 \\
4x_1 & & & + & 5x_3 & = & 2
\end{array}
$$

has coefficient matrix

$$
\begin{bmatrix}
3 & -2 & 1 \\
4 & 0 & 5
\end{bmatrix}
$$

and augmented matrix

$$
\left[\begin{array}{ccc|c}
3 & -2 & 1 & 9 \\
4 & 0 & 5 & 2
\end{array}\right].
$$

Notice that the absence of x_2 in the second equation simply means its coefficient is zero. $\diamond$

Each equation of a linear system corresponds to a row of its augmented matrix, and thus each step in the elimination process corresponds to a **row operation**. There are three types of row operations.

1. Divide a row by a nonzero scalar.

2. Subtract a scalar multiple of one row from another row.

3. Exchange two rows.

We will explain the need for the third operation momentarily. The most important fact is that *row operations do not change the set of solutions of the system*. The goal of elimination is to put the augmented matrix in **reduced row echelon form**. A matrix is in reduced row echelon form if the following conditions hold.

Properties of Reduced Row Echelon Form

1. The first nonzero entry in each row equals 1. These entries are called the **pivot** entries.

2. Each pivot is further to the right than the pivot of the row immediately above.

3. All other entries in the column of any pivot are zero.

4. If a row has all zero entries, then so does every row below.

Example 6.2. The following is a list of all possible 2×3 reduced row echelon form matrices.

$$\begin{bmatrix} 1 & 0 & * \\ 0 & 1 & * \end{bmatrix} \quad \begin{bmatrix} 1 & * & 0 \\ 0 & 0 & 1 \end{bmatrix} \quad \begin{bmatrix} 0 & 1 & 0 \\ 0 & 0 & 1 \end{bmatrix} \quad \begin{bmatrix} 1 & * & * \\ 0 & 0 & 0 \end{bmatrix} \quad \begin{bmatrix} 0 & 1 & * \\ 0 & 0 & 0 \end{bmatrix} \quad \begin{bmatrix} 0 & 0 & 1 \\ 0 & 0 & 0 \end{bmatrix} \quad \begin{bmatrix} 0 & 0 & 0 \\ 0 & 0 & 0 \end{bmatrix}$$

The asterisks can be any real numbers, including zero. $\diamond$

Two matrices are said to be **row equivalent** if one can be obtained from the other by a sequence of row operations. Since row operations are reversible, this relationship is symmetric. It turns out that every matrix is row equivalent to a unique matrix in reduced row echelon form.

Proposition 6.1. Let A be any $m \times n$ matrix. Then A is row equivalent to exactly one reduced row echelon form matrix. This matrix is called the reduced row echelon form of A and is denoted $\mathrm{rref}(A)$.

The examples in this section illustrate how one might construct an algorithm for finding the reduced row echelon form of a matrix A. The proof of its uniqueness is somewhat technical and can be found in Appendix C.

Example 6.3. Find the reduced row echelon form of

$$A = \begin{bmatrix} 1 & 1 & 0 & 0 & 2 \\ 2 & 2 & 0 & 1 & 6 \\ 0 & 1 & -1 & 1 & 3 \\ -1 & -2 & 1 & 1 & -1 \end{bmatrix}.$$

Solution. Subtracting twice the first row from the second and adding the first row to the fourth results in

$$\begin{bmatrix} 1 & 1 & 0 & 0 & 2 \\ 0 & 0 & 0 & 1 & 2 \\ 0 & 1 & -1 & 1 & 3 \\ 0 & -1 & 1 & 1 & 1 \end{bmatrix}.$$

Notice that the first nonzero entry in the third row is to the *left* of the first nonzero entry in the second row. This violates one of the conditions of echelon form. The solution is to exchange the second row with the third row.

$$\begin{bmatrix} 1 & 1 & 0 & 0 & 2 \\ 0 & 1 & -1 & 1 & 3 \\ 0 & 0 & 0 & 1 & 2 \\ 0 & -1 & 1 & 1 & 1 \end{bmatrix}$$

Now we can use the second row to eliminate the other nonzero entries in the second column. Subtracting the second row from the first and adding the second row to the fourth gives

$$\begin{bmatrix} 1 & 0 & 1 & -1 & -1 \\ 0 & 1 & -1 & 1 & 3 \\ 0 & 0 & 0 & 1 & 2 \\ 0 & 0 & 0 & 2 & 4 \end{bmatrix}.$$

The first nonzero entry in the third row is in the fourth column, so we use it to eliminate the other entries in the fourth column. Adding the third row to the first, subtracting the third row from the second, and subtracting twice the third row from the fourth we get

$$\begin{bmatrix} 1 & 0 & 1 & 0 & 1 \\ 0 & 1 & -1 & 0 & 1 \\ 0 & 0 & 0 & 1 & 2 \\ 0 & 0 & 0 & 0 & 0 \end{bmatrix},$$

which is in reduced row echelon form.   ◇

Given a system whose augmented matrix is in reduced row echelon form, it is very easy to determine the set of solutions. We identify the variables as one of two types. Those variables whose corresponding column contains a pivot are called **pivot variables**. The remaining variables are called **free variables**. By the properties of reduced row echelon form, every nonzero equation of the system either contains a pivot variable, or is the equation $0 = 1$. That is, any equation which actually contains a variable contains a pivot variable. Moreover, each pivot variable appears in *exactly one* equation of the system and it is *the only pivot variable* in that equation. Thus, given any choice of the free variables, we can solve for the pivot variables, and the only possible inconsistency that can arise is an equation of the form $0 = 1$.

Example 6.4. Find the set of solutions of the system

$$
\begin{aligned}
x_1 + 2x_2 + x_3 + x_4 &= 7 \\
x_1 + 2x_2 + 2x_3 - x_4 &= 12 \\
2x_1 + 4x_2 + 6x_4 &= 4.
\end{aligned}
$$

Solution. The augmented matrix of this system is

$$
\left[\begin{array}{cccc|c}
1 & 2 & 1 & 1 & 7 \\
1 & 2 & 2 & -1 & 12 \\
2 & 4 & 0 & 6 & 4
\end{array}\right].
$$

Its reduced row echelon form is

$$
\left[\begin{array}{cccc|c}
1 & 2 & 0 & 3 & 2 \\
0 & 0 & 1 & -2 & 5 \\
0 & 0 & 0 & 0 & 0
\end{array}\right].
$$

(Verify this!) Thus the system reduces to

$$
\begin{aligned}
x_1 + 2x_2 + 3x_4 &= 2 \\
x_3 - 2x_4 &= 5 \\
0 &= 0.
\end{aligned}
$$

Solving for the pivot variables x_1 and x_3 in terms of the free variables x_2 and x_4 gives $x_1 = 2 - 2x_2 - 3x_4$ and $x_3 = 5 + 2x_4$. The solution therefore takes the form

$$
\begin{bmatrix} x_1 \\ x_2 \\ x_3 \\ x_4 \end{bmatrix}
=
\begin{bmatrix} 2 - 2x_2 - 3x_4 \\ x_2 \\ 5 + 2x_4 \\ x_4 \end{bmatrix}
=
\begin{bmatrix} 2 \\ 0 \\ 5 \\ 0 \end{bmatrix}
+ x_2 \begin{bmatrix} -2 \\ 1 \\ 0 \\ 0 \end{bmatrix}
+ x_4 \begin{bmatrix} -3 \\ 0 \\ 2 \\ 1 \end{bmatrix}.
$$

This is a parametric representation of a plane in $\mathbf{R}^4$. $\diamond$

Example 6.5. Find the set of solutions of the system

$$
\begin{aligned}
x_1 + 2x_2 + x_3 + x_4 &= 8 \\
x_1 + 2x_2 + 2x_3 - x_4 &= 12 \\
2x_1 + 4x_2 + 6x_4 &= 4.
\end{aligned}
$$

Solution. Notice that this is exactly the same system as in Example 6.4 except for the right hand side of the first equation. Since

$$
\mathrm{rref}
\left[\begin{array}{cccc|c}
1 & 2 & 1 & 1 & 8 \\
1 & 2 & 2 & -1 & 12 \\
2 & 4 & 0 & 6 & 4
\end{array}\right]
=
\left[\begin{array}{cccc|c}
1 & 2 & 0 & 3 & 0 \\
0 & 0 & 1 & -2 & 0 \\
0 & 0 & 0 & 0 & 1
\end{array}\right]
$$

the system reduces to

$$
\begin{aligned}
x_1 + 2x_2 + 3x_4 &= 0 \\
x_3 - 2x_4 &= 0 \\
0 &= 1.
\end{aligned}
$$

The last equation is impossible so the system has no solutions. $\diamond$

44

Given a system whose augmented matrix is in reduced row echelon form, the size of the solution set is determined by two factors – the absence or presence of the equation $0 = 1$, and the number of free variables. The system has no solutions if the equation $0 = 1$ appears. If the system does not contain the equation $0 = 1$, the system is consistent. In this case, if there are no free variables, there is a unique solution. If there are free variables (one or more) then there are infinitely many solutions, one for each choice of values for the free variables. These observations are summarized in the following proposition.

Proposition 6.2. Given a system whose augmented matrix is in reduced row echelon form, there are three possibilities.

1. **No solutions.** One of the equations is $0 = 1$.

2. **Exactly one solution.** There are no free variables, and no equation $0 = 1$.

3. **Infinitely many solutions.** There is at least one free variable, and no equation $0 = 1$.

Since, by Proposition 6.1, every matrix is row equivalent to a unique reduced row echelon form matrix, and since row operations on the augmented matrix do not change the set of solutions of the system, the three possibilities listed above apply to *any* system of linear equations. So *every linear system has no solutions, exactly one solution, or infinitely many solutions.*

Exercises

In Exercises 1 through 6 express the given system as an augmented matrix, use Gaussian elimination to put the system in reduced row echelon form, and determine whether the system has no solutions, one solution (find it) or infinitely many solutions.

6.1.
$$\begin{aligned} w \qquad\quad +\ y \qquad\qquad &= 5 \\ w + 2x + 3y + 4z &= 13 \\ w + 2x + \ y + 2z &= 5. \end{aligned}$$

6.2.
$$\begin{aligned} x + 2y + 3z &= 1 \\ 2x + \ y - 2z &= 1. \end{aligned}$$

6.3.
$$\begin{aligned} x - 2y + \ z &= 0 \\ 2x + 2y - \ z &= 8 \\ 3x + \ y + 2z &= 0 \\ x - 2y + 3z &= -7. \end{aligned}$$

6.4.
$$\begin{aligned} w + 2x - \ y - \ z &= 1 \\ 2w + 4x - 2y + 3z &= 3 \\ -w + \ x - 2y + 4z &= 2. \end{aligned}$$

$$
\begin{array}{rrrrr}
u & + & 2v & + & 3w & = & -1 \\
6.5. & u & + & 2v & + & 4w & = & -2 \\
-2u & - & 4v & - & 4w & = & 2.
\end{array}
$$

6.5.
$$
\begin{aligned}
u + 2v + 3w &= -1 \\
u + 2v + 4w &= -2 \\
-2u - 4v - 4w &= 2.
\end{aligned}
$$

6.6.
$$
\begin{aligned}
x + y + z &= 3 \\
x + 2y + 3z &= 0 \\
x + 3y + 4z &= -2.
\end{aligned}
$$

6.7. In each part, find the reduced row echelon form of the given augmented matrix. Write the system of equations corresponding to the original augmented matrix and to the reduced row echelon form matrix. Find all solutions.

(a) $\begin{bmatrix} 2 & 3 & 1 & | & 0 \\ -1 & 4 & 0 & | & 0 \\ -6 & 2 & -2 & | & 0 \end{bmatrix}$

(b) $\begin{bmatrix} 2 & 3 & 1 & | & -3 \\ -1 & 4 & 0 & | & 1 \\ -6 & 2 & -2 & | & 6 \end{bmatrix}$

In Exercises 8 through 12, write the vector $\mathbf{v}$ as a linear combination of the vectors in the given set, or show that $\mathbf{v}$ is not in the span.

6.8. $\left\{ \begin{bmatrix} 2 \\ 3 \\ 2 \end{bmatrix}, \begin{bmatrix} -4 \\ 1 \\ 8 \end{bmatrix}, \begin{bmatrix} 5 \\ 2 \\ 4 \end{bmatrix} \right\} \qquad \mathbf{v} = \begin{bmatrix} 4 \\ 3 \\ 1 \end{bmatrix}$

6.9. $\left\{ \begin{bmatrix} 2 \\ 3 \\ 2 \end{bmatrix}, \begin{bmatrix} -4 \\ 1 \\ 8 \end{bmatrix}, \begin{bmatrix} -8 \\ 9 \\ 30 \end{bmatrix} \right\} \qquad \mathbf{v} = \begin{bmatrix} 0 \\ -2 \\ 1 \end{bmatrix}$

6.10. $\left\{ \begin{bmatrix} 1 \\ -4 \\ 5 \end{bmatrix}, \begin{bmatrix} -2 \\ 3 \\ 1 \end{bmatrix}, \begin{bmatrix} 1 \\ 0 \\ 4 \end{bmatrix} \right\} \qquad \mathbf{v} = \begin{bmatrix} -6 \\ 18 \\ -9 \end{bmatrix}$

6.11. $\left\{ \begin{bmatrix} 7 \\ 5 \\ -2 \end{bmatrix}, \begin{bmatrix} 2 \\ -3 \\ 1 \end{bmatrix} \right\} \qquad \mathbf{v} = \begin{bmatrix} 2 \\ -2 \\ 1 \end{bmatrix}$

6.12. $\left\{ \begin{bmatrix} -4 \\ 2 \end{bmatrix}, \begin{bmatrix} 1 \\ 3 \end{bmatrix} \right\} \qquad \mathbf{v} = \begin{bmatrix} -4 \\ 9 \end{bmatrix}$

6.13. Find the coefficients of the quadratic polynomial $p(x) = ax^2 + bx + c$ which passes through the points $(1, 1)$, $(2, 2)$ and $(-1, 5)$.

6.14. Is there a polynomial $p(x) = x^3 + ax^2 + bx + c$ which satisfies $p(-2) = 2$, $p(-1) = 3$, $p(1) = 0$ and $p(2) = 8$?

6.15. Suppose $f(t) = A \cos t + B \sin t + Ce^t$ and $f(0) = 2$, $f'(0) = 0$, $f''(0) = 6$. Find A, B and C.

7 Matrix-Vector Products

In this section we will investigate the structure of solution sets of linear systems. First we introduce some important notation. Given a linear system

$$
\begin{array}{ccccccccc}
a_{11}x_1 & + & a_{12}x_2 & + & \cdots & + & a_{1n}x_n & = & b_1 \\
a_{21}x_1 & + & a_{22}x_2 & + & \cdots & + & a_{2n}x_n & = & b_2 \\
\vdots & & \vdots & & & & \vdots & & \vdots \\
a_{m1}x_1 & + & a_{m2}x_2 & + & \cdots & + & a_{mn}x_n & = & b_m
\end{array}
\tag{7.1}
$$

we may rewrite it as a single vector equation

$$
\begin{bmatrix}
a_{11}x_1 & + & a_{12}x_2 & + & \cdots & + & a_{1n}x_n \\
a_{21}x_1 & + & a_{22}x_2 & + & \cdots & + & a_{2n}x_n \\
\vdots & & \vdots & & & & \vdots \\
a_{m1}x_1 & + & a_{m2}x_2 & + & \cdots & + & a_{mn}x_n
\end{bmatrix}
=
\begin{bmatrix}
b_1 \\ b_2 \\ \vdots \\ b_m
\end{bmatrix}.
\tag{7.2}
$$

Let A denote the coefficient matrix of the system, and let $\mathbf{x}$ denote the vector of unknowns x_1 through x_n. Then we define the **matrix-vector product** of the matrix A with the vector $\mathbf{x}$ to be the vector

$$
A\mathbf{x} =
\begin{bmatrix}
a_{11} & a_{12} & \cdots & a_{1n} \\
a_{21} & a_{22} & \cdots & a_{2n} \\
\vdots & \vdots & & \vdots \\
a_{m1} & a_{m2} & \cdots & a_{mn}
\end{bmatrix}
\begin{bmatrix}
x_1 \\ x_2 \\ \vdots \\ x_n
\end{bmatrix}
=
\begin{bmatrix}
a_{11}x_1 & + & a_{12}x_2 & + & \cdots & + & a_{1n}x_n \\
a_{21}x_1 & + & a_{22}x_2 & + & \cdots & + & a_{2n}x_n \\
\vdots & & \vdots & & & & \vdots \\
a_{m1}x_1 & + & a_{m2}x_2 & + & \cdots & + & a_{mn}x_n
\end{bmatrix}.
$$

The system (7.1) can now be written concisely as

$$
A\mathbf{x} = \mathbf{b}
$$

where $\mathbf{b}$ is the vector on the right hand side of (7.2).

There are two important ways of viewing the product $A\mathbf{x}$. The first is to write $A\mathbf{x}$ as a sum of n vectors and factor out the components x_i of $\mathbf{x}$ to get

$$
A\mathbf{x} = x_1
\begin{bmatrix}
a_{11} \\ a_{21} \\ \vdots \\ a_{m1}
\end{bmatrix}
+ x_2
\begin{bmatrix}
a_{12} \\ a_{22} \\ \vdots \\ a_{m2}
\end{bmatrix}
+ \cdots + x_n
\begin{bmatrix}
a_{1n} \\ a_{2n} \\ \vdots \\ a_{mn}
\end{bmatrix},
$$

the linear combinations of the *columns* of A obtained by using the components of $\mathbf{x}$ as coefficients. So if we let $\mathbf{v}_1, \mathbf{v}_2, \ldots, \mathbf{v}_n$ denote the columns of A then

$$Ax = \begin{bmatrix} | & | & & | \\ \mathbf{v}_1 & \mathbf{v}_2 & \cdots & \mathbf{v}_n \\ | & | & & | \end{bmatrix} \begin{bmatrix} x_1 \\ x_2 \\ \vdots \\ x_n \end{bmatrix} = x_1\mathbf{v}_1 + x_2\mathbf{v}_2 + \cdots + x_n\mathbf{v}_n. \tag{7.3}$$

So Ax is the linear combination of the columns of A whose coefficients are the components of $\mathbf{x}$.

On the other hand, we can view the product in terms of the rows of A. To do this correctly we need to introduce some notation. When we speak of a vector $\mathbf{v}$ in $\mathbf{R}^n$ we always mean a **column vector**. We define the **transpose** of the column vector $\mathbf{v}$ to be the **row vector** $\mathbf{v}^T$ whose components are the same as the components of $\mathbf{v}$, but are written horizontally instead of vertically. That is,

$$\mathbf{v} = \begin{bmatrix} v_1 \\ v_2 \\ \vdots \\ v_n \end{bmatrix} \quad \Longrightarrow \quad \mathbf{v}^T = \begin{bmatrix} v_1 & v_2 & \cdots & v_n \end{bmatrix}.$$

Now we observe that the first component of the product Ax is the dot product of the vector

$$\mathbf{w}_1 = \begin{bmatrix} a_{11} \\ a_{12} \\ \vdots \\ a_{1n} \end{bmatrix}$$

with $\mathbf{x}$, and that the row vector $\mathbf{w}_1^T$ is the first row of the matrix A. Likewise, component i of Ax is the dot product of

$$\mathbf{w}_i = \begin{bmatrix} a_{i1} \\ a_{i2} \\ \vdots \\ a_{in} \end{bmatrix}$$

with $\mathbf{x}$, and $\mathbf{w}_i^T$ is row i of A. Thus

$$Ax = \begin{bmatrix} \rule{1em}{0.4pt} & \mathbf{w}_1^T & \rule{1em}{0.4pt} \\ \rule{1em}{0.4pt} & \mathbf{w}_2^T & \rule{1em}{0.4pt} \\ & \vdots & \\ \rule{1em}{0.4pt} & \mathbf{w}_m^T & \rule{1em}{0.4pt} \end{bmatrix} \begin{bmatrix} | \\ \mathbf{x} \\ | \end{bmatrix} = \begin{bmatrix} \mathbf{w}_1 \cdot \mathbf{x} \\ \mathbf{w}_2 \cdot \mathbf{x} \\ \vdots \\ \mathbf{w}_m \cdot \mathbf{x} \end{bmatrix}.$$

Example 7.1. Let

$$A = \begin{bmatrix} \overset{a_{11}}{1} & \overset{a_{12}}{2} & \overset{a_{13}}{3} \\ 2 & -1 & 3 \end{bmatrix} \quad \text{and} \quad \mathbf{x} = \begin{bmatrix} 3 \\ 2 \\ -1 \end{bmatrix}.$$

Then

$$A\mathbf{x} = 3\begin{bmatrix} 1 \\ 2 \end{bmatrix} + 2\begin{bmatrix} 2 \\ -1 \end{bmatrix} - 1\begin{bmatrix} 3 \\ 3 \end{bmatrix} = \begin{bmatrix} 4 \\ 1 \end{bmatrix}$$

or, equivalently

$$A\mathbf{x} = \begin{bmatrix} 1(3) + 2(2) + 3(-1) \\ 2(3) - 1(2) + 3(-1) \end{bmatrix} = \begin{bmatrix} 4 \\ 1 \end{bmatrix}.$$

$\diamond$

Notice that the product $A\mathbf{x}$ only makes sense if <u>the number of columns of A equals</u> the number <u>of components of $\mathbf{x}$</u>, i.e. when <u>$\mathbf{x}$ is in $\mathbf{R}^n$ and A is $m \times n$</u> for some m. The vector $A\mathbf{x}$ then has m components and is therefore a vector in $\mathbf{R}^m$. <u>We can therefore think of</u> <u>multiplication by A as a function</u> which takes vectors in $\mathbf{R}^n$ to vectors in $\mathbf{R}^m$.

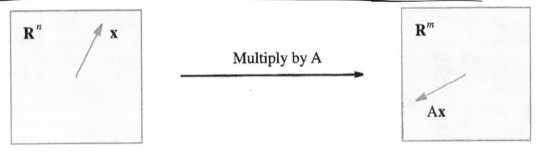

We now prove the <u>two most important properties of matrix-vector products.</u>

Proposition 7.1. Let A be an $m \times n$ matrix. Then

1. $\underline{A(\mathbf{x} + \mathbf{y}) = A\mathbf{x} + A\mathbf{y}}$

2. $A(c\mathbf{x}) = cA\mathbf{x}$

for any vectors $\mathbf{x}$, $\mathbf{y}$ in $\mathbf{R}^n$ and any scalar $c \in \mathbf{R}$.

Proof. Let $\mathbf{v}_1$ through $\mathbf{v}_n$ denote the columns of A, let x_1 through x_n denote the components of $\mathbf{x}$ and let y_1 through y_n denote the components of $\mathbf{y}$. Then, using equation (7.3),

$$A(\mathbf{x} + \mathbf{y}) = (x_1 + y_1)\mathbf{v}_1 + (x_2 + y_2)\mathbf{v}_2 + \cdots + (x_n + y_n)\mathbf{v}_n$$
$$= (x_1\mathbf{v}_1 + x_2\mathbf{v}_2 + \cdots + x_n\mathbf{v}_n) + (y_1\mathbf{v}_1 + y_2\mathbf{v}_2 + \cdots + y_n\mathbf{v}_n)$$
$$= A\mathbf{x} + A\mathbf{y}$$

and

$$A(c\mathbf{x}) = (cx_1)\mathbf{v}_1 + (cx_2)\mathbf{v}_2 + \cdots + (cx_n)\mathbf{v}_n$$
$$= c(x_1\mathbf{v}_1 + x_2\mathbf{v}_2 + \cdots + x_n\mathbf{v}_n)$$
$$= cA\mathbf{x}.$$

□

It follows by repeated application of these properties that

$$A(c_1\mathbf{x}_1 + c_2\mathbf{x}_2 + \cdots + c_k\mathbf{x}_k) = c_1A\mathbf{x}_1 + c_2A\mathbf{x}_2 + \cdots + c_kA\mathbf{x}_k,$$

the product of A with a linear combination of $\mathbf{x}_1$ through $\mathbf{x}_k$ equals the same linear combination of $A\mathbf{x}_1$ through $A\mathbf{x}_k$.

Exercises

In Exercises 1 through 6 calculate the matrix-vector product, or state that the product is not defined.

7.1. $A = \begin{bmatrix} 2 & 0 & 1 \\ 3 & -4 & 2 \\ 5 & 1 & -3 \end{bmatrix} \qquad \mathbf{v} = \begin{bmatrix} 3 \\ -4 \\ 1 \end{bmatrix}.$

7.2. $A = \begin{bmatrix} 3 & 1 & 8 \\ -4 & 5 & 2 \end{bmatrix} \qquad \mathbf{v} = \begin{bmatrix} 2 \\ -1 \\ 0 \end{bmatrix}.$

7.3. $A = \begin{bmatrix} 3 & 1 & 8 \\ -4 & 5 & 2 \end{bmatrix} \qquad \mathbf{v} = \begin{bmatrix} 4 \\ -5 \end{bmatrix}.$

7.4. $A = \begin{bmatrix} 5 & -7 & 2 & 0 \\ 5 & -1 & 3 & 1 \end{bmatrix} \qquad \mathbf{v} = \begin{bmatrix} -2 \\ 5 \end{bmatrix}.$

7.5. $A = \begin{bmatrix} 5 & 5 \\ -7 & -1 \\ 2 & 3 \\ 0 & 1 \end{bmatrix} \qquad \mathbf{v} = \begin{bmatrix} -2 \\ 5 \end{bmatrix}.$

7.6. $A = \begin{bmatrix} 3 \\ 0 \\ -2 \\ 1 \end{bmatrix} \qquad \mathbf{v} = \begin{bmatrix} 8 \\ 2 \\ 3 \\ 1 \end{bmatrix}.$

8 Null Space

Given an $m \times n$ matrix A, we say that a linear system $A\mathbf{x} = \mathbf{b}$ is **homogeneous** if $\mathbf{b} = \mathbf{0}$, and **inhomogeneous if $\mathbf{b} \neq \mathbf{0}$**. Given an $m \times n$ matrix A, the **null space** of A is

$$N(A) = \{\mathbf{x} \in \mathbf{R}^n \mid A\mathbf{x} = \mathbf{0}\},$$

the set of all solutions of the homogeneous linear system $A\mathbf{x} = \mathbf{0}$. If we think of multiplication by A as a function which sends a vector $\mathbf{x}$ in $\mathbf{R}^n$ to a vector $A\mathbf{x}$ in $\mathbf{R}^m$, the null space is then the set of vectors which are sent to the zero vector.

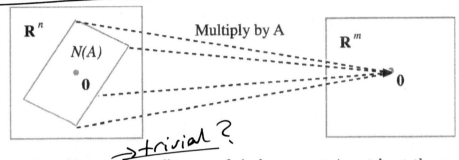

Observe that, since $A\mathbf{0} = \mathbf{0}$, ⟶ trivial ? the null space of A always contains at least the zero vector. So every homogeneous system is consistent. Furthermore, if $\mathbf{x}$ and $\mathbf{y}$ are solutions of $A\mathbf{x} = \mathbf{0}$, the properties of matrix-vector products imply that

$$A(\mathbf{x} + \mathbf{y}) = A\mathbf{x} + A\mathbf{y} = \mathbf{0} + \mathbf{0} = \mathbf{0}$$

and

$$A(c\mathbf{x}) = cA\mathbf{x} = c\mathbf{0} = \mathbf{0}$$

for any scalar c. Thus sums and scalar multiples of solutions of homogeneous linear systems are also solutions. These facts are summarized as follows.

Proposition 8.1. Let A be any $m \times n$ matrix. Then

1. $N(A)$ contains the zero vector.

2. If $\mathbf{x}$ and $\mathbf{y}$ are in $N(A)$, then $\mathbf{x} + \mathbf{y}$ is in $N(A)$.

3. If $\mathbf{x}$ is in $N(A)$, then $c\mathbf{x}$ is in $N(A)$ for any scalar c.

Repeated application of these properties shows that any linear combination of vectors in $N(A)$ is a vector in $N(A)$. This implies that $N(A)$ can be expressed as the span of some collection of vectors.

The null space of A is found by performing Gaussian elimination on the system $A\mathbf{x} = \mathbf{0}$. The task is simplified by observing that the final column of zeros in the augmented matrix cannot possibly become nonzero during elimination. So if we let $R = \mathrm{rref}(A)$, the system $A\mathbf{x} = \mathbf{0}$ reduces to $R\mathbf{x} = \mathbf{0}$. So

$$N(A) = N(\mathrm{rref}(A)),$$

the null space of A equals the null space of $\mathrm{rref}(A)$.

Example 8.1. Let

$$A = \begin{bmatrix} 1 & 1 & 1 & 1 \\ 1 & 2 & 3 & 4 \\ 4 & 3 & 2 & 1 \end{bmatrix}.$$

Since

$$\mathrm{rref}(A) = \begin{bmatrix} 1 & 0 & -1 & -2 \\ 0 & 1 & 2 & 3 \\ 0 & 0 & 0 & 0 \end{bmatrix}$$

the system $A\mathbf{x} = \mathbf{0}$ reduces to

$$\begin{aligned} x_1 \quad - \quad x_3 \quad - \quad 2x_4 &= 0 \\ x_2 + 2x_3 + 3x_4 &= 0. \end{aligned}$$

Solving for the pivot variables in terms of the free variables gives $x_1 = x_3 + 2x_4$ and $x_2 = -2x_3 - 3x_4$, so

$$\begin{bmatrix} x_1 \\ x_2 \\ x_3 \\ x_4 \end{bmatrix} = \begin{bmatrix} x_3 + 2x_4 \\ -2x_3 - 3x_4 \\ x_3 \\ x_4 \end{bmatrix} = x_3 \begin{bmatrix} 1 \\ -2 \\ 1 \\ 0 \end{bmatrix} + x_4 \begin{bmatrix} 2 \\ -3 \\ 0 \\ 1 \end{bmatrix}.$$

Thus

$$N(A) = \mathrm{span}\left(\begin{bmatrix} 1 \\ -2 \\ 1 \\ 0 \end{bmatrix}, \begin{bmatrix} 2 \\ -3 \\ 0 \\ 1 \end{bmatrix} \right).$$

Next let us consider an inhomogeneous system

$$A\mathbf{x} = \mathbf{b} \qquad \mathbf{b} \neq \mathbf{0}.$$

Suppose $\mathbf{x}$ and $\mathbf{y}$ are solutions of this system. Then

$$A(\mathbf{x} + \mathbf{y}) = A\mathbf{x} + A\mathbf{y} = \mathbf{b} + \mathbf{b} = 2\mathbf{b} \neq \mathbf{b}$$

so $\mathbf{x} + \mathbf{y}$ is not a solution. Likewise, for any scalar $c \neq 1$,

$$A(c\mathbf{x}) = cA\mathbf{x} = c\mathbf{b} \neq \mathbf{b}$$

so $c\mathbf{x}$ is not a solution. Thus the set of solutions of any inhomogeneous system is *not* closed under addition or scalar multiplication, and cannot be expressed as a span. However, there is a very nice relationship between the set of solutions of an inhomogeneous system $A\mathbf{x} = \mathbf{b}$ and the set of solutions of the corresponding homogeneous system $A\mathbf{x} = \mathbf{0}$.

Proposition 8.2. Suppose $\mathbf{x}_p$ is any particular solution of the inhomogeneous system $A\mathbf{x} = \mathbf{b}$. Then the set of solutions of the system $A\mathbf{x} = \mathbf{b}$ consists of all vectors of the form

$$\boxed{\mathbf{x}_p + \mathbf{x}_h}$$

where $\mathbf{x}_h$ is a solution of $A\mathbf{x} = \mathbf{0}$.

Proof. First we show that every vector of the form $\mathbf{x}_p + \mathbf{x}_h$ is a solution of $A\mathbf{x} = \mathbf{b}$. By the first property of matrix-vector products,

$$A(\mathbf{x}_p + \mathbf{x}_h) = A\mathbf{x}_p + A\mathbf{x}_h = \mathbf{b} + \mathbf{0} = \mathbf{b}$$

so $\mathbf{x}_p + \mathbf{x}_h$ is a solution of $A\mathbf{x} = \mathbf{b}$. Next we show that every solution of $A\mathbf{x} = \mathbf{b}$ equals $\mathbf{x}_p + \mathbf{x}_h$ for some solution $\mathbf{x}_h$ of $A\mathbf{x} = \mathbf{0}$. Suppose $\mathbf{x}$ is any solution of $A\mathbf{x} = \mathbf{b}$. Then

$$A(\mathbf{x} - \mathbf{x}_p) = A\mathbf{x} - A\mathbf{x}_p = \mathbf{b} - \mathbf{b} = \mathbf{0}$$

so $\mathbf{x} - \mathbf{x}_p$ is a solution of $A\mathbf{x} = \mathbf{0}$. Call this solution $\mathbf{x}_h$. Then $\mathbf{x} - \mathbf{x}_p = \mathbf{x}_h$, so $\mathbf{x} = \mathbf{x}_p + \mathbf{x}_h$. $\square$

Geometrically this means that the entire set of solutions of $A\mathbf{x} = \mathbf{b}$ is obtained by translating the set of solutions of $A\mathbf{x} = \mathbf{0}$ (the null space of A) by the fixed vector $\mathbf{x}_p$.

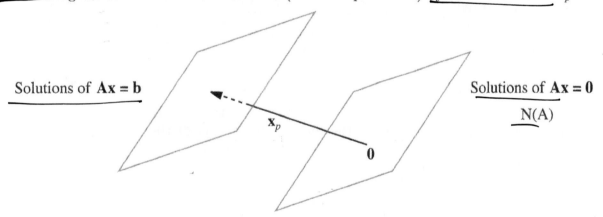

Solutions of $A\mathbf{x} = \mathbf{b}$

Solutions of $A\mathbf{x} = \mathbf{0}$

N(A)

$\mathbf{x}_p$

$\mathbf{0}$

Example 8.2. Let

$$A = \begin{bmatrix} 1 & -3 \\ -1 & 3 \end{bmatrix} \quad \text{and} \quad \mathbf{b} = \begin{bmatrix} -4 \\ 4 \end{bmatrix}.$$

The system $A\mathbf{x} = \mathbf{b}$ has solution

$$\begin{bmatrix} x_1 \\ x_2 \end{bmatrix} = \begin{bmatrix} -4 \\ 0 \end{bmatrix} + x_2 \begin{bmatrix} 3 \\ 1 \end{bmatrix}$$

while the system $A\mathbf{x} = \mathbf{0}$ has solution

$$\begin{bmatrix} x_1 \\ x_2 \end{bmatrix} = x_2 \begin{bmatrix} 3 \\ 1 \end{bmatrix}.$$

Thus in this case the solution sets are parallel lines.

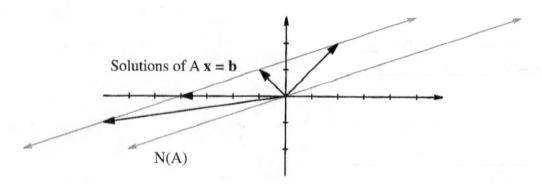

The set of solutions of $A\mathbf{x} = \mathbf{b}$ is obtained by translating the null space of A by *any* solution of $A\mathbf{x} = \mathbf{b}$. ◇

This relationship between solutions of homogeneous and inhomogeneous equations is dependent upon the existence of at least one solution of the inhomogeneous equation. While a homogeneous equation $A\mathbf{x} = \mathbf{0}$ always has at least one solution, namely $\mathbf{x} = \mathbf{0}$, the inhomogeneous equation $A\mathbf{x} = \mathbf{b}$ may or may not have solutions.

Example 8.3. Let

$$A = \begin{bmatrix} 1 & -3 \\ -1 & 3 \end{bmatrix} \quad \text{and} \quad \mathbf{b} = \begin{bmatrix} -3 \\ 4 \end{bmatrix}.$$

The system $A\mathbf{x} = \mathbf{b}$ reduces to

$$\begin{array}{rcl} x_1 \quad - \quad 3x_2 & = & 0 \\ 0 & = & 1 \end{array}$$

and therefore has no solutions. ◇

There is an important relationship between vectors in the null space of a matrix A and the columns of A. Recall that $A\mathbf{x}$ is the linear combination of the columns of A whose coefficients are the components of $\mathbf{x}$. Thus, if $A\mathbf{x} = \mathbf{0}$ we have

$$x_1\mathbf{v}_1 + x_2\mathbf{v}_2 + \cdots + x_n\mathbf{v}_n = \mathbf{0}$$

where $\mathbf{v}_1$ through $\mathbf{v}_n$ are the columns of A. Thus each element of $N(A)$ gives rise to a linear combination of the columns of A which equals the zero vector. The null space always contains the zero vector, which corresponds to the trivial combination. If the null space of A contains any nonzero vectors then the columns of A are linearly dependent.

Example 8.4. Let

$$\mathbf{v}_1 = \begin{bmatrix} 1 \\ 1 \\ 4 \end{bmatrix}, \quad \mathbf{v}_2 = \begin{bmatrix} 1 \\ 2 \\ 3 \end{bmatrix}, \quad \mathbf{v}_3 = \begin{bmatrix} 1 \\ 3 \\ 2 \end{bmatrix}, \quad \mathbf{v}_4 = \begin{bmatrix} 1 \\ 4 \\ 1 \end{bmatrix}.$$

These are the columns of the matrix A in Example 8.1. Since $N(A)$ contains nonzero vectors, the set $\{\mathbf{v}_1, \mathbf{v}_2, \mathbf{v}_3, \mathbf{v}_4\}$ is linearly dependent. In fact, from the vectors which span $N(A)$ we see that

$$\mathbf{v}_1 - 2\mathbf{v}_2 + \mathbf{v}_3 = \mathbf{0}$$

and

$$2\mathbf{v}_1 - 3\mathbf{v}_2 + \mathbf{v}_4 = \mathbf{0}.$$

◇

The columns of A are linearly independent if and only if $N(A)$ contains *only* the zero vector. That is, the zero vector is the *only* solution of $A\mathbf{x} = \mathbf{0}$. By Proposition 6.2, this is the case only when the reduced system $R\mathbf{x} = \mathbf{0}$ has no free variables ($R = \text{rref}(A)$). So every variable must be a pivot variable, and since each variable corresponds to a column of the coefficient matrix, this is the case if and only if each column of $\text{rref}(A)$ contains a pivot. We summarize these conclusions as follows.

Proposition 8.3. Let A be an $m \times n$ matrix. Then the following statements are equivalent. (This means that if one statement holds then so do the others, and if one statement fails then so do the others.)

1. The columns of A are linearly independent.

2. $N(A) = \{\mathbf{0}\}$.

3. $\text{rref}(A)$ has a pivot in each column.

One case in which the third statement necessarily fails is when A has more columns than rows. By definition there cannot be more than one pivot in any one row of $\text{rref}(A)$, so if there are fewer rows than columns, then there cannot be a pivot in every column of $\text{rref}(A)$. So by Proposition 8.3, the columns of A are linearly dependent. Since the columns of an $m \times n$ matrix form a collection of n vectors in $\mathbf{R}^m$, we can rephrase this result as follows.

Proposition 8.4. Any set of n vectors in $\mathbf{R}^m$ with $n > m$ is linearly dependent.

Exercises

For Exercises 1 through 9, express the null space of the given matrix A as a span of linearly independent vectors or show that $N(A) = \{\mathbf{0}\}$.

8.1. $A = \begin{bmatrix} 1 & 8 & 3 \\ -1 & -6 & -7 \\ 1 & 2 & 15 \\ -1 & -4 & -11 \end{bmatrix}$

8.2. $A = \begin{bmatrix} 0 & 1 & 0 \\ 0 & 0 & 0 \\ 0 & 0 & 0 \end{bmatrix}$

8.3. $A = \begin{bmatrix} 1 & 3 & -1 & 9 \\ 1 & 1 & 3 & 1 \\ 2 & 7 & -4 & 22 \end{bmatrix}$

8.4. $A = \begin{bmatrix} 0 & 1 & 1 \\ 0 & 0 & 1 \\ 0 & 0 & 0 \end{bmatrix}$

8.5. $A = \begin{bmatrix} -2 & 4 & -6 & 14 \\ 4 & 2 & 1 & 13 \\ 1 & -1 & -4 & 3 \\ 3 & -2 & 4 & -4 \end{bmatrix}$

8.6. $A = \begin{bmatrix} 2 & 3 & -1 \\ -4 & -6 & 2 \\ 8 & 12 & -4 \end{bmatrix}$

8.7. $A = \begin{bmatrix} 3 & 2 \\ 1 & -1 \\ 4 & 0 \\ 2 & 1 \end{bmatrix}$

8.8. $A = \begin{bmatrix} 3 & 2 & 1 \\ 0 & 2 & 1 \\ 0 & 0 & 1 \end{bmatrix}$

8.9. $A = \begin{bmatrix} 1 & -2 & 0 & 2 \\ 1 & 1 & 3 & -1 \end{bmatrix}$

8.10. In each part, express in parametric form the set of *all* solutions $\mathbf{x}$ of $A\mathbf{x} = A\mathbf{c}$ where A is the matrix from Exercise 9. Hint: $A\mathbf{x} = A\mathbf{c}$ is the same as $A(\mathbf{x} - \mathbf{c}) = \mathbf{0}$.

(a) $\mathbf{c} = \begin{bmatrix} 1 \\ 2 \\ 3 \\ 7 \end{bmatrix}$ (b) $\mathbf{c} = \begin{bmatrix} -3 \\ 2 \\ 4 \\ 2 \end{bmatrix}$ (c) $\mathbf{c} = \begin{bmatrix} \pi/6 \\ \sqrt{e} \\ \sqrt[3]{2} \\ 195 \end{bmatrix}$

8.11. Express in parametric form the set of solutions to the equation

$$\begin{bmatrix} 1 & 8 & -3 \\ -1 & -6 & -7 \\ 1 & 2 & 15 \\ -1 & -4 & -11 \end{bmatrix} \begin{bmatrix} x_1 \\ x_2 \\ x_3 \end{bmatrix} = \begin{bmatrix} 3 \\ 2 \\ 0 \\ 1 \end{bmatrix}.$$

8.12. Express in parametric form the set of solutions of the equation

$$\begin{bmatrix} 1 & -2 & 0 & 2 \\ 1 & 1 & 3 & -1 \end{bmatrix} \begin{bmatrix} x_1 \\ x_2 \\ x_3 \\ x_4 \end{bmatrix} = \begin{bmatrix} 5 \\ 11 \end{bmatrix}.$$

8.13. Express in parametric form the set of solutions to the equation

$$\begin{bmatrix} 1 & 3 & -1 & 9 \\ 1 & 1 & 3 & 1 \\ 2 & 7 & -4 & 22 \end{bmatrix} \begin{bmatrix} x_1 \\ x_2 \\ x_3 \\ x_4 \end{bmatrix} = \begin{bmatrix} 7 \\ 9 \\ 13 \end{bmatrix}.$$

In Exercises 14 through 17, (a) express $N(A)$ as a span of linearly independent vectors or show that $N(A) = \{\mathbf{0}\}$, (b) graph $N(A)$, (c) find *all* solutions of $A\mathbf{x} = \mathbf{b}$ and (d) graph the set of solutions of $A\mathbf{x} = \mathbf{b}$.

8.14. $A = \begin{bmatrix} 2 & 4 \\ -1 & -2 \end{bmatrix}$ $\quad \mathbf{b} = \begin{bmatrix} 6 \\ -3 \end{bmatrix}.$

8.15. $A = \begin{bmatrix} 3 & 6 \\ 1 & 4 \end{bmatrix}$ $\quad \mathbf{b} = \begin{bmatrix} 2 \\ 5 \end{bmatrix}.$

8.16. $A = \begin{bmatrix} 3 & -3 & -6 \\ 2 & -1 & -2 \\ 3 & 2 & 4 \end{bmatrix}$ $\quad \mathbf{b} = \begin{bmatrix} 3 \\ 4 \\ 13 \end{bmatrix}.$

8.17. $A = \begin{bmatrix} 1 & 3 & -4 \\ -3 & -9 & 6 \\ 2 & 6 & -3 \end{bmatrix}$ $\quad \mathbf{b} = \begin{bmatrix} -6 \\ 12 \\ -7 \end{bmatrix}.$

In Exercises 18 through 23 find a matrix A such that $N(A)$ is the given set S, or explain why no such matrix can exist.

8.18. $S = \text{span}\left(\begin{bmatrix} 1 \\ 0 \end{bmatrix}\right)$

8.19. $S = \left\{\begin{bmatrix} 0 \\ 0 \end{bmatrix}\right\}$

8.20. $S = \left\{\begin{bmatrix} 1 \\ 0 \end{bmatrix}\right\}$

8.21. $S = \mathbf{R}^2$

8.22. $S = \text{span}\left(\begin{bmatrix} 2 \\ 3 \end{bmatrix}\right)$

8.23. $S = \text{span}\left(\begin{bmatrix} 1 \\ 0 \end{bmatrix}\right) \cup \text{span}\left(\begin{bmatrix} 2 \\ 3 \end{bmatrix}\right)$

In Exercises 24 through 29, determine whether or not the given set of vectors is linearly independent. If linearly dependent, express one of the vectors as a linear combination of the others.

8.24. $\left\{ \begin{bmatrix} 1 \\ 4 \\ 2 \end{bmatrix}, \begin{bmatrix} -2 \\ 4 \\ 2 \end{bmatrix}, \begin{bmatrix} 3 \\ 1 \\ -1 \end{bmatrix}, \begin{bmatrix} 2 \\ 2 \\ 3 \end{bmatrix} \right\}$

8.25. $\left\{ \begin{bmatrix} 4 \\ 1 \\ 3 \end{bmatrix}, \begin{bmatrix} 1 \\ 1 \\ 1 \end{bmatrix}, \begin{bmatrix} 1 \\ -1 \\ 1 \end{bmatrix} \right\}$

8.26. $\left\{ \begin{bmatrix} 2 \\ 1 \\ 2 \end{bmatrix}, \begin{bmatrix} 4 \\ 2 \\ 9 \end{bmatrix}, \begin{bmatrix} -2 \\ -1 \\ 3 \end{bmatrix} \right\}$

8.27. $\left\{ \begin{bmatrix} 1 \\ 4 \\ 2 \\ 1 \end{bmatrix}, \begin{bmatrix} 0 \\ 1 \\ -2 \\ 3 \end{bmatrix}, \begin{bmatrix} 2 \\ 5 \\ 10 \\ -7 \end{bmatrix} \right\}$

8.28. $\left\{ \begin{bmatrix} -1 \\ 4 \\ 2 \\ 1 \end{bmatrix}, \begin{bmatrix} -2 \\ 1 \\ -2 \\ 3 \end{bmatrix}, \begin{bmatrix} 5 \\ 5 \\ 10 \\ -7 \end{bmatrix} \right\}$

8.29. $\left\{ \begin{bmatrix} 1 \\ 2 \\ 3 \\ 4 \end{bmatrix}, \begin{bmatrix} 5 \\ 6 \\ 7 \\ 8 \end{bmatrix}, \begin{bmatrix} 9 \\ 10 \\ 11 \\ 12 \end{bmatrix}, \begin{bmatrix} 13 \\ 14 \\ 15 \\ 16 \end{bmatrix} \right\}$

9 Column Space

Given an $m \times n$ matrix A, we would like to know for which vectors $\mathbf{b}$ in $\mathbf{R}^m$ the system $A\mathbf{x} = \mathbf{b}$ has a solution. First write

$$A = \begin{bmatrix} | & | & & | \\ \mathbf{v}_1 & \mathbf{v}_2 & \cdots & \mathbf{v}_n \\ | & | & & | \end{bmatrix}$$

and recall that

$$A\mathbf{x} = x_1\mathbf{v}_1 + x_2\mathbf{v}_2 + \cdots + x_n\mathbf{v}_n$$

is the linear combination of the columns of A whose coefficients are the components of $\mathbf{x}$. Thus the system $A\mathbf{x} = \mathbf{b}$ has a solution if and only if $\mathbf{b}$ can be written as a linear combination of the columns of A. Motivated by this fact, we define the **column space** of A to be

$$C(A) = \text{span}(\mathbf{v}_1, \mathbf{v}_2, \ldots, \mathbf{v}_n),$$

the span of the columns of A. Since every such linear combination takes the form $A\mathbf{x}$ for some $\mathbf{x}$ in $\mathbf{R}^n$ and since conversely every vector of the form $A\mathbf{x}$ is such a linear combination we can also express the column space as

$$C(A) = \{A\mathbf{x} \mid \mathbf{x} \in \mathbf{R}^n\}.$$

Since the columns of A are vectors in $\mathbf{R}^m$, or equivalently, since $A\mathbf{x}$ is in $\mathbf{R}^m$ for every $\mathbf{x}$ in $\mathbf{R}^n$, the column space of A is a subset of $\mathbf{R}^m$. The following fact is an immediate consequence of the definition.

Proposition 9.1. The system $A\mathbf{x} = \mathbf{b}$ has a solution if and only if $\mathbf{b}$ is in $C(A)$.

Example 9.1. Let

$$A = \begin{bmatrix} 1 & 1 & 1 & 1 \\ 1 & 2 & 3 & 4 \\ 4 & 3 & 2 & 1 \end{bmatrix}.$$

Then the column space is

$$C(A) = \text{span} \left\{ \begin{bmatrix} 1 \\ 1 \\ 4 \end{bmatrix}, \begin{bmatrix} 1 \\ 2 \\ 3 \end{bmatrix}, \begin{bmatrix} 1 \\ 3 \\ 2 \end{bmatrix}, \begin{bmatrix} 1 \\ 4 \\ 1 \end{bmatrix} \right\}.$$

We know however from Example 8.4 that the third and fourth vectors are linear combinations of the first two. Since the first two are linearly independent,

$$C(A) = \text{span} \left(\begin{bmatrix} 1 \\ 1 \\ 4 \end{bmatrix}, \begin{bmatrix} 1 \\ 2 \\ 3 \end{bmatrix} \right)$$

and the column space of A is a plane passing through the origin in $\mathbf{R}^3$.

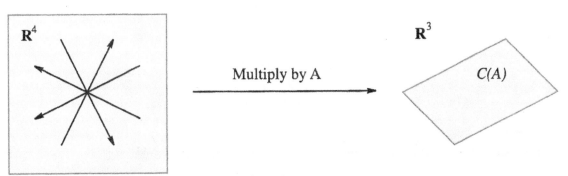

This plane is also the set of all vectors obtained by multiplying vectors in $\mathbf{R}^4$ by the matrix A. So the system $A\mathbf{x} = \mathbf{b}$ has solutions if and only if $\mathbf{b}$ is in this plane. $\diamond$

This description of the column space as a span of a set of vectors is useful in the sense that we can easily generate vectors in $C(A)$ by forming linear combinations of the spanning vectors. However, suppose we wish to know whether or not a given vector $\mathbf{b}$ is in the column space of A. We would then need to solve a system of equations. By regarding $\mathbf{b}$ as an unknown it is possible to derive conditions which determine whether or not $\mathbf{b}$ is in the column space.

Example 9.2. Let A be the matrix from Example 9.1. We will perform elimination on the system $A\mathbf{x} = \mathbf{b}$ with $\mathbf{b}$ left as an unknown. The augmented matrix for this system is

$$\begin{bmatrix} 1 & 1 & 1 & 1 & | & b_1 \\ 1 & 2 & 3 & 4 & | & b_2 \\ 4 & 3 & 2 & 1 & | & b_3 \end{bmatrix}.$$

Performing the row operations which place the coefficient matrix A in reduced row echelon form gives

$$\begin{bmatrix} 1 & 0 & -1 & -2 & | & 2b_1 - b_2 \\ 0 & 1 & 2 & 3 & | & b_2 - b_1 \\ 0 & 0 & 0 & 0 & | & -5b_1 + b_2 + b_3 \end{bmatrix}.$$

The only way an inconsistency can arise in this system is if $-5b_1 + b_2 + b_3 \neq 0$. Otherwise, the system has at least one solution, in which case $\mathbf{b}$ is in the column space of A. So $\mathbf{b}$ is in the column space of A if and only if

$$-5b_1 + b_2 + b_3 = 0.$$

This is the equation of the plane in $\mathbf{R}^3$ spanned by the columns of A. If

$$\mathbf{b}_1 = \begin{bmatrix} 2 \\ 7 \\ 3 \end{bmatrix} \quad \text{and} \quad \mathbf{b}_2 = \begin{bmatrix} 2 \\ 6 \\ 3 \end{bmatrix}$$

we see that $\mathbf{b}_1$ is in $C(A)$ since $-5(2)+7+3 = 0$, but $\mathbf{b}_2$ is not in $C(A)$ since $-5(2)+6+3 \neq 0$. Thus $A\mathbf{x} = \mathbf{b}_1$ has solutions, while $A\mathbf{x} = \mathbf{b}_2$ does not. $\diamond$

In general, each row of zeros in $\mathrm{rref}(A)$ leads to an equation that $\mathbf{b}$ must satisfy in order to be in $C(A)$.

Example 9.3. Let

$$A = \begin{bmatrix} 1 & 3 & 4 \\ 2 & 7 & 9 \\ -1 & 1 & 0 \\ 3 & 3 & 6 \end{bmatrix}.$$

Performing elimination on the augmented matrix for $A\mathbf{x} = \mathbf{b}$, we get

$$\begin{bmatrix} 1 & 0 & 1 & | & 7b_1 - 3b_2 \\ 0 & 1 & 1 & | & b_2 - 2b_1 \\ 0 & 0 & 0 & | & b_3 - 4b_2 + 9b_1 \\ 0 & 0 & 0 & | & b_4 + 6b_2 - 15b_1 \end{bmatrix}.$$

60

The system is consistent if and only if

$$
\begin{array}{rrrrl}
9b_1 & - & 4b_2 & + & b_3 & & = 0 \\
-15b_1 & + & 6b_2 & & & + \ b_4 & = 0
\end{array}
$$

so $\mathbf{b} \in C(A)$ if and only if $\mathbf{b}$ satisfies both equations. If we let

$$
B = \begin{bmatrix} 9 & -4 & 1 & 0 \\ -15 & 6 & 0 & 1 \end{bmatrix}
$$

this means that $\mathbf{b}$ satisfies $B\mathbf{b} = \mathbf{0}$, so $\mathbf{b}$ is in the null space of B. In other words $C(A) = N(B)$. $\diamond$

If $\mathrm{rref}(A)$ does not contain a row of zeros then the system $A\mathbf{b} = \mathbf{b}$ is consistent for all $\mathbf{b}$ in $\mathbf{R}^m$.

Example 9.4. Let

$$
A = \begin{bmatrix} 1 & 2 & 3 \\ 2 & 3 & 1 \end{bmatrix}.
$$

Row reducing $A\mathbf{x} = \mathbf{b}$ gives

$$
\left[\begin{array}{ccc|c} 1 & 0 & -7 & -3b_1 + 2b_2 \\ 0 & 1 & 5 & 2b_1 - b_2 \end{array} \right].
$$

The free variable x_3 can be chosen arbitrarily and then the pivot variables are given by $x_1 = 7x_3 - 3b_1 + 2b_2$ and $x_2 = -5x_3 + 2b_1 - b_2$. There is no inconsistency, so every vector $\mathbf{b}$ in $\mathbf{R}^2$ is in the column space of A. $\diamond$

Proposition 9.2. Let A be an $m \times n$ matrix. Then the following statements are equivalent.

1. The columns of A span $\mathbf{R}^m$.

2. $C(A) = \mathbf{R}^m$.

3. $\mathrm{rref}(A)$ has a pivot in each row.

Proof. The equivalence of 1 and 2 follows from the definition of $C(A)$, so we just need to show that 2 and 3 are equivalent. Suppose 3 holds, and let $\mathbf{b}$ be any vector in $\mathbf{R}^m$. The augmented matrix for the system $A\mathbf{x} = \mathbf{b}$ is $[A \mid \mathbf{b}]$, and the reduced row echelon form of this matrix is $[R \mid \mathbf{c}]$ for some vector $\mathbf{c}$, where $R = \mathrm{rref}(A)$. By Proposition 6.2, the reduced system $R\mathbf{x} = \mathbf{c}$ is inconsistent if and only if it contains the equation $0 = 1$. Since $\mathrm{rref}(A)$ has a pivot in each row, it does not contain a row of zeros, and the equation $0 = 1$ does not appear in the reduced system. Hence the original system $A\mathbf{x} = \mathbf{b}$ is consistent. By

Proposition 9.1 this implies $\mathbf{b}$ is in $C(A)$. Since this holds for all $\mathbf{b}$ in $\mathbf{R}^m$, 2 holds. Now suppose 3 fails, so that $\operatorname{rref}(A)$ has a row of zeros. Then, as illustrated in the examples above, this leads to an equation that must be satisfied by the components of $\mathbf{b}$ in order for $\mathbf{b}$ to be in $C(A)$. Thus not every $\mathbf{b}$ in $\mathbf{R}^m$ is in $C(A)$, so 2 fails. This proves that 2 and 3 are equivalent. $\qquad\square$

An interesting case of this proposition is the case $m = n$, where A is a **square matrix**. In this case, the presence of a pivot in each row means that there are n pivots. Since each column can contain at most one pivot, there must be a pivot in each column. The only $n \times n$ matrix in reduced row echelon form with these properties is the matrix

$$I_n = \begin{bmatrix} 1 & 0 & \cdots & 0 \\ 0 & 1 & \cdots & 0 \\ \vdots & \vdots & \ddots & \vdots \\ 0 & 0 & \cdots & 1 \end{bmatrix},$$

called the $n \times n$ **identity matrix**. Using Proposition 8.3, we reach the following conclusion.

Proposition 9.3. Let A be an $n \times n$ square matrix. Then the following statements are equivalent.

1. The columns of A span $\mathbf{R}^n$.

2. The columns of A are linearly independent.

3. $C(A) = \mathbf{R}^n$.

4. $N(A) = \{\mathbf{0}\}$.

5. $\operatorname{rref}(A) = I_n$.

So a set of n vectors in $\mathbf{R}^n$ is linearly independent if and only if it spans $\mathbf{R}^n$, and to test whether or not this is the case, we form a matrix A whose columns are these vectors and compute $\operatorname{rref}(A)$.

The next example illustrates the relationship between the column space and null space of a matrix.

Example 9.5. Let

$$A = \begin{bmatrix} 1 & -2 & 3 \\ 2 & -4 & 6 \end{bmatrix}.$$

Since the second and third columns are scalar multiples of the first column, the column space is

$$C(A) = \operatorname{span}\left(\begin{bmatrix} 1 \\ 2 \end{bmatrix} \right),$$

a line in $\mathbf{R}^2$. Since

$$\mathrm{rref}(A) = \begin{bmatrix} 1 & -2 & 3 \\ 0 & 0 & 0 \end{bmatrix}$$

it follows that the null space is

$$N(A) = \mathrm{span}\left(\begin{bmatrix} 2 \\ 1 \\ 0 \end{bmatrix}, \begin{bmatrix} -3 \\ 0 \\ 1 \end{bmatrix} \right),$$

a plane in $\mathbf{R}^3$. For each vector $\mathbf{b}$ in the column space of A, the system $A\mathbf{x} = \mathbf{b}$ has a solution. By Proposition 8.2, each set of solutions is a translation of the null space of A.

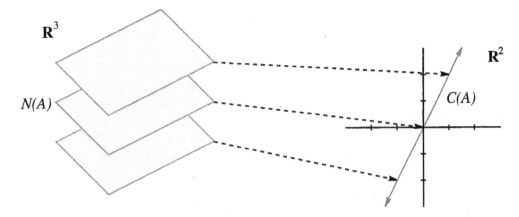

Multiplication by the matrix A sends every vector in $N(A)$ to the zero vector in $\mathbf{R}^2$. Each plane parallel to $N(A)$ is sent to a different vector in $C(A)$. ◇

Exercises

In Exercises 1 through 3 find conditions on the components of the vector $\mathbf{b}$ which are necessary and sufficient for $\mathbf{b}$ to be in the column space of the matrix A.

9.1. $A = \begin{bmatrix} 1 & 8 & 3 \\ -1 & -6 & -7 \\ 1 & 2 & 15 \\ -1 & -4 & -11 \end{bmatrix}$ $\qquad \mathbf{b} = \begin{bmatrix} b_1 \\ b_2 \\ b_3 \\ b_4 \end{bmatrix}$

9.2. $A = \begin{bmatrix} 1 & 3 & -1 & 9 \\ 1 & 1 & 3 & 1 \\ 2 & 7 & -4 & 22 \end{bmatrix}$ $\qquad \mathbf{b} = \begin{bmatrix} b_1 \\ b_2 \\ b_3 \end{bmatrix}$

9.3. $A = \begin{bmatrix} 1 & 1 \\ -2 & 1 \\ 0 & 3 \\ 2 & -1 \end{bmatrix}$ $\qquad \mathbf{b} = \begin{bmatrix} b_1 \\ b_2 \\ b_3 \\ b_4 \end{bmatrix}$

9.4. Which of the following vectors are in the column space of the matrix A from Exercise 3? Hint: Work Exercise 3 first.

(a) $\begin{bmatrix} 1 \\ 2 \\ 4 \\ 2 \end{bmatrix}$ (b) $\begin{bmatrix} 0 \\ 3 \\ 3 \\ -3 \end{bmatrix}$ (c) $\begin{bmatrix} 1 \\ 2 \\ 4 \\ -2 \end{bmatrix}$

(d) $\begin{bmatrix} -2 \\ -2 \\ -6 \\ 2 \end{bmatrix}$ (e) $\begin{bmatrix} 2 \\ 1 \\ 3 \\ -1 \end{bmatrix}$ (f) $\begin{bmatrix} 2 \\ -4 \\ 0 \\ 4 \end{bmatrix}$

In Exercises 5 through 10 find a 2×2 matrix A such that $C(A) = S$ or explain why no such matrix exists.

9.5. $S = \left\{ \begin{bmatrix} x_1 \\ x_2 \end{bmatrix} \in \mathbf{R}^2 : x_1 + x_2 = 0 \right\}.$

9.6. $S = \left\{ \begin{bmatrix} x_1 \\ x_2 \end{bmatrix} \in \mathbf{R}^2 : x_1 + x_2 = 2 \right\}.$

9.7. $S = \left\{ \begin{bmatrix} 0 \\ 0 \end{bmatrix} \right\}.$

9.8. $S = \left\{ \begin{bmatrix} 1 \\ 0 \end{bmatrix} \right\}.$

9.9. $S = \mathbf{R}^2$

9.10. $S = \operatorname{span}\left(\begin{bmatrix} 1 \\ 0 \end{bmatrix} \right) \cup \operatorname{span}\left(\begin{bmatrix} 0 \\ 1 \end{bmatrix} \right)$

In Exercises 11 through 19 (a) graph $N(A)$, (b) graph $C(A)$ on a separate graph, (c) find all solutions of $A\mathbf{x} = \mathbf{b}$, and (d) show that the set of solutions to $A\mathbf{x} = \mathbf{b}$ is a translate of $N(A)$.

9.11. $A = \begin{bmatrix} 1 & 3 \\ 2 & 6 \end{bmatrix}$ $\mathbf{b} = \begin{bmatrix} -2 \\ -4 \end{bmatrix}$

9.12. $A = \begin{bmatrix} 1 & 2 \\ 3 & 4 \end{bmatrix}$ $\mathbf{b} = \begin{bmatrix} 1 \\ -2 \end{bmatrix}$

9.13. $A = \begin{bmatrix} -1 & 3 & 4 \\ -2 & 6 & 8 \end{bmatrix}$ $\mathbf{b} = \begin{bmatrix} 2 \\ 4 \end{bmatrix}$

9.14. $A = \begin{bmatrix} -1 & 3 & 4 \\ -2 & 6 & 5 \end{bmatrix}$ $\mathbf{b} = \begin{bmatrix} -3 \\ 1 \end{bmatrix}$

9.15. $A = \begin{bmatrix} 1 & 2 \\ 3 & 6 \\ 2 & 4 \end{bmatrix}$ $\quad b = \begin{bmatrix} 3 \\ 9 \\ 6 \end{bmatrix}$

9.16. $A = \begin{bmatrix} 1 & -2 \\ 3 & 0 \\ 2 & 4 \end{bmatrix}$ $\quad b = \begin{bmatrix} 4 \\ 6 \\ 0 \end{bmatrix}$

9.17. $A = \begin{bmatrix} 1 & -2 & 3 \\ -1 & 2 & -3 \\ 2 & -4 & 6 \end{bmatrix}$ $\quad b = \begin{bmatrix} -4 \\ 4 \\ -8 \end{bmatrix}$

9.18. $A = \begin{bmatrix} 2 & 1 & 3 \\ 4 & 0 & 6 \\ -2 & 1 & -3 \end{bmatrix}$ $\quad b = \begin{bmatrix} 1 \\ 4 \\ -3 \end{bmatrix}$

9.19. $A = \begin{bmatrix} 2 & 3 & 5 \\ 1 & 4 & -1 \\ 0 & 2 & 5 \end{bmatrix}$ $\quad b = \begin{bmatrix} -7 \\ 1 \\ -12 \end{bmatrix}$

10 Subspaces of $\mathbf{R}^n$

The null space and column space of a matrix are examples of sets called subspaces. A **linear subspace** of $\mathbf{R}^n$ is a subset V of $\mathbf{R}^n$ satisfying the following properties.

1. V contains the zero vector.

2. If $\mathbf{v}$ and $\mathbf{w}$ are in V then $\mathbf{v} + \mathbf{w}$ is in V.

3. If $\mathbf{v}$ is in V, the $c\mathbf{v}$ is in V for any scalar c.

Sets which satisfy condition 2 are said to be **closed under addition**, and sets which satisfy condition 3 are said to be **closed under scalar multiplication**. Thus subspaces are sets which contain the zero vector and are closed under both addition and scalar multiplication.

Example 10.1. The subset $\{0\}$ of $\mathbf{R}^n$ consisting of just the zero vector is a subspace of $\mathbf{R}^n$, since $0 + 0 = 0$ and $c0 = 0$ for any scalar c. This is called the **trivial** subspace. $\diamond$

Example 10.2. $\mathbf{R}^n$ is a subspace of itself. A subspace V of $\mathbf{R}^n$ is called **proper** if $V \neq \mathbf{R}^n$. $\diamond$

Example 10.3. The span of any nonempty set of vectors in $\mathbf{R}^n$ is a subspace of $\mathbf{R}^n$. To see this, suppose $V = \text{span}(\mathbf{v}_1, \mathbf{v}_2, \ldots, \mathbf{v}_k)$. The trivial combination of these vectors equals the zero vector, so V contains the zero vector. If $\mathbf{v}$ and $\mathbf{w}$ are in V then

$$\mathbf{v} = a_1 \mathbf{v}_1 + a_2 \mathbf{v}_2 + \cdots + a_k \mathbf{v}_k$$

and

$$\mathbf{w} = b_1\mathbf{v}_1 + b_2\mathbf{v}_2 + \cdots + b_k\mathbf{v}_k.$$

So

$$\mathbf{v} + \mathbf{w} = (a_1 + b_1)\mathbf{v}_1 + (a_2 + b_2)\mathbf{v}_2 + \cdots + (a_k + b_k)\mathbf{v}_k$$

and

$$c\mathbf{v} = (ca_1)\mathbf{v}_1 + (ca_2)\mathbf{v}_2 + \cdots + (ca_k)\mathbf{v}_k$$

are both linear combinations of $\mathbf{v}_1$ through $\mathbf{v}_k$ and are therefore in V. For instance, in $\mathbf{R}^3$ any line or plane which passes through the origin is a subspace.

Lines and planes which do not pass through the origin are not subspaces. The subsets in the next two examples are also not subspaces.

Example 10.4. Consider the upper half-plane

$$H = \left\{ \begin{bmatrix} x_1 \\ x_2 \end{bmatrix} \in \mathbf{R}^2 \;\middle|\; x_2 \geq 0 \right\}.$$

Suppose

$$\mathbf{v} = \begin{bmatrix} v_1 \\ v_2 \end{bmatrix} \qquad \text{and} \qquad \mathbf{w} = \begin{bmatrix} w_1 \\ w_2 \end{bmatrix}$$

are in H. Then $v_2 \geq 0$ and $w_2 \geq 0$, so

$$\mathbf{v} + \mathbf{w} = \begin{bmatrix} v_1 + w_1 \\ v_2 + w_2 \end{bmatrix}$$

is in H since $v_2 + w_2 \geq 0$. Thus H is closed under addition.

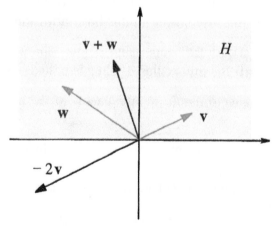

However, H is not closed under scalar multiplication. For instance, suppose $v_2 > 0$. Then

$$-2\mathbf{v} = \begin{bmatrix} -2v_1 \\ -2v_2 \end{bmatrix}$$

is not in H since $-2v_2 < 0$. So H is not a subspace. ◇

Example 10.5. Let

$$\mathbf{v}_1 = \begin{bmatrix} 2 \\ 1 \end{bmatrix} \quad \text{and} \quad \mathbf{v}_2 = \begin{bmatrix} -3 \\ 1 \end{bmatrix}.$$

By Example 10.3 both $V_1 = \text{span}(\mathbf{v}_1)$ and $V_2 = \text{span}(\mathbf{v}_2)$ are subspaces. Let $V = V_1 \cup V_2$, the union of V_1 and V_2. Let $\mathbf{v}$ be in V and let c be any scalar. Then either $\mathbf{v}$ is in V_1 in which case $c\mathbf{v} \in V_1$, or $\mathbf{v}$ is in V_2 in which case $c\mathbf{v} \in V_2$. In either case $c\mathbf{v}$ is in $V_1 \cup V_2 = V$, so V is closed under scalar multiplication. However, V is not closed under addition, since for instance both $\mathbf{v}_1$ and $\mathbf{v}_2$ are in V, but

$$\mathbf{v}_1 + \mathbf{v}_2 = \begin{bmatrix} -1 \\ 2 \end{bmatrix}$$

is not in V_1 or V_2, and thus is not in V.

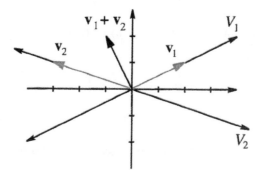

So V is not a subspace. ◇

As mentioned above, the null space and column space of a matrix are subspaces.

Proposition 10.1. Let A be an m by n matrix. Then

1. The column space of A is a subspace of $\mathbf{R}^m$.

2. The null space of A is a subspace of $\mathbf{R}^n$.

Proof. The first statement follows from Example 10.3 since the column space of A is the span of the columns of A. The second statement follows immediately from Proposition 8.1. □

The set of solutions of a homogeneous linear system $A\mathbf{x} = \mathbf{0}$ is a subspace, namely the null space of A. However, the set of solutions of an inhomogeneous system $A\mathbf{x} = \mathbf{b}$ (if there are solutions) is not a subspace, but rather a translation of the null space of A. We say that a subset A of $\mathbf{R}^n$ is an **affine linear subspace** if A is a translation of some subspace V of $\mathbf{R}^n$. That is, A is an affine subspace if

$$A = \{\mathbf{x}_0 + \mathbf{v} \mid \mathbf{v} \in V\}$$

for some subspace V and some fixed vector $\mathbf{x}_0$.

Example 10.6. Recall that any line in $\mathbf{R}^n$ can be described parametrically as

$$L = \{\mathbf{x}_0 + t\mathbf{v} \mid t \in \mathbf{R}\}.$$

So L is a translation of the subspace $V = \operatorname{span}(\mathbf{v})$, and therefore an affine subspace. Likewise, any plane in $\mathbf{R}^n$ can be described as

$$P = \{\mathbf{x}_0 + s\mathbf{v}_1 + t\mathbf{v}_2 \mid t \in \mathbf{R}\}.$$

So P is a translation of the subspace $V = \operatorname{span}(\mathbf{v}_1, \mathbf{v}_2)$, and therefore an affine subspace. In $\mathbf{R}^3$ a plane can also be described by an equation of the form

$$a_1 x_1 + a_2 x_2 + a_3 x_3 = b.$$

The set of solutions of this inhomogeneous equation are a translation of the null space of the matrix

$$A = \begin{bmatrix} a_1 & a_2 & a_3 \end{bmatrix}.$$

$\diamond$

We emphasize that affine subspaces are *not* always subspaces. Only the ones which pass through the origin are subspaces. See the exercises.

Exercises

In Exercises 11 through 20 determine whether or not the given set is a subspace of $\mathbf{R}^n$. If it is, show that the three subspace properties are satisfied, and if it is not, show by example that one of the properties fails.

10.11. The line $3x - 2y = 2$.

10.12. The line $3x - 2y = 0$.

10.13. The set of solutions of $A\mathbf{x} = \mathbf{0}$, where A is any $m \times n$ matrix.

10.14. The set of solutions of $A\mathbf{x} = \mathbf{b}$, where A is any $m \times n$ matrix, and $\mathbf{b}$ is any vector in $\mathbf{R}^m$.

10.15. The set of solutions of $A\mathbf{x} = \mathbf{x}$, where A is any $n \times n$ matrix.

10.16. The first quadrant in $\mathbf{R}^2$. That is,

$$\left\{ \begin{bmatrix} x_1 \\ x_2 \end{bmatrix} \in \mathbf{R}^2 \,\middle|\, x_1 \geq 0 \text{ and } x_2 \geq 0 \right\}.$$

10.17. The union of the first and third quadrants in $\mathbf{R}^2$. That is,

$$\left\{ \begin{bmatrix} x_1 \\ x_2 \end{bmatrix} \in \mathbf{R}^2 \,\middle|\, (x_1 \geq 0 \text{ and } x_2 \geq 0) \text{ or } (x_1 \leq 0 \text{ and } x_2 \leq 0) \right\}.$$

10.18. The intersection of the planes $x + y - z = 3$ and $2x - y + 3z = 0$.

10.19. The intersection of the planes $x - y + 2z = 0$ and $2x + y + 4z = 0$.

10.20. The unit disk in $\mathbf{R}^2$. That is

$$\left\{ \begin{bmatrix} x_1 \\ x_2 \end{bmatrix} \in \mathbf{R} \,\middle|\, x_1^2 + x_2^2 \leq 1 \right\}.$$

10.21. Show that if V and W are subspaces of $\mathbf{R}^n$ then their intersection $V \cap W$ is also a subspace of $\mathbf{R}^n$.

10.22. Let $V + W = \{\mathbf{v} + \mathbf{w} \mid \mathbf{v} \text{ is in } V \text{ and } \mathbf{w} \text{ is in } W\}$. Show that if V and W are subspaces then $V + W$ is a subspace.

10.23. Show that every subspace of $\mathbf{R}^2$ is one of the following: the trivial subspace $\{\mathbf{0}\}$, a line through the origin, or $\mathbf{R}^2$ itself.

10.24. Show that if A is an affine subspace of $\mathbf{R}^n$ and A contains the origin, then A is a subspace of $\mathbf{R}^n$.

11   Basis for a Subspace

A **basis** for a subspace V of $\mathbf{R}^n$ is a linearly independent set of vectors $\{\mathbf{v}_1, \mathbf{v}_2, \ldots, \mathbf{v}_k\}$ such that $V = \mathrm{span}(\mathbf{v}_1, \mathbf{v}_2 \ldots, \mathbf{v}_k)$. A basis can be thought of as an economical way of describing a subspace, in that

1. its span is the subspace – so it describes the subspace, and

2. its vectors are independent – there is no redundancy.

Given a basis for a subspace, every vector in the subspace can be described *uniquely* in terms of the basis vectors.

Proposition 11.1. Suppose $\{\mathbf{v}_1, \mathbf{v}_2, \ldots, \mathbf{v}_k\}$ is a basis for a subspace V of $\mathbf{R}^n$. Then every vector $\mathbf{v}$ in V can be expressed uniquely as a linear combination of $\mathbf{v}_1, \mathbf{v}_2, \ldots, \mathbf{v}_k$.

Proof. By definition, $\{\mathbf{v}_1, \mathbf{v}_2, \ldots, \mathbf{v}_k\}$ spans V, so every $\mathbf{v}$ in V can be written

$$\mathbf{v} = c_1\mathbf{v}_1 + c_2\mathbf{v}_2 + \cdots + c_k\mathbf{v}_k$$

for some scalars $c_1, c_2, \ldots, c_k$. To prove uniqueness, suppose in addition that

$$\mathbf{v} = d_1\mathbf{v}_1 + d_2\mathbf{v}_2 + \cdots + d_k\mathbf{v}_k.$$

Then, subtracting this from the previous equation gives

$$\mathbf{0} = (c_1 - d_1)\mathbf{v}_1 + (c_2 - d_2)\mathbf{v}_2 + \cdots + (c_k - d_k)\mathbf{v}_k.$$

Again by the definition of a basis, $\mathbf{v}_1, \mathbf{v}_2, \ldots, \mathbf{v}_k$ are linearly independent, so $c_1 - d_1 = 0$, $c_2 - d_2 = 0, \ldots, c_k - d_k = 0$. Thus $c_1 = d_1$, $c_2 = d_2$, $\ldots$, $c_k = d_k$ and the two expressions are the same. $\square$

Bases, however are not unique.

Example 11.1. The set $\{\mathbf{e}_1, \mathbf{e}_2, \ldots, \mathbf{e}_n\}$ is linearly independent and spans $\mathbf{R}^n$, and is therefore a basis for $\mathbf{R}^n$. This is called the **standard basis** for $\mathbf{R}^n$. $\diamond$

Example 11.2. Let

$$\mathbf{v}_1 = \begin{bmatrix} 1 \\ 2 \\ 4 \end{bmatrix}, \quad \mathbf{v}_2 = \begin{bmatrix} 2 \\ 1 \\ -1 \end{bmatrix}, \quad \text{and} \quad \mathbf{v}_3 = \begin{bmatrix} 3 \\ 4 \\ 5 \end{bmatrix}.$$

Let A be the matrix whose columns are $\mathbf{v}_1$, $\mathbf{v}_2$ and $\mathbf{v}_3$. Since

$$\text{rref}(A) = \begin{bmatrix} 1 & 0 & 0 \\ 0 & 1 & 0 \\ 0 & 0 & 1 \end{bmatrix},$$

Proposition 9.3 implies that the columns of A are linearly independent and span $\mathbf{R}^3$. Thus $\{\mathbf{v}_1, \mathbf{v}_2, \mathbf{v}_3\}$ is a basis for $\mathbf{R}^3$. $\diamond$

By Proposition 9.3, any set of n linearly independent vectors in $\mathbf{R}^n$ spans $\mathbf{R}^n$, and is therefore a basis for $\mathbf{R}^n$. By the same result, any set of n vectors which spans $\mathbf{R}^n$ must be linearly independent, and therefore is a basis for $\mathbf{R}^n$.

Example 11.3. The sets $\left\{\begin{bmatrix} 1 \\ 0 \end{bmatrix}, \begin{bmatrix} 0 \\ 1 \end{bmatrix}, \begin{bmatrix} 2 \\ 3 \end{bmatrix}\right\}$ and $\left\{\begin{bmatrix} 1 \\ 2 \end{bmatrix}\right\}$ are not bases for $\mathbf{R}^2$. The first is a linearly dependent set and the second does not span $\mathbf{R}^2$. $\diamond$

The proof that every subspace of $\mathbf{R}^n$ has a basis is somewhat technical, and can be found in Appendix B. Since almost every subspace we will encounter is either the null space or column space of a matrix, we demonstrate how to find bases for these subspaces.

Finding a Basis for the Null Space

Given a matrix A we find a spanning set for $N(A)$ by finding $R = \text{rref}(A)$ and solving $R\mathbf{x} = \mathbf{0}$. It turns out that the spanning set found by this method is always linearly independent and thus forms a basis for $N(A)$.

Example 11.4. Let

$$A = \begin{bmatrix} 1 & 1 & 1 & 1 & 1 \\ 1 & 1 & 2 & 4 & 4 \end{bmatrix}.$$

Then

$$R = \mathrm{rref}(A) = \begin{bmatrix} 1 & 1 & 0 & -2 & -2 \\ 0 & 0 & 1 & 3 & 3 \end{bmatrix}.$$

Solving $R\mathbf{x} = \mathbf{0}$ for the pivot variables x_1 and x_3 in terms of the free variables x_2, x_4 and x_5 we get

$$\begin{bmatrix} x_1 \\ x_2 \\ x_3 \\ x_4 \\ x_5 \end{bmatrix} = \begin{bmatrix} -x_2 + 2x_4 + 2x_5 \\ x_2 \\ -3x_4 - 3x_5 \\ x_4 \\ x_5 \end{bmatrix} = x_2 \begin{bmatrix} -1 \\ 1 \\ 0 \\ 0 \\ 0 \end{bmatrix} + x_4 \begin{bmatrix} 2 \\ 0 \\ -3 \\ 1 \\ 0 \end{bmatrix} + x_5 \begin{bmatrix} 2 \\ 0 \\ -3 \\ 0 \\ 1 \end{bmatrix}$$

so

$$N(A) = \mathrm{span}\left(\begin{bmatrix} -1 \\ 1 \\ 0 \\ 0 \\ 0 \end{bmatrix}, \begin{bmatrix} 2 \\ 0 \\ -3 \\ 1 \\ 0 \end{bmatrix}, \begin{bmatrix} 2 \\ 0 \\ -3 \\ 0 \\ 1 \end{bmatrix} \right).$$

It is clear that these vectors are linearly independent since each contains a 1 in an entry which is zero in the other two vectors. These entries correspond to the appearance of the free variables x_2, x_4 and x_5 in entries 2, 4, and 5 of the solution. ◇

In general, if $R = \mathrm{rref}(A)$, the solution of $R\mathbf{x} = \mathbf{0}$ is always a linear combination in which the coefficients are the free variables. The vector $\mathbf{v}_k$ whose coefficient is the free variable x_k has a 1 in the kth component, while each of the remaining vectors will have a zero in the kth component. Thus $\mathbf{v}_k$ cannot be a linear combination of the other vectors. Since this is true for each free variable, the spanning vectors are linearly independent and thus form a basis for the null space of A.

Finding a Basis for the Column Space

By definition, the columns of A span the column space of A. The question is whether or not these vectors are linearly independent and, if not, which vectors should be removed to form a basis. The answer can be determined by looking at the reduced row echelon form R of A. The key is that, although the column spaces of A and R may be different, they share the same null space.

Example 11.5. Let

$$A = \underbrace{\begin{bmatrix} 1 & 0 & -1 & 0 & 4 \\ 2 & 1 & 0 & 0 & 9 \\ -1 & 2 & 5 & 1 & -5 \\ 1 & -1 & -3 & -2 & 9 \end{bmatrix}}_{\mathbf{v}_1 \quad \mathbf{v}_2 \quad \mathbf{v}_3 \quad \mathbf{v}_4 \quad \mathbf{v}_5}.$$

71

The reduced row echelon form of A is

$$R = \begin{bmatrix} 1 & 0 & -1 & 0 & 4 \\ 0 & 1 & 2 & 0 & 1 \\ 0 & 0 & 0 & 1 & -3 \\ 0 & 0 & 0 & 0 & 0 \end{bmatrix}.$$

$$\underbrace{}$$
$$\mathbf{w}_1 \quad \mathbf{w}_2 \quad \mathbf{w}_3 \quad \mathbf{w}_4 \quad \mathbf{w}_5$$

It is clear that the columns of R which contain pivots form a linearly independent set, since each such column contains a 1 where the others contain a zero. Furthermore, the remaining columns can be expressed as linear combinations of $\mathbf{w}_1$, $\mathbf{w}_2$ and $\mathbf{w}_4$. In particular, $\mathbf{w}_3 = -1\mathbf{w}_1 + 2\mathbf{w}_2$ and $\mathbf{w}_5 = 4\mathbf{w}_1 + \mathbf{w}_2 - 3\mathbf{w}_4$. So $\{\mathbf{w}_1, \mathbf{w}_2, \mathbf{w}_4\}$ spans the column space of R and is therefore a basis for the column space of R.

These vectors however *not* form a basis for the column space of A. It turns out that the *corresponding columns* of A form a basis for the column space of A. That is,

$$\{\mathbf{v}_1, \mathbf{v}_2, \mathbf{v}_4\} = \left\{ \begin{bmatrix} 1 \\ 2 \\ -1 \\ 1 \end{bmatrix}, \begin{bmatrix} 0 \\ 1 \\ 2 \\ -1 \end{bmatrix}, \begin{bmatrix} 0 \\ 0 \\ 1 \\ -2 \end{bmatrix} \right\}$$

is a basis for the column space of A. To see that $\{\mathbf{v}_1, \mathbf{v}_2, \mathbf{v}_4\}$ spans $C(A)$ we need to express $\mathbf{v}_3$ and $\mathbf{v}_5$ as linear combinations of these vectors. Since the null spaces of R and A are the same, exactly the same relations hold among the columns of R and the columns of A. The fact that $\mathbf{w}_3 = -1\mathbf{w}_1 + 2\mathbf{w}_2$ implies that

$$\begin{bmatrix} -1 \\ 2 \\ -1 \\ 0 \\ 0 \end{bmatrix}$$

is in $N(R) = N(A)$, so $\mathbf{v}_3 = -\mathbf{v}_1 + 2\mathbf{v}_2$ (Check!). Likewise, because $\mathbf{w}_5 = 4\mathbf{w}_1 + \mathbf{w}_2 - 3\mathbf{w}_4$ it follows that $\mathbf{v}_5 = 4\mathbf{v}_1 + \mathbf{v}_2 - 3\mathbf{v}_4$. To show that $\{\mathbf{v}_1, \mathbf{v}_2, \mathbf{v}_4\}$ is linearly independent, suppose that

$$c_1\mathbf{v}_1 + c_2\mathbf{v}_2 + c_4\mathbf{v}_4 = \mathbf{0}.$$

This means that the vector

$$\begin{bmatrix} c_1 \\ c_2 \\ 0 \\ c_4 \\ 0 \end{bmatrix}$$

is in the null space of A, and thus in the null space of R. Hence

$$c_1\mathbf{w}_1 + c_2\mathbf{w}_2 + c_4\mathbf{w}_4 = \mathbf{0}.$$

But since $\{\mathbf{w}_1, \mathbf{w}_2, \mathbf{w}_4\}$ is linearly independent, this implies $c_1 = c_2 = c_4 = 0$. ◇

We now summarize the observations made in this example.

Proposition 11.2. Given any matrix A, the columns of $R = \operatorname{rref}(A)$ which contain pivots form a basis for $C(R)$, and the *corresponding columns* of A form a basis for $C(A)$.

Exercises

In Exercises 1 through 4, find bases for the column space and null space of each of the given matrices.

11.1.
$$\begin{bmatrix} 1 & 2 & 1 & 0 & 5 \\ 2 & 2 & 0 & 2 & 4 \\ 3 & 2 & 0 & 0 & 3 \\ 4 & 2 & 0 & -2 & 2 \\ 5 & 2 & 0 & -4 & 1 \end{bmatrix}$$

11.2.
$$\begin{bmatrix} 1 & 0 & 2 & 3 & 1 & -1 \\ 2 & -1 & -2 & 5 & 4 & 0 \\ 3 & -1 & 0 & 8 & 5 & -1 \\ 4 & -1 & 2 & 1 & 8 & 0 \end{bmatrix}$$

11.3.
$$\begin{bmatrix} 1 & 2 & 0 & 1 \\ 3 & -1 & -1 & 2 \\ -2 & 5 & 6 & 3 \\ 5 & 5 & 4 & 8 \\ 0 & 2 & 5 & 4 \end{bmatrix}$$

11.4.
$$\begin{bmatrix} 1 & 1 & 1 & 1 & 0 \\ 1 & 1 & 1 & 0 & 1 \\ 1 & 1 & 0 & 1 & 1 \\ 1 & 0 & 1 & 1 & 1 \end{bmatrix}$$

In Exercises 5 through 11 find a basis for the given set.

11.5. $\operatorname{span}\left(\begin{bmatrix} 2 \\ 1 \\ 3 \end{bmatrix}, \begin{bmatrix} -4 \\ 3 \\ 8 \end{bmatrix}, \begin{bmatrix} -14 \\ 3 \\ -3 \end{bmatrix} \right)$

11.6. $\operatorname{span}\left(\begin{bmatrix} 1 \\ -5 \\ 7 \\ 4 \end{bmatrix}, \begin{bmatrix} 2 \\ 0 \\ -3 \\ 4 \end{bmatrix}, \begin{bmatrix} 1 \\ 2 \\ 5 \\ -3 \end{bmatrix}, \begin{bmatrix} 1 \\ 3 \\ 0 \\ -2 \end{bmatrix} \right)$

73

11.7. span $\left(\begin{bmatrix} 2 \\ 1 \\ 0 \\ 1 \\ 0 \end{bmatrix}, \begin{bmatrix} 1 \\ 0 \\ 1 \\ 0 \\ 2 \end{bmatrix}, \begin{bmatrix} 4 \\ 1 \\ 2 \\ 1 \\ 4 \end{bmatrix}, \begin{bmatrix} 0 \\ 1 \\ -2 \\ 1 \\ -4 \end{bmatrix} \right)$

11.8. The plane $3x + 2y - 4z = 0$ in $\mathbf{R}^3$.

11.9. The hyperplane $ax + by + cz + dw = 0$ in $\mathbf{R}^4$.

11.10. The intersection of the planes $2x + 3y + z = 0$ and $3x - 2y + z = 0$.

11.11. The set of solutions of

$$
\begin{array}{rcrcrcrcrcrcr}
x_1 & + & x_2 & + & x_3 & - & x_4 & - & x_5 & - & x_6 & = & 0 \\
2x_1 & + & 2x_2 & - & x_3 & + & x_4 & + & 2x_5 & + & x_6 & = & 0 \\
-x_1 & - & x_2 & + & 2x_3 & - & 2x_4 & - & 3x_5 & - & 2x_6 & = & 0
\end{array}
$$

In Exercises 12 through 15, determine whether the statement is true or false. If true, explain why. If false, give a counterexample.

11.12. Let A be an $m \times n$ matrix and let $R = \mathrm{rref}(A)$. Then if $S = \{\mathbf{v}_1, \ldots, \mathbf{v}_k\}$ is a basis for $C(R)$, then S is a basis for $C(A)$.

11.13. Let A be an $m \times n$ matrix and let $R = \mathrm{rref}(A)$. Then if $S = \{\mathbf{v}_1, \ldots, \mathbf{v}_k\}$ is a basis for $N(R)$, then S is a basis for $N(A)$.

11.14. If $\{\mathbf{v}_1, \mathbf{v}_2, \mathbf{v}_3\}$ is a basis for a subspace V of $\mathbf{R}^n$, then $\{2\mathbf{v}_1 - \mathbf{v}_2, \mathbf{v}_1 + \mathbf{v}_2 + 2\mathbf{v}_3, \mathbf{v}_1 + \mathbf{v}_3\}$ is also a basis for V.

11.15. If $\{\mathbf{v}_1, \mathbf{v}_2, \mathbf{v}_3\}$ is a basis for a subspace V of $\mathbf{R}^n$, then $\{3\mathbf{v}_1 - 2\mathbf{v}_2 + \mathbf{v}_3, -\mathbf{v}_1 + 4\mathbf{v}_2 - \mathbf{v}_3, 2\mathbf{v}_1 + \mathbf{v}_2 + 4\mathbf{v}_3\}$ is also a basis for V.

12 Dimension of a Subspace

The **dimension** of a nontrivial subspace V is the number of elements in any basis for V and is denoted $\dim(V)$. The trivial subspace is defined to have dimension zero.

Example 12.1. The standard basis $\{\mathbf{e}_1, \mathbf{e}_2, \ldots, \mathbf{e}_n\}$ for $\mathbf{R}^n$ has n elements, so the dimension of $\mathbf{R}^n$ is n. $\diamond$

Example 12.2. The plane P defined by $x - 4y + 5z = 0$ has a basis

$$
\left\{ \begin{bmatrix} 4 \\ 1 \\ 0 \end{bmatrix}, \begin{bmatrix} -5 \\ 0 \\ 1 \end{bmatrix} \right\}
$$

so $\dim(P) = 2$. $\diamond$

Before we proceed any further there is an important issue that needs to be addressed. A subspace may have many different bases. What if one basis had more elements than another? What would the dimension of the subspace be then? The answer is that this cannot happen. The proof of this relies upon the following fact.

Proposition 12.1. If a set of m vectors spans a subspace V and $n > m$ then any set of n vectors in V must be linearly dependent.

Proof. Suppose

$$V = \text{span}(\mathbf{v}_1, \mathbf{v}_2, \ldots, \mathbf{v}_m)$$

and let $\{\mathbf{w}_1, \mathbf{w}_2, \ldots, \mathbf{w}_n\}$ be any set of vectors in V with $n > m$. We can then write

$$\mathbf{w}_1 = a_{11}\mathbf{v}_1 + a_{21}\mathbf{v}_2 + \cdots + a_{m1}\mathbf{v}_m$$
$$\mathbf{w}_2 = a_{12}\mathbf{v}_1 + a_{22}\mathbf{v}_2 + \cdots + a_{m2}\mathbf{v}_m$$
$$\vdots$$
$$\mathbf{w}_n = a_{1n}\mathbf{v}_1 + a_{2n}\mathbf{v}_2 + \cdots + a_{mn}\mathbf{v}_m$$

for some real numbers a_{ij}. The m by n matrix

$$A = \begin{bmatrix} a_{11} & a_{12} & \cdots & a_{1n} \\ a_{21} & a_{22} & \cdots & a_{2n} \\ \vdots & \vdots & & \vdots \\ a_{m1} & a_{m2} & \cdots & a_{mn} \end{bmatrix}$$

has more columns than rows, so there cannot be a pivot in each column of $\text{rref}(A)$. So by Proposition 8.3, A must have a nontrivial null space. Let

$$\mathbf{c} = \begin{bmatrix} c_1 \\ c_2 \\ \vdots \\ c_n \end{bmatrix}$$

be any nonzero element of $N(A)$. Then

$$c_1\mathbf{w}_1 + c_2\mathbf{w}_2 + \cdots + c_n\mathbf{w}_n = (a_{11}c_1 + a_{12}c_2 + \cdots + a_{1n}c_n)\mathbf{v}_1$$
$$+ (a_{21}c_1 + a_{22}c_2 + \cdots + a_{2n}c_n)\mathbf{v}_2$$
$$\vdots$$
$$+ (a_{m1}c_1 + a_{m2}c_2 + \cdots + a_{mn}c_n)\mathbf{v}_m$$
$$= 0\mathbf{v}_1 + 0\mathbf{v}_2 + \cdots + 0\mathbf{v}_m = \mathbf{0}$$

since the coefficients of $\mathbf{v}_1, \mathbf{v}_2, \ldots, \mathbf{v}_m$ are exactly the components of $A\mathbf{c}$, which equals $\mathbf{0}$ since $\mathbf{c}$ is in the null space of A. Since $\mathbf{c}$ is nonzero, this implies that the set $\{\mathbf{w}_1, \mathbf{w}_2, \ldots, \mathbf{w}_n\}$ is linearly dependent. $\square$

We can now prove that the definition of dimension makes sense.

Proposition 12.2. Let V be a subspace of $\mathbf{R}^n$. Then every basis for V has the same number of elements.

Proof. Suppose $\mathcal{B}_1 = \{\mathbf{v}_1, \ldots, \mathbf{v}_{d_1}\}$ and $\mathcal{B}_2 = \{\mathbf{w}_1, \ldots, \mathbf{w}_{d_2}\}$ are bases for V. Since $\mathcal{B}_1$ spans V and $\mathcal{B}_2$ is linearly independent, it follows from Proposition 12.1 that $d_2 \leq d_1$. On the other hand, since $\mathcal{B}_2$ spans V and $\mathcal{B}_1$ is linearly independent, it follows that $d_1 \leq d_2$. Hence $d_1 = d_2$. $\square$

Once the dimension d of a subspace V is known, to verify that a set of d elements of V is a basis, it suffices to verify *either* that the set spans V *or* that it is linearly independent. The other property comes for free.

Proposition 12.3. Let V be a subspace with dimension d, and let $S = \{\mathbf{v}_1, \mathbf{v}_2, \ldots, \mathbf{v}_d\}$ be any set of d vectors in V. Then the following statements are equivalent.

1. S is linearly independent.

2. S spans V.

3. S is a basis for V.

That is, any one of the statements implies the other two. Thus, for example, any set of n linearly independent vectors in $\mathbf{R}^n$ is a basis for $\mathbf{R}^n$. Also, any set of n vectors which spans $\mathbf{R}^n$ is a basis for $\mathbf{R}^n$.

Proof. By definition, 3 implies 1 and 2, and 1 and 2 together imply 3. Thus we only need to show that 1 and 2 are equivalent.

First suppose 1 holds, so S is linearly independent. Let $\mathbf{v}$ be any vector in V and consider the set $\{\mathbf{v}, \mathbf{v}_1, \ldots, \mathbf{v}_d\}$. This set consists of $d + 1$ vectors in V, and V can be spanned by d vectors, so by Proposition 12.1 this set must be linearly dependent. Thus

$$c_0 \mathbf{v} + c_1 \mathbf{v}_1 + \cdots + c_d \mathbf{v}_d = \mathbf{0}.$$

Since S is linearly independent, c_0 must be nonzero. Thus

$$\mathbf{v} = -\frac{1}{c_0}(c_1 \mathbf{v}_1 + \cdots + c_d \mathbf{v}_d)$$

so $\mathbf{v}$ is in $\mathrm{span}(\mathbf{v}_1, \ldots, \mathbf{v}_d)$. Since $\mathbf{v}$ is arbitrary, this proves that $V = \mathrm{span}(\mathbf{v}_1, \ldots, \mathbf{v}_d)$. Thus 1 implies 2.

Now suppose 2 holds, and that S is linearly dependent. Then one of the $\mathbf{v}_i$ is a linear combination of the others, so V can be spanned by $d - 1$ vectors. But any basis for V consists of d linearly independent vectors. This contradicts Proposition 12.1, so S must be linearly independent. So 2 implies 1, and thus 1 and 2 are equivalent. $\square$

We conclude this section by considering the dimensions of the column space and null space of a matrix. Let A be an m by n matrix. We define the **rank** (or column rank) of A by

$$\text{rank}(A) = \dim(C(A)),$$

the dimension of the column space of A, and the **nullity** of A by

$$\text{nullity}(A) = \dim(N(A)),$$

the dimension of the null space of A. We have seen that the columns of A which correspond to the pivot columns of $R = \text{rref}(A)$ form a basis for the column space of A. Thus the rank of A equals the number of pivots in $\text{rref}(A)$. We have also seen that there is one basis vector of the null space of A for each free variable of $A\mathbf{x} = \mathbf{0}$. Thus the nullity of A is simply the number of free variables. Since there are n variables, and the number of pivot variables is $\text{rank}(A)$, the nullity of A must be $n - \text{rank}(A)$. We therefore have the following result.

Proposition 12.4. (Rank-Nullity Theorem) Let A be any m by n matrix. Then

$$\text{rank}(A) + \text{nullity}(A) = n.$$

That is,

$$\dim(C(A)) + \dim(N(A)) = n.$$

Exercises

In Exercises 1 through 11 compute the rank and nullity of the matrix A and state what this implies about the existence and/or uniqueness of solutions $\mathbf{x}$ of $A\mathbf{x} = \mathbf{b}$.

12.1. $A = \begin{bmatrix} 1 & 2 & 3 \\ 1 & 1 & 1 \end{bmatrix}$

12.2. $A = \begin{bmatrix} 1 & 2 \\ 2 & 1 \end{bmatrix}$

12.3. $A = \begin{bmatrix} 1 & 1 \\ 2 & 2 \\ -1 & -1 \end{bmatrix}$

12.4. $A = \begin{bmatrix} 0 & 1 \\ 1 & 0 \\ 2 & 2 \end{bmatrix}$

12.5. $A = \begin{bmatrix} -1 & 2 & 4 \\ 2 & -4 & -8 \end{bmatrix}$

12.6. $A = \begin{bmatrix} 1 & 1 & 1 \\ 1 & 2 & 3 \\ 3 & 2 & 1 \end{bmatrix}$

12.7. $A = \begin{bmatrix} 0 & 1 & 1 & 0 \\ 2 & -1 & -1 & 2 \\ 1 & 2 & 2 & 4 \end{bmatrix}$

12.8. $A = \begin{bmatrix} 7 & 3 & 9 & 1 \\ 3 & 7 & 1 & 9 \\ 9 & 1 & 13 & -3 \\ 1 & 9 & -3 & 13 \end{bmatrix}$

12.9. $A = \begin{bmatrix} 1 & -1 & 2 & -2 \\ -1 & 1 & -2 & 2 \\ 2 & -2 & 4 & -4 \\ -2 & 2 & -4 & 4 \end{bmatrix}$

12.10. $A = \begin{bmatrix} 1 & -2 & 3 & 1 \\ 0 & 0 & 0 & 1 \\ 2 & 1 & 2 & 1 \\ -1 & 0 & -1 & 1 \end{bmatrix}$

12.11. $A = \begin{bmatrix} 1 & -2 & 3 & 1 \\ 0 & 0 & 0 & 1 \\ 2 & 1 & 2 & 1 \\ -1 & -3 & 1 & 1 \end{bmatrix}$

12.12. Evaluate each of the following assertions as always true, sometimes true, or never true.

(a) A set of 3 vectors in $\mathbf{R}^4$ is linearly independent.

(b) A set of 3 vectors in $\mathbf{R}^4$ spans $\mathbf{R}^4$.

(c) A set of 4 vectors in $\mathbf{R}^3$ is linearly independent.

(d) A set of 4 vectors in $\mathbf{R}^3$ spans $\mathbf{R}^3$.

(e) A set of 4 vectors which spans $\mathbf{R}^4$ is linearly independent.

(f) A set of 4 linearly independent vectors in $\mathbf{R}^4$ spans $\mathbf{R}^4$.

12.13. Determine whether each of the following statements is true or false.

(a) For a subspace V with dimension d, any d vectors which span V form a basis for V.

(b) For a subspace V with dimension d, any d vectors which are linearly independent form a basis for V.

78

(c) If $\{\mathbf{v}_1, \dots, \mathbf{v}_k\}$ span a subspace V, then V is k-dimensional.

(d) If $\{\mathbf{v}_1, \dots, \mathbf{v}_k\}$ is a basis for a subspace V, then any k linear combinations of $\mathbf{v}_1$ through $\mathbf{v}_k$ forms a basis for V.

(e) If $\{\mathbf{v}_1, \dots, \mathbf{v}_k\}$ is a basis for a subspace V, then every basis for V consists of k linear combinations of $\mathbf{v}_1$ through $\mathbf{v}_k$.

13   Linear Transformations

Thus far we have been concerned with the linear subsets of $\mathbf{R}^n$ (subspaces). We now turn our attention to linear functions on $\mathbf{R}^n$. A **function** from a set X to a set Y is a rule f which assigns to each element x of X an element of Y, which we denote by $f(x)$. The set X is called the **domain** of f and the set Y is called the **codomain** of f. The domain can be thought of as the set of all possible inputs for f, while the codomain is the set in which the outputs lie. We write $f : X \to Y$ to denote that f is a function with domain X and codomain Y. We will be mostly concerned with functions whose domain is $\mathbf{R}^n$, or some subset of $\mathbf{R}^n$, and whose codomain is $\mathbf{R}^m$, or a subset of $\mathbf{R}^m$. Functions whose codomain is a subset of $\mathbf{R}$ are called **real valued**, or **scalar valued**. Functions whose codomain is a subset of $\mathbf{R}^m$ for $m \geq 2$ are called **vector valued**, and are denoted using boldface letters.

Example 13.1. The formula $\mathbf{f}(x_1, x_2, x_3) = (x_1^2 + x_2^2 + x_3^2, x_1 x_2 x_3)$ defines a function from $\mathbf{R}^3$ to $\mathbf{R}^2$. $\diamond$

By making the usual identification of points in $\mathbf{R}^n$ with vectors in $\mathbf{R}^n$, we may view a function $\mathbf{f} : \mathbf{R}^n \to \mathbf{R}^m$ as a function which sends vectors in $\mathbf{R}^n$ to vectors in $\mathbf{R}^m$. Linear functions are precisely those functions which are well behaved with respect to the vector operations of addition and scalar multiplication. A **linear transformation** (linear function) is a function $\mathbf{T} : \mathbf{R}^n \to \mathbf{R}^m$ which satisfies

1. $\mathbf{T}(\mathbf{x} + \mathbf{y}) = \mathbf{T}(\mathbf{x}) + \mathbf{T}(\mathbf{y})$

2. $\mathbf{T}(c\mathbf{x}) = c\mathbf{T}(\mathbf{x})$

for all $\mathbf{x}$ and $\mathbf{y}$ in $\mathbf{R}^n$ and all scalars c in $\mathbf{R}$. The first property says that adding $\mathbf{x}$ and $\mathbf{y}$ and then applying $\mathbf{T}$ is equivalent to applying $\mathbf{T}$ to $\mathbf{x}$ and $\mathbf{y}$ and then adding the resulting vectors.

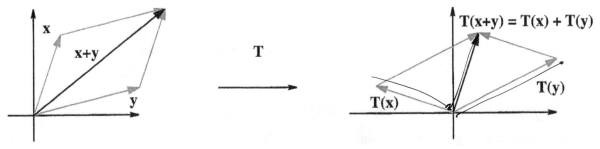

79

The second property says that scaling first and then applying **T** is equivalent to applying **T** first and then scaling.

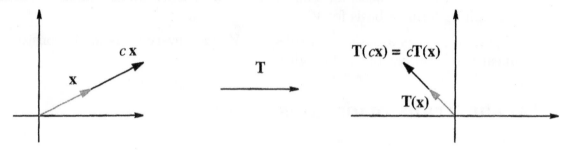

Example 13.2. Let $\mathbf{T} : \mathbf{R}^2 \to \mathbf{R}^2$ be defined by $\mathbf{T}(x_1, x_2) = (2x_1 - 3x_2, x_1 + x_2)$. Since

$$\mathbf{T}(\mathbf{x} + \mathbf{y}) = \begin{bmatrix} 2(x_1 + y_1) - 3(x_2 + y_2) \\ (x_1 + y_1) + (x_2 + y_2) \end{bmatrix} = \begin{bmatrix} 2x_1 - 3x_2 \\ x_1 + x_2 \end{bmatrix} + \begin{bmatrix} 2y_1 - 3y_2 \\ y_1 + y_2 \end{bmatrix} = \mathbf{T}(\mathbf{x}) + \mathbf{T}(\mathbf{y})$$

and

$$\mathbf{T}(c\mathbf{x}) = \begin{bmatrix} 2(cx_1) - 3(cx_2) \\ cx_1 + cx_2 \end{bmatrix} = c \begin{bmatrix} 2x_1 - 3x_2 \\ x_1 + x_2 \end{bmatrix} = c\mathbf{T}(\mathbf{x}),$$

T is a linear transformation. $\diamond$

Example 13.3. Let $\mathbf{f} : \mathbf{R}^3 \to \mathbf{R}^2$ be the function defined in Example 13.1. Making the arbitrary choice

$$\mathbf{x} = \begin{bmatrix} 1 \\ 1 \\ 1 \end{bmatrix}$$

we see that $\mathbf{f}(\mathbf{x}) = \mathbf{f}(1, 1, 1) = (3, 1)$, while $\mathbf{f}(2\mathbf{x}) = \mathbf{f}(2, 2, 2) = (12, 8)$. Thus $\mathbf{f}(2\mathbf{x}) \neq 2\mathbf{f}(\mathbf{x})$, so $\mathbf{f}$ is not a linear transformation, since the second property fails. $\diamond$

Matrices and Linear Transformations

The properties which define linear transformations are identical to those of matrix-vector products. It follows therefore that multiplication by any matrix defines a linear transformation.

Proposition 13.1. Let A be an $m \times n$ matrix, and let **T** be the function from $\mathbf{R}^n$ to $\mathbf{R}^m$ defined by $\mathbf{T}(\mathbf{x}) = A\mathbf{x}$. Then **T** is a linear transformation.

Proof. By Proposition 7.1,

$$\mathbf{T}(\mathbf{x} + \mathbf{y}) = A(\mathbf{x} + \mathbf{y}) = A\mathbf{x} + A\mathbf{y} = \mathbf{T}(\mathbf{x}) + \mathbf{T}(\mathbf{y})$$

and

$$\mathbf{T}(c\mathbf{x}) = A(c\mathbf{x}) = cA\mathbf{x} = c\mathbf{T}(\mathbf{x})$$

for any vectors $\mathbf{x}$ and $\mathbf{y}$ in $\mathbf{R}^n$ and any scalar c in $\mathbf{R}$. $\square$

Example 13.4. The linear transformation $\mathbf{T} : \mathbf{R}^3 \to \mathbf{R}^2$ defined by multiplication by the matrix

$$A = \begin{bmatrix} 2 & -3 & 4 \\ 6 & 1 & -2 \end{bmatrix} \begin{bmatrix} x_1 \\ x_2 \\ x_3 \end{bmatrix}$$

is given by $\mathbf{T}(x_1, x_2, x_3) = (2x_1 - 3x_2 + 4x_3, 6x_1 + x_2 - 2x_3)$. ◇

The remarkable fact is that every linear transformation is equivalent to multiplication by some matrix.

Proposition 13.2. Let $\mathbf{T} : \mathbf{R}^n \to \mathbf{R}^m$ be a linear transformation. Then $\mathbf{T}$ is equivalent to multiplication by the matrix

$$A = \begin{bmatrix} | & | & & | \\ \mathbf{T}(\mathbf{e}_1) & \mathbf{T}(\mathbf{e}_2) & \cdots & \mathbf{T}(\mathbf{e}_n) \\ | & | & & | \end{bmatrix}$$

where $\mathbf{e}_1$ through $\mathbf{e}_n$ are the standard basis vectors in $\mathbf{R}^n$. That is, $\mathbf{T}(\mathbf{x}) = A\mathbf{x}$ for all $\mathbf{x}$ in $\mathbf{R}^n$.

We say that the **matrix of a linear transformation T** (with respect to the standard basis) is the matrix A defined above.

Proof. First, recall that any vector $\mathbf{x}$ may be written in terms of the standard basis vectors as

$$\mathbf{x} = x_1\mathbf{e}_1 + x_2\mathbf{e}_2 + \cdots + x_n\mathbf{e}_n.$$

Using the linearity of $\mathbf{T}$ we then have

$$\mathbf{T}(\mathbf{x}) = \mathbf{T}(x_1\mathbf{e}_1 + x_2\mathbf{e}_2 + \cdots + x_n\mathbf{e}_n)$$
$$= x_1\mathbf{T}(\mathbf{e}_1) + x_2\mathbf{T}(\mathbf{e}_2) + \cdots + x_n\mathbf{T}(\mathbf{e}_n).$$

The final expression is exactly the product of the matrix A with the vector $\mathbf{x}$. □

Example 13.5. The linear transformation $\mathbf{T} : \mathbf{R}^2 \to \mathbf{R}^2$ defined in Example 13.2 satisfies

$$\mathbf{T}(\mathbf{e}_1) = \begin{bmatrix} 2 \\ 1 \end{bmatrix} \quad \text{and} \quad \mathbf{T}(\mathbf{e}_2) = \begin{bmatrix} -3 \\ 1 \end{bmatrix},$$

so the matrix for $\mathbf{T}$ is

$$A = \begin{bmatrix} 2 & -3 \\ 1 & 1 \end{bmatrix},$$

and thus $\mathbf{T}(\mathbf{x}) = A\mathbf{x}$ for all $\mathbf{x}$ in $\mathbf{R}^2$. ◇

Images and Preimages

Given a function $f : X \to Y$ and a subset S of X, each element of S is then sent by f to some element $f(x)$ of Y. The set of all such elements $f(x)$ is called the **image** of S under f, and is denoted $f(S)$. That is,

$$f(S) = \{f(x) \mid x \text{ is in } S\}.$$

Example 13.6. Let $\mathbf{T}$ be the linear transformation from Example 13.2 and let the line L be parametrized by $\{\mathbf{x}_0 + t\mathbf{v} \mid t \in \mathbf{R}\}$, where

$$\mathbf{x}_0 = \begin{bmatrix} 0 \\ -1 \end{bmatrix} \qquad \text{and} \qquad \mathbf{v} = \begin{bmatrix} 1 \\ 1 \end{bmatrix}.$$

By linearity

$$\mathbf{T}(\mathbf{x}_0 + t\mathbf{v}) = \mathbf{T}(\mathbf{x}_0) + t\mathbf{T}(\mathbf{v}),$$

so

$$\mathbf{T}(L) = \{\mathbf{T}(\mathbf{x}_0) + t\mathbf{T}(\mathbf{v}) \mid t \in \mathbf{R}\}.$$

This is precisely the line passing through $\mathbf{T}(\mathbf{x}_0)$, parallel to the line spanned by $\mathbf{T}(\mathbf{v})$. Since

$$\mathbf{T}(\mathbf{x}_0) = \begin{bmatrix} 2 & -3 \\ 1 & 1 \end{bmatrix} \begin{bmatrix} 0 \\ -1 \end{bmatrix} = \begin{bmatrix} 3 \\ -1 \end{bmatrix} \qquad \text{and} \qquad \mathbf{T}(\mathbf{v}) = \begin{bmatrix} 2 & -3 \\ 1 & 1 \end{bmatrix} \begin{bmatrix} 1 \\ 1 \end{bmatrix} = \begin{bmatrix} -1 \\ 2 \end{bmatrix}$$

the image of L under $\mathbf{T}$ is the line which passes through the points $(3, -1)$ and $(2, 1)$.

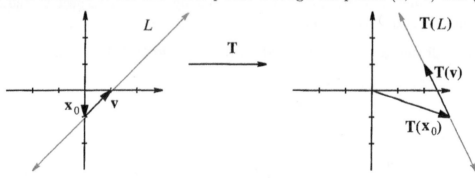

In general, the image under a linear transformation $\mathbf{T}$ of a line $\{\mathbf{x}_0 + t\mathbf{v} \mid t \in \mathbf{R}\}$ is a line $\mathbf{T}(\mathbf{x}_0) + t\mathbf{T}(\mathbf{v})$, unless $\mathbf{T}(\mathbf{v})$ equals the zero vector, in which case the image consists only of the point $\mathbf{T}(\mathbf{x}_0)$. By the same reasoning, it follows that the image under a linear transformation $\mathbf{T}$ of the line segment

$$\{\mathbf{x}_0 + t(\mathbf{x}_1 - \mathbf{x}_0) \mid 0 \le t \le 1\}$$

between $\mathbf{x}_0$ and $\mathbf{x}_1$ is the line segment

$$\{\mathbf{T}(\mathbf{x}_0) + t(\mathbf{T}(\mathbf{x}_1) - \mathbf{T}(\mathbf{x}_0)) \mid 0 \le t \le 1\}$$

between $\mathbf{T}(\mathbf{x}_0)$ and $\mathbf{T}(\mathbf{x}_1)$. Thus the image of any polygonal region may be found by determining the image of its vertices and then "connecting the dots" in order with line segments.

Example 13.7. Consider again the linear transformation **T** from Example 13.2, and let R be the region bounded by the polygon with vertices $(0,0)$, $(1,1)$, $(1,-1)$, $(-1,-1)$, and $(-1,1)$, in that order. Since $\mathbf{T}(0,0) = (0,0)$, $\mathbf{T}(1,1) = (-1,2)$, $\mathbf{T}(1,-1) = (5,0)$, $\mathbf{T}(-1,-1) = (1,-2)$ and $\mathbf{T}(-1,1) = (-5,0)$, the image of R under **T** is the polygon shown below.

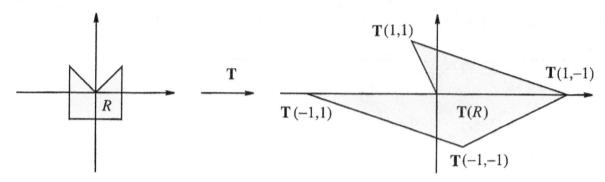

$\Diamond$

We next show that the image of a subspace under a linear transformation is a subspace.

Proposition 13.3. Let $\mathbf{T} : \mathbf{R}^n \to \mathbf{R}^m$ be a linear transformation, and let V be a subspace of $\mathbf{R}^n$. Then $\mathbf{T}(V)$ is a subspace of $\mathbf{R}^m$.

Proof. We need to show that the image $\mathbf{T}(V)$ is closed under addition and scalar multiplication. So consider two elements $\mathbf{T}(\mathbf{x})$ and $\mathbf{T}(\mathbf{y})$ in $\mathbf{T}(V)$, where $\mathbf{x}$ and $\mathbf{y}$ are necessarily in V. By linearity, their sum is

$$\mathbf{T}(\mathbf{x}) + \mathbf{T}(\mathbf{y}) = \mathbf{T}(\mathbf{x} + \mathbf{y}).$$

Since V is a subspace, $\mathbf{x} + \mathbf{y}$ is in V, so $\mathbf{T}(\mathbf{x} + \mathbf{y})$, and hence $\mathbf{T}(\mathbf{x}) + \mathbf{T}(\mathbf{y})$, is in $\mathbf{T}(V)$. So $\mathbf{T}(V)$ is closed under addition. Next, for any scalar c we have

$$c\mathbf{T}(\mathbf{x}) = \mathbf{T}(c\mathbf{x}).$$

Once again using the fact that V is a subspace, since $\mathbf{x}$ is in V it follows that $c\mathbf{x}$ is in V. Thus $\mathbf{T}(c\mathbf{x})$, and hence $c\mathbf{T}(\mathbf{x})$, is in $\mathbf{T}(V)$, so $\mathbf{T}(V)$ is closed under scalar multiplication. $\square$

We leave it as an exercise to verify that if $\{\mathbf{v}_1, \ldots, \mathbf{v}_k\}$ spans V then $\{\mathbf{T}(\mathbf{v}_1), \ldots, \mathbf{T}(\mathbf{v}_k)\}$ spans $\mathbf{T}(V)$.

Example 13.8. Let $\mathbf{T} : \mathbf{R}^3 \to \mathbf{R}^3$ be the linear transformation whose matrix is

$$A = \begin{bmatrix} 3 & -1 & 1 \\ 2 & 0 & 2 \\ 1 & 1 & 3 \end{bmatrix}$$

and let V be the plane $x_1 + 4x_2 - 6x_3 = 0$. The vectors

$$\mathbf{v}_1 = \begin{bmatrix} -4 \\ 1 \\ 0 \end{bmatrix} \qquad \text{and} \qquad \mathbf{v}_2 = \begin{bmatrix} 6 \\ 0 \\ 1 \end{bmatrix}$$

form a basis for (and hence span) V. Thus the vectors

$$\mathbf{T}(\mathbf{v}_1) = \begin{bmatrix} -13 \\ -8 \\ -3 \end{bmatrix} \qquad \text{and} \qquad \mathbf{T}(\mathbf{v}_2) = \begin{bmatrix} 19 \\ 14 \\ 9 \end{bmatrix}$$

span $\mathbf{T}(V)$. Since $\mathbf{T}(\mathbf{v}_1)$ and $\mathbf{T}(\mathbf{v}_2)$ are linearly independent they form a basis for $\mathbf{T}(V)$. It is not in general true however that if $\{\mathbf{v}_1, \ldots, \mathbf{v}_k\}$ is a basis for a subspace V, then $\{\mathbf{T}(\mathbf{v}_1), \ldots, \mathbf{T}(\mathbf{v}_k)\}$ is a basis for $\mathbf{T}(V)$, since these vectors could be linearly dependent. $\diamond$

As a special case of Proposition 13.3, let V be all of $\mathbf{R}^n$. The image of $\mathbf{R}^n$ under a linear transformation $\mathbf{T} : \mathbf{R}^n \to \mathbf{R}^m$ is called the **image** of $\mathbf{T}$, and is denoted $\operatorname{im}(\mathbf{T})$. That is,

$$\operatorname{im}(\mathbf{T}) = \{\mathbf{T}(\mathbf{x}) \mid \mathbf{x} \in \mathbf{R}^n\}.$$

Now let A be the matrix for $\mathbf{T}$. Then $\mathbf{T}(\mathbf{x}) = A\mathbf{x}$ for each $\mathbf{x}$ in $\mathbf{R}^n$, so that

$$\operatorname{im}(\mathbf{T}) = \{A\mathbf{x} \mid \mathbf{x} \in \mathbf{R}^n\} = C(A).$$

Hence the image of $\mathbf{T}$ is precisely the column space of A.

Another important concept is that of a preimage. Given a function $f : X \to Y$, and a subset S of the codomain Y, we might wish to know which elements x in X are sent by f into S. The **preimage** of S under f is the set

$$f^{-1}(S) = \{x \text{ in } X \mid f(x) \text{ is in } S\}.$$

Example 13.9. Let $\mathbf{T} : \mathbf{R}^2 \to \mathbf{R}^2$ be the linear transformation with matrix

$$A = \begin{bmatrix} 1 & 3 \\ 2 & 6 \end{bmatrix}$$

and let $S = \{(0,0), (1,2)\}$. The preimage of S consists of all points in $\mathbf{R}^2$ which are sent by $\mathbf{T}$ to either of these points. Thus we need to solve the systems

$$A\mathbf{x} = \begin{bmatrix} 0 \\ 0 \end{bmatrix} \qquad \text{and} \qquad A\mathbf{x} = \begin{bmatrix} 1 \\ 2 \end{bmatrix}.$$

The solutions of these systems are

$$\left\{ t \begin{bmatrix} -3 \\ 1 \end{bmatrix} \;\middle|\; t \in \mathbf{R} \right\} \qquad \text{and} \qquad \left\{ \begin{bmatrix} 1 \\ 0 \end{bmatrix} + t \begin{bmatrix} -3 \\ 1 \end{bmatrix} \;\middle|\; t \in \mathbf{R} \right\},$$

respectively, so the preimage $f^{-1}(S)$ consists of two parallel lines.

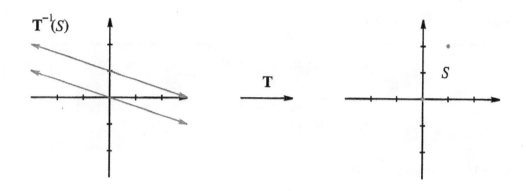

It is left as an exercise to show that the preimage of a subspace under a linear transformation is a subspace. One important example is the preimage of the trivial subspace. The kernel of a linear transformation $\mathbf{T} : \mathbf{R}^n \to \mathbf{R}^m$ is the set

$$\ker(\mathbf{T}) = \{\mathbf{x} \text{ in } \mathbf{R}^n \mid \mathbf{T}(\mathbf{x}) = \mathbf{0}\}.$$

If A is the matrix for $\mathbf{T}$, then a vector $\mathbf{x}$ is in the kernel of $\mathbf{T}$ if and only if $A\mathbf{x} = \mathbf{0}$. Hence the kernel of $\mathbf{T}$ is precisely the null space of A.

Sums and Scalar Multiples of Linear Transformations

Given two linear transformations $\mathbf{S} : \mathbf{R}^n \to \mathbf{R}^m$ and $\mathbf{T} : \mathbf{R}^n \to \mathbf{R}^m$, their **sum** is the transformation defined by $(\mathbf{S} + \mathbf{T})(\mathbf{x}) = \mathbf{S}(\mathbf{x}) + \mathbf{T}(\mathbf{x})$. We also define a scalar multiple c of the transformation $\mathbf{T}$ by $(c\mathbf{T})(\mathbf{x}) = c\mathbf{T}(\mathbf{x})$. It is left as an exercise to verify that sums and scalar multiples (and hence linear combinations) of linear transformations are linear transformations. By Proposition 13.2, the jth column of the matrix for $\mathbf{S} + \mathbf{T}$ is

$$(\mathbf{S} + \mathbf{T})(\mathbf{e}_j) = \mathbf{S}(\mathbf{e}_j) + \mathbf{T}(\mathbf{e}_j),$$

the sum of the jth column of the matrix for $\mathbf{S}$ and the jth column of the matrix for $\mathbf{T}$. Since

$$(c\mathbf{S})(\mathbf{e}_j) = c\mathbf{S}(\mathbf{e}_j),$$

for any scalar c, the jth column of the matrix for $c\mathbf{S}$ is c times the jth column of the matrix for $\mathbf{S}$. In view of these facts, we define the sum of two $m \times n$ matrices A and B by

$$
\begin{aligned}
A + B &= \begin{bmatrix} a_{11} & a_{12} & \cdots & a_{1n} \\ a_{21} & a_{22} & \cdots & a_{2n} \\ \vdots & \vdots & & \vdots \\ a_{m1} & a_{m2} & \cdots & a_{mn} \end{bmatrix} + \begin{bmatrix} b_{11} & b_{12} & \cdots & b_{1n} \\ b_{21} & b_{22} & \cdots & b_{2n} \\ \vdots & \vdots & & \vdots \\ b_{m1} & b_{m2} & \cdots & b_{mn} \end{bmatrix} \\
&= \begin{bmatrix} a_{11} + b_{11} & a_{12} + b_{12} & \cdots & a_{1n} + b_{1n} \\ a_{21} + b_{21} & a_{22} + b_{22} & \cdots & a_{2n} + b_{2n} \\ \vdots & \vdots & & \vdots \\ a_{m1} + b_{m1} & a_{m2} + b_{m2} & \cdots & a_{mn} + b_{mn} \end{bmatrix}
\end{aligned}
$$

and the scalar multiple c of A by

$$cA = c \begin{bmatrix} a_{11} & a_{12} & \cdots & a_{1n} \\ a_{21} & a_{22} & \cdots & a_{2n} \\ \vdots & \vdots & & \vdots \\ a_{m1} & a_{m2} & \cdots & a_{mn} \end{bmatrix} = \begin{bmatrix} ca_{11} & ca_{12} & \cdots & ca_{1n} \\ ca_{21} & ca_{22} & \cdots & ca_{2n} \\ \vdots & \vdots & & \vdots \\ ca_{m1} & ca_{m2} & \cdots & ca_{mn} \end{bmatrix}.$$

We then have the following result.

Proposition 13.4. Suppose $\mathbf{S} : \mathbf{R}^n \to \mathbf{R}^m$ and $\mathbf{T} : \mathbf{R}^n \to \mathbf{R}^m$ are linear transformations with matrices A and B, respectively. Then the matrix for $\mathbf{S} + \mathbf{T}$ is $A + B$ and, for any scalar c, the matrix for $c\mathbf{S}$ is cA.

As with vectors, we denote by $-A$ the matrix $(-1)A$, and by O the **zero matrix**, all of whose entries are zero. With this notation, matrices obey exactly the same properties as vectors.

Proposition 13.5. Let A, B and C be $m \times n$ matrices and let c and d be real numbers. Then

1. $A + B = B + A$
2. $A + (B + C) = (A + B) + C$
3. $A + O = A$
4. $A + (-A) = O$

5. $c(dA) = (cd)A$
6. $(c + d)A = cA + dA$
7. $c(A + B) = cA + cB$
8. $1A = A$

Exercises

In Exercises 1 through 6, for the given function $\mathbf{f} : \mathbf{R}^n \to \mathbf{R}^m$, determine whether the function is a linear transformation. If it is, find the matrix A such that $\mathbf{f}(\mathbf{x}) = A\mathbf{x}$ for all $\mathbf{x} \in \mathbf{R}^n$. If it is not, show that it does not satisfy at least one of the conditions necessary for a function to be a linear transformation.

13.1. $\mathbf{f}(x_1, x_2) = (3x_1, -2x_1 + 5x_2)$

13.2. $\mathbf{f}(x_1, x_2) = (-x_2, x_1 + 1)$

13.3. $\mathbf{f}(x_1, x_2) = (x_1^2 + 3x_2, -5x_1 + 2x_1)$

13.4. $\mathbf{f}(x_1, x_2) = (1, 2)$

13.5. $\mathbf{f}(x_1, x_2) = (0, 0)$

13.6. $\mathbf{f}(x_1, x_2, x_3) = (3x_1 - 2x_3, x_2 + 4x_3, -x_1 + x_2)$

13.7. Suppose $\mathbf{T} : \mathbf{R}^2 \to \mathbf{R}^2$ is a linear transformation satisfying

$$\mathbf{T}\left(\begin{bmatrix} 2 \\ 1 \end{bmatrix}\right) = \begin{bmatrix} 2 \\ 1 \end{bmatrix} \qquad \mathbf{T}\left(\begin{bmatrix} -1 \\ 2 \end{bmatrix}\right) = \begin{bmatrix} 1 \\ -2 \end{bmatrix}.$$

   (a) For which matrix A is $\mathbf{T}$ equivalent to multiplication by A?

   (b) Describe $\mathbf{T}$ geometrically.

13.8. Suppose $\mathbf{T} : \mathbf{R}^2 \to \mathbf{R}^2$ is a linear transformation satisfying

$$\mathbf{T}\left(\begin{bmatrix} 4 \\ 3 \end{bmatrix}\right) = \begin{bmatrix} 11 \\ 0 \end{bmatrix} \qquad \mathbf{T}\left(\begin{bmatrix} 3 \\ 1 \end{bmatrix}\right) = \begin{bmatrix} 7 \\ -5 \end{bmatrix}.$$

For which matrix A is $\mathbf{T}$ equivalent to multiplication by A?

13.9. Let R_1 be the triangle with vertices $(0,0)$, $(1,1)$ and $(-1,1)$, and let R_2 be the triangle with vertices $(0,0)$, $(2,2)$ and $(2,-2)$. There are exactly two linear transformations $\mathbf{T} : \mathbf{R}^2 \to \mathbf{R}^2$ such that $\mathbf{T}(R_1) = R_2$. Find the matrices for these transformations.

In Exercises 10 through 16 sketch the image of the figure shown below under the linear transformation defined by the given matrix.

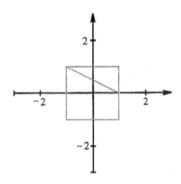

13.10. $\begin{bmatrix} 1 & 0 \\ 0 & 1 \end{bmatrix}$

13.11. $\begin{bmatrix} 1 & 0 \\ 0 & 3 \end{bmatrix}$

13.12. $\begin{bmatrix} 1 & -1 \\ 1 & 1 \end{bmatrix}$

13.13. $\begin{bmatrix} 1 & 2 \\ 2 & 4 \end{bmatrix}$

13.14. $\begin{bmatrix} 0 & 0 \\ 0 & 0 \end{bmatrix}$

13.15. $\begin{bmatrix} 1 & 2 \\ 3 & 4 \end{bmatrix}$

13.16. $\begin{bmatrix} 1 & 2 \\ 0 & 1 \end{bmatrix}$

13.17. Show that if $\{\mathbf{v}_1, \dots, \mathbf{v}_k\}$ spans V then $\{\mathbf{T}(\mathbf{v}_1), \dots, \mathbf{T}(\mathbf{v}_k)\}$ spans $\mathbf{T}(V)$.

13.18. Give an example of a linear transformation $\mathbf{T} : \mathbf{R}^2 \to \mathbf{R}^2$ and a basis $\{\mathbf{v}_1, \mathbf{v}_2\}$ for $\mathbf{R}^2$ such that $\{\mathbf{T}(\mathbf{v}_1), \mathbf{T}(\mathbf{v}_2)\}$ is not a basis for $\mathbf{T}(\mathbf{R}^2)$.

13.19. Given linear transformations $\mathbf{S} : \mathbf{R}^n \to \mathbf{R}^m$ and $\mathbf{T} : \mathbf{R}^n \to \mathbf{R}^m$, show the following.

(a) $\mathbf{S} + \mathbf{T}$ is a linear transformation.

(b) $c\mathbf{S}$ is a linear transformation.

13.20. Show that if $\{\mathbf{v}_1, \mathbf{v}_2, \dots, \mathbf{v}_k\}$ spans V then $\{\mathbf{T}(\mathbf{v}_1), \mathbf{T}(\mathbf{v}_2), \dots, \mathbf{T}(\mathbf{v}_k)\}$ spans $\mathbf{T}(V)$.

13.21. Show by example that it is not always true that if $\{\mathbf{v}_1, \mathbf{v}_2, \dots, \mathbf{v}_k\}$ is a basis for V then $\{\mathbf{T}(\mathbf{v}_1), \mathbf{T}(\mathbf{v}_2), \dots, \mathbf{T}(\mathbf{v}_k)\}$ is a basis for $\mathbf{T}(V)$.

13.22. Show that if $\{\mathbf{v}_1, \mathbf{v}_2, \dots, \mathbf{v}_k\}$ is a linearly dependent set and $\mathbf{T}$ is a linear transformation, then $\{\mathbf{T}(\mathbf{v}_1), \mathbf{T}(\mathbf{v}_2), \dots, \mathbf{T}(\mathbf{v}_k)\}$ is also linearly dependent.

1. Let $\mathbf{T} : \mathbf{R}^n \to \mathbf{R}^m$ be a linear transformation, and let V be a subspace of $\mathbf{R}^m$. Show that the preimage $\mathbf{T}^{-1}(V)$ is a subspace of $\mathbf{R}^n$.

14   Examples of Linear Transformations

In this section we consider a number of important examples of linear transformations. We begin with one of the simplest.

The Identity Transformation

The function $\mathbf{I_{R^n}} : \mathbf{R}^n \to \mathbf{R}^n$ defined by $\mathbf{I_{R^n}}(\mathbf{x}) = \mathbf{x}$ is called the **identity transformation** on $\mathbf{R}^n$. It is easy to see that this transformation is linear. Since $\mathbf{I_{R^n}}(\mathbf{e}_i) = \mathbf{e}_i$ for $i = 1, \dots, n$, the matrix for $\mathbf{I_{R^n}}$ is

$$\begin{bmatrix} 1 & 0 & \cdots & 0 \\ 0 & 1 & \cdots & 0 \\ \vdots & \vdots & \ddots & \vdots \\ 0 & 0 & \cdots & 1 \end{bmatrix},$$

the $n \times n$ identity matrix I_n. The identity transformation does essentially nothing, sending each vector in $\mathbf{R}^n$ to itself.

Example 14.1. Consider the triangle in $\mathbf{R}^2$ with vertices $(1,1)$, $(-1,1)$ and $(-1,0)$. Its image under the identity transformation is itself.

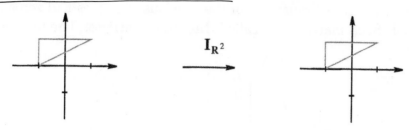

$\diamond$

Scaling Transformations

A **scaling transformation** on $\mathbf{R}^n$ is a transformation $\mathbf{T} : \mathbf{R}^n \to \mathbf{R}^n$ defined by $\mathbf{T}(\mathbf{x}) = \alpha\mathbf{x}$ for some scalar $\alpha \in \mathbf{R}$. Depending on the size of α, scaling transformations either stretch ($|\alpha| > 1$) or contract ($|\alpha| < 1$) vectors, and if α is negative, the transformation reflects vectors through the origin. Since this transformation is α times the identity transformation, its matrix must be

$$\alpha I_n = \begin{bmatrix} \alpha & 0 & \cdots & 0 \\ 0 & \alpha & \cdots & 0 \\ \vdots & \vdots & \ddots & \vdots \\ 0 & 0 & \cdots & \alpha \end{bmatrix}.$$

Example 14.2. The image under $\mathbf{T}$ of the triangle from Example 14.1 is shown below for $\alpha = 2$ and $\alpha = -\frac{1}{2}$.

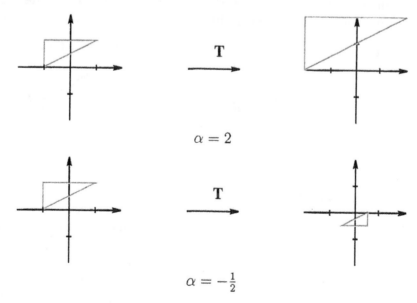

$\diamond$

Diagonal Matrices

The matrices of the transformations in the previous examples had zeros in all entries off the main diagonal. Such matrices are called **diagonal** matrices. The most general diagonal matrix takes the form

$$D = \begin{bmatrix} d_1 & 0 & \cdots & 0 \\ 0 & d_2 & \cdots & 0 \\ \vdots & \vdots & \ddots & \vdots \\ 0 & 0 & \cdots & d_n \end{bmatrix}.$$

The transformation $\mathbf{T} : \mathbf{R}^n \to \mathbf{R}^n$ defined by $\mathbf{T}(\mathbf{x}) = D\mathbf{x}$ then has the effect of stretching, contracting or reflecting vectors along the ith coordinate axis by the factor d_i.

Example 14.3. Shown below is the image under $\mathbf{T}$ of the triangle from Example 14.1, with $d_1 = 2$ and $d_2 = -1$.

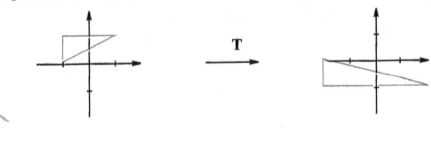

$\diamond$

Rotations in $\mathbf{R}^2$

Another important type of linear transformation is a **rotation**. We define $\mathbf{Rot}_\theta : \mathbf{R}^2 \to \mathbf{R}^2$ to be the function which rotates vectors in $\mathbf{R}^2$ counterclockwise through the angle θ.

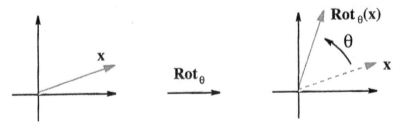

The figure below illustrates that scaling and then rotating is equivalent to rotating and then scaling, so that $\mathbf{Rot}_\theta(c\mathbf{x}) = c\mathbf{Rot}_\theta(\mathbf{x})$.

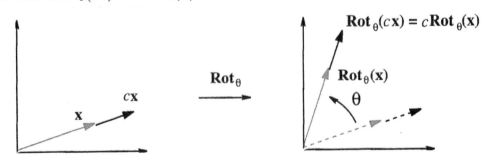

90

Next notice that adding $\mathbf{x}$ and $\mathbf{y}$ and then rotating is the same as rotating and then adding, so $\mathbf{Rot}_\theta(\mathbf{x}+\mathbf{y}) = \mathbf{Rot}_\theta(\mathbf{x}) + \mathbf{Rot}_\theta(\mathbf{y})$.

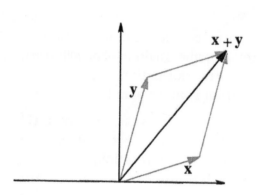
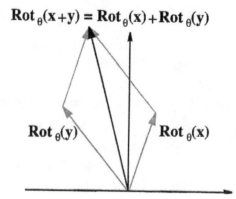

Thus $\mathbf{Rot}_\theta$ is a linear transformation. To find its matrix we evaluate $\mathbf{Rot}_\theta$ on $\mathbf{e}_1$ and $\mathbf{e}_2$ and use Proposition 13.2.

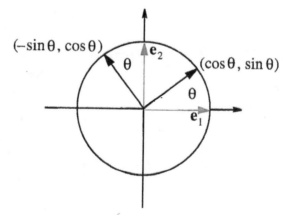

From the figure we see that

$$\mathbf{Rot}_\theta(\mathbf{e}_1) = \begin{bmatrix} \cos\theta \\ \sin\theta \end{bmatrix} \qquad \text{and} \qquad \mathbf{Rot}_\theta(\mathbf{e}_2) = \begin{bmatrix} -\sin\theta \\ \cos\theta \end{bmatrix}.$$

Hence the matrix for $\mathbf{Rot}_\theta$ is

$$\begin{bmatrix} \cos\theta & -\sin\theta \\ \sin\theta & \cos\theta \end{bmatrix}.$$

Example 14.4. The matrix for a 45° ($\pi/4$ radian) rotation is

$$\begin{bmatrix} \sqrt{2}/2 & -\sqrt{2}/2 \\ \sqrt{2}/2 & \sqrt{2}/2 \end{bmatrix}.$$

$$\mathbf{Rot}_{\pi/4}$$

Rotations in $\mathbf{R}^3$

Given a line in $\mathbf{R}^3$ which passes through the origin we can define a linear transformation which rotates all points in $\mathbf{R}^3$ about this line through some angle θ. For arbitrarily lines it is quite difficult to determine the matrix for such a transformation. However, if the line happens to be one of the coordinate axes, the calculation is much simpler.

Example 14.5. Let $\mathbf{T} : \mathbf{R}^3 \to \mathbf{R}^3$ be the transformation which rotates vectors in $\mathbf{R}^3$ about the x-axis through angle θ, where the direction is such that the positive y-axis is rotated toward the positive z-axis. Then since the x-axis is fixed by the rotation, $\mathbf{T}(\mathbf{e}_1) = \mathbf{e}_1$. The effect on the yz-plane is that of an ordinary rotation in $\mathbf{R}^2$, so

$$\mathbf{T}(\mathbf{e}_2) = (\cos \theta)\mathbf{e}_2 + (\sin \theta)\mathbf{e}_3 = \begin{bmatrix} 0 \\ \cos \theta \\ \sin \theta \end{bmatrix}$$

$$\mathbf{T}(\mathbf{e}_3) = (-\sin \theta)\mathbf{e}_2 + (\cos \theta)\mathbf{e}_3 = \begin{bmatrix} 0 \\ -\sin \theta \\ \cos \theta \end{bmatrix}.$$

Therefore the matrix for $\mathbf{T}$ is

$$\begin{bmatrix} 1 & 0 & 0 \\ 0 & \cos \theta & -\sin \theta \\ 0 & \sin \theta & \cos \theta \end{bmatrix}.$$

Projections

Given a line L in $\mathbf{R}^n$ which passes through the origin, the **orthogonal projection** of a vector $\mathbf{x}$ onto L is the vector $\mathbf{Proj}_L(\mathbf{x})$ in L such that the difference vector $\mathbf{x} - \mathbf{Proj}_L(\mathbf{x})$ is orthogonal to L.

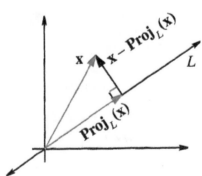

Suppose L is spanned by the vector $\mathbf{v}$. To derive a formula for $\mathbf{Proj}_L(\mathbf{x})$ in terms of $\mathbf{x}$ and $\mathbf{v}$ first observe that $\mathbf{Proj}_L(\mathbf{x}) = c\mathbf{v}$ for some scalar c. Since orthogonal vectors have dot product zero, we have

$$\mathbf{v} \cdot (\mathbf{x} - c\mathbf{v}) = 0.$$

Solving for c we get

$$c = \frac{\mathbf{x} \cdot \mathbf{v}}{\mathbf{v} \cdot \mathbf{v}}$$

and thus we arrive at

$$\mathbf{Proj}_L(\mathbf{x}) = \left(\frac{\mathbf{x} \cdot \mathbf{v}}{\mathbf{v} \cdot \mathbf{v}}\right) \mathbf{v}$$

where $\mathbf{v}$ is any vector which spans the line L. By using a unit vector $\mathbf{u}$ which spans L, the formula simplifies to

$$\mathbf{Proj}_L(\mathbf{x}) = (\mathbf{x} \cdot \mathbf{u})\mathbf{u}.$$

Since

$$\begin{aligned}
\mathbf{Proj}_L(\mathbf{x} + \mathbf{y}) &= ((\mathbf{x} + \mathbf{y}) \cdot \mathbf{u})\mathbf{u} \\
&= (\mathbf{x} \cdot \mathbf{u} + \mathbf{y} \cdot \mathbf{u})\mathbf{u} \\
&= (\mathbf{x} \cdot \mathbf{u})\mathbf{u} + (\mathbf{y} \cdot \mathbf{u})\mathbf{u} \\
&= \mathbf{Proj}_L(\mathbf{x}) + \mathbf{Proj}_L(\mathbf{y})
\end{aligned}$$

and

$$\begin{aligned}
\mathbf{Proj}_L(c\mathbf{x}) &= ((c\mathbf{x}) \cdot \mathbf{u})\mathbf{u} \\
&= c(\mathbf{x} \cdot \mathbf{u})\mathbf{u} \\
&= c\mathbf{Proj}_L(\mathbf{x}),
\end{aligned}$$

$\mathbf{Proj}_L$ is a linear transformation. We again use Proposition 13.2 to find the matrix for a projection. If L is the line in $\mathbf{R}^2$ spanned by the unit vector

$$\mathbf{u} = \begin{bmatrix} u_1 \\ u_2 \end{bmatrix}$$

then

$$\mathbf{Proj}_L(\mathbf{e}_1) = (\mathbf{e}_1 \cdot \mathbf{u})\mathbf{u} = u_1\mathbf{u} = \begin{bmatrix} u_1^2 \\ u_1 u_2 \end{bmatrix}$$

$$\mathbf{Proj}_L(\mathbf{e}_2) = (\mathbf{e}_2 \cdot \mathbf{u})\mathbf{u} = u_2\mathbf{u} = \begin{bmatrix} u_1 u_2 \\ u_2^2 \end{bmatrix}.$$

So the matrix for $\mathbf{Proj}_L$ is

$$\begin{bmatrix} u_1^2 & u_1 u_2 \\ u_1 u_2 & u_2^2 \end{bmatrix}.$$

Example 14.6. If L is the line $y = -x$ then

$$\mathbf{u} = \begin{bmatrix} \sqrt{2}/2 \\ -\sqrt{2}/2 \end{bmatrix}$$

is a unit vector which spans L, so the matrix for $\mathbf{Proj}_L$ is

$$\begin{bmatrix} \frac{1}{2} & -\frac{1}{2} \\ -\frac{1}{2} & \frac{1}{2} \end{bmatrix}.$$

The image under $\mathbf{Proj}_L$ of a triangle is shown below.

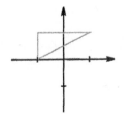 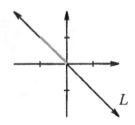

If L is the line in $\mathbf{R}^3$ spanned by the unit vector $\mathbf{u}$ then

$$\mathbf{Proj}_L(\mathbf{e}_1) = \begin{bmatrix} u_1^2 \\ u_1 u_2 \\ u_1 u_3 \end{bmatrix} \qquad \mathbf{Proj}_L(\mathbf{e}_2) = \begin{bmatrix} u_1 u_2 \\ u_2^2 \\ u_2 u_3 \end{bmatrix} \qquad \mathbf{Proj}_L(\mathbf{e}_3) = \begin{bmatrix} u_1 u_3 \\ u_2 u_3 \\ u_3^2 \end{bmatrix}$$

where u_1, u_2 and u_3 are the components of $\mathbf{u}$. Thus the matrix for $\mathbf{Proj}_L$ is

$$\begin{bmatrix} u_1^2 & u_1 u_2 & u_1 u_3 \\ u_1 u_2 & u_2^2 & u_2 u_3 \\ u_1 u_3 & u_2 u_3 & u_3^2 \end{bmatrix}.$$

Reflections

Given a line L in $\mathbf{R}^n$ which passes through the origin, the **reflection** through L of a vector $\mathbf{x}$ is the vector $\mathbf{Ref}_L(\mathbf{x})$ which is the *mirror image* of $\mathbf{x}$ on the opposite side of L.

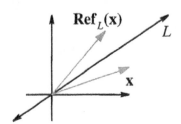

To derive a formula for $\mathbf{Ref}_L$, we let $\mathbf{w} = \mathbf{Proj}_L(\mathbf{x}) - \mathbf{x}$ as shown below.

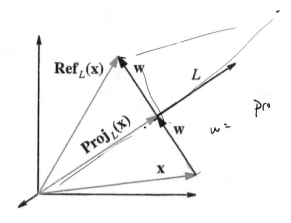

Then

$$\mathbf{Ref}_L(\mathbf{x}) = \mathbf{x} + 2\mathbf{w} = 2\mathbf{Proj}_L(\mathbf{x}) - \mathbf{x} = 2\mathbf{Proj}_L(\mathbf{x}) - \mathbf{I}_{\mathbf{R}^n}(\mathbf{x}) = (2\mathbf{Proj}_L - \mathbf{I}_{\mathbf{R}^n})(\mathbf{x}),$$

so $\mathbf{Ref}_L = 2\mathbf{Proj}_L - \mathbf{I}_{\mathbf{R}^n}$. Since $\mathbf{Proj}_L$ is linear and the identity function is linear, it follows that $\mathbf{Ref}_L$ is a linear transformation, since a linear combination of linear transformations is a linear transformation.

Example 14.7. Let L be the line $y = -x$. Using the result of Example 14.6, it follows that the matrix for $\mathbf{Ref}_L = 2\mathbf{Proj}_L - \mathbf{I}_{\mathbf{R}^2}$ is

$$2 \begin{bmatrix} \frac{1}{2} & -\frac{1}{2} \\ -\frac{1}{2} & \frac{1}{2} \end{bmatrix} - \begin{bmatrix} 1 & 0 \\ 0 & 1 \end{bmatrix} = \begin{bmatrix} 0 & -1 \\ -1 & 0 \end{bmatrix}.$$

The image under $\mathbf{Ref}_L$ of a triangle is shown below.

Other Examples

The linear transformations we have considered thus far are interesting geometrically, but by no means do they represent all possible linear transformations. There are many linear transformations which do not fall into any of the categories listed above. Here is one such example.

Example 14.8. Consider the linear transformation $\mathbf{T} : \mathbf{R}^2 \to \mathbf{R}^2$ whose matrix is

$$A = \begin{bmatrix} 1 & 0 \\ 1 & 1 \end{bmatrix}.$$

This gives the formula $\mathbf{T}(x_1, x_2) = (x_1, x_1 + x_2)$. Thus $\mathbf{T}$ fixes the first component and adds the first component to the second. Points on the (vertical) x_2-axis are therefore left fixed, while points to the right of the axis are shifted upward and points to the left are shifted downward. The image under $\mathbf{T}$ of a triangle is shown below.

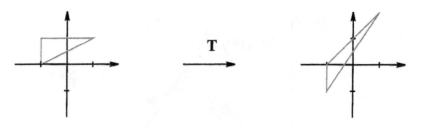

This transformation is an example of a **shear**.   ◇

In the next section we will see how linear transformations can be composed to form new linear transformations.

Exercises

In Exercises 1 through 9, (a) sketch the graph of the figure shown under the linear transformation described and (b) find the matrix A associated with this linear transformation.

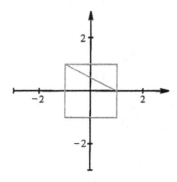

14.1. Counterclockwise rotation by $\pi/3$ radians.

14.2. Rotation by π radians.

14.3. Reflection across the y-axis.

14.4. Reflection across the line $y = \frac{1}{2}x$.

14.5. Projection onto the x-axis.

14.6. Projection onto the line $y = 2x$.

14.7. Scaling by a factor $\alpha = 2$.

14.8. Scaling by a factor $\alpha = 1/2$.

14.9. Reflection through the origin.

14.10. Let $\mathbf{T} : \mathbf{R}^2 \rightarrow \mathbf{R}^2$ be the linear transformation which stretches vectors by a factor 2 along the x-axis and reflects vectors across the x-axis. Find the matrix A associated with this transformation.

14.11. Let $\mathbf{T} : \mathbf{R}^2 \rightarrow \mathbf{R}^2$ be the linear transformation which leaves points on the x-axis fixed, but shifts points off the x-axis horizontally by $2y$. Find the matrix A such that $\mathbf{T}$ is equivalent to multiplication by A.

14.12. Let $\mathbf{T} : \mathbf{R}^3 \rightarrow \mathbf{R}^3$ be the linear transformation which reflects vectors through the xy-plane. Find the matrix A associated with this transformation.

14.13. Let $\mathbf{Proj}_L : \mathbf{R}^3 \rightarrow \mathbf{R}^3$ be the linear transformation which projects vectors onto the line L spanned by $\mathbf{b}$. Find the matrix for $\mathbf{Proj}_L$ for each of the following vectors $\mathbf{b}$.

(a) $\begin{bmatrix} 1 \\ 2 \\ 2 \end{bmatrix}$ (b) $\begin{bmatrix} -3 \\ 0 \\ 4 \end{bmatrix}$ (c) $\begin{bmatrix} 0 \\ 1 \\ 0 \end{bmatrix}$ (d) $\begin{bmatrix} 1 \\ 1 \\ 1 \end{bmatrix}$

14.14. Let $\mathbf{T} : \mathbf{R}^3 \rightarrow \mathbf{R}^3$ be the rotation about the y-axis through angle θ, where the direction is such that the positive x-axis is rotated toward the positive z-axis.

14.15. Let $\mathbf{T} : \mathbf{R}^3 \rightarrow \mathbf{R}^3$ be the rotation about the z-axis through angle θ, where the direction is such that the positive y-axis is rotated toward the positive x-axis.

15   Composition and Matrix Multiplication

Let $f : X \rightarrow Y$ and $g : Y \rightarrow Z$ be functions. The **composition** of g with f is the function $g \circ f : X \rightarrow Z$ defined by

$$(g \circ f)(x) = g(f(x))$$

for x in X.

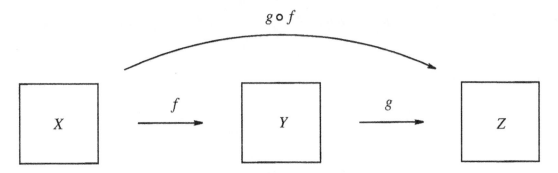

Example 15.1. Let $\mathbf{f} : \mathbf{R}^2 \rightarrow \mathbf{R}^2$ and $\mathbf{g} : \mathbf{R}^2 \rightarrow \mathbf{R}^2$ be defined by

$$\mathbf{f}(x, y) = (x - y^2, y + x^2)$$
$$\mathbf{g}(x, y) = (y - x, y + x).$$

$$A x \qquad m\times 3 \qquad 3\times 1$$

$$\begin{bmatrix} -a_1- \\ -a_2- \\ -a_m- \end{bmatrix} \begin{bmatrix} x_1 \\ x_2 \\ x_3 \end{bmatrix} = \begin{bmatrix} a_1\cdot \\ a_2\cdot \\ a_3\cdot \end{bmatrix} \begin{bmatrix} a_1 & a_2 & a_3 \\ | & | & | \\ | & | & | \end{bmatrix} \begin{bmatrix} x_1 \\ x_2 \\ x_3 \end{bmatrix} = \begin{bmatrix} \quad \end{bmatrix}$$

Then $\mathbf{f} \circ \mathbf{g} : \mathbf{R}^2 \to \mathbf{R}^2$ is given by

$$\begin{aligned}
(\mathbf{f} \circ \mathbf{g})(x,y) &= \mathbf{f}(\mathbf{g}(x,y)) \\
&= \mathbf{f}(y-x, y+x) \\
&= ((y-x)-(y+x)^2), (y+x)+(y-x)^2) \\
&= (y-x-y^2-2xy-x^2, y+x+y^2-2xy+x^2).
\end{aligned}$$

The composition $\mathbf{g} \circ \mathbf{f} : \mathbf{R}^2 \to \mathbf{R}^2$ also makes sense, and is given by

$$\begin{aligned}
(\mathbf{g} \circ \mathbf{f})(x,y) &= \mathbf{g}(\mathbf{f}(x,y)) \\
&= \mathbf{g}(x-y^2, y+x^2) \\
&= ((y+x^2)-(x-y^2), (y+x^2)+(x-y^2)) \\
&= (y+x^2-x+y^2, y+x^2+x-y^2).
\end{aligned}$$

Notice, however, that $\mathbf{f} \circ \mathbf{g}$ and $\mathbf{g} \circ \mathbf{f}$ are not the same function. ◇

Example 15.2. Let $\mathbf{f} : \mathbf{R} \to \mathbf{R}^3$ be given by $\mathbf{f}(t) = (\cos t, \sin t, t^2)$ and let $\mathbf{g} : \mathbf{R}^3 \to \mathbf{R}^2$ be defined by $\mathbf{g}(x,y,z) = (x^2+y^2+z^2, x-y)$. Then $\mathbf{g} \circ \mathbf{f} : \mathbf{R} \to \mathbf{R}^2$ is defined by

$$\begin{aligned}
(\mathbf{g} \circ \mathbf{f})(t) &= \mathbf{g}(\mathbf{f}(t)) \\
&= \mathbf{g}(\cos t, \sin t, t^2) \\
&= (1+t^4, \cos t - \sin t),
\end{aligned}$$

but the composition $\mathbf{f} \circ \mathbf{g}$ is not defined. ◇

These examples illustrate that composition is not in general commutative. Composition is however associative.

Proposition 15.1. Let $f : X \to Y$, $g : Y \to Z$ and $h : Z \to W$. Then

$$(h \circ g) \circ f = h \circ (g \circ f).$$

Proof. Let x be in X. Then

$$\begin{aligned}
((h \circ g) \circ f)(x) &= (h \circ g)(f(x)) \\
&= h(g(f(x))) \\
&= h((g \circ f)(x)) \\
&= (h \circ (g \circ f))(x).
\end{aligned}$$

Since this holds for every x in X, the functions $(h \circ g) \circ f$ and $h \circ (g \circ f)$ are the same. □

The parentheses in the formulas above are therefore unnecessary, and we can write without ambiguity $h \circ g \circ f$. For a function $f : X \to X$ it makes sense to compose f with itself. We write f^2 to denote $f \circ f$, f^3 to denote $f \circ f \circ f$, and so on. We now focus our attention on compositions of linear transformations. First we show that any such composition is itself a linear transformation.

Proposition 15.2. Let $\mathbf{T} : \mathbf{R}^k \to \mathbf{R}^n$ and $\mathbf{S} : \mathbf{R}^n \to \mathbf{R}^m$ be linear transformations. Then their composition $\mathbf{S} \circ \mathbf{T} : \mathbf{R}^k \to \mathbf{R}^m$ is also a linear transformation.

Proof. Let $\mathbf{x}$ and $\mathbf{y}$ be in $\mathbf{R}^k$. Then

$$
\begin{aligned}
(\mathbf{S} \circ \mathbf{T})(\mathbf{x} + \mathbf{y}) &= \mathbf{S}(\mathbf{T}(\mathbf{x} + \mathbf{y})) \\
&= \mathbf{S}(\mathbf{T}(\mathbf{x}) + \mathbf{T}(\mathbf{y})) \\
&= \mathbf{S}(\mathbf{T}(\mathbf{x})) + \mathbf{S}(\mathbf{T}(\mathbf{y})) \\
&= (\mathbf{S} \circ \mathbf{T})(\mathbf{x}) + (\mathbf{S} \circ \mathbf{T})(\mathbf{y})
\end{aligned}
$$

and for any scalar c,

$$
\begin{aligned}
(\mathbf{S} \circ \mathbf{T})(c\mathbf{x}) &= \mathbf{S}(\mathbf{T}(c\mathbf{x})) \\
&= \mathbf{S}(c\mathbf{T}(\mathbf{x})) \\
&= c\mathbf{S}(\mathbf{T}(\mathbf{x})) \\
&= c(\mathbf{S} \circ \mathbf{T})(\mathbf{x})
\end{aligned}
$$

so $\mathbf{S} \circ \mathbf{T}$ is linear. $\qquad\square$

Now suppose that $\mathbf{S}$ and $\mathbf{T}$ have matrices A and B, respectively. What is the matrix for $\mathbf{S} \circ \mathbf{T}$ in terms of A and B? The answer is found by evaluating $\mathbf{S} \circ \mathbf{T}$ on the standard basis vectors $\mathbf{e}_1$ through $\mathbf{e}_k$ in $\mathbf{R}^k$. Column j of the matrix for $\mathbf{S} \circ \mathbf{T}$ must be

$$(\mathbf{S} \circ \mathbf{T})(\mathbf{e}_j) = \mathbf{S}(\mathbf{T}(\mathbf{e}_j)) = A(B\mathbf{e}_j).$$

But $B\mathbf{e}_j$ is column j of B, so column j of the matrix for $\mathbf{S} \circ \mathbf{T}$ equals A times column j of B. This motivates the following definition. The **matrix product** AB of an m by n matrix A with an n by k matrix B is the m by k matrix

$$
AB = A \begin{bmatrix} \mid & \mid & & \mid \\ \mathbf{b}_1 & \mathbf{b}_2 & \cdots & \mathbf{b}_k \\ \mid & \mid & & \mid \end{bmatrix} = \begin{bmatrix} \mid & \mid & & \mid \\ A\mathbf{b}_1 & A\mathbf{b}_2 & \cdots & A\mathbf{b}_k \\ \mid & \mid & & \mid \end{bmatrix}
$$

where $\mathbf{b}_1, \mathbf{b}_2, \ldots, \mathbf{b}_k$ denote the columns of B. That is, the columns of AB are obtained by multiplying A by the columns of B. Now, since for any vector $\mathbf{x}$, the components of $A\mathbf{x}$ are the dot products of the *rows* of A with $\mathbf{x}$, each entry of AB is the dot product of a row of A with a column of B. More precisely, if $\mathbf{a}_1^T, \mathbf{a}_2^T, \ldots, \mathbf{a}_m^T$ denote the rows of A then

$$
AB = \begin{bmatrix} \text{---} & \mathbf{a}_1^T & \text{---} \\ \text{---} & \mathbf{a}_2^T & \text{---} \\ & \vdots & \\ \text{---} & \mathbf{a}_m^T & \text{---} \end{bmatrix} \begin{bmatrix} \mid & \mid & & \mid \\ \mathbf{b}_1 & \mathbf{b}_2 & \cdots & \mathbf{b}_k \\ \mid & \mid & & \mid \end{bmatrix} = \begin{bmatrix} \mathbf{a}_1 \cdot \mathbf{b}_1 & \mathbf{a}_1 \cdot \mathbf{b}_2 & \cdots & \mathbf{a}_1 \cdot \mathbf{b}_k \\ \mathbf{a}_2 \cdot \mathbf{b}_1 & \mathbf{a}_2 \cdot \mathbf{b}_2 & \cdots & \mathbf{a}_2 \cdot \mathbf{b}_k \\ \vdots & \vdots & & \vdots \\ \mathbf{a}_m \cdot \mathbf{b}_1 & \mathbf{a}_m \cdot \mathbf{b}_2 & \cdots & \mathbf{a}_m \cdot \mathbf{b}_k \end{bmatrix}.
$$

Thus the entry in row i, column j of AB is the dot product of row i of A with column j of B. Let a_{ij} and b_{ij} denote the entries in row i column j of A and B, respectively, and let c_{ij} denote the entry in row i column j of the product $C = AB$. Then the ij^{th} entry of the product can be expressed as the sum

$$c_{ij} = \sum_{l=1}^{n} a_{il}b_{lj}.$$

Observe that the product AB is defined only if the number of columns of A equals the number of rows of B. The product has the same number of rows as A and the same number of columns as B. So the product of an m by n matrix with an n by k matrix is an m by k matrix. The heuristic for remembering this is the following:

$$(m \times n)(n \times k) \longrightarrow (m \times k).$$

The adjacent n's cancel.

Example 15.3. Let

$$A = \begin{bmatrix} 2 & 1 & -1 \\ -1 & 3 & 2 \end{bmatrix} \qquad \text{and} \qquad B = \begin{bmatrix} 1 & 2 & 3 & 4 \\ -1 & 0 & 2 & 1 \\ 3 & 3 & 1 & 2 \end{bmatrix}.$$

Then

$$AB = \begin{bmatrix} -2 & 1 & 7 & 7 \\ 2 & 4 & 5 & 3 \end{bmatrix},$$

while the product BA is not defined since B has 4 columns but A has only 2 rows. $\diamond$

Example 15.4. Let

$$A = \begin{bmatrix} 4 & 1 & -2 \end{bmatrix} \qquad \text{and} \qquad B = \begin{bmatrix} 1 \\ -1 \\ 3 \end{bmatrix}.$$

Then

$$AB = \begin{bmatrix} -3 \end{bmatrix} \qquad \text{and} \qquad BA = \begin{bmatrix} 4 & 1 & -2 \\ -4 & -1 & 2 \\ 12 & 3 & -6 \end{bmatrix}.$$

$\diamond$

In view of the discussion above, we have the following result.

Proposition 15.3. Let $\mathbf{T} : \mathbf{R}^k \to \mathbf{R}^n$ and $\mathbf{S} : \mathbf{R}^n \to \mathbf{R}^m$ be linear transformations with matrices B and A, respectively. Then the product AB is the matrix for the composition $\mathbf{S} \circ \mathbf{T} : \mathbf{R}^k \to \mathbf{R}^m$.

Example 15.5. Consider the rotations $\mathbf{Rot}_\theta$ and $\mathbf{Rot}_\phi$. The matrix for the composition $\mathbf{Rot}_\theta \circ \mathbf{Rot}_\phi$ is

$$\begin{bmatrix} \cos\theta & -\sin\theta \\ \sin\theta & \cos\theta \end{bmatrix} \begin{bmatrix} \cos\phi & -\sin\phi \\ \sin\phi & \cos\phi \end{bmatrix} = \begin{bmatrix} \cos\theta\cos\phi - \sin\theta\sin\phi & -\cos\theta\sin\phi - \sin\theta\cos\phi \\ \sin\theta\cos\phi + \cos\theta\sin\phi & -\sin\theta\sin\phi + \cos\theta\cos\phi \end{bmatrix}$$

$$= \begin{bmatrix} \cos(\theta+\phi) & -\sin(\theta+\phi) \\ \sin(\theta+\phi) & \cos(\theta+\phi) \end{bmatrix},$$

which, as expected, is the matrix for the rotation through the angle $\theta + \phi$. Thus

$$\mathbf{Rot}_\theta \circ \mathbf{Rot}_\phi = \mathbf{Rot}_{\theta+\phi}.$$

Likewise,

$$\mathbf{Rot}_\phi \circ \mathbf{Rot}_\theta = \mathbf{Rot}_{\theta+\phi}.$$

This is one instance in which composition *does* commute. ◇

Example 15.6. Let L_1 be the x-axis and let L_2 be the line $y = x$. The composition $\mathbf{Proj}_{L_1} \circ \mathbf{Proj}_{L_2}$ has matrix

$$\begin{bmatrix} 1 & 0 \\ 0 & 0 \end{bmatrix} \begin{bmatrix} 1/2 & 1/2 \\ 1/2 & 1/2 \end{bmatrix} = \begin{bmatrix} 1/2 & 1/2 \\ 0 & 0 \end{bmatrix}$$

while the composition $\mathbf{Proj}_{L_2} \circ \mathbf{Proj}_{L_1}$ has matrix

$$\begin{bmatrix} 1/2 & 1/2 \\ 1/2 & 1/2 \end{bmatrix} \begin{bmatrix} 1 & 0 \\ 0 & 0 \end{bmatrix} = \begin{bmatrix} 1/2 & 0 \\ 1/2 & 0 \end{bmatrix}.$$

◇

We now list some properties of matrix multiplication.

Proposition 15.4. Let A, B, C be matrices for which the sums and products below are defined. Then

1. $A(BC) = (AB)C$.

2. $A(B + C) = AB + AC$.

3. $(A + B)C = AC + BC$.

Proof. The first property follows from the associativity of composition. The others are left as exercises. □

If A is an $n \times n$ matrix, it makes sense to multiply A by itself. In this case we write $A^2 = AA$, $A^3 = AAA$, and so on.

Example 15.7. Let L be the line $y = x$. The matrix for $\mathbf{Proj}_L$ is

$$A = \begin{bmatrix} 1/2 & 1/2 \\ 1/2 & 1/2 \end{bmatrix}.$$

Its square

$$A^2 = \begin{bmatrix} 1/2 & 1/2 \\ 1/2 & 1/2 \end{bmatrix} \begin{bmatrix} 1/2 & 1/2 \\ 1/2 & 1/2 \end{bmatrix} = \begin{bmatrix} 1/2 & 1/2 \\ 1/2 & 1/2 \end{bmatrix} = A$$

is the matrix for $(\mathbf{Proj}_L)^2$. Thus $\mathbf{Proj}_L \circ \mathbf{Proj}_L = \mathbf{Proj}_L$. Think about why this makes sense geometrically. ◇

Exercises

15.1. Compute the following matrix products where possible.

(a) $\begin{bmatrix} 1 & -1 \\ 0 & 1 \end{bmatrix} \begin{bmatrix} 1 & 2 \\ -3 & 4 \end{bmatrix}$ (b) $\begin{bmatrix} 1 & 2 \\ -3 & 4 \end{bmatrix} \begin{bmatrix} 1 & 1 \\ 0 & 1 \end{bmatrix}$ (c) $\begin{bmatrix} 1 & -2 \\ -2 & 4 \end{bmatrix} \begin{bmatrix} 12 & 6 & -2 \\ 6 & 3 & -1 \end{bmatrix}$

(d) $\begin{bmatrix} 1 & 2 & 3 \\ 4 & 5 & 6 \end{bmatrix} \begin{bmatrix} 10 & 11 \\ 12 & 13 \end{bmatrix}$ (e) $\begin{bmatrix} 10 & 11 \\ 12 & 13 \end{bmatrix} \begin{bmatrix} 1 & 2 & 3 \\ 4 & 5 & 6 \end{bmatrix}$ (f) $\begin{bmatrix} 0 & 1 & 0 & 0 \\ 0 & 0 & 1 & 0 \\ 0 & 0 & 0 & 1 \\ 1 & 0 & 0 & 0 \end{bmatrix} \begin{bmatrix} 0 & 0 \\ 9 & 7 \\ 9 & 8 \\ 9 & 9 \end{bmatrix}$

(g) $\begin{bmatrix} 1 & 2 & 3 \end{bmatrix} \begin{bmatrix} 1 \\ 2 \\ 3 \end{bmatrix}$ (h) $\begin{bmatrix} 1 \\ 2 \\ 3 \end{bmatrix} \begin{bmatrix} 1 & 2 & 3 \end{bmatrix}$ (i) $\begin{bmatrix} 1 & 1 \\ 0 & 1 \end{bmatrix}^8$

15.2. For all 2×2 matrices A, B and C, verify directly that $A(BC) = (AB)C$.

1. (a) Prove part (2) of Proposition 15.4.

   (b) Prove part (3) of Proposition 15.4.

15.3. Let $\mathbf{T} : \mathbf{R}^2 \to \mathbf{R}^2$ be the linear transformation defined by first rotating counterclockwise through an angle of $\pi/4$ radians and then reflecting across the line $x_2 = -x_1$. What is the matrix for $\mathbf{T}$?

15.4. Let $\mathbf{T} : \mathbf{R}^3 \to \mathbf{R}^3$ be the linear transformation which rotates vectors 30° about the x-axis in the direction from the positive y-axis toward the positive z-axis. Let $\mathbf{S} : \mathbf{R}^3 \to \mathbf{R}^3$ be the linear transformation which rotates vectors 45° about the z-axis in the direction from the positive x-axis toward the positive y-axis. Find the matrices representing the transformations $\mathbf{T}, \mathbf{S}, \mathbf{T} \circ \mathbf{S}$ and $\mathbf{S} \circ \mathbf{T}$.

15.5. Let $\mathbf{T} : \mathbf{R}^2 \to \mathbf{R}^2$ be rotation in the counterclockwise direction through the angle $\pi/2$ radians followed by projection onto the line which makes an angle θ with the positive x-axis.

102

(a) Find the matrix for **T** in terms of θ.

(b) What is the kernel of **T**?

(c) What is the image of **T**?

15.6. Let $\mathbf{T} : \mathbf{R}^2 \to \mathbf{R}^2$ be projection onto the line which makes an angle θ with the positive x-axis followed by rotation in the counterclockwise direction through the angle $\pi/2$ radians.

(a) Find the matrix for **T** in terms of θ.

(b) What is the kernel of **T**?

(c) What is the image of **T**?

For Exercises 7 through 10, let $\mathbf{Ref}_\theta : \mathbf{R}^2 \to \mathbf{R}^2$ be reflection across the line which makes an angle θ with the positive x-axis. Let $\mathbf{Rot}_\phi : \mathbf{R}^2 \to \mathbf{R}^2$ be rotation in the counterclockwise direction through the angle ϕ.

15.7. Show that the matrix A associated with $\mathbf{Ref}_\theta$ is given by

$$A = \begin{bmatrix} \cos(2\theta) & \sin(2\theta) \\ \sin(2\theta) & -\cos(2\theta) \end{bmatrix}.$$

15.8. Using the matrix A from Exercise 7,

(a) find the matrix for $\mathbf{Ref}_\theta \circ \mathbf{Rot}_\phi$,

(b) find an angle α (depending on θ and ϕ) such that $\mathbf{Ref}_\theta \circ \mathbf{Rot}_\phi = \mathbf{Ref}_\alpha$.

15.9. Using the matrix A from Exercise 7,

(a) find the matrix for $\mathbf{Rot}_\phi \circ \mathbf{Ref}_\theta$,

(b) find an angle β (depending on θ and ϕ) such that $\mathbf{Rot}_\phi \circ \mathbf{Ref}_\theta = \mathbf{Ref}_\beta$.

15.10. Using the matrix A from Exercise 7,

(a) find the matrix for $\mathbf{Ref}_\theta \circ \mathbf{Ref}_\phi$,

(b) find an angle α (depending on θ and ϕ) such that $\mathbf{Ref}_\theta \circ \mathbf{Ref}_\phi = \mathbf{Rot}_\alpha$.

16   Inverses

The **identity function** on a set X is the function $I_X : X \to X$ such that $I_X(x) = x$ for every x in X. A function $f : X \to Y$ is called **invertible** if there is a function $f^{-1} : Y \to X$ such that

$$f^{-1} \circ f = I_X \quad \text{and} \quad f \circ f^{-1} = I_Y.$$

The function f^{-1}, if it exists, is called the **inverse function** of f.

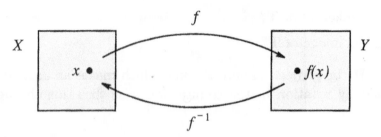

Applying f to x and then applying f^{-1} to the result yields x, so f^{-1} reverses the action of f. Likewise f reverses the action of f^{-1}. The following result allows us to speak of *the* inverse function.

Proposition 16.1. Let $f : X \to Y$ be invertible. Then the inverse of f is unique.

Proof. Suppose that both $g : Y \to X$ and $h : Y \to X$ are both inverses of f. Then,

$$g = I_X \circ g = (h \circ f) \circ g = h \circ (f \circ g) = h \circ I_Y = h.$$

$\square$

Inverse functions are very useful in solving equations of the form $f(x) = y$. The next result states that invertibility is equivalent to the existence and uniqueness of solutions.

Proposition 16.2. A function $f : X \to Y$ is invertible if and only if for every $y \in Y$, the equation $f(x) = y$ has a unique solution x in X.

Proof. First suppose f is invertible. Apply f^{-1} to both sides of $f(x) = y$ to see that

$$x = I_X(x) = (f^{-1} \circ f)(x) = f^{-1}(f(x)) = f^{-1}(y),$$

so $x = f^{-1}(y)$ is the only possible solution of $f(x) = y$. To see that this is in fact a solution, apply f to get

$$f(x) = f(f^{-1}(y)) = (f \circ f^{-1})(y) = I_Y(y) = y.$$

Now suppose that, for every y in Y, the equation $f(x) = y$ has a unique solution x in X. Then define

$$f^{-1}(y) = \text{ the unique solution } x \text{ of } f(x) = y.$$

To verify that this is actually the inverse of f notice that, since $f^{-1}(y)$ is an element x such that $f(x) = y$, we have $f(f^{-1}(y)) = y$. Since this holds for every y in Y, we have $f \circ f^{-1} = I_Y$. Next consider some element x_0 of X. By definition $f^{-1}(f(x_0))$ is the unique solution x of $f(x) = f(x_0)$. But it is clear that the solution must be $x = x_0$, so $f^{-1}(f(x_0)) = x_0$. Since this holds for every x_0 in X, we have $f^{-1} \circ f = I_X$. $\square$

Example 16.1. Let $\mathbf{f} : \mathbf{R}^2 \to \mathbf{R}^2$ be defined by $\mathbf{f}(x_1, x_2) = (x_1 + \sqrt[3]{x_2}, x_1)$. The equation $\mathbf{f}(x_1, x_2) = (y_1, y_2)$ consists of two equations

$$y_1 = x_1 + \sqrt[3]{x_2}$$
$$y_2 = x_1.$$

The second equation implies $x_1 = y_2$. Solving for x_2 in the first equation then gives $x_2 = (y_1 - y_2)^3$. Thus the inverse of $\mathbf{f}$ is given by

$$\mathbf{f}^{-1}(y_1, y_2) = \left(y_2, (y_1 - y_2)^3\right).$$

It is easy now to see that $\mathbf{f} \circ \mathbf{f}^{-1} = \mathbf{f}^{-1} \circ \mathbf{f} = \mathbf{I}_{\mathbf{R}^2}$. $\diamond$

There are two obstacles to invertibility. The first is that the equation $f(x) = y$ may not have solutions for some y.

Example 16.2. Let $\mathbf{f} : \mathbf{R} \to \mathbf{R}^2$ be defined by $\mathbf{f}(x) = (x + 1, 2x - 1)$. Consider the point $(2, 3) \in \mathbf{R}^2$. If we attempt to solve $\mathbf{f}(x) = (2, 3)$ we get the two equations $x + 1 = 2$ and $2x - 1 = 3$. The first implies $x = 1$ while the second implies $x = 2$. Hence there is no x such that $\mathbf{f}(x) = (2, 3)$, and thus $\mathbf{f}$ is not invertible. Geometrically, the image of $\mathbf{R}$ under $\mathbf{f}$ is a line in $\mathbf{R}^2$, so clearly there are many points in $\mathbf{R}^2$ which are not in the range of $\mathbf{f}$. $\diamond$

A function $f : X \to Y$ is **onto** (or **surjective**) if, for every $y \in Y$ there is at least one x in X such that $f(x) = y$. That is, $f(X) = Y$, the image of X under f equals Y. The function in Example 16.2 is not onto. The second obstacle to invertibility is that the equation $f(x) = y$ may have more than one solution for some y.

Example 16.3. Let $\mathbf{f} : \mathbf{R}^3 \to \mathbf{R}^2$ be defined by $\mathbf{f}(x_1, x_2, x_3) = (x_1 + x_2 + x_3, x_1 x_2 x_3)$. Notice that $\mathbf{f}(1, 1, -1) = \mathbf{f}(1, -1, 1) = (1, -1)$, so the equation $\mathbf{f}(\mathbf{x}) = (1, -1)$ has at least two solutions. Therefore $\mathbf{f}$ is not invertible. $\diamond$

A function $f : X \to Y$ is **one to one** (or **injective**) if, for every y in Y there is at most one x in X such that $f(x) = y$. The function in Example 16.3 is not one to one. The following proposition is an immediate consequence of Proposition 16.2.

Proposition 16.3. A function $f : X \to Y$ is invertible if and only if f is both onto and one to one.

Inverse of a Linear Transformation

Next suppose $\mathbf{T} : \mathbf{R}^n \to \mathbf{R}^m$ is a linear transformation. Under what conditions is $\mathbf{T}$ invertible, and if $\mathbf{T}$ is invertible, what is its inverse? To answer the first part of this question, suppose A is the $(m \times n)$ matrix for $\mathbf{T}$. By Proposition 16.3, $\mathbf{T}$ is invertible if and only if $\mathbf{T}$ is both onto and one to one.

For $\mathbf{T}$ to be onto, the equation $\mathbf{T}(\mathbf{x}) = \mathbf{y}$, which is equivalent to the system $A\mathbf{x} = \mathbf{y}$, must have at least one solution $\mathbf{x}$ for each $\mathbf{y}$ in $\mathbf{R}^m$. Recall that the set of $\mathbf{y}$ for which this system has a solution is the column space of A. So $C(A)$ must equal $\mathbf{R}^m$. By Proposition 9.2, this happens if and only if $\text{rref}(A)$ has a pivot in each of its m rows, so $\text{rank}(A) = m$.

Proposition 16.4. The linear transformation $\mathbf{T} : \mathbf{R}^n \to \mathbf{R}^m$ is onto if and only if its matrix A has rank m.

For $\mathbf{T}$ to be one to one, the system $A\mathbf{x} = \mathbf{y}$, must have at most one solution $\mathbf{x}$ for each $\mathbf{y}$ in $\mathbf{R}^m$. By Proposition 8.2 every solution set of $A\mathbf{x} = \mathbf{y}$ is a translation of the null space of A. So in order for solutions to be unique, the null space must be trivial. By Proposition 8.3, this occurs if and only if $\mathrm{rref}(A)$ has a pivot in each of its n rows, so $\mathrm{rank}(A) = n$.

Proposition 16.5. The linear transformation $\mathbf{T} : \mathbf{R}^n \to \mathbf{R}^m$ is one to one if and only if its matrix A has rank n.

Example 16.4. Let $\mathbf{T} : \mathbf{R}^2 \to \mathbf{R}^3$ be the linear transformation with matrix

$$A = \begin{bmatrix} 1 & 2 \\ 3 & 4 \\ 5 & 6 \end{bmatrix}.$$

Since

$$\mathrm{rref}(A) = \begin{bmatrix} 1 & 0 \\ 0 & 1 \\ 0 & 0 \end{bmatrix},$$

A has rank 2, so $\mathbf{T}$ is one to one but not onto, and hence not invertible. $\diamond$

Example 16.5. Let $\mathbf{T} : \mathbf{R}^4 \to \mathbf{R}^3$ be the linear transformation with matrix

$$A = \begin{bmatrix} 1 & 1 & 1 & 1 \\ 1 & 2 & 4 & 8 \\ 1 & 3 & 9 & 27 \end{bmatrix}.$$

Since

$$\mathrm{rref}(A) = \begin{bmatrix} 1 & 0 & 0 & 6 \\ 0 & 1 & 0 & -11 \\ 0 & 0 & 1 & 6 \end{bmatrix},$$

A has rank 3, so $\mathbf{T}$ is onto but not one to one, and hence not invertible. $\diamond$

In order for $\mathbf{T}$ to be both onto and one to one, we must have $\mathrm{rank}(A) = m = n$, so A must be a square matrix. Thus only linear transformations from $\mathbf{R}^n$ to $\mathbf{R}^n$ can be invertible, and the test for invertibility follows directly from Proposition 9.3.

Proposition 16.6. Let $\mathbf{T} : \mathbf{R}^n \to \mathbf{R}^n$ be a linear transformation with matrix A. Then $\mathbf{T}$ is invertible if and only if $\mathrm{rref}(A) = I_n$.

Example 16.6. Let $\mathbf{T} : \mathbf{R}^3 \to \mathbf{R}^3$ be the linear transformation with matrix

$$A = \begin{bmatrix} 1 & 2 & 3 \\ 4 & 5 & 6 \\ 7 & 8 & 9 \end{bmatrix}.$$

Since

$$\text{rref}(A) = \begin{bmatrix} 1 & 0 & -1 \\ 0 & 1 & 2 \\ 0 & 0 & 0 \end{bmatrix},$$

A has rank 2, and therefore $\mathbf{T}$ is not invertible. $\diamond$

Example 16.7. Let

$$A = \begin{bmatrix} 1 & -1 & -1 \\ -1 & 2 & 3 \\ 1 & 1 & 4 \end{bmatrix}.$$

Since $\text{rref}(A) = I_3$, the linear transformation $\mathbf{T} : \mathbf{R}^3 \to \mathbf{R}^3$ with matrix A is invertible. $\diamond$

Now suppose $\mathbf{T} : \mathbf{R}^n \to \mathbf{R}^n$ is an invertible linear transformation. We leave it as an exercise to verify that its inverse $\mathbf{T}^{-1} : \mathbf{R}^n \to \mathbf{R}^n$ is also a linear transformation. If A is the matrix for $\mathbf{T}$, then we denote by A^{-1} the matrix for $\mathbf{T}^{-1}$. The matrix A^{-1} is called the **inverse matrix** of A, and we say that A is an **invertible matrix**. Since

$$\mathbf{T} \circ \mathbf{T}^{-1} = \mathbf{T}^{-1} \circ \mathbf{T} = \mathbf{I}_{\mathbf{R}^n},$$

and since the matrix for $\mathbf{I}_{\mathbf{R}^n}$ is the $n \times n$ identity matrix I_n, it follows that

$$\boxed{AA^{-1} = A^{-1}A = I_n.}$$

Example 16.8. Geometrically it is clear that the rotation $\mathbf{Rot}_\theta$ is invertible, with inverse $\mathbf{Rot}_{-\theta}$. So

$$A = \begin{bmatrix} \cos\theta & -\sin\theta \\ \sin\theta & \cos\theta \end{bmatrix} \implies A^{-1} = \begin{bmatrix} \cos(-\theta) & -\sin(-\theta) \\ \sin(-\theta) & \cos(-\theta) \end{bmatrix} = \begin{bmatrix} \cos\theta & \sin\theta \\ -\sin\theta & \cos\theta \end{bmatrix}.$$

It is easy to verify directly that $AA^{-1} = A^{-1}A = I_2$. $\diamond$

Next we consider the task of finding the inverse of a linear transformation. Suppose $\mathbf{T} : \mathbf{R}^n \to \mathbf{R}^n$ is an invertible linear transformation. The columns of the matrix for $\mathbf{T}^{-1}$ are

$$\mathbf{x}_1 = \mathbf{T}^{-1}(\mathbf{e}_1) \qquad \mathbf{x}_2 = \mathbf{T}^{-1}(\mathbf{e}_2) \qquad \ldots \qquad \mathbf{x}_n = \mathbf{T}^{-1}(\mathbf{e}_n).$$

Thus $\mathbf{x}_1$ through $\mathbf{x}_n$ satisfy

$$\mathbf{T}(\mathbf{x}_1) = \mathbf{e}_1 \qquad \mathbf{T}(\mathbf{x}_2) = \mathbf{e}_2 \qquad \ldots \qquad \mathbf{T}(\mathbf{x}_n) = \mathbf{e}_n$$

or, in terms of the matrix A for $\mathbf{T}$,

$$A\mathbf{x}_1 = \mathbf{e}_1 \qquad A\mathbf{x}_2 = \mathbf{e}_2 \qquad \ldots \qquad A\mathbf{x}_n = \mathbf{e}_n.$$

The invertibility of $\mathbf{T}$ guarantees a unique solution to each of these equations.

Example 16.9. Let

$$A = \begin{bmatrix} 1 & -1 & -1 \\ -1 & 2 & 3 \\ 1 & 1 & 4 \end{bmatrix}.$$

Solving $A\mathbf{x}_1 = \mathbf{e}_1$ we obtain

$$\left[\begin{array}{ccc|c} 1 & -1 & -1 & 1 \\ -1 & 2 & 3 & 0 \\ 1 & 1 & 4 & 0 \end{array}\right] \longrightarrow \left[\begin{array}{ccc|c} 1 & 0 & 0 & 5 \\ 0 & 1 & 0 & 7 \\ 0 & 0 & 1 & -3 \end{array}\right]$$

so

$$\mathbf{x}_1 = \begin{bmatrix} 5 \\ 7 \\ -3 \end{bmatrix}$$

is the first column of A^{-1}. We could continue in the same way to find $\mathbf{x}_2$ and $\mathbf{x}_3$, but it is more efficient to do all the calculations simultaneously. Since the same elimination steps take place in all three calculations, we may simply augment the matrix A with three columns $\mathbf{e}_1$, $\mathbf{e}_2$ and $\mathbf{e}_3$. Doing so we obtain

$$\left[\begin{array}{ccc|ccc} 1 & -1 & -1 & 1 & 0 & 0 \\ -1 & 2 & 3 & 0 & 1 & 0 \\ 1 & 1 & 4 & 0 & 0 & 1 \end{array}\right] \longrightarrow \left[\begin{array}{ccc|ccc} 1 & 0 & 0 & 5 & 3 & -1 \\ 0 & 1 & 0 & 7 & 5 & -2 \\ 0 & 0 & 1 & -3 & -2 & 1 \end{array}\right]$$

To the right of the divider appear $\mathbf{x}_1$, $\mathbf{x}_2$ and $\mathbf{x}_3$. Thus

$$A^{-1} = \begin{bmatrix} 5 & 3 & -1 \\ 7 & 5 & -2 \\ -3 & -2 & 1 \end{bmatrix}.$$

Observe that $AA^{-1} = A^{-1}A = I_3$. $\diamond$

This example illustrates a general procedure for finding the inverse of a matrix A.

Proposition 16.7. If A is an invertible matrix, then $\mathrm{rref}[A \mid I_n] = [I_n \mid A^{-1}]$.

Example 16.10. Let

$$A = \begin{bmatrix} 1 & 1 & 1 \\ 1 & 2 & 4 \\ 1 & 3 & 9 \end{bmatrix}.$$

Then

$$\left[\begin{array}{ccc|ccc} 1 & 1 & 1 & 1 & 0 & 0 \\ 1 & 2 & 4 & 0 & 1 & 0 \\ 1 & 3 & 9 & 0 & 0 & 1 \end{array}\right] \longrightarrow \left[\begin{array}{ccc|ccc} 1 & 0 & 0 & 3 & -3 & 1 \\ 0 & 1 & 0 & -5/2 & 4 & -3/2 \\ 0 & 0 & 1 & 1/2 & -1 & 1/2 \end{array}\right],$$

so

$$A^{-1} = \begin{bmatrix} 3 & -3 & 1 \\ -5/2 & 4 & -3/2 \\ 1/2 & -1 & 1/2 \end{bmatrix}.$$

$\Diamond$

Inverse functions satisfy the following properties.

Proposition 16.8. Let $f : X \to Y$ and $g : Y \to Z$ be invertible functions. Then

1. f^{-1} is invertible and $(f^{-1})^{-1} = f$,

2. $g \circ f$ is invertible and $(g \circ f)^{-1} = f^{-1} \circ g^{-1}$.

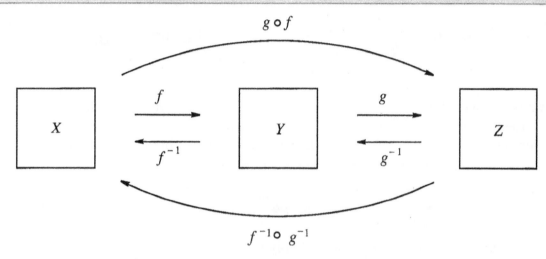

Proof. By definition, f^{-1} is invertible if there exists a function $h : X \to Y$ such that

$$h \circ f^{-1} = I_Y$$
$$f^{-1} \circ h = I_X.$$

But f is exactly such a function, so it is the inverse of f^{-1}. Next, since

$$(g \circ f) \circ (f^{-1} \circ g^{-1}) = g \circ (f \circ f^{-1}) \circ g^{-1}$$
$$= g \circ I_Y \circ g^{-1}$$
$$= g \circ g^{-1}$$
$$= I_Z$$

and

$$(f^{-1} \circ g^{-1}) \circ (g \circ f) = f^{-1} \circ (g^{-1} \circ g) \circ f$$
$$= f^{-1} \circ I_Y \circ f$$
$$= f^{-1} \circ f$$
$$= I_X$$

$f^{-1} \circ g^{-1}$ is the inverse of $g \circ f$. $\square$

As an immediate corollary, we have the corresponding results for invertible matrices.

Proposition 16.9. Let A and B be $n \times n$ invertible matrices. Then

1. A^{-1} is invertible and $(A^{-1})^{-1} = A$,

2. AB is invertible and $(AB)^{-1} = B^{-1}A^{-1}$.

Repeated application of the second identity yields formulas for inverses of longer products. For instance, $(ABC)^{-1} = ((AB)C)^{-1} = C^{-1}(AB)^{-1} = C^{-1}B^{-1}A^{-1}$.

Example 16.11. Express the inverse of $B^{-1}ACA^{-1}$ as a product of A, B, C and their inverses.
Solution.

$$(B^{-1}ACA^{-1})^{-1} = (A^{-1})^{-1}C^{-1}A^{-1}(B^{-1})^{-1} = AC^{-1}A^{-1}B.$$

$\diamond$

There are explicit formulas for the inverse of a matrix, but it is actually more efficient in most cases to use Gaussian elimination to find inverses. One case worth noting is the formula for the inverse of a 2×2 matrix. If A is a 2×2 invertible matrix then its inverse is

$$A^{-1} = \begin{bmatrix} a & b \\ c & d \end{bmatrix}^{-1} = \frac{1}{ad - bc}\begin{bmatrix} d & -b \\ -c & a \end{bmatrix}.$$

This formula can be verified directly by multiplying by A.

Example 16.12. Let

$$A = \begin{bmatrix} 1 & 2 \\ 3 & 4 \end{bmatrix}.$$

Then

$$A^{-1} = \frac{1}{-2}\begin{bmatrix} 4 & -2 \\ -3 & 1 \end{bmatrix}.$$

$\diamond$

Notice that this formula makes sense only when $ad - bc \neq 0$. The expression $ad - bc$ is the subject of the next section.

Exercises

In Exercises 1 through 10, find the inverses of the given matrix, or demonstrate that the matrix is not invertible.

16.1. $\begin{bmatrix} 1 & 0 & 3 \\ 4 & 4 & 2 \\ 2 & 5 & -4 \end{bmatrix}$

16.2. $\begin{bmatrix} 0 & 1 & 1 \\ 1 & 0 & 1 \\ 1 & 1 & 0 \end{bmatrix}$

16.3. $\begin{bmatrix} 0 & -1 \\ 1 & 0 \end{bmatrix}$

16.4. $\begin{bmatrix} 3 & -1 \\ -3 & 1 \end{bmatrix}$

16.5. $\begin{bmatrix} 3 & -1 \\ 1 & -3 \end{bmatrix}$

16.6. $\begin{bmatrix} 2 & 0 & -1 \\ 1 & 1 & 0 \\ 1 & 1 & 2 \end{bmatrix}$

16.7. $\begin{bmatrix} 1 & 1 & 1 \\ 1 & 2 & 3 \\ 1 & 4 & 9 \end{bmatrix}$

16.8. $\begin{bmatrix} 4 & 2 & 0 \\ 1 & 2 & 1 \\ 1 & -1 & 8 \end{bmatrix}$

16.9. $\begin{bmatrix} 0 & 0 & 3 \\ 0 & -2 & 0 \\ 4 & 0 & 0 \end{bmatrix}$

16.10. $\begin{bmatrix} 3 & 10 & 3 & 8 \\ 3 & -2 & 8 & 7 \\ 2 & 1 & 4 & -5 \\ 5 & 11 & 7 & 3 \end{bmatrix}$

16.11. Simplify the expression $(I_n + A)(I_n - A)$. (Here I_n refers to the $n \times n$ identity matrix, and A is an arbitrary matrix of the same size.)

16.12. Simplify the expression $(B + A)(B - A)$, where A, B are $n \times n$ matrices. Beware!

16.13. Let

$$A = \begin{bmatrix} a & b \\ b & -a \end{bmatrix}$$

and suppose you know that $A^{-1} = A$. What can you say about a and b?

111

16.14. For which choices of the constant k is the matrix

$$\begin{bmatrix} 1 & 1 & 1 \\ 1 & 2 & k \\ 1 & 4 & k^2 \end{bmatrix}$$

invertible?

16.15. Find two invertible matrices whose sum is not invertible.

16.16. Assume A is an invertible matrix.

(a) If $A\mathbf{x} = \lambda\mathbf{x}$ where $\lambda \neq 0$ is a scalar, what is $A^{-1}\mathbf{x}$?

(b) If $A\mathbf{u} = \mathbf{v}$, what is $A^{-1}(2\mathbf{v})$?

(c) If $A\mathbf{u}_1 = 2\mathbf{v}_1$ and $A\mathbf{u}_2 = 3\mathbf{v}_2$, what is $A^{-1}(3\mathbf{v}_1 + 2\mathbf{v}_2)$?

16.17. Suppose A is a matrix which satisfies

$$A\begin{bmatrix} 1 \\ 2 \\ 0 \end{bmatrix} = \begin{bmatrix} 2 \\ 4 \\ 0 \end{bmatrix} \qquad A\begin{bmatrix} 1 \\ 0 \\ 1 \end{bmatrix} = \begin{bmatrix} 1 \\ 0 \\ 1 \end{bmatrix} \qquad A\begin{bmatrix} 0 \\ 3 \\ -1 \end{bmatrix} = \begin{bmatrix} 0 \\ -3 \\ 1 \end{bmatrix}$$

and let

$$C = \begin{bmatrix} 1 & 1 & 0 \\ 2 & 0 & 3 \\ 0 & 1 & -1 \end{bmatrix}.$$

(a) Explain without calculating C^{-1} why

$$C^{-1}AC = \begin{bmatrix} 2 & 0 & 0 \\ 0 & 1 & 0 \\ 0 & 0 & -1 \end{bmatrix}$$

Hint: The jth column of a matrix M is $M\mathbf{e}_j$, where $\mathbf{e}_j$ is the jth standard basis vector. Apply this to the matrix $M = C^{-1}AC$.

(b) Calculate C^{-1}.

(c) Using the results from parts (a) and (b), calculate A.

16.18. Suppose $\mathbf{T} : \mathbf{R}^n \to \mathbf{R}^n$ is an invertible linear transformation. Show that $\mathbf{T}^{-1} : \mathbf{R}^n \to \mathbf{R}^n$ is also a linear transformation.

16.19. Consider the linear transformations defined by the following matrices. Which are one to one? Which are onto? For those which are both one to one and onto, find the inverse.

(a) $\begin{bmatrix} 1 & 2 & 3 \\ 4 & 5 & 6 \end{bmatrix}$ (b) $\begin{bmatrix} 1 & 4 \\ 2 & 5 \\ 3 & 6 \end{bmatrix}$ (c) $\begin{bmatrix} 1 & 2 & 3 \\ 4 & 5 & 6 \\ 7 & 8 & 9 \end{bmatrix}$ (d) $\begin{bmatrix} 1 & 2 & 0 \\ 2 & 3 & 2 \\ 0 & 2 & 1 \end{bmatrix}$

16.20. Which of the following are true for all linear transformations $\mathbf{T} : \mathbf{R}^n \to \mathbf{R}^m$?

    (a) If $n < m$ then $\mathbf{T}$ must be onto.

    (b) If $n < m$ then $\mathbf{T}$ must be one to one.

    (c) If $n < m$ then $\mathbf{T}$ cannot be onto.

    (d) If $n < m$ then $\mathbf{T}$ cannot be one to one.

    (e) If $n > m$ then $\mathbf{T}$ must be onto.

    (f) If $n > m$ then $\mathbf{T}$ must be one to one.

    (g) If $n > m$ then $\mathbf{T}$ cannot be onto.

    (h) If $n > m$ then $\mathbf{T}$ cannot be one to one.

16.21. Suppose $\mathbf{T} : \mathbf{R}^n \to \mathbf{R}^m$ is a linear transformation that is one to one.

    (a) Show that if $\mathbf{T}(\mathbf{v}) = \mathbf{0}$, then $\mathbf{v} = \mathbf{0}$.

    (b) Show that if the vectors $\{\mathbf{v}_1, \mathbf{v}_2, \dots , \mathbf{v}_k\}$ are linearly independent, then so are the vectors $\{\mathbf{T}(\mathbf{v}_1), \mathbf{T}(\mathbf{v}_2), \dots , \mathbf{T}(\mathbf{v}_k)\}$.

    (c) Find an example of a linear transformation $\mathbf{S}$ and linearly independent vectors $\mathbf{v}_1$ and $\mathbf{v}_2$ such that $\mathbf{S}(\mathbf{v}_1)$ and $S(\mathbf{v}_2)$ are linearly dependent.

16.22. Suppose C and A are $n \times n$ matrices and C is invertible.

    (a) If $m \geq 1$ explain why $C^{-1}A^m C = (C^{-1}AC)^m$.

    (b) If $B = C^{-1}AC$ explain why $CBC^{-1} = A$.

16.23. Let

$$A = \begin{bmatrix} 1 & -2 \\ 1 & 4 \end{bmatrix} \qquad C = \begin{bmatrix} 1 & 2 \\ -1 & -1 \end{bmatrix}.$$

    (a) Find C^{-1}.

    (b) Calculate $C^{-1}AC$.

    (c) Calculate A^7 using the result from part (b). Hint: Let $D = (C^{-1}AC)^7 = C^{-1}A^7 C$. Then $CDC^{-1} = A^7$.

17   Determinants

The **determinant** of a 2×2 matrix

$$A = \begin{bmatrix} a & b \\ c & d \end{bmatrix}$$

is the number

$$\det(A) = \begin{vmatrix} a & b \\ c & d \end{vmatrix} = ad - bc.$$

The vertical lines in place of brackets signify the determinant. Notice that the determinant appears in the formula for the inverse of A,

$$A^{-1} = \frac{1}{\det(A)} \begin{bmatrix} d & -b \\ -c & a \end{bmatrix}.$$

Thus if $\det(A)$ is nonzero then A is invertible. It is left as an exercise to verify that A is not invertible if $\det(A) = 0$.

Proposition 17.1. A 2×2 matrix A is invertible if and only if $\det(A) \neq 0$.

Example 17.1. Let

$$A = \begin{bmatrix} 1 & 2 \\ -2 & -4 \end{bmatrix} \quad \text{and} \quad B = \begin{bmatrix} 2 & 3 \\ 4 & 0 \end{bmatrix}.$$

Then $\det(A) = 0$ and $\det(B) = -12$, so B is invertible, but A is not invertible. $\diamond$

The determinant of a 3 by 3 matrix is defined as follows.

$$\begin{vmatrix} a_{11} & a_{12} & a_{13} \\ a_{21} & a_{22} & a_{23} \\ a_{31} & a_{32} & a_{33} \end{vmatrix} = a_{11} \begin{vmatrix} a_{22} & a_{23} \\ a_{32} & a_{33} \end{vmatrix} - a_{12} \begin{vmatrix} a_{21} & a_{23} \\ a_{31} & a_{33} \end{vmatrix} + a_{13} \begin{vmatrix} a_{21} & a_{22} \\ a_{31} & a_{32} \end{vmatrix}$$

Each term is an entry from the first row multiplied by the determinant of the 2 by 2 matrix obtained by removing the row and column of that entry from the original 3 by 3 matrix.

Example 17.2.

$$\begin{vmatrix} 1 & 2 & 4 \\ 2 & -1 & 3 \\ 4 & 0 & -1 \end{vmatrix} = 1 \begin{vmatrix} -1 & 3 \\ 0 & -1 \end{vmatrix} - 2 \begin{vmatrix} 2 & 3 \\ 4 & -1 \end{vmatrix} + 4 \begin{vmatrix} 2 & -1 \\ 4 & 0 \end{vmatrix}$$
$$= 1(1) - 2(-14) + 4(4) = 45.$$

$\diamond$

We define recursively the determinant of any $n \times n$ matrix A. Let a_{ij} denote the entry in the ith row, j^{th} column of A, and let A_{ij} denote the $(n-1) \times (n-1)$ matrix obtained by removing the ith row and j^{th} column from A. Then we define

$$\det(A) = a_{11} \det(A_{11}) - a_{12} \det(A_{12}) + \cdots + (-1)^{n+1} a_{1n} \det(A_{1n}).$$

Each term is again an entry from the first row multiplied by the determinant of an $(n-1) \times (n-1)$ matrix, and the signs alternate $+, -, +, -$.

Example 17.3.

$$
\begin{vmatrix} 1 & 2 & 3 & 4 \\ 1 & 0 & 2 & 0 \\ 0 & 1 & 2 & 3 \\ 2 & 3 & 0 & 0 \end{vmatrix} = 1 \cdot \begin{vmatrix} 0 & 2 & 0 \\ 1 & 2 & 3 \\ 3 & 0 & 0 \end{vmatrix} - 2 \cdot \begin{vmatrix} 1 & 2 & 0 \\ 0 & 2 & 3 \\ 2 & 0 & 0 \end{vmatrix} + 3 \cdot \begin{vmatrix} 1 & 0 & 0 \\ 0 & 1 & 3 \\ 2 & 3 & 0 \end{vmatrix} - 4 \cdot \begin{vmatrix} 1 & 0 & 2 \\ 0 & 1 & 2 \\ 2 & 3 & 0 \end{vmatrix}
$$

$$
= 1 \left(0 \cdot \begin{vmatrix} 2 & 3 \\ 0 & 0 \end{vmatrix} - 2 \cdot \begin{vmatrix} 1 & 3 \\ 3 & 0 \end{vmatrix} + 0 \cdot \begin{vmatrix} 1 & 2 \\ 3 & 0 \end{vmatrix} \right) - 2 \left(1 \cdot \begin{vmatrix} 2 & 3 \\ 0 & 0 \end{vmatrix} - 2 \begin{vmatrix} 0 & 3 \\ 2 & 0 \end{vmatrix} + 0 \cdot \begin{vmatrix} 0 & 2 \\ 2 & 0 \end{vmatrix} \right)
$$

$$
+ 3 \left(1 \cdot \begin{vmatrix} 1 & 3 \\ 3 & 0 \end{vmatrix} - 0 \cdot \begin{vmatrix} 0 & 3 \\ 2 & 0 \end{vmatrix} + 0 \cdot \begin{vmatrix} 0 & 1 \\ 2 & 3 \end{vmatrix} \right) - 4 \left(1 \begin{vmatrix} 1 & 2 \\ 3 & 0 \end{vmatrix} - 0 \cdot \begin{vmatrix} 0 & 2 \\ 2 & 0 \end{vmatrix} + 2 \begin{vmatrix} 0 & 1 \\ 2 & 3 \end{vmatrix} \right)
$$

$$
= 1(18) - 2(12) + 3(-9) - 4(-10)
$$

$$
= 7
$$

$\diamond$

In this example the calculations were simplified by the presence of zeros in the first rows of the three by three determinants. It turns out that determinants may be expanded along any row. The formula for expansion along row i is

$$
\det(A) = \sum_{j=1}^{n} (-1)^{i+j} a_{ij} \det(A_{ij}).
$$

The sign of each term is determined by the following checkerboard pattern.

$$
\begin{bmatrix} + & - & + & \cdots \\ - & + & - & \cdots \\ + & - & + & \cdots \\ \vdots & \vdots & \vdots & \ddots \end{bmatrix}
$$

Expanding along a row which contains zeros simplifies the calculations.

Example 17.4. Expanding along the fourth row gives

$$
\begin{vmatrix} 1 & 2 & 3 & 4 \\ 1 & 0 & 2 & 0 \\ 0 & 1 & 2 & 3 \\ 2 & 3 & 0 & 0 \end{vmatrix} = -2 \cdot \begin{vmatrix} 2 & 3 & 4 \\ 0 & 2 & 0 \\ 1 & 2 & 3 \end{vmatrix} + 3 \cdot \begin{vmatrix} 1 & 3 & 4 \\ 1 & 2 & 0 \\ 0 & 2 & 3 \end{vmatrix},
$$

and expanding each of the remaining determinants along the second row gives

$$
-2 \cdot 2 \cdot \begin{vmatrix} 2 & 4 \\ 1 & 3 \end{vmatrix} + 3 \left(-1 \cdot \begin{vmatrix} 3 & 4 \\ 2 & 3 \end{vmatrix} + 2 \begin{vmatrix} 1 & 4 \\ 0 & 3 \end{vmatrix} \right) = -2 \cdot 2 \cdot 2 + 3 \cdot (-1 + 6) = 7.
$$

$\diamond$

One may also expand along any column. The formula for expansion along column j is

$$\det(A) = \sum_{i=1}^{n}(-1)^{i+j}a_{ij}\det(A_{ij}).$$

Example 17.5. Expanding the matrix

$$A = \begin{bmatrix} 2 & -1 & 3 & 5 \\ 0 & 3 & 5 & 7 \\ 0 & 0 & -2 & 1 \\ 0 & 0 & 0 & -1 \end{bmatrix}$$

along the first column we get

$$\det(A) = 2 \cdot \begin{vmatrix} 3 & 5 & 7 \\ 0 & -2 & 1 \\ 0 & 0 & -1 \end{vmatrix} = (2) \cdot (3) \cdot \begin{vmatrix} -2 & 1 \\ 0 & -1 \end{vmatrix} = (2) \cdot (3) \cdot (-2) \cdot (-1) = 12,$$

the product of the diagonal entries. $\diamond$

A matrix is called **upper triangular** if all entries below the diagonal are zero. Likewise a matrix is called **lower triangular** if all entries above the diagonal are zero. The determinant of any upper or lower triangular matrix is the product of its diagonal entries. We now list the basic properties of determinants.

Proposition 17.2.

1. (Determinants are Alternating) Exchanging two rows reverses the sign of the determinant. That is, if A and B agree in all but two rows, which are swapped, then $\det(B) = -\det(A)$.

2. (Determinants are Multilinear) The determinant is linear in each row.

   (a) If row i of A is the sum of row i of B and row i of C, and all the other rows of A, B and C agree, then $\det(A) = \det(B) + \det(C)$.

   (b) If row i of A equals a scalar multiple c of row i of B, and all the other rows of A and B agree, then $\det(A) = c\det(B)$.

The first property applies in the case of a single row exchange, with all other rows held fixed. Likewise, the second property applies *one row at a time*, with all other rows held fixed. In particular it does *not* imply that $\det(A+B) = \det(A) + \det(B)$. Determinants are *not* linear, but rather *linear in each row*. One important consequence of the first property is that the determinant of any matrix with two identical rows is necessarily zero.

Example 17.6. Let

$$A = \begin{bmatrix} 1 & 2 & 4 \\ 4 & 5 & -1 \\ 1 & 2 & 4 \end{bmatrix}.$$

By Property 1, if we exchange the first and third rows of A, this reverses the sign of the determinant. But since the first and third rows of A are the same, this implies

$$\det(A) = \det \begin{bmatrix} 1 & 2 & 4 \\ 4 & 5 & -1 \\ 1 & 2 & 4 \end{bmatrix} = -\det \begin{bmatrix} 1 & 2 & 4 \\ 4 & 5 & -1 \\ 1 & 2 & 4 \end{bmatrix} = -\det(A)$$

and thus $\det(A) = 0$. ◇

Now suppose that for some matrix A we form a matrix B whose entries are the same as those of A, except in row i, which equals row i of A minus a scalar multiple of row j of A ($j \neq i$). By Property 2,

$$\det(B) = \begin{vmatrix} \vdots \\ — \ \mathbf{v}_i^T - c\mathbf{v}_j^T \ — \\ \vdots \\ — \quad \mathbf{v}_j^T \quad — \\ \vdots \end{vmatrix} = \begin{vmatrix} \vdots \\ — \ \mathbf{v}_i^T \ — \\ \vdots \\ — \ \mathbf{v}_j^T \ — \\ \vdots \end{vmatrix} - c \begin{vmatrix} \vdots \\ — \ \mathbf{v}_j^T \ — \\ \vdots \\ — \ \mathbf{v}_j^T \ — \\ \vdots \end{vmatrix}.$$

The last matrix has a repeated row, so its determinant is zero, so we are left with

$$\begin{vmatrix} \vdots \\ — \ \mathbf{v}_i^T \ — \\ \vdots \\ — \ \mathbf{v}_j^T \ — \\ \vdots \end{vmatrix} = \det(A).$$

Thus subtracting a multiple of one row from another does not change the determinant. This makes it possible to compute determinants by performing Gaussian elimination. For larger matrices this is actually much more efficient than using the recursive formula.

Example 17.7.

$$\begin{vmatrix} 1 & 2 & 2 & 1 \\ 1 & 2 & 4 & 2 \\ 2 & 7 & 5 & 2 \\ -1 & 4 & -6 & 3 \end{vmatrix} = \begin{vmatrix} 1 & 2 & 2 & 1 \\ 0 & 0 & 2 & 1 \\ 0 & 3 & 1 & 0 \\ 0 & 6 & -4 & 4 \end{vmatrix} = - \begin{vmatrix} 1 & 2 & 2 & 1 \\ 0 & 3 & 1 & 0 \\ 0 & 0 & 2 & 1 \\ 0 & 6 & -4 & 4 \end{vmatrix} = - \begin{vmatrix} 1 & 2 & 2 & 1 \\ 0 & 3 & 1 & 0 \\ 0 & 0 & 2 & 1 \\ 0 & 0 & -6 & 4 \end{vmatrix}$$

$$= - \begin{vmatrix} 1 & 2 & 2 & 1 \\ 0 & 3 & 1 & 0 \\ 0 & 0 & 2 & 1 \\ 0 & 0 & 0 & 7 \end{vmatrix} = -(1)(3)(2)(7) = -42$$

◇

This method of calculating the determinant also reveals an important connection between the determinant and invertibility. Given an $n \times n$ matrix A, consider the effect on the determinant of each elimination step in going from A to $\mathrm{rref}(A)$. Dividing a row by a nonzero scalar divides the determinant by that scalar, subtracting a multiple of one row from another does not change the determinant, and exchanging two rows reverses the sign of the determinant. At the end, we reach the determinant of $\mathrm{rref}(A)$, so the determinant of A is some nonzero multiple of the determinant of $\mathrm{rref}(A)$. Now recall that A is invertible if and only if $\mathrm{rref}(A) = I_n$. So if A is invertible, then since $\det(I_n) = 1$, it follows that $\det(A)$ is nonzero. On the other hand, if A is not invertible, then $\mathrm{rref}(A)$ has fewer than n pivots, and thus has a row of zeros. Expanding the determinant along that row gives $\det(\mathrm{rref}(A)) = 0$, and consequently $\det(A) = 0$. We therefore have the following generalization of Proposition 17.1.

Proposition 17.3. An $n \times n$ matrix A is invertible if and only if $\det(A) \neq 0$.

The determinant may therefore be used as a test for invertibility.

Example 17.8. The upper triangular matrix

$$A = \begin{bmatrix} 4 & 8 & 2 & -5 \\ 0 & 7 & -2 & 9 \\ 0 & 0 & -3 & 1 \\ 0 & 0 & 0 & 1 \end{bmatrix}$$

has determinant $(4)(7)(-3)(1) = -84$ and is therefore invertible, while in the matrix

$$B = \begin{bmatrix} 3 & 2 & 1 & -2 \\ 1 & -1 & 8 & 7 \\ 6 & 4 & 2 & -4 \\ 2 & 2 & -1 & 4 \end{bmatrix}$$

the third row is twice the first row. Using the linearity of the determinant in the third row gives

$$\det(B) = 2 \begin{vmatrix} 3 & 2 & 1 & -2 \\ 1 & -1 & 8 & 7 \\ 3 & 2 & 1 & -2 \\ 2 & 2 & -1 & 4 \end{vmatrix} = 0$$

since the first and third rows of the new matrix are equal. Thus B is not invertible. $\diamond$

Although determinants are not linear, they are multiplicative.

Proposition 17.4. If A and B are $n \times n$ matrices, then $\det(AB) = \det(A)\det(B)$.

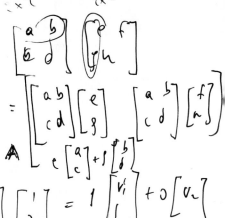

$$\begin{bmatrix} 1 & 0 \\ 0 & 1 \end{bmatrix} = ($$

$\dfrac{v_2 \cdot v_1}{v_1 \cdot v_2}$ M_1

From this we deduce the formula for the determinant of the inverse of a matrix. Suppose A is an $n \times n$ invertible matrix. Then $AA^{-1} = I_n$. Taking the determinant of both sides gives

$$1 = \det(I_n) = \det(AA^{-1}) = \det(A)\det(A^{-1}),$$

so

$$\boxed{\det(A^{-1}) = \frac{1}{\det(A)}.}$$

Determinants and Area

Let $\mathbf{T} : \mathbf{R}^2 \to \mathbf{R}^2$ be the linear transformation whose matrix is

$$A = \begin{bmatrix} a & b \\ c & d \end{bmatrix}$$

and let S denote the square generated by the standard bases vectors $\mathbf{e}_1$ and $\mathbf{e}_2$. The image $\mathbf{T}(S)$ of S under $\mathbf{T}$ is the parallelogram generated by the vectors

$$\mathbf{v}_1 = \mathbf{T}(\mathbf{e}_1) = \begin{bmatrix} a \\ c \end{bmatrix} \qquad \text{and} \qquad \mathbf{v}_2 = \mathbf{T}(\mathbf{e}_2) = \begin{bmatrix} b \\ d \end{bmatrix}.$$

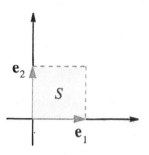

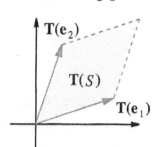

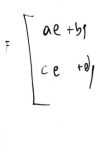

$$F \begin{bmatrix} ae+bf \\ ce+df \end{bmatrix}$$

The area of the square S is 1. What is the area of $\mathbf{T}(S)$? The area of a parallelogram is its base times its height, as shown below.

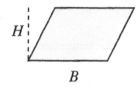

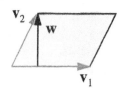

In terms of $\mathbf{v}_1$ and $\mathbf{v}_2$, the base is $B = \|\mathbf{v}_1\|$ and the height is $H = \|\mathbf{w}\|$ where $\mathbf{w} = \mathbf{v}_2 - \mathbf{Proj}_L(\mathbf{v}_2)$ and L is the line spanned by $\mathbf{v}_1$. By the Pythagorean Theorem,

$$\|\mathbf{w}\|^2 = \|\mathbf{v}_2\|^2 - \|\mathbf{Proj}_L(\mathbf{v}_2)\|^2 = \mathbf{v}_2 \cdot \mathbf{v}_2 - \left(\frac{\mathbf{v}_2 \cdot \mathbf{v}_1}{\mathbf{v}_1 \cdot \mathbf{v}_1}\right)^2 \mathbf{v}_1 \cdot \mathbf{v}_1.$$

It is easier to work with B^2H^2, the square of the area. Doing so, we find that

$$B^2H^2 = (\mathbf{v}_1 \cdot \mathbf{v}_1)\left[\mathbf{v}_2 \cdot \mathbf{v}_2 - \left(\frac{\mathbf{v}_2 \cdot \mathbf{v}_1}{\mathbf{v}_1 \cdot \mathbf{v}_1}\right)^2 \mathbf{v}_1 \cdot \mathbf{v}_1\right]$$
$$= (\mathbf{v}_1 \cdot \mathbf{v}_1)(\mathbf{v}_2 \cdot \mathbf{v}_2) - (\mathbf{v}_2 \cdot \mathbf{v}_1)^2$$
$$= (a^2 + c^2)(b^2 + d^2) - (ab + cd)^2$$
$$= a^2d^2 + c^2b^2 - 2abcd$$
$$= (ad - bc)^2$$
$$= (\det(A))^2.$$

Taking square roots we find that $BH = |\det(A)|$.

Proposition 17.5. Let A be any 2 by 2 matrix. The area of the parallelogram generated by the columns of A is $|\det(A)|$.

Example 17.9. Let

$$\mathbf{v} = \begin{bmatrix} -3 \\ 4 \end{bmatrix} \quad \text{and} \quad \mathbf{w} = \begin{bmatrix} 5 \\ 2 \end{bmatrix}.$$

The area of the parallelogram formed by $\mathbf{v}$ and $\mathbf{w}$ is

$$\left| \det \begin{bmatrix} -3 & 5 \\ 4 & 2 \end{bmatrix} \right| = |-6 - 20| = 26.$$

$\diamond$

Next, consider the effect of $\mathbf{T}$ on rectangles of different sizes. Let R be the rectangle generated by $c_1\mathbf{e}_1$ and $c_2\mathbf{e}_2$ for some positive scalars c_1 and c_2. The area of R is then c_1c_2, and $\mathbf{T}(R)$ is the parallelogram generated by $c_1\mathbf{T}(\mathbf{e}_1) = c_1\mathbf{v}_1$ and $c_2\mathbf{T}(\mathbf{e}_2) = c_2\mathbf{v}_2$.

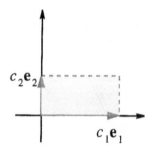
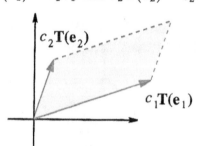

The area of $\mathbf{T}(R)$ is therefore

$$\left| \det \begin{bmatrix} c_1a & c_2b \\ c_1c & c_2d \end{bmatrix} \right| = c_1c_2 |\det(A)|,$$

exactly $|\det(A)|$ times the area of R. Thus the determinant of A can be interpreted as an area expansion factor for the transformation $\mathbf{T}$. The remarkable fact is that this property holds for arbitrary regions, not just rectangles.

Proposition 17.6. Let $\mathbf{T} : \mathbf{R}^2 \to \mathbf{R}^2$ be a linear transformation with matrix A, and let R be a region in $\mathbf{R}^2$. Then the area of $\mathbf{T}(R)$ is $|\det(A)|$ times the area of R.

We will not provide a rigorous proof of this fact, but here is the idea of why it is true. Imagine subdividing R into many small rectangles. Then the image of R is subdivided into many small parallelograms, each of which has area $|\det(A)|$ times the area of the corresponding rectangle in R.

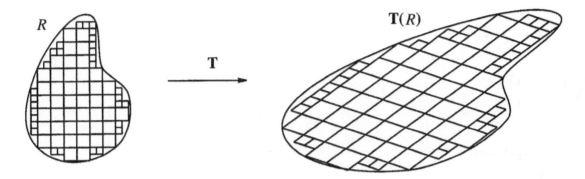

The formula then follows since the area of R is the sum of the areas of these rectangles and the area of $\mathbf{T}(R)$ is the sum of the areas of the parallelograms.

Example 17.10. Let R be the region enclosed by the ellipse

$$\frac{x^2}{4} + y^2 = 1$$

and let $\mathbf{T}$ be the linear transformation defined by the matrix

$$A = \begin{bmatrix} 1 & -1 \\ 1 & 1 \end{bmatrix}.$$

The image of R under $\mathbf{T}$ is also an ellipse. The area of an ellipse with major axis a and minor axis b is πab. Thus the area of R is 2π ($a = 2$ and $b = 1$). Since $|\det A| = 2$, the area of $\mathbf{T}(R)$ is 4π.

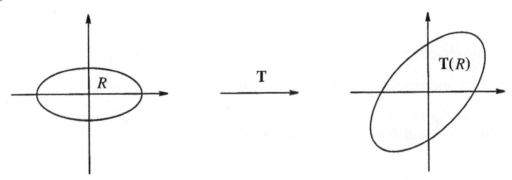

Exercises

Compute the determinant of each matrix in Exercises 1 through 8 and state whether or not the matrix is invertible.

17.1. $\begin{bmatrix} 4 & 6 \\ 4 & 9 \end{bmatrix}$

17.2. $\begin{bmatrix} 4 & 6 \\ 6 & 9 \end{bmatrix}$

17.3. $\begin{bmatrix} 0 & 2 & -1 \\ 3 & 2 & 2 \\ -5 & 1 & 2 \end{bmatrix}$

17.4. $\begin{bmatrix} 1 & 2 & 5 \\ 1 & 2 & 3 \\ 1 & 2 & 1 \end{bmatrix}$

17.5. $\begin{bmatrix} 0 & 0 & 1 \\ 0 & 1 & 0 \\ 1 & 0 & 0 \end{bmatrix}$

17.6. $\begin{bmatrix} 1 & 1 & 2 & 1 \\ 0 & 1 & 3 & 2 \\ 2 & -1 & 0 & 4 \\ 1 & 1 & 1 & 1 \end{bmatrix}$

17.7. $\begin{bmatrix} 1 & 1 & 1 & 1 \\ 2 & 1 & 1 & 2 \\ 0 & 1 & 2 & 4 \\ 3 & 3 & 4 & 5 \end{bmatrix}$

17.8. $\begin{bmatrix} 0 & 1 & 2 & 3 \\ 1 & 2 & 4 & 7 \\ 2 & 4 & 8 & 15 \\ 3 & 7 & 15 & 30 \end{bmatrix}$

17.9. (a) Verify Property 1 of Proposition 17.2 for all 2×2 matrices.

(b) Verify Property 2 of Proposition 17.2 for all 2×2 matrices.

17.10. For all 2×2 matrices A and B, verify that $\det(AB) = \det(A)\det(B)$.

17.11. Find 2×2 matrices A and B such that $\det(A+B) \neq \det(A) + \det(B)$. Find 2×2 matrices A and B such that $\det(A + B) = \det(A) + \det(B)$.

17.12. Let

$$A = \begin{bmatrix} a & b \\ c & d \end{bmatrix}$$

and suppose $ad - bc = 0$. Show that A is not invertible.

17.13. The **trace** of a square matrix A is the sum of the entries on the main diagonal. That is,

$$\mathrm{tr}(A) = \sum_{i=1}^{n} a_{ii}$$

where a_{ii} is the entry in row i column i of A.

(a) Show that for any 2×2 matrix A the following identity holds.

$$A^2 - \mathrm{tr}(A)A + \det(A)I_2 = \begin{bmatrix} 0 & 0 \\ 0 & 0 \end{bmatrix}$$

where I_2 is the 2×2 identity matrix and for scalars c the matrix cA is obtained by multiplying each entry of A by c.

(b) Show for any two $n \times n$ matrices A and B that $\mathrm{tr}(AB) = \mathrm{tr}(BA)$.

17.14. Let A be an $n \times n$ matrix and c any real number. How are $\det(A)$ and $\det(cA)$ related?

17.15. (a) Suppose R is the quadrilateral with vertices $(0, 0)$, $(2, 1)$, $(3, -3)$ and $(4, -1)$. Find the area of R.

(b) If $\mathbf{T}$ is the linear transformation with matrix

$$A = \begin{bmatrix} -3 & 2 \\ -1 & 2 \end{bmatrix}$$

and R is the region from part (a), find the area of the region $\mathbf{T}(R)$.

17.16. Let $\mathbf{T}$ be the linear transformation given by multiplication by

$$A = \begin{bmatrix} 2 & 1 \\ -1 & 2 \end{bmatrix}$$

and let R be the region bounded by the triangle with vertices $(1, 1)$, $(4, -1)$ and $(5, 5)$.

(a) Find the area of R.

(b) Find the area of the region $\mathbf{T}(R)$.

17.17. Let A be a 3×3 matrix with columns $\mathbf{u}$, $\mathbf{v}$ and $\mathbf{w}$ in order from left to right. Show that $\det(A) = \mathbf{u} \cdot (\mathbf{v} \times \mathbf{w})$.

17.18. Let C be the cube in $\mathbf{R}^3$ generated by the standard basis vectors $\mathbf{e}_1$, $\mathbf{e}_2$ and $\mathbf{e}_3$, and let $\mathbf{T} : \mathbf{R}^3 \to \mathbf{R}^3$ be a linear transformation with matrix A. Use the result of the previous exercise to show that the volume of $\mathbf{T}(C)$ is $|\det(A)|$. See Exercise 26 of Section 4.

18 Transpose of a Matrix

Given an $m \times n$ matrix A, the **transpose** of A is the $n \times m$ matrix A^T whose entry in row i column j is the entry in row j column i of A. In other words, the rows of A become the columns of A^T, and the columns of A become the rows of A^T.

Example 18.1.

$$A = \begin{bmatrix} 1 & 2 & 8 \\ 0 & -2 & 7 \\ 3 & 1 & 2 \\ 4 & 4 & 1 \end{bmatrix} \qquad \Longrightarrow \qquad A^T = \begin{bmatrix} 1 & 0 & 3 & 4 \\ 2 & -2 & 1 & 4 \\ 8 & 7 & 2 & 1 \end{bmatrix}$$

$\diamond$

Just as A defines a linear transformation from $\mathbf{R}^n$ to $\mathbf{R}^m$, A^T defines a linear transformation from $\mathbf{R}^m$ to $\mathbf{R}^n$. In this section and the next, we will explore the relationship between these two transformations. First we list some properties of the transpose.

Proposition 18.1. Let A and B be matrices for which the following expressions are defined.

1. $(A^T)^T = A$.

2. $(A + B)^T = A^T + B^T$.

3. $(AB)^T = B^T A^T$.

4. If A is invertible, then A^T is invertible and $(A^T)^{-1} = (A^{-1})^T$.

5. If A is a square matrix, then $\det(A^T) = \det(A)$.

Proof. The first two properties are easy to see. For the third, let $C = AB$, and let $D = B^T A^T$. We will use a_{ij}, b_{ij}, c_{ij} and d_{ij} to denote the entries in row i, column j of A, B, C and D, respectively. Likewise, we denote by a'_{ij}, b'_{ij} and c'_{ij} the entries in row i, column j of A^T, B^T and C^T, respectively. Using this notation, we may write the ij^{th} entry of C^T as

$$c'_{ij} = c_{ji} = \sum_{l=1}^{n} a_{jl} b_{li} = \sum_{l=1}^{n} a'_{lj} b'_{il} = \sum_{l=1}^{n} b'_{il} a'_{lj} = d_{ij}.$$

So $C^T = (AB)^T$ and $D = B^T A^T$ share the same entries, and therefore are equal. To verify the fourth property, let A be an invertible matrix. Taking the transpose of $AA^{-1} = A^{-1}A = I_n$ and using the third property gives

$$(A^{-1})^T A^T = A^T (A^{-1})^T = I_n^T = I_n,$$

124

so $(A^{-1})^T$ is the inverse of A^T. To prove the equivalence of the determinants we use induction on the size of the matrix. If A is a 2×2 matrix, it is clear that $\det(A^T) = \det(A)$. Now suppose the result holds for all $k \times k$ matrices and suppose A is $(k+1) \times (k+1)$. Expanding the determinant of A^T along column j we have

$$\det(A^T) = \sum_{i=1}^{n} (-1)^{i+j} a'_{ij} \det(A'_{ij}),$$

where, as before, a'_{ij} is the entry in row i column j of A^T and A'_{ij} is the $k \times k$ matrix obtained by removing row i and column j from A^T. But $A'_{ij} = (A_{ji})^T$, so by the induction hypothesis, $\det(A'_{ij}) = \det((A_{ji})^T) = \det(A_{ji})$. Thus, since $a'_{ij} = a_{ji}$,

$$\det(A^T) = \sum_{i=1}^{n} (-1)^{i+j} a_{ji} \det(A_{ji}),$$

which is precisely the expansion of the determinant of A along row j. $\qquad\square$

Dot Products and Transposes

As discussed in Section 7, given a column vector

$$\mathbf{v} = \begin{bmatrix} v_1 \\ \vdots \\ v_n \end{bmatrix}$$

in $\mathbf{R}^n$, its transpose

$$\mathbf{v}^T = \begin{bmatrix} v_1 & \cdots & v_n \end{bmatrix}$$

is a row vector. Multiplying the $1 \times n$ row vector $\mathbf{v}^T$ and the $n \times 1$ column vector $\mathbf{w}$ as matrices gives

$$\mathbf{v}^T \mathbf{w} = \begin{bmatrix} v_1 & \cdots & v_n \end{bmatrix} \begin{bmatrix} w_1 \\ \vdots \\ w_n \end{bmatrix} = v_1 w_1 + \cdots + v_n w_n,$$

precisely the dot product of $\mathbf{v}$ and $\mathbf{w}$. Thus

$$\mathbf{v} \cdot \mathbf{w} = \mathbf{v}^T \mathbf{w}.$$

Given an $m \times n$ matrix A, and a vector $\mathbf{x}$, the product $A\mathbf{x}$ is in $\mathbf{R}^m$, so if $\mathbf{y}$ is a vector in $\mathbf{R}^m$, the dot product $A\mathbf{x} \cdot \mathbf{y}$ is defined. On the other hand, A^T is $n \times m$, so $A^T \mathbf{y}$ is in $\mathbf{R}^n$, and the dot product $\mathbf{x} \cdot A^T \mathbf{y}$ makes sense. Remarkably, these two quantities are always equal.

125

Proposition 18.2. Let A be an $m \times n$ matrix. Then

$$Ax \cdot y = x \cdot A^T y$$

for all vectors x in $\mathbf{R}^n$ and y in $\mathbf{R}^m$.

Proof. Using the expression above for dot products, and the formula for the transpose of a product, we have

$$Ax \cdot y = (Ax)^T y = x^T A^T y = x \cdot A^T y.$$

$$x^T A^T y \qquad x \cdot A^T y$$

$\square$

Row Space and Left Null Space

Given an $m \times n$ matrix A, we now consider the column space and null space of A^T. Since the columns of A^T are the rows of A, the column space of A^T is the span of the rows of A. We therefore refer to $C(A^T)$ as the **row space** of A. Vectors x in null space of A^T satisfy $A^T x = 0$. Taking the transpose of both sides, and viewing the left side as the product of the $n \times m$ matrix A^T with the $m \times 1$ matrix x, we get $x^T A = 0^T$. This says that for vectors x in $N(A^T)$, multiplying A on the *left* by the row vector x^T results in the zero row vector. For this reason, we call $N(A^T)$ the **left null space** of A. So we now have four subspaces associated with the matrix A.

The Four Subspaces Associated with an $m \times n$ matrix A

1. $N(A)$, the null space of A, a subspace of $\mathbf{R}^n$.

2. $C(A)$, the column space of A, a subspace of $\mathbf{R}^m$.

3. $N(A^T)$, the left null space of A, a subspace of $\mathbf{R}^m$.

4. $C(A^T)$, the row space of A, a subspace of $\mathbf{R}^n$.

Example 18.2. Let

$$A = \begin{bmatrix} 2 & -1 & -3 \\ -4 & 2 & 6 \end{bmatrix} \begin{bmatrix} x \\ y \\ z \end{bmatrix} = \begin{bmatrix} 2x - y - 3z \\ -4x + 2y + 6z \end{bmatrix}$$

$$A^T = \begin{bmatrix} 2 & -4 \\ -1 & 2 \\ -3 & 6 \end{bmatrix} \begin{bmatrix} x \\ y \end{bmatrix} = \begin{bmatrix} 2x - 4y \\ -x + 2y \\ -3x + 6y \end{bmatrix} = x \begin{bmatrix} 2 \\ -1 \\ -3 \end{bmatrix} + y \begin{bmatrix} -4 \\ 2 \\ 6 \end{bmatrix} = x \begin{bmatrix} 1 \\ -2 \end{bmatrix} + y \begin{bmatrix} -1 \\ 2 \end{bmatrix} + z \begin{bmatrix} -1 \\ 2 \end{bmatrix}$$

The four subspaces are

$$N(A) = \text{span} \left(\begin{bmatrix} 1 \\ 2 \\ 0 \end{bmatrix}, \begin{bmatrix} 3 \\ 0 \\ 2 \end{bmatrix} \right)$$

$$C(A) = \text{span} \left(\begin{bmatrix} -1 \\ 2 \end{bmatrix} \right)$$

$$N(A^T) = \text{span} \left(\begin{bmatrix} 2 \\ 1 \end{bmatrix} \right)$$

$$C(A^T) = \text{span} \left(\begin{bmatrix} 2 \\ -1 \\ -3 \end{bmatrix} \right).$$

They are shown in the figure below.

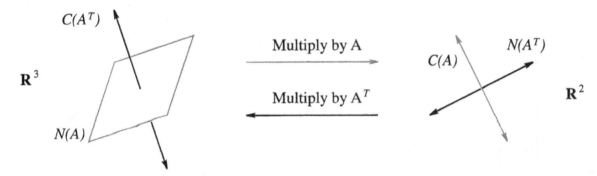

Multiplication by A sends vectors from $\mathbf{R}^3$ into $C(A)$, and vectors from $N(A)$ to the zero vector in $\mathbf{R}^2$, while multiplication by A^T sends vectors from $\mathbf{R}^2$ into $C(A^T)$, and vectors from $N(A^T)$ to the zero vector in $\mathbf{R}^3$. It is interesting to note that the line $C(A)$ is actually perpendicular to the line $N(A^T)$, and the line $C(A^T)$ is perpendicular to the plane $N(A)$. As we shall see in the next section, this is not a coincidence. $\diamond$

We conclude this section by proving that the row space and column space have the same dimension.

Proposition 18.3. Let A be any matrix. Then $\text{rank}(A^T) = \text{rank}(A)$.

Proof. Recall that $\text{rank}(A)$ equals the number of pivots in $\text{rref}(A)$. Since $\text{rank}(A^T)$ is the dimension of the row space of A, let us consider the rows of A and $\text{rref}(A)$. At each stage of the elimination process, the current rows are linear combinations of the rows of A. Hence the rows of $\text{rref}(A)$ are linear combinations of the rows of A, which implies that any vector in the row space of $\text{rref}(A)$ is in the row space of A. By reversing the elimination steps, we can produce A from $\text{rref}(A)$ through a sequence of row operations. Thus, by the same reasoning, any vector in the row space of A is in the row space of $\text{rref}(A)$, and consequently the row space of A equals the row space of $\text{rref}(A)$. It is easy to see that the rows of $\text{rref}(A)$ which contain pivots (the nonzero rows) form a basis for the row space of rref(A), since each such row contains a one in a component where all the other rows contain a zero. This implies that the dimension of the row space of rref(A), and hence the dimension of row space of A, equals the number of pivots in rref(A). $\square$

Exercises

For each matrix A in Exercises 1 through 5 compute A^T, $A^T A$, and $A A^T$.

18.1. $A = \begin{bmatrix} 4 & 2 & 1 \\ 3 & -1 & 5 \end{bmatrix}$

18.2. $A = \begin{bmatrix} 3 & 1 & 2 & 4 \end{bmatrix}$

18.3. $A = \begin{bmatrix} 2 & 1 & 3 \\ 1 & 5 & 4 \\ 3 & 4 & 7 \end{bmatrix}$

18.4. $A = \begin{bmatrix} 5 \\ 1 \\ 0 \\ 2 \end{bmatrix}$

18.5. $A = \begin{bmatrix} 0 & 2 \\ 1 & 3 \\ 6 & 1 \\ 4 & 6 \end{bmatrix}$

For each $m \times n$ matrix A in Exercises 6 through 9, (a) find a basis for $C(A), N(A), C(A^T)$ and $N(A^T)$, (b) graph $N(A)$ and $C(A^T)$ in $\mathbf{R}^n$, $N(A^T)$ and $C(A)$ in $\mathbf{R}^m$. Note that rank(A) = rank(A^T).

18.6. $A = \begin{bmatrix} 1 & 2 \\ 3 & 6 \end{bmatrix}$

18.7. $A = \begin{bmatrix} 1 & 3 & -3 \\ 4 & -2 & 16 \end{bmatrix}$

18.8. $A = \begin{bmatrix} 3 & 4 \\ -6 & 0 \\ 2 & 1 \end{bmatrix}$

18.9. $A = \begin{bmatrix} 3 & 0 & 2 \\ 2 & 4 & -2 \\ 4 & -4 & 6 \end{bmatrix}$

In Exercises 10 through 13, answer true or false. Answer true only if the statement is true for all matrices A, and explain why the statement is true. Otherwise, give a counterexample.

18.10. If $S = \{\mathbf{v}_1, \ldots, \mathbf{v}_k\}$ is a basis for the row space of rref(A), then S is a basis for the row space of A.

18.11. If $S = \{\mathbf{v}_1, \ldots, \mathbf{v}_k\}$ is a basis for the left null space of rref(A), then S is a basis for the left null space of A.

18.12. If the left null space of A has dimension d, then the null space of A also has dimension d.

18.13. If $C(A) = \mathbf{R}^m$, then $C(A^T) = \mathbf{R}^n$.

18.14. Let A be an $m \times n$ matrix.

 (a) What is rank(A) + nullity(A)?

 (b) What is rank(A^T) + nullity(A^T)?

 (c) Use Proposition 18.3 along with parts (a) and (b) to derive a relationship between nullity(A^T) and nullity(A).

19 Orthogonal Complements

Let V be a subspace of $\mathbf{R}^n$. The **orthogonal complement** of V is the set

$$V^\perp = \{\mathbf{x} \in \mathbf{R}^n \mid \mathbf{x} \cdot \mathbf{v} = 0 \text{ for every } \mathbf{v} \text{ in } V\}.$$

That is, $V^\perp$ (read "V perp") consists of all vectors which are orthogonal to every vector in V.

Example 19.1. Let V be the line spanned by

$$\mathbf{v} = \begin{bmatrix} 3 \\ 1 \\ 2 \end{bmatrix}.$$

Any vector

$$\mathbf{x} = \begin{bmatrix} x_1 \\ x_2 \\ x_3 \end{bmatrix}$$

in $V^\perp$ must be orthogonal to $\mathbf{v}$. In addition, $\mathbf{x}$ must be orthogonal to every scalar multiple of $\mathbf{v}$. But if $\mathbf{x}$ is orthogonal to $\mathbf{v}$, orthogonality to scalar multiples of $\mathbf{v}$ comes for free because

$$\mathbf{x} \cdot (c\mathbf{v}) = c(\mathbf{x} \cdot \mathbf{v}) = c0 = 0.$$

Thus $\mathbf{x}$ is in $V^\perp$ if and only if $3x_1 + x_2 + 2x_3 = 0$. So $V^\perp$ is the plane passing through the origin with normal vector $\mathbf{v}$.

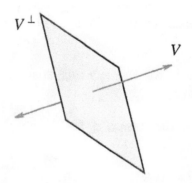

Notice that $V^{\perp}$ is also a subspace. ◇

Proposition 19.1. Let V be a subspace of $\mathbf{R}^n$. Then $V^{\perp}$ is also a subspace.

Proof. Since $\mathbf{0} \cdot \mathbf{v} = 0$ for any vector $\mathbf{v}$, and in particular for elements of V, it follows that $\mathbf{0}$ is in $V^{\perp}$. Next, suppose $\mathbf{x}$ and $\mathbf{y}$ are in $V^{\perp}$. Then $\mathbf{x} \cdot \mathbf{v} = 0$ and $\mathbf{y} \cdot \mathbf{v} = 0$ for every vector $\mathbf{v}$ in V. It then follows that

$$(\mathbf{x} + \mathbf{y}) \cdot \mathbf{v} = \mathbf{x} \cdot \mathbf{v} + \mathbf{y} \cdot \mathbf{v} = 0 + 0 = 0$$

and

$$(c\mathbf{x}) \cdot \mathbf{v} = c(\mathbf{x} \cdot \mathbf{v}) = c0 = 0$$

for every vector $\mathbf{v}$ in V, so both $\mathbf{x} + \mathbf{y}$ and $c\mathbf{x}$ are in $V^{\perp}$. □

We now state the relationship between the four subspaces associated with a matrix A.

Proposition 19.2. Let A be any matrix.

1. $N(A) = C(A^T)^{\perp}$.

2. $N(A^T) = C(A)^{\perp}$.

So the null space consists of all vectors which are orthogonal to everything in the row space, and likewise the left null space consists of all vectors orthogonal to everything in the column space.

Proof. Write A as

$$A = \begin{bmatrix} \text{---} & \mathbf{w}_1^T & \text{---} \\ \text{---} & \mathbf{w}_2^T & \text{---} \\ & \vdots & \\ \text{---} & \mathbf{w}_m^T & \text{---} \end{bmatrix}$$

in terms of its rows. If $\mathbf{x}$ is in the null space of A, then

$$A\mathbf{x} = \begin{bmatrix} \mathbf{w}_1 \cdot \mathbf{x} \\ \mathbf{w}_2 \cdot \mathbf{x} \\ \vdots \\ \mathbf{w}_m \cdot \mathbf{x} \end{bmatrix} = \begin{bmatrix} 0 \\ 0 \\ \vdots \\ 0 \end{bmatrix}$$

so $\mathbf{x}$ is orthogonal to each row of A. By linearity of the dot product,

$$(c_1\mathbf{w}_1 + c_2\mathbf{w}_2 + \cdots + c_m\mathbf{w}_m) \cdot \mathbf{x} = c_1\mathbf{w}_1 \cdot \mathbf{x} + c_2\mathbf{w}_2 \cdot \mathbf{x} + \cdots + c_m\mathbf{w}_m \cdot \mathbf{x}$$
$$= 0$$

so $\mathbf{x}$ is orthogonal to any vector in the row space of A. Hence $\mathbf{x}$ is in $C(A^T)^\perp$. Conversely, suppose $\mathbf{x}$ is some vector in $C(A^T)^\perp$. Then $\mathbf{x}$ is orthogonal to every vector in the row space of A. In particular, $\mathbf{x}$ is orthogonal to each row of A, so $A\mathbf{x} = \mathbf{0}$, and therefore $\mathbf{x}$ is in the null space of A. Thus $C(A^T)^\perp = N(A)$. The second statement follows by replacing A with A^T (and hence A^T with $(A^T)^T = A$) in the first statement. $\square$

An important consequence of this is that a subspace and its orthogonal complement have complementary dimensions.

Proposition 19.3. Let V be a subspace of $\mathbf{R}^n$. Then $\dim(V) + \dim(V^\perp) = n$.

Proof. If $V = \{\mathbf{0}\}$, then $V^\perp = \mathbf{R}^n$, and the statement holds. Otherwise, let $\{\mathbf{v}_1, \ldots, \mathbf{v}_k\}$ be a basis for V, and let A be the matrix whose columns consist of these basis vectors. Then $V = C(A)$, so $V^\perp = C(A)^\perp = N(A^T)$, by Proposition 19.2. The matrix A^T is $k \times n$, so by the Rank-Nullity Theorem, $\dim(C(A^T)) + \dim(N(A^T)) = n$. By Proposition 18.3, $\dim(C(A^T)) = \dim(C(A))$, so $\dim(C(A)) + \dim(N(A^T)) = n$. $\square$

Proposition 19.4. Let V be a subspace of $\mathbf{R}^n$.

1. $V \cap V^\perp = \{\mathbf{0}\}$.

2. $V + V^\perp = \mathbf{R}^n$. That is, every vector $\mathbf{x}$ in $\mathbf{R}^n$ can be written as a sum $\mathbf{v} + \mathbf{w}$ of a vector $\mathbf{v}$ in V and a vector $\mathbf{w}$ in $V^\perp$. Furthermore, this expression is unique.

Proof. To prove the first statement, suppose $\mathbf{v}$ is in both V and $V^\perp$. Then $\mathbf{v}$ is orthogonal to itself, so $\|\mathbf{v}\|^2 = \mathbf{v} \cdot \mathbf{v} = 0$, which implies $\mathbf{v} = \mathbf{0}$.

If $V = \{\mathbf{0}\}$, then $V^\perp = \mathbf{R}^n$, so $\mathbf{x} = \mathbf{0} + \mathbf{x}$ is a sum of a vector in V and a vector in $V^\perp$. If $V = \mathbf{R}^n$, then $V^\perp = \{\mathbf{0}\}$, so $\mathbf{x} = \mathbf{x} + \mathbf{0}$ is a sum of a vector in V and a vector in $V^\perp$. Otherwise, V has dimension $0 < k < n$ and $V^\perp$ has dimension $0 < n - k < n$, so let $\{\mathbf{v}_1, \ldots, \mathbf{v}_k\}$ be a basis for V, let $\{\mathbf{w}_1, \ldots, \mathbf{w}_{n-k}\}$ be a basis for $V^\perp$, and suppose that

$$c_1\mathbf{v}_1 + \cdots + c_k\mathbf{v}_k + d_1\mathbf{w}_1 + \cdots + d_{n-k}\mathbf{w}_{n-k} = \mathbf{0}$$

131

for some scalars. Moving the vectors in $V^\perp$ to the right side, we have

$$\mathbf{v} = c_1\mathbf{v}_1 + \cdots + c_k\mathbf{v}_k = -(d_1\mathbf{w}_1 + \cdots + d_{n-k}\mathbf{w}_{n-k}).$$

Since $\mathbf{v}$ is in both V and $V^\perp$, it equals $\mathbf{0}$ by the first statement, so

$$c_1\mathbf{v}_1 + \cdots + c_k\mathbf{v}_k = \mathbf{0}$$

and

$$d_1\mathbf{w}_1 + \cdots + d_{n-k}\mathbf{w}_{n-k} = \mathbf{0}.$$

By independence, c_1 through c_k and d_1 through d_{n-k} must all be zero. So the set

$$\{\mathbf{v}_1,\ldots,\mathbf{v}_k,\mathbf{w}_1,\ldots,\mathbf{w}_{n-k}\}$$

is linearly independent, and since it consists of n vectors, by Proposition 12.3 it is a basis for $\mathbf{R}^n$. Any vector $\mathbf{x}$ in $\mathbf{R}^n$ may then be written

$$\mathbf{x} = \underbrace{c_1\mathbf{v}_1 + \cdots + c_k\mathbf{v}_k}_{\text{in } V} + \underbrace{d_1\mathbf{w}_1 + \cdots + d_{n-k}\mathbf{w}_{n-k}}_{\text{in } V^\perp}.$$

To see that such expressions are unique, suppose $\mathbf{x} = \mathbf{v}_1 + \mathbf{w}_1 = \mathbf{v}_2 + \mathbf{w}_2$, where $\mathbf{v}_1$ and $\mathbf{v}_2$ are in V and $\mathbf{w}_1$ and $\mathbf{w}_2$ are in $V^\perp$. Then $\mathbf{v}_1 - \mathbf{v}_2 = \mathbf{w}_2 - \mathbf{w}_1$ is a vector in both V and $V^\perp$, and is therefore the zero vector. So $\mathbf{v}_1 = \mathbf{v}_2$ and $\mathbf{w}_1 = \mathbf{w}_2$. $\square$

Proposition 19.5. $(V^\perp)^\perp = V.$

Proof. First let $\mathbf{x}$ be a vector in $(V^\perp)^\perp$. By Proposition 19.4, $\mathbf{x} = \mathbf{v} + \mathbf{w}$ for some $\mathbf{v}$ in V and $\mathbf{w}$ in $V^\perp$. Since $\mathbf{x}$ is orthogonal to $\mathbf{w}$ and $\mathbf{w}$ is orthogonal to $\mathbf{v}$, taking the dot product of both sides with $\mathbf{w}$ gives

$$0 = \mathbf{x} \cdot \mathbf{w} = \mathbf{v} \cdot \mathbf{w} + \mathbf{w} \cdot \mathbf{w} = \|\mathbf{w}\|^2.$$

Thus $\mathbf{w} = \mathbf{0}$, and $\mathbf{x} = \mathbf{v}$ is in V. Conversely, suppose $\mathbf{v}$ is a vector in V. Applying Proposition 19.4 to the subspace $V^\perp$, we may write $\mathbf{v} = \mathbf{w} + \mathbf{x}$ for some $\mathbf{w}$ in $V^\perp$ and some $\mathbf{x}$ in $(V^\perp)^\perp$. Again taking the dot product with $\mathbf{w}$ gives

$$0 = \mathbf{v} \cdot \mathbf{w} = \mathbf{w} \cdot \mathbf{w} + \mathbf{x} \cdot \mathbf{w} = \|\mathbf{w}\|^2.$$

So $\mathbf{w} = \mathbf{0}$ and $\mathbf{v} = \mathbf{x}$ is in $(V^\perp)^\perp$. $\square$

The importance of this result is that if a subspace W is the orthogonal complement of a subspace V, then $W = V^\perp$, so by Proposition 19.5, $W^\perp = (V^\perp)^\perp = V$, and therefore V is the orthogonal complement of W. Thus there is a symmetry in the definition. For instance, according to Proposition 19.2 we have

1. $C(A^T) = N(A)^\perp$.

2. $C(A) = N(A^T)^\perp$.

Example 19.2. Find the set V of all vectors in $\mathbf{R}^4$ which are orthogonal to every solution of

$$\begin{array}{rrrrrrrrl} 2x_1 & + & x_2 & - & 3x_3 & + & x_4 & = & 0 \\ -2x_1 & + & 3x_2 & - & x_3 & + & 2x_4 & = & 0. \end{array}$$

Solution. The set of solutions is the null space of the matrix

$$A = \begin{bmatrix} 2 & 1 & -3 & 1 \\ -2 & 3 & -1 & 2 \end{bmatrix}$$

so the set of vectors we are seeking is $V = N(A)^\perp = C(A^T)$, the row space of A. The vectors

$$\begin{bmatrix} 2 \\ 1 \\ -3 \\ 1 \end{bmatrix} \quad \text{and} \quad \begin{bmatrix} -2 \\ 3 \\ -1 \\ 2 \end{bmatrix}$$

form a basis for V. $\diamond$

We conclude this section by illustrating further the relationship between the column space and row space of a matrix.

Proposition 19.6. Given any vector $\mathbf{b}$ in the column space of A, there exists a unique vector $\mathbf{x}_0$ in the row space of A such that $A\mathbf{x}_0 = \mathbf{b}$. Furthermore, among all solutions of $A\mathbf{x} = \mathbf{b}$, $\mathbf{x}_0$ has the smallest magnitude.

Proof. For any $\mathbf{b}$ in $C(A)$, there is at least one solution $\mathbf{x}$ of $A\mathbf{x} = \mathbf{b}$. By Proposition 19.4, $\mathbf{x} = \mathbf{x}_0 + \mathbf{y}$ for some $\mathbf{x}_0$ in $C(A^T)$ and some $\mathbf{y}$ in $C(A^T)^\perp = N(A)$. Thus

$$A\mathbf{x}_0 = A(\mathbf{x} - \mathbf{y}) = A\mathbf{x} - A\mathbf{y} = \mathbf{b} - \mathbf{0} = \mathbf{b},$$

so $\mathbf{x}_0$ is an element of the row space which satisfies $A\mathbf{x}_0 = \mathbf{b}$. To prove that this is the only such vector in the row space, suppose $\mathbf{x}_1$ is in the row space and satisfies $A\mathbf{x}_1 = \mathbf{b}$. Then since $C(A^T)$ is a subspace, $\mathbf{x}_1 - \mathbf{x}_0$ is in $C(A^T)$, and since

$$A(\mathbf{x}_1 - \mathbf{x}_0) = A\mathbf{x}_1 - A\mathbf{x}_0 = \mathbf{b} - \mathbf{b} = \mathbf{0},$$

$\mathbf{x}_1 - \mathbf{x}_0$ is in $N(A) = C(A^T)^\perp$. Thus by the first part of Proposition 19.4, $\mathbf{x}_1 - \mathbf{x}_0 = \mathbf{0}$, so $\mathbf{x}_1 = \mathbf{x}_0$, which proves uniqueness.

For any solution $\mathbf{x}$ of $A\mathbf{x} = \mathbf{b}$, we see as above that $\mathbf{x} - \mathbf{x}_0$ is in $N(A) = C(A^T)^\perp$ and is therefore orthogonal to $\mathbf{x}_0$. Hence, by the Pythagorean Theorem,

$$\|\mathbf{x}\|^2 = \|(\mathbf{x} - \mathbf{x}_0) + \mathbf{x}_0\|^2 = \|\mathbf{x} - \mathbf{x}_0\|^2 + \|\mathbf{x}_0\|^2 \geq \|\mathbf{x}_0\|^2,$$

so $\|\mathbf{x}_0\| \leq \|\mathbf{x}\|$. $\square$

Example 19.3. Let

$$A = \begin{bmatrix} 3 & -2 \\ 6 & -4 \end{bmatrix} \quad \text{and} \quad b = \begin{bmatrix} 9 \\ 18 \end{bmatrix}.$$

Then

$$N(A) = \text{span}\left(\begin{bmatrix} 2 \\ 3 \end{bmatrix} \right), \quad C(A^T) = \text{span}\left(\begin{bmatrix} 3 \\ -2 \end{bmatrix} \right),$$

and the set of solutions of $A\mathbf{x} = \mathbf{b}$ is

$$\left\{ \begin{bmatrix} 3 \\ 0 \end{bmatrix} + t \begin{bmatrix} 2 \\ 3 \end{bmatrix} \;\middle|\; t \in \mathbf{R} \right\}.$$

To find the solution $\mathbf{x}_0$ in $C(A^T)$, we use the fact that, for any solution $\mathbf{x}$, the difference $\mathbf{x} - \mathbf{x}_0$ in orthogonal to the line $L = C(A^T)$. Thus $\mathbf{x}_0$ must be the orthogonal projection of $\mathbf{x}$ onto $C(A^T)$. Choosing any solution, say

$$\mathbf{x} = \begin{bmatrix} 3 \\ 0 \end{bmatrix},$$

and letting

$$\mathbf{u} = \frac{1}{13} \begin{bmatrix} 3 \\ -2 \end{bmatrix}$$

denote one of the unit vectors which spans $C(A^T)$, we then find that

$$\mathbf{x}_0 = \text{Proj}_L(\mathbf{x}) = (\mathbf{x} \cdot \mathbf{u})\mathbf{u} = \begin{bmatrix} 27/13 \\ -18/13 \end{bmatrix}.$$

This solution $\mathbf{x}_0$ has the smallest magnitude among all solutions of $A\mathbf{x} = \mathbf{b}$. It is closest to the origin, and the only solution orthogonal to the null space of A. ◇

The solution $\mathbf{x}_0$ will generally be the orthogonal projection of any solution $\mathbf{x}$ onto the row space. In the next section we consider orthogonal projections onto arbitrary subspaces.

Exercises

In Exercises 1 through 16, for the subspace V given, find a basis for $V^\perp$.

19.1. $V = \mathrm{span}\left(\begin{bmatrix} 2 \\ 5 \end{bmatrix}\right)$

19.2. $V = \mathrm{span}\left(\begin{bmatrix} 2 \\ 5 \end{bmatrix}, \begin{bmatrix} 1 \\ 4 \end{bmatrix}\right)$

19.3. $V = \mathrm{span}\left(\begin{bmatrix} 3 \\ -2 \\ 1 \end{bmatrix}\right)$

19.4. $V = \mathrm{span}\left(\begin{bmatrix} 2 \\ 0 \\ 4 \end{bmatrix}, \begin{bmatrix} 3 \\ -2 \\ 1 \end{bmatrix}\right)$

19.5. $V = \mathrm{span}\left(\begin{bmatrix} 2 \\ 0 \\ 4 \end{bmatrix}, \begin{bmatrix} 3 \\ -2 \\ 1 \end{bmatrix}, \begin{bmatrix} -5 \\ 4 \\ 0 \end{bmatrix}\right)$

19.6. $V = \mathrm{span}\left(\begin{bmatrix} 2 \\ 0 \\ 4 \end{bmatrix}, \begin{bmatrix} 3 \\ -2 \\ 1 \end{bmatrix}, \begin{bmatrix} 5 \\ 2 \\ 1 \end{bmatrix}\right)$

19.7. $V = \mathrm{span}\left(\begin{bmatrix} 5 \\ 2 \\ -2 \\ 1 \end{bmatrix}\right)$

19.8. $V = \mathrm{span}\left(\begin{bmatrix} 5 \\ 2 \\ -2 \\ 1 \end{bmatrix}, \begin{bmatrix} 2 \\ 3 \\ 0 \\ 5 \end{bmatrix}\right)$

19.9. V is the line in $\mathbf{R}^2$ which satisfies the equation $-x + 7y = 0$.

19.10. V is the plane in $\mathbf{R}^3$ which satisfies the equation $4x - 2y + z = 0$.

19.11. V is the hyperplane in $\mathbf{R}^4$ given by $3x + 2y - z + 7w = 0$.

19.12. V is the set of solutions to the system

$$\begin{aligned} 3x_1 + 2x_2 &= 0 \\ -x_1 + 5x_2 &= 0 \end{aligned}$$

19.13. V is the set of solutions to the system

$$\begin{aligned} 3x_1 - x_2 + 7x_3 &= 0 \\ 2x_1 + 4x_2 + x_3 &= 0 \end{aligned}$$

19.14. V is the set of solutions to the system

$$
\begin{aligned}
x_1 &- 3x_2 &+ 4x_3 &= 0 \\
x_1 &+ 6x_2 &- 5x_3 &= 0 \\
4x_1 &+ 6x_2 &- 2x_3 &= 0
\end{aligned}
$$

19.15. V is the set of solutions to the system

$$
\begin{aligned}
3x_1 &- 7x_2 &+ 4x_3 &+ x_4 &= 0 \\
2x_1 & & + 5x_3 &- 4x_4 &= 0
\end{aligned}
$$

19.16. V is the set of solutions to the system

$$
\begin{aligned}
-x_1 &+ 3x_2 &+ 4x_3 &- 5x_4 &= 0 \\
4x_1 &- 6x_2 &+ 11x_3 &- 4x_4 &= 0 \\
2x_1 &- 4x_2 &+ x_3 &+ 2x_4 &= 0
\end{aligned}
$$

In Exercises 17 through 22, find a basis for each of the four subspaces. Notice that $N(A) = C(A^T)^\perp$ and $N(A^T) = C(A)^\perp$.

19.17. $A = \begin{bmatrix} 2 & 3 & -1 \\ 4 & 0 & 2 \end{bmatrix}$

19.18. $A = \begin{bmatrix} 4 & 2 \\ -3 & 1 \\ 2 & 5 \end{bmatrix}$

19.19. $A = \begin{bmatrix} 2 & -1 & 3 \\ 4 & 2 & 0 \\ 8 & -2 & 9 \end{bmatrix}$

19.20. $A = \begin{bmatrix} 1 & 0 & 4 & -5 \\ 2 & 2 & -5 & 9 \\ 3 & 2 & -1 & 4 \\ 8 & 6 & -7 & 17 \end{bmatrix}$

19.21. $A = \begin{bmatrix} 1 & 1 & 0 & 1 \\ 0 & 1 & 1 & 1 \\ 1 & 1 & 1 & 0 \\ 2 & 1 & 0 & 0 \end{bmatrix}$

19.22. $A = \begin{bmatrix} 2 & -1 & 0 & 5 \\ 3 & 8 & 1 & -4 \\ 3 & -11 & -1 & 19 \end{bmatrix}$

19.23. Let V, W be subspaces of $\mathbf{R}^n$. Show that if $V \subseteq W$, then $W^\perp \subseteq V^\perp$.

19.24. For any subspaces X and Y define $X+Y \equiv \{\mathbf{u} = \mathbf{x}+\mathbf{y} : \mathbf{x} \in X, \mathbf{y} \in Y\}$. Let V, W be subspaces of $\mathbf{R}^n$. Use the following steps to show that $(V \cap W)^\perp = V^\perp + W^\perp$.

    (a) Show that $V \cap W \subseteq (V^\perp + W^\perp)^\perp$.

    (b) Show that $(V^\perp + W^\perp)^\perp \subseteq V \cap W$. *Hint:* Use the result from Exercise 23 to show that $(V^\perp + W^\perp)^\perp \subseteq V$ and $(V^\perp + W^\perp)^\perp \subseteq W$.

    (c) Use the fact that for any subspace U, $(U^\perp)^\perp = U$ to conclude that $(V \cap W)^\perp = V^\perp + W^\perp$.

19.25. Let V, W be subspaces of $\mathbf{R}^n$. Use the following steps to show that $(V \cup W)^\perp = V^\perp \cap W^\perp$.

    (a) $(V \cup W)^\perp \subseteq V^\perp \cap W^\perp$.

    (b) $V^\perp \cap W^\perp \subseteq (V \cup W)^\perp$.

19.26. Suppose

$$\left\{ \begin{bmatrix} 3 \\ -1 \\ 2 \end{bmatrix}, \begin{bmatrix} 1 \\ 1 \\ -1 \end{bmatrix} \right\}$$

is a basis for the left null space of A. For which vectors $\mathbf{b}$ does the system $A\mathbf{x} = \mathbf{b}$ have a solution?

    (a) $\mathbf{b} = \begin{bmatrix} 2 \\ -10 \\ -8 \end{bmatrix}$ (b) $\mathbf{b} = \begin{bmatrix} 3 \\ -1 \\ 2 \end{bmatrix}$ (c) $\mathbf{b} = \begin{bmatrix} 4 \\ 0 \\ 1 \end{bmatrix}$ (d) $\mathbf{b} = \begin{bmatrix} -1 \\ 5 \\ 4 \end{bmatrix}$

19.27. Suppose

$$\left\{ \begin{bmatrix} 1 \\ 2 \\ 3 \end{bmatrix} \right\}$$

is a basis for the left null space of A. For which vectors $\mathbf{b}$ does the system $A\mathbf{x} = \mathbf{b}$ have a solution?

    (a) $\mathbf{b} = \begin{bmatrix} 1 \\ 1 \\ -1 \end{bmatrix}$ (b) $\mathbf{b} = \begin{bmatrix} 1 \\ 2 \\ 3 \end{bmatrix}$ (c) $\mathbf{b} = \begin{bmatrix} -1 \\ 5 \\ -3 \end{bmatrix}$ (d) $\mathbf{b} = \begin{bmatrix} 3 \\ -2 \\ 1 \end{bmatrix}$

19.28. Let A be an $m \times n$ matrix and suppose that the system $A\mathbf{x} = \mathbf{b}$ has a unique solution for some $\mathbf{b}$ in $\mathbf{R}^m$. What does this imply about the row space of A?

In Exercises 26 through 29 find the solution of $A\mathbf{x} = \mathbf{b}$ which lies in the row space of A.

19.26. $A = \begin{bmatrix} 1 & -2 & 3 \\ 2 & -4 & 6 \end{bmatrix}$, $\mathbf{b} = \begin{bmatrix} 3 \\ 6 \end{bmatrix}$

19.27. $A = \begin{bmatrix} 3 & -6 \\ -2 & 4 \end{bmatrix}$, $\quad \mathbf{b} = \begin{bmatrix} -3 \\ 2 \end{bmatrix}$

19.28. $A = \begin{bmatrix} 5 & 2 \\ -5 & -2 \end{bmatrix}$, $\quad \mathbf{b} = \begin{bmatrix} -3 \\ 3 \end{bmatrix}$

19.29. $A = \begin{bmatrix} 1 & 2 & -1 & 3 \\ -1 & -2 & 1 & -3 \\ 2 & 4 & -2 & 6 \end{bmatrix}$, $\quad \mathbf{b} = \begin{bmatrix} 2 \\ -2 \\ 4 \end{bmatrix}$

20   Orthogonal Projections

Let V be a subspace of $\mathbf{R}^n$. By Proposition 19.4 any vector $\mathbf{x}$ in $\mathbf{R}^n$ may be written uniquely as a sum

$$\mathbf{x} = \mathbf{v} + \mathbf{w}$$

where $\mathbf{v}$ is in V and $\mathbf{w}$ is in $V^\perp$. We can therefore define a function $\mathbf{Proj}_V : \mathbf{R}^n \to \mathbf{R}^n$, called the **projection** onto the subspace V, by $\mathbf{Proj}_V(\mathbf{x}) = \mathbf{v}$.

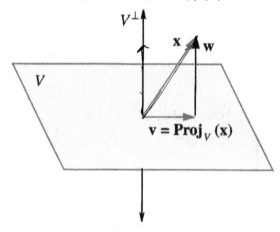

We claim that $\mathbf{Proj}_V$ is a linear transformation. We will show this in the case that V is a nontrivial proper subspace of $\mathbf{R}^n$ – the cases $V = \{\mathbf{0}\}$ and $V = \mathbf{R}^n$ are left for the reader to consider. Let $\{\mathbf{v}_1, \ldots, \mathbf{v}_k\}$ be a basis for V and let A be the $n \times k$ matrix whose columns are these vectors. Then $V = C(A)$, so that $\mathbf{Proj}_V(\mathbf{x}) = A\mathbf{y}$ for some vector $\mathbf{y}$ in $\mathbf{R}^k$. By definition, $\mathbf{x} - \mathbf{Proj}_V(\mathbf{x})$ is a vector $\mathbf{w}$ in $V^\perp = C(A)^\perp$. But by Proposition 19.2, $C(A)^\perp = N(A^T)$, so $\mathbf{x} - A\mathbf{y}$ is in the null space of A^T. Thus

$$A^T(\mathbf{x} - A\mathbf{y}) = 0 \qquad \Longrightarrow \qquad A^T A\mathbf{y} = A^T\mathbf{x}.$$

It turns out that the $k \times k$ matrix $A^T A$ is invertible. To see this, suppose that $\mathbf{z}$ is in the null space of $A^T A$. Then $A^T A\mathbf{z} = \mathbf{0}$. Multiplying on the left by $\mathbf{z}^T$ gives $\mathbf{z}^T A^T A\mathbf{z} = 0$. Since $\mathbf{z}^T A^T = (A\mathbf{z})^T$, this implies that $A\mathbf{z} \cdot A\mathbf{z} = 0$, and therefore $\|A\mathbf{z}\|^2 = 0$. Since only the zero vector has length zero, this implies $A\mathbf{z} = \mathbf{0}$. But since the columns of A are linearly independent, $N(A) = \{\mathbf{0}\}$, so $\mathbf{z} = \mathbf{0}$. Hence the null space of $A^T A$ is trivial, and since $A^T A$ is a square matrix, it must be invertible. We may therefore solve the above equation for $\mathbf{y}$ to get $\mathbf{y} = (A^T A)^{-1} A^T \mathbf{x}$ and therefore

$$\mathbf{Proj}_V(\mathbf{x}) = A(A^T A)^{-1} A^T \mathbf{x}.$$

Example 20.1. Find the matrix for the projection onto the subspace

$$V = \mathrm{span}\left(\begin{bmatrix}1\\0\\0\\1\end{bmatrix}, \begin{bmatrix}0\\1\\0\\1\end{bmatrix}\right)$$

of $\mathbf{R}^4$.

Solution.

$$A = \begin{bmatrix}1 & 0\\0 & 1\\0 & 0\\1 & 1\end{bmatrix} \implies A^T A = \begin{bmatrix}2 & 1\\1 & 2\end{bmatrix} \implies (A^T A)^{-1} = \frac{1}{3}\begin{bmatrix}2 & -1\\-1 & 2\end{bmatrix}$$

so

$$A(A^T A)^{-1} A^T = \frac{1}{3}\begin{bmatrix}1 & 0\\0 & 1\\0 & 0\\1 & 1\end{bmatrix}\begin{bmatrix}2 & -1\\-1 & 2\end{bmatrix}\begin{bmatrix}1 & 0 & 0 & 1\\0 & 1 & 0 & 1\end{bmatrix} = \frac{1}{3}\begin{bmatrix}2 & -1 & 0 & 1\\-1 & 2 & 0 & 1\\0 & 0 & 0 & 0\\1 & 1 & 0 & 2\end{bmatrix}.$$

$\diamond$

The following result states that the projections onto V and $V^\perp$ are complementary, in that they sum to the identity function.

Proposition 20.1. Let V be a subspace of $\mathbf{R}^n$. Then $\mathbf{Proj}_V + \mathbf{Proj}_{V^\perp} = I_{\mathbf{R}^n}$.

Proof. Applying Proposition 19.4 to $V^\perp$, we can express any vector $\mathbf{x}$ in $\mathbf{R}^n$ uniquely as $\mathbf{w}+\mathbf{v}$ where $\mathbf{w}$ is in $V^\perp$ and $\mathbf{v}$ is in $(V^\perp)^\perp = V$. By definition $\mathbf{w} = \mathbf{Proj}_{V^\perp}(\mathbf{x})$ and $\mathbf{v} = \mathbf{Proj}_V(\mathbf{x})$, so $\mathbf{x} = \mathbf{Proj}_V(\mathbf{x}) + \mathbf{Proj}_{V^\perp}(\mathbf{x})$. $\square$

Example 20.2. Find the matrix for the projection onto the plane $x_1 + x_2 + x_3 = 0$ in $\mathbf{R}^3$.
Solution. Call the plane V. Then V is the null space of the matrix $A = \begin{bmatrix}1 & 1 & 1\end{bmatrix}$, and thus $V^\perp = N(A)^\perp = C(A^T)$ is the row space of A. That is,

$$V^\perp = \mathrm{span}\left(\begin{bmatrix}1\\1\\1\end{bmatrix}\right).$$

139

Call B the matrix consisting of this single column vector. Then

$$B(B^TB)^{-1}B^T = \begin{bmatrix} 1 \\ 1 \\ 1 \end{bmatrix} [3]^{-1} \begin{bmatrix} 1 & 1 & 1 \end{bmatrix} = \frac{1}{3}\begin{bmatrix} 1 & 1 & 1 \\ 1 & 1 & 1 \\ 1 & 1 & 1 \end{bmatrix}$$

is the matrix for $\mathbf{Proj}_{V^\perp}$. Since $\mathbf{Proj}_V = \mathbf{I}_{\mathbf{R}^3} - \mathbf{Proj}_{V^\perp}$, the matrix for $\mathbf{Proj}_V$ is

$$\begin{bmatrix} 1 & 0 & 0 \\ 0 & 1 & 0 \\ 0 & 0 & 1 \end{bmatrix} - \frac{1}{3}\begin{bmatrix} 1 & 1 & 1 \\ 1 & 1 & 1 \\ 1 & 1 & 1 \end{bmatrix} = \frac{1}{3}\begin{bmatrix} 2 & -1 & -1 \\ -1 & 2 & -1 \\ -1 & -1 & 2 \end{bmatrix}.$$

$\diamond$

Geometrically, the orthogonal projection of a vector $\mathbf{x}$ onto a subspace V is the closest point in V to the point $\mathbf{x}$.

Proposition 20.2. Let V be a subspace of $\mathbf{R}^n$, and let $\mathbf{x}$ be any vector in $\mathbf{R}^n$. Then

$$\|\mathbf{x} - \mathbf{Proj}_V(\mathbf{x})\| \leq \|\mathbf{x} - \mathbf{v}\|$$

for every $\mathbf{v}$ in V, and equality holds if and only if $\mathbf{v} = \mathbf{Proj}_V(\mathbf{x})$.

Proof. Let $\mathbf{v}$ be any vector in V and write

$$\mathbf{x} - \mathbf{v} = \underbrace{\mathbf{x} - \mathbf{Proj}_V(\mathbf{x})}_{\mathbf{a}} + \underbrace{\mathbf{Proj}_V(\mathbf{x}) - \mathbf{v}}_{\mathbf{b}}.$$

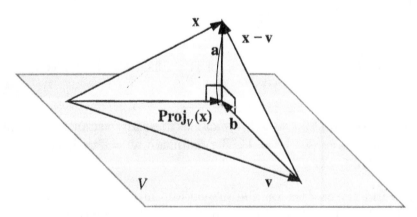

By definition $\mathbf{a} = \mathbf{x} - \mathbf{Proj}_V(\mathbf{x})$ is in $V^\perp$, and since V is a subspace, $\mathbf{b} = \mathbf{Proj}_V(\mathbf{x}) - \mathbf{v}$ is in V. So $\mathbf{a}$ and $\mathbf{b}$ are orthogonal, and the Pythagorean Theorem implies

$$\begin{aligned} \|\mathbf{x} - \mathbf{v}\|^2 &= \|\mathbf{a} + \mathbf{b}\|^2 \\ &= \|\mathbf{a}\|^2 + \|\mathbf{b}\|^2 \\ &= \|\mathbf{x} - \mathbf{Proj}_V(\mathbf{x})\|^2 + \|\mathbf{Proj}_V(\mathbf{x}) - \mathbf{v}\|^2. \end{aligned}$$

Hence

$$\|\mathbf{x} - \mathbf{Proj}_V(\mathbf{x})\| \le \|\mathbf{x} - \mathbf{v}\|$$

and we have equality only if $\mathbf{v} = \mathbf{Proj}_V(\mathbf{x})$. $\qquad\square$

Example 20.3. Find the distance between the point $(3, 2, 1)$ and the plane $x_1 + x_2 + x_3 = 0$.
Solution. Using the matrix for the orthogonal projection onto the plane found in Example 20.2, we have

$$\frac{1}{3}\begin{bmatrix} 2 & -1 & -1 \\ -1 & 2 & -1 \\ -1 & -1 & 2 \end{bmatrix}\begin{bmatrix} 3 \\ 2 \\ 1 \end{bmatrix} = \begin{bmatrix} 1 \\ 0 \\ -1 \end{bmatrix}.$$

Thus $(1, 0, -1)$ is the closest point in the plane to $(3, 2, 1)$, and the distance between these points is $2\sqrt{3}$. $\qquad\diamond$

Least Squares Approximation

Next suppose we seek a solution to a linear system $A\mathbf{x} = \mathbf{b}$, but the right hand side $\mathbf{b}$ is not in the column space of A, so that the system has no solutions. To obtain an approximate solution, we attempt to find an $\mathbf{x}$ which minimizes the length of the difference vector $A\mathbf{x} - \mathbf{b}$. For such an $\mathbf{x}$, by Proposition 20.2, $A\mathbf{x}$ must be the projection of $\mathbf{b}$ onto $V = C(A)$.

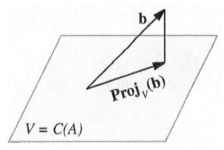

Thus we seek a solution $\mathbf{x}^*$ of $A\mathbf{x}^* = \mathbf{Proj}_V(\mathbf{b})$. The right hand side is in $C(A)$, so this system certainly has a solution. Now $\mathbf{x}^*$ is a solution if and only if

$$A\mathbf{x}^* - \mathbf{b} = \mathbf{Proj}_V(\mathbf{b}) - \mathbf{b}$$

is in $V^\perp = C(A)^\perp = N(A^T)$. Thus $\mathbf{x}^*$ is a solution if and only if $A^T(A\mathbf{x}^* - \mathbf{b}) = 0$. This equation simplifies conveniently to

$$A^T A\mathbf{x}^* = A^T \mathbf{b}$$

which is just A^T multiplied by the original system $A\mathbf{x} = \mathbf{b}$. A solution $\mathbf{x}^*$ of this system is called a **least-squares** solution of the system $A\mathbf{x} = \mathbf{b}$. Although this system always has a solution, we emphasize that solutions of this system are *not* solutions of the original system $A\mathbf{x} = \mathbf{b}$, which we assumed had no solutions. A least-squares solution minimizes the error $\|A\mathbf{x} - \mathbf{b}\|$. The term least-squares comes from the fact that the error (squared) is the sum of the squares of the error in each equation of the system.

Example 20.4. The system

$$\begin{aligned} 2x_1 - x_2 &= 2 \\ x_1 + 2x_2 &= 1 \\ x_1 + x_2 &= 4 \end{aligned}$$

has no solutions. (Check!) To find the least squares solution, notice that

$$A^T A = \begin{bmatrix} 6 & 1 \\ 1 & 6 \end{bmatrix} \quad \text{and} \quad A^T \mathbf{b} = \begin{bmatrix} 9 \\ 4 \end{bmatrix}$$

so the system $A^T A \mathbf{x}^* = A^T \mathbf{b}$ takes the form

$$\begin{aligned} 6x_1^* + x_2^* &= 9 \\ x_1^* + 6x_2^* &= 4. \end{aligned}$$

The solution of this system is

$$\mathbf{x}^* = \begin{bmatrix} 10/7 \\ 3/7 \end{bmatrix},$$

and the error is

$$\| A\mathbf{x}^* - \mathbf{b} \| = \left\| \begin{bmatrix} 3/7 \\ 9/7 \\ -15/7 \end{bmatrix} \right\| = 3\sqrt{35}/7.$$

$\diamond$

Example 20.5. To find the line $f(x) = ax + b$ which best fits the data $f(-1) = 0$, $f(0) = 1$, $f(1) = 2$, and $f(2) = 1$, we consider the resulting system

$$\begin{aligned} -a + b &= 0 \\ b &= 1 \\ a + b &= 2 \\ 2a + b &= 1. \end{aligned}$$

Since

$$A^T A = \begin{bmatrix} -1 & 0 & 1 & 2 \\ 1 & 1 & 1 & 1 \end{bmatrix} \begin{bmatrix} -1 & 1 \\ 0 & 1 \\ 1 & 1 \\ 2 & 1 \end{bmatrix} = \begin{bmatrix} 6 & 2 \\ 2 & 4 \end{bmatrix} \quad \text{and} \quad A^T \mathbf{b} = \begin{bmatrix} -1 & 0 & 1 & 2 \\ 1 & 1 & 1 & 1 \end{bmatrix} \begin{bmatrix} 0 \\ 1 \\ 2 \\ 1 \end{bmatrix} = \begin{bmatrix} 4 \\ 4 \end{bmatrix},$$

the system $A^T A \mathbf{x}^* = A^T \mathbf{b}$ is

$$\begin{aligned} 6x_1^* + 2x_2^* &= 4 \\ 2x_1^* + 4x_2^* &= 4. \end{aligned}$$

The solution is

$$\mathbf{x}^* = \begin{bmatrix} 2/5 \\ 4/5 \end{bmatrix},$$

and thus $f(x) = \frac{2}{5}x + \frac{4}{5}$ is the line which best fits the given data.

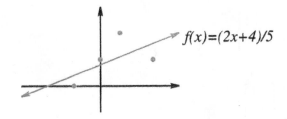

$f(x)=(2x+4)/5$

◇

Exercises

In Exercises 1 through 7, find the matrix for the orthogonal projection onto the subspace V.

20.1. $V = \text{span}\left(\begin{bmatrix} 2 \\ 1 \end{bmatrix}\right)$

20.2. V is the line $4x_1 + 2x_2 = 0$.

20.3. $V = \text{span}\left(\begin{bmatrix} 2 \\ 1 \\ -3 \end{bmatrix}\right)$

20.4. $V = \text{span}\left(\begin{bmatrix} 2 \\ 1 \\ -3 \end{bmatrix}, \begin{bmatrix} 4 \\ 0 \\ 2 \end{bmatrix}\right)$

20.5. V is the plane $-x_1 + 2x_2 + 3x_3 = 0$.

20.6. $V = \text{span}\left(\begin{bmatrix} 1 \\ 1 \\ 0 \end{bmatrix}, \begin{bmatrix} 3 \\ 1 \\ 2 \end{bmatrix}, \begin{bmatrix} -2 \\ 0 \\ 1 \end{bmatrix}\right)$

20.7. $V = \text{span}\left(\begin{bmatrix} -4 \\ 2 \\ 0 \\ 5 \end{bmatrix}\right)$

In Exercises 8 and 9, find the distance between the point in $\mathbf{R}^3$ and the plane in $\mathbf{R}^3$.

20.8. $(1, 0, 1)$ and $3x_1 - 2x_2 + x_3 = 0$.

20.9. $(1, 2, 3)$ and $x_1 - x_3 = 0$.

In Exercises 10 through 12, find the least squares solution of the system $A\mathbf{x} = \mathbf{b}$.

20.10. $A = \begin{bmatrix} 1 & 2 \\ -2 & 0 \\ 3 & 1 \end{bmatrix}$ $\mathbf{b} = \begin{bmatrix} 1 \\ 4 \\ 0 \end{bmatrix}$

20.11. $A = \begin{bmatrix} 4 & 1 \\ -2 & 5 \\ 1 & 3 \end{bmatrix}$ $\quad \mathbf{b} = \begin{bmatrix} 1 \\ 0 \\ 1 \end{bmatrix}$

20.12. $A = \begin{bmatrix} 1 & 2 \\ 0 & -1 \\ 3 & 1 \\ 2 & 4 \end{bmatrix}$ $\quad \mathbf{b} \begin{bmatrix} -1 \\ 0 \\ 1 \\ 0 \end{bmatrix}$

20.13. Consider the data points $(1,2), (2,4)$ and $(4,6)$.

    (a) Find the line $f(x) = ax + b$ which best fits the data points.

    (b) Sketch the data points and the linear approximation from part (a).

    (c) Find a quadratic polynomial $f(x) = ax^2 + bx + c$ which contains all three data points.

20.14. Consider the data points $(-2,1), (0,2)$ and $(2,4)$.

    (a) Find the line $f(x) = ax + b$ which best fits the data points.

    (b) Sketch the data points and the linear approximation from part (a).

    (c) Find a quadratic polynomial $f(x) = ax^2 + bx + c$ which contains all three data points.

20.15. Find a quadratic polynomial $f(x) = ax^2 + bx + c$ which best fits the data points $(-1,1)$, $(0,4)$, $(1,3)$ and $(2,5)$.

20.16. Let $P : \mathbf{R}^n \to \mathbf{R}^n$ be the matrix associated with orthogonal projection onto a subspace V of $\mathbf{R}^n$. Show that $P^2 = I_n$.

20.17. We say a matrix A is **symmetric** if $A = A^T$. Show that the matrix P associated with orthogonal projection onto a subspace V of $\mathbf{R}^n$ is a symmetric matrix.

20.18. Show that if A is invertible, then the least squares solution $\mathbf{x}^*$ of $A\mathbf{x} = \mathbf{b}$ is the same as the actual solution of $A\mathbf{x} = \mathbf{b}$.

In Exercises 19 through 22, find the solution of $A\mathbf{x} = \mathbf{b}$ which has the smallest magnitude. That is, find the unique solution in $C(A^T)$.

20.19. $A = \begin{bmatrix} 1 & 2 & 3 \\ 2 & -1 & 1 \end{bmatrix}$, $\quad \mathbf{b} = \begin{bmatrix} 6 \\ 2 \end{bmatrix}$

20.20. $A = \begin{bmatrix} 1 & 2 & 3 \\ 4 & 5 & 6 \\ 7 & 8 & 9 \end{bmatrix}$, $\quad \mathbf{b} = \begin{bmatrix} 1 \\ 4 \\ 7 \end{bmatrix}$

20.21. $A = \begin{bmatrix} 0 & 1 & 1 \\ 1 & 2 & 1 \\ 1 & 1 & 0 \end{bmatrix}$, $\quad \mathbf{b} = \begin{bmatrix} 2 \\ 3 \\ 1 \end{bmatrix}$

20.22. $A = \begin{bmatrix} 0 & 0 & 1 & 1 \\ 1 & 1 & 0 & 0 \\ 0 & 1 & 1 & 0 \end{bmatrix}$, $\quad \mathbf{b} = \begin{bmatrix} 5 \\ 1 \\ 3 \end{bmatrix}$

21 Systems of Coordinates

Each basis for a subspace V of $\mathbf{R}^n$ determines a different **coordinate system** on V. Suppose $\mathcal{B} = \{\mathbf{v}_1, \mathbf{v}_2, \ldots, \mathbf{v}_k\}$ is a basis for V, and recall that by Proposition 11.1 any vector $\mathbf{v}$ in V can be written uniquely as a linear combination

$$\mathbf{v} = c_1 \mathbf{v}_1 + c_2 \mathbf{v}_2 + \cdots + c_n \mathbf{v}_k$$

of the basis vectors. We call the coefficients $c_1, c_2, \ldots, c_k$ the **coordinates** of $\mathbf{v}$ with respect to the basis $\mathcal{B}$ and write

$$[\mathbf{v}]_{\mathcal{B}} = \begin{bmatrix} c_1 \\ c_2 \\ \vdots \\ c_k \end{bmatrix}.$$

Notice that there are k components to this vector, each corresponding to the coefficient of one of the basis vectors.

Example 21.1. Let

$$\mathbf{v}_1 = \begin{bmatrix} 1 \\ 2 \\ 3 \end{bmatrix} \qquad \text{and} \qquad \mathbf{v}_2 = \begin{bmatrix} 1 \\ 0 \\ 1 \end{bmatrix},$$

and define $V = \text{span}(\mathbf{v}_1, \mathbf{v}_2)$. Then $\mathcal{B} = \{\mathbf{v}_1, \mathbf{v}_2\}$ is a basis for V. The vector

$$\mathbf{v} = 2\mathbf{v}_1 - 3\mathbf{v}_2 = \begin{bmatrix} -1 \\ 4 \\ 3 \end{bmatrix}$$

is a linear combination of $\mathbf{v}_1$ and $\mathbf{v}_2$ and is therefore in V. Its coordinates with respect to $\mathcal{B}$ are

$$[\mathbf{v}]_{\mathcal{B}} = \begin{bmatrix} 2 \\ -3 \end{bmatrix}.$$

Notice that, although $\mathbf{v}$ is a vector in $\mathbf{R}^3$, it has two coordinates with respect to the basis $\mathcal{B}$ for the two-dimensional subspace V and is thus represented by a vector with two components. $\diamond$

Example 21.2. Let $\mathcal{S} = \{\mathbf{e}_1, \mathbf{e}_2, \ldots, \mathbf{e}_n\}$ be the standard basis for $\mathbf{R}^n$. Given any vector $\mathbf{x}$ in $\mathbf{R}^n$, we have

$$\mathbf{x} = \begin{bmatrix} x_1 \\ x_2 \\ \vdots \\ x_n \end{bmatrix} = x_1 \mathbf{e}_1 + x_2 \mathbf{e}_2 + \cdots + x_n \mathbf{e}_n$$

so the coordinates of $\mathbf{x}$ with respect to $\mathcal{S}$ are

$$[\mathbf{x}]_{\mathcal{S}} = \begin{bmatrix} x_1 \\ x_2 \\ \vdots \\ x_n \end{bmatrix}.$$

Thus our usual representation of a vector in $\mathbf{R}^n$ is in terms of its coordinates with respect to the standard basis. We call these coordinates the **standard coordinates**. ◇

Example 21.3. Let

$$\mathbf{v}_1 = \begin{bmatrix} 2 \\ 1 \end{bmatrix} \quad \text{and} \quad \mathbf{v}_2 = \begin{bmatrix} 1 \\ 2 \end{bmatrix}.$$

Then $\mathcal{B} = \{\mathbf{v}_1, \mathbf{v}_2\}$ is a basis for $\mathbf{R}^2$. Given a vector

$$\mathbf{x} = \begin{bmatrix} 4 \\ 5 \end{bmatrix}$$

its $\mathcal{B}$ coordinates are found by solving $\mathbf{x} = c_1 \mathbf{v}_1 + c_2 \mathbf{v}_2$. The solution is $c_1 = 1$ and $c_2 = 2$, so

$$[\mathbf{x}]_{\mathcal{B}} = \begin{bmatrix} 1 \\ 2 \end{bmatrix}.$$

On the other hand, suppose we are given the coordinates of a vector with respect to $\mathcal{B}$, say

$$[\mathbf{y}]_{\mathcal{B}} = \begin{bmatrix} -2 \\ 3 \end{bmatrix}.$$

Then, in standard coordinates

$$\mathbf{y} = -2\mathbf{v}_1 + 3\mathbf{v}_2 = \begin{bmatrix} -1 \\ 4 \end{bmatrix}.$$

◇

We can visualize coordinate systems by drawing the "graph paper" generated by the basis vectors.

Example 21.4. The graph paper generated by the standard basis $\mathcal{S} = \{\mathbf{e}_1, \mathbf{e}_2\}$ for $\mathbf{R}^2$ is shown below.

146

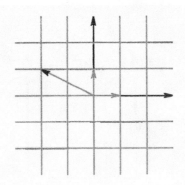

The vector shown,

$$\mathbf{x} = \begin{bmatrix} -2 \\ 1 \end{bmatrix}$$

is obtained by moving from the origin -2 units along the $\mathbf{e}_1$-axis and 1 unit along the $\mathbf{e}_2$-axis.
◇

Example 21.5. The graph paper generated by the basis $\mathcal{B}$ in Example 21.3 is shown below.

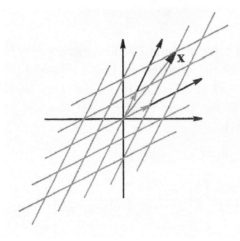

The vector shown is

$$\mathbf{x} = \begin{bmatrix} 4 \\ 5 \end{bmatrix}.$$

From Example 21.3, its $\mathcal{B}$ coordinates are

$$[\mathbf{x}]_\mathcal{B} = \begin{bmatrix} 1 \\ 2 \end{bmatrix}.$$

Geometrically $\mathbf{x}$ is obtained by moving from the origin 1 unit along the $\mathbf{v}_1$-axis and 2 units along the $\mathbf{v}_2$-axis.
◇

Change of Basis Matrix

To recover the standard coordinates of a vector from its $\mathcal{B}$ coordinates we use the matrix

$$C = \begin{bmatrix} | & | & & | \\ \mathbf{v}_1 & \mathbf{v}_2 & \cdots & \mathbf{v}_k \\ | & | & & | \end{bmatrix}$$

whose columns are the vectors in $\mathcal{B}$. Since

$$\mathbf{v} = c_1 \mathbf{v}_1 + c_2 \mathbf{v}_2 + \cdots + c_k \mathbf{v}_k = \begin{bmatrix} | & | & & | \\ \mathbf{v}_1 & \mathbf{v}_2 & \cdots & \mathbf{v}_k \\ | & | & & | \end{bmatrix} \begin{bmatrix} c_1 \\ c_2 \\ \vdots \\ c_k \end{bmatrix}$$

we have

$$\mathbf{v} = C[\mathbf{v}]_{\mathcal{B}}.$$

Thus the standard coordinates are obtained by multiplying the $\mathcal{B}$ coordinates by C, and we therefore refer to the matrix C as the **change of basis matrix** for the basis $\mathcal{B}$. On the other hand, to find the $\mathcal{B}$ coordinates of a vector $\mathbf{v}$ in V, we need to solve the system $C[\mathbf{v}]_{\mathcal{B}} = \mathbf{v}$ for $[\mathbf{v}]_{\mathcal{B}}$. Since the columns of C are basis vectors of V, we are guaranteed that this system has a unique solution for every $\mathbf{v}$ in V.

Example 21.6. Let V be the plane spanned by

$$\mathbf{v}_1 = \begin{bmatrix} 1 \\ 2 \\ 3 \end{bmatrix} \qquad \text{and} \qquad \mathbf{v}_2 = \begin{bmatrix} 1 \\ 0 \\ 1 \end{bmatrix},$$

and suppose that the coordinates of some vector $\mathbf{v}$ in V with respect to the basis $\mathcal{B} = \{\mathbf{v}_1, \mathbf{v}_2\}$ are

$$[\mathbf{v}]_{\mathcal{B}} = \begin{bmatrix} 7 \\ -4 \end{bmatrix}.$$

Then since the change of basis matrix is

$$C = \begin{bmatrix} 1 & 1 \\ 2 & 0 \\ 3 & 1 \end{bmatrix},$$

the standard coordinates of $\mathbf{v}$ are

$$\mathbf{v} = C[\mathbf{v}]_{\mathcal{B}} = \begin{bmatrix} 1 & 1 \\ 2 & 0 \\ 3 & 1 \end{bmatrix} \begin{bmatrix} 7 \\ -4 \end{bmatrix} = \begin{bmatrix} 3 \\ 14 \\ 17 \end{bmatrix}.$$

On the other hand, it can be seen by taking the cross product of the vectors $\mathbf{v}_1$ and $\mathbf{v}_2$ that the plane has equation $x + y - z = 0$. So, for example, the vector

$$\mathbf{w} = \begin{bmatrix} 8 \\ -6 \\ 2 \end{bmatrix}$$

is in V. What are its $\mathcal{B}$ coordinates? To find out, we must solve $C[\mathbf{w}]_{\mathcal{B}} = \mathbf{w}$ for the components c_1 and c_2 of $[\mathbf{w}]_{\mathcal{B}}$. That is, we must solve

$$\begin{bmatrix} 1 & 1 \\ 2 & 0 \\ 3 & 1 \end{bmatrix} \begin{bmatrix} c_1 \\ c_2 \end{bmatrix} = \begin{bmatrix} 8 \\ -6 \\ 2 \end{bmatrix}$$

for c_1 and c_2. The unique solution is $c_1 = -3$, $c_2 = 11$. Thus

$$[\mathbf{w}]_{\mathcal{B}} = \begin{bmatrix} -3 \\ 11 \end{bmatrix}$$

are the $\mathcal{B}$ coordinates of $\mathbf{w}$. $\diamond$

In the case $V = \mathbf{R}^n$, $\mathcal{B}$ is a basis for $\mathbf{R}^n$, and the matrix C is invertible, and we therefore have the relation

$$\boxed{[\mathbf{v}]_{\mathcal{B}} = C^{-1}\mathbf{v}}$$

so the $\mathcal{B}$ coordinates are obtained by multiplying the standard coordinates by C^{-1}.

Example 21.7. Consider once again the basis from Example 21.3. The change of basis matrix is

$$C = \begin{bmatrix} 2 & 1 \\ 1 & 2 \end{bmatrix}$$

so the $\mathcal{B}$ coordinates of

$$\mathbf{v} = \begin{bmatrix} 4 \\ 5 \end{bmatrix}$$

are

$$[\mathbf{v}]_{\mathcal{B}} = C^{-1}\mathbf{v} = \frac{1}{3} \begin{bmatrix} 2 & -1 \\ -1 & 2 \end{bmatrix} \begin{bmatrix} 4 \\ 5 \end{bmatrix} = \begin{bmatrix} 1 \\ 2 \end{bmatrix}$$

which agrees with our earlier calculation.

$\diamond$

Matrix of a Linear Transformation

One reason for studying bases other than the standard basis is to better understand linear transformations. Let $\mathbf{T} : \mathbf{R}^n \to \mathbf{R}^n$ be a linear transformation. Recall that the matrix A for $\mathbf{T}$ is the matrix such that

$$\mathbf{T}(\mathbf{v}) = A\mathbf{v}$$

for all $\mathbf{v}$ in $\mathbf{R}^n$. Now let $\mathcal{B} = \{\mathbf{v}_1, \ldots, \mathbf{v}_n\}$ be a basis for $\mathbf{R}^n$. We say that B is the matrix for $\mathbf{T}$ with respect to $\mathcal{B}$ if

$$[\mathbf{T}(\mathbf{v})]_\mathcal{B} = B[\mathbf{v}]_\mathcal{B}$$

for all $\mathbf{v}$ in $\mathbf{R}^n$. That is, B is the matrix which sends the $\mathcal{B}$-coordinates of $\mathbf{v}$ to the $\mathcal{B}$-coordinates of $\mathbf{T}(\mathbf{v})$. The matrix A is simply the matrix for $\mathbf{T}$ with respect to the standard basis. The relationship between A and B can be found in terms of the change of basis matrix C for $\mathcal{B}$. Using the definition above we have

$$B[\mathbf{v}]_\mathcal{B} = [\mathbf{T}(\mathbf{v})]_\mathcal{B} = C^{-1}\mathbf{T}(\mathbf{v}) = C^{-1}A\mathbf{v} = C^{-1}AC[\mathbf{v}]_\mathcal{B}.$$

Thus

$$B = C^{-1}AC.$$

This relationship is illustrated in the following diagram.

In the diagram, both rows represent the action of the linear transformation $\mathbf{T}$ on some vector $\mathbf{v}$ in $\mathbf{R}^n$. The top row states that this action is performed in standard coordinates by multiplying by the matrix A, while the bottom row states that it is performed in $\mathcal{B}$ coordinates by multiplying by the matrix B. So both A and B represent the same linear transformation $\mathbf{T}$, but in different systems of coordinates.

The relation $B = C^{-1}AC$ can be understood as two different ways of obtaining the $\mathcal{B}$-coordinates of $\mathbf{T}(\mathbf{v})$ from the $\mathcal{B}$-coordinates of $\mathbf{v}$. Beginning from $[\mathbf{v}]_\mathcal{B}$ in the lower left corner, to obtain $[\mathbf{T}(\mathbf{v})]_\mathcal{B}$ we can either multiply by B, or multiply first by C, then by A and then by C^{-1}, i.e. multiply by $C^{-1}AC$. The latter method corresponds to first changing to standard coordinates, computing $\mathbf{T}(\mathbf{v})$ in standard coordinates, and then changing back to $\mathcal{B}$ coordinates.

The equation $B = C^{-1}AC$ may be solved for A by multiplying on the left by C and on the right by C^{-1}. This results in

$$\boxed{A = CBC^{-1}.}$$

The purpose of considering coordinate systems other than the standard coordinates is that for an appropriately chosen basis $\mathcal{B}$, the matrix for a transformation with respect to $\mathcal{B}$ is very simple, and thus provides greater insight into the nature of the transformation.

Example 21.8. Let $\mathbf{T} : \mathbf{R}^2 \to \mathbf{R}^2$ be the transformation with matrix

$$A = \begin{bmatrix} 3 & -2 \\ 2 & -2 \end{bmatrix}$$

with respect to the standard basis and let

$$\mathcal{B} = \left\{ \begin{bmatrix} 2 \\ 1 \end{bmatrix}, \begin{bmatrix} 1 \\ 2 \end{bmatrix} \right\}.$$

The matrix for $\mathbf{T}$ with respect to $\mathcal{B}$ is

$$B = C^{-1}AC = \frac{1}{3} \begin{bmatrix} 2 & -1 \\ -1 & 2 \end{bmatrix} \begin{bmatrix} 3 & -2 \\ 2 & -2 \end{bmatrix} \begin{bmatrix} 2 & 1 \\ 1 & 2 \end{bmatrix} = \begin{bmatrix} 2 & 0 \\ 0 & -1 \end{bmatrix}.$$

So in $\mathcal{B}$-coordinates, $\mathbf{T}$ is represented by a diagonal matrix. It scales the first coordinate by 2 and the second by -1. For instance, if

$$[\mathbf{x}]_{\mathcal{B}} = \begin{bmatrix} 1 \\ -2 \end{bmatrix}$$

then

$$[\mathbf{T}(\mathbf{x})]_{\mathcal{B}} = \begin{bmatrix} 2 \\ 2 \end{bmatrix}.$$

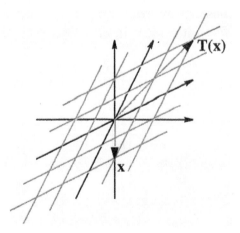

Figure 21.1.

In standard coordinates

$$\mathbf{x} = 1 \begin{bmatrix} 2 \\ 1 \end{bmatrix} - 2 \begin{bmatrix} 1 \\ 2 \end{bmatrix} = \begin{bmatrix} 0 \\ -3 \end{bmatrix}$$

and

$$\mathbf{T}(\mathbf{x}) = 2 \begin{bmatrix} 2 \\ 1 \end{bmatrix} + 2 \begin{bmatrix} 1 \\ 2 \end{bmatrix} = \begin{bmatrix} 6 \\ 6 \end{bmatrix}.$$

It is of course faster to just multiply by A. But suppose we wanted to apply the transformation $\mathbf{T}$ ten times. This would involve multiplying by A ten times, or equivalently, multiplying by A^{10}. Unfortunately computing A^{10} directly is rather tedious. Instead, let's use the relation $A = CBC^{-1}$.

$$A^2 = CBC^{-1}CBC^{-1} = CB^2C^{-1}$$
$$A^3 = A^2A = CB^2C^{-1}CBC^{-1} = CB^3C^{-1}$$
$$\vdots$$
$$A^{10} = CB^{10}C^{-1}$$

The point is that powers of B are very easy to compute.

$$B^2 = \begin{bmatrix} 4 & 0 \\ 0 & 1 \end{bmatrix} \qquad B^3 = \begin{bmatrix} 8 & 0 \\ 0 & -1 \end{bmatrix} \qquad \cdots \qquad B^{10} = \begin{bmatrix} 2^{10} & 0 \\ 0 & (-1)^{10} \end{bmatrix}$$

Thus

$$A^{10} = \begin{bmatrix} 2 & 1 \\ 1 & 2 \end{bmatrix} \begin{bmatrix} 1024 & 0 \\ 0 & 1 \end{bmatrix} \frac{1}{3} \begin{bmatrix} 2 & -1 \\ -1 & 2 \end{bmatrix} = \frac{1}{3} \begin{bmatrix} 2 & 1 \\ 1 & 2 \end{bmatrix} \begin{bmatrix} 2048 & -1024 \\ -1 & 2 \end{bmatrix} = \begin{bmatrix} 1365 & -682 \\ 682 & -340 \end{bmatrix}.$$

$\diamond$

Now suppose that we do not know the matrix for a linear transformation $\mathbf{T}$. We can find its matrix B with respect to a basis $\mathcal{B}$ by evaluating $\mathbf{T}$ on the basis vectors $\{\mathbf{v}_1, \mathbf{v}_2, \ldots, \mathbf{v}_n\}$ in $\mathcal{B}$. By definition $[\mathbf{T}(\mathbf{v})]_{\mathcal{B}} = B[\mathbf{v}]_{\mathcal{B}}$ for all $\mathbf{v}$ in $\mathbf{R}^n$. Observe that

$$\mathbf{v}_1 = 1\mathbf{v}_1 + 0\mathbf{v}_2 + \cdots + 0\mathbf{v}_n$$

so

$$[\mathbf{v}_1]_{\mathcal{B}} = \begin{bmatrix} 1 \\ 0 \\ \vdots \\ 0 \end{bmatrix} = \mathbf{e}_1,$$

and likewise $[\mathbf{v}_j]_{\mathcal{B}} = \mathbf{e}_j$ for each j. Thus

$$[\mathbf{T}(\mathbf{v}_j)]_{\mathcal{B}} = B\mathbf{e}_j$$

is the jth column of B. So

$$B = \begin{bmatrix} \Big| & \Big| & & \Big| \\ [\mathbf{T}(\mathbf{v}_1)]_{\mathcal{B}} & [\mathbf{T}(\mathbf{v}_2)]_{\mathcal{B}} & \cdots & [\mathbf{T}(\mathbf{v}_n)]_{\mathcal{B}} \\ \Big| & \Big| & & \Big| \end{bmatrix}$$

is the matrix for $\mathbf{T}$ with respect to $\mathcal{B}$. Knowing the matrix B then allows us to find the matrix for $\mathbf{T}$ in standard coordinates via the relation $A = CBC^{-1}$.

Example 21.9. Let $\mathbf{T}$ be the linear transformation defined by reflection across the line $y = 3x$ in $\mathbf{R}^2$. A nice way to express this transformation is in terms of the vector

$$\mathbf{v}_1 = \begin{bmatrix} 1 \\ 3 \end{bmatrix}$$

which spans the line $y = 3x$ and the vector

$$\mathbf{v}_2 = \begin{bmatrix} -3 \\ 1 \end{bmatrix}$$

which is perpendicular to the line. It is clear geometrically that $\mathbf{T}(\mathbf{v}_1) = \mathbf{v}_1$ and $\mathbf{T}(\mathbf{v}_2) = -\mathbf{v}_2$.

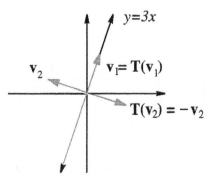

In terms of the basis $\mathcal{B} = \{\mathbf{v}_1, \mathbf{v}_2\}$

$$\begin{aligned} \mathbf{T}(\mathbf{v}_1) &= 1\mathbf{v}_1 + 0\mathbf{v}_2 \\ \mathbf{T}(\mathbf{v}_2) &= 0\mathbf{v}_1 + (-1)\mathbf{v}_2, \end{aligned}$$

and therefore

$$[\mathbf{T}(\mathbf{v}_1)]_{\mathcal{B}} = \begin{bmatrix} 1 \\ 0 \end{bmatrix} \quad \text{and} \quad [\mathbf{T}(\mathbf{v}_2)]_{\mathcal{B}} = \begin{bmatrix} 0 \\ -1 \end{bmatrix}.$$

So the matrix for $\mathbf{T}$ with respect to $\mathcal{B}$ is

$$B = \begin{bmatrix} 1 & 0 \\ 0 & -1 \end{bmatrix}.$$

In standard coordinates, the matrix for $\mathbf{T}$ is

$$A = CBC^{-1} = \begin{bmatrix} 1 & -3 \\ 3 & 1 \end{bmatrix} \begin{bmatrix} 1 & 0 \\ 0 & -1 \end{bmatrix} \frac{1}{10} \begin{bmatrix} 1 & 3 \\ -3 & 1 \end{bmatrix} = \begin{bmatrix} -\frac{4}{5} & \frac{3}{5} \\ \frac{3}{5} & \frac{4}{5} \end{bmatrix}.$$

$\diamond$

Example 21.10. Let V be the plane $x_1 + 2x_2 + 5x_3 = 0$ in $\mathbf{R}^3$. Find the matrix for $\mathbf{Proj}_V$, the orthogonal projection onto V.

Solution. Let

$$\mathbf{v}_1 = \begin{bmatrix} -2 \\ 1 \\ 0 \end{bmatrix}, \qquad \mathbf{v}_2 = \begin{bmatrix} -5 \\ 0 \\ 1 \end{bmatrix} \qquad \text{and} \qquad \mathbf{v}_3 = \begin{bmatrix} 1 \\ 2 \\ 5 \end{bmatrix}.$$

Then $\{\mathbf{v}_1, \mathbf{v}_2\}$ is a basis for V and $\{\mathbf{v}_3\}$ is a basis for $V^\perp$, so $\mathcal{B} = \{\mathbf{v}_1, \mathbf{v}_2, \mathbf{v}_3\}$ is a basis for $\mathbf{R}^3$. Since

$$\mathbf{Proj}_V(\mathbf{v}_1) = \mathbf{v}_1 = 1\mathbf{v}_1 + 0\mathbf{v}_2 + 0\mathbf{v}_3$$
$$\mathbf{Proj}_V(\mathbf{v}_2) = \mathbf{v}_2 = 0\mathbf{v}_1 + 1\mathbf{v}_2 + 0\mathbf{v}_3$$
$$\mathbf{Proj}_V(\mathbf{v}_3) = \mathbf{0} = 0\mathbf{v}_1 + 0\mathbf{v}_2 + 0\mathbf{v}_3$$

the matrix for $\mathbf{Proj}_V$ with respect to $\mathcal{B}$ is

$$B = \begin{bmatrix} 1 & 0 & 0 \\ 0 & 1 & 0 \\ 0 & 0 & 0 \end{bmatrix}.$$

The change of basis matrix and its inverse are

$$C = \begin{bmatrix} -2 & -5 & 1 \\ 1 & 0 & 2 \\ 0 & 1 & 5 \end{bmatrix} \qquad \text{and} \qquad C^{-1} = \frac{1}{30} \begin{bmatrix} -2 & 26 & -10 \\ -5 & -10 & 5 \\ 1 & 2 & 5 \end{bmatrix}$$

so the matrix for $\mathbf{Proj}_V$ in standard coordinates is

$$A = CBC^{-1} = \frac{1}{30} \begin{bmatrix} 29 & -2 & -5 \\ -2 & 26 & -10 \\ -5 & -10 & 5 \end{bmatrix}.$$

$\diamond$

Similar Matrices

Motivated by the preceding discussion, we make the following definition. Let A and B be $n \times n$ matrices. We say A is **similar** to B if

$$\boxed{A = CBC^{-1}}$$

for some matrix C. As mentioned earlier, this relation means that A and B represent the same linear transformation, but in different coordinates. Similar matrices have the following properties, which we leave as exercises.

Proposition 21.1.

1. Any $n \times n$ matrix A is similar to itself.

2. If A is similar to B then B is similar to A.

3. If A is similar to B and B is similar to C, then A is similar to C.

4. If A is similar to B then $\det(A) = \det(B)$.

5. If A is similar to B and A is invertible, then B is invertible and A^{-1} is similar to B^{-1}.

6. If A is similar to B, then A^k is similar to B^k for any positive integer k.

Linear Transformations on Subspaces

Given a subspace V of $\mathbf{R}^n$, we say that a function $\mathbf{T} : V \to V$ is a linear transformation on V if

1. $\mathbf{T}(\mathbf{x} + \mathbf{y}) = \mathbf{T}(\mathbf{x}) + \mathbf{T}(\mathbf{y})$

2. $\mathbf{T}(c\mathbf{x}) = c\mathbf{T}(\mathbf{x})$

for all $\mathbf{x}$ and $\mathbf{y}$ in V and all scalars c in $\mathbf{R}$. Note that the transformation need not be defined on all of $\mathbf{R}^n$. In the same way as we did above, we define the matrix for $\mathbf{T}$ with respect to a basis $\mathcal{B} = \{\mathbf{v}_1, \dots, \mathbf{v}_k\}$ of V to be the matrix B such that

$$[\mathbf{T}(\mathbf{v})]_{\mathcal{B}} = B[\mathbf{v}]_{\mathcal{B}}$$

for all $\mathbf{v}$ in V. By the same reasoning as above, it follows that

$$B = \begin{bmatrix} \big[\mathbf{T}(\mathbf{v}_1)\big]_{\mathcal{B}} & \big[\mathbf{T}(\mathbf{v}_2)\big]_{\mathcal{B}} & \cdots & \big[\mathbf{T}(\mathbf{v}_k)\big]_{\mathcal{B}} \end{bmatrix}.$$

Notice that B is a $k \times k$ matrix.

Example 21.11. Let

$$\mathbf{v}_1 = \begin{bmatrix} 2 \\ 1 \\ 2 \end{bmatrix} \quad \text{and} \quad \mathbf{v}_2 = \begin{bmatrix} -2 \\ 2 \\ 1 \end{bmatrix}$$

and let $V = \mathrm{span}(\mathbf{v}_1, \mathbf{v}_2)$. Define $\mathbf{T} : V \to V$ to be the transformation which reflects vectors in V across the line spanned by $\mathbf{v}_1$. Then $\mathbf{T}(\mathbf{v}_1) = \mathbf{v}_1$, and since $\mathbf{v}_2$ is orthogonal to $\mathbf{v}_1$, $\mathbf{T}(\mathbf{v}_2) = -\mathbf{v}_2$. So in terms of the basis $\mathcal{B} = \{\mathbf{v}_1, \mathbf{v}_2\}$,

$$[\mathbf{T}(\mathbf{v}_1)]_{\mathcal{B}} = \begin{bmatrix} 1 \\ 0 \end{bmatrix} \quad \text{and} \quad [\mathbf{T}(\mathbf{v}_2)]_{\mathcal{B}} = \begin{bmatrix} 0 \\ -1 \end{bmatrix}$$

and thus the matrix for $\mathbf{T}$ with respect to $\mathcal{B}$ is

$$B = \begin{bmatrix} 1 & 0 \\ 0 & -1 \end{bmatrix}.$$

$\diamond$

Exercises

21.1. Let

$$\mathcal{B} = \left\{ \begin{bmatrix} 3 \\ 1 \end{bmatrix}, \begin{bmatrix} 1 \\ 2 \end{bmatrix} \right\}$$

(a) Write each vector $\mathbf{v}$ in standard coordinates.

i. $[\mathbf{v}]_{\mathcal{B}} = \begin{bmatrix} 2 \\ -1 \end{bmatrix}$

ii. $[\mathbf{v}]_{\mathcal{B}} = \begin{bmatrix} 1 \\ 2 \end{bmatrix}$

(b) Find $[\mathbf{v}]_{\mathcal{B}}$ for each vector $\mathbf{v}$.

i. $\mathbf{v} = \begin{bmatrix} 2 \\ -1 \end{bmatrix}$

ii. $\mathbf{v} = \begin{bmatrix} 9 \\ 8 \end{bmatrix}$

21.2. Let

$$\mathcal{B} = \left\{ \begin{bmatrix} -4 \\ 1 \end{bmatrix}, \begin{bmatrix} 3 \\ 5 \end{bmatrix} \right\}$$

(a) Write the following vectors in standard coordinates.

i. $[\mathbf{v}]_{\mathcal{B}} = \begin{bmatrix} 2 \\ 4 \end{bmatrix}$

ii. $[\mathbf{v}]_{\mathcal{B}} = \begin{bmatrix} 1 \\ 3 \end{bmatrix}$

(b) Write the following vectors in $\mathcal{B}$ coordinates.

i. $\mathbf{v} = \begin{bmatrix} 2 \\ 4 \end{bmatrix}$

ii. $\mathbf{v} = \begin{bmatrix} 1 \\ 3 \end{bmatrix}$

21.3. Let

$$\mathcal{B} = \left\{ \begin{bmatrix} 1 \\ 0 \\ -1 \end{bmatrix}, \begin{bmatrix} 0 \\ 1 \\ 1 \end{bmatrix}, \begin{bmatrix} 1 \\ 1 \\ -1 \end{bmatrix} \right\}$$

(a) Write each vector $\mathbf{v}$ in standard coordinates.

    i. $[\mathbf{v}]_{\mathcal{B}} = \begin{bmatrix} 0 \\ 1 \\ 1 \end{bmatrix}$

    ii. $[\mathbf{v}]_{\mathcal{B}} = \begin{bmatrix} 2 \\ 3 \\ -1 \end{bmatrix}$

(b) Find $[\mathbf{v}]_{\mathcal{B}}$ for each vector $\mathbf{v}$.

    i. $\mathbf{v} = \begin{bmatrix} 0 \\ 1 \\ 1 \end{bmatrix}$

    ii. $\mathbf{v} = \begin{bmatrix} 2 \\ 2 \\ -1 \end{bmatrix}$

21.4. Let

$$\mathcal{B} = \left\{ \begin{bmatrix} 1 \\ 0 \\ -1 \end{bmatrix}, \begin{bmatrix} 0 \\ 1 \\ 1 \end{bmatrix} \right\}$$

(a) Write each vector $\mathbf{v}$ in standard coordinates.

    i. $[\mathbf{v}]_{\mathcal{B}} = \begin{bmatrix} 3 \\ 5 \end{bmatrix}$

    ii. $[\mathbf{v}]_{\mathcal{B}} = \begin{bmatrix} -4 \\ 2 \end{bmatrix}$

(b) Find $[\mathbf{v}]_{\mathcal{B}}$ for each vector $\mathbf{v}$.

    i. $\mathbf{v} = \begin{bmatrix} 2 \\ -4 \\ -6 \end{bmatrix}$

    ii. $\mathbf{v} = \begin{bmatrix} 1 \\ 5 \\ 4 \end{bmatrix}$

21.5. Let

$$\mathcal{B} = \left\{ \begin{bmatrix} 2 \\ 1 \\ 0 \end{bmatrix}, \begin{bmatrix} 1 \\ 0 \\ 3 \end{bmatrix}, \begin{bmatrix} -1 \\ 2 \\ 3 \end{bmatrix} \right\}$$

(a) Write each vector $\mathbf{v}$ in standard coordinates.

i. $[\mathbf{v}]_{\mathcal{B}} = \begin{bmatrix} 4 \\ 3 \\ 1 \end{bmatrix}$

ii. $[\mathbf{v}]_{\mathcal{B}} = \begin{bmatrix} 1 \\ 2 \\ 5 \end{bmatrix}$

(b) Find $[\mathbf{v}]_{\mathcal{B}}$ for each vector $\mathbf{v}$.

i. $\mathbf{v} = \begin{bmatrix} 0 \\ 3 \\ 4 \end{bmatrix}$

ii. $\mathbf{v} = \begin{bmatrix} 1 \\ -2 \\ 3 \end{bmatrix}$

21.6. Let

$$\mathcal{B} = \left\{ \begin{bmatrix} 3 \\ 1 \\ -4 \\ 2 \end{bmatrix}, \begin{bmatrix} -2 \\ 5 \\ 1 \\ 1 \end{bmatrix} \right\}.$$

(a) Write each vector $\mathbf{v}$ in standard coordinates.

i. $[\mathbf{v}]_{\mathcal{B}} = \begin{bmatrix} 2 \\ -1 \end{bmatrix}$

ii. $[\mathbf{v}]_{\mathcal{B}} = \begin{bmatrix} 1 \\ 2 \end{bmatrix}$

(b) Find $[\mathbf{v}]_{\mathcal{B}}$ for each vector $\mathbf{v}$.

i. $\mathbf{v} = \begin{bmatrix} 8 \\ -3 \\ -9 \\ 3 \end{bmatrix}$

ii. $\mathbf{v} = \begin{bmatrix} -12 \\ 13 \\ 11 \\ -1 \end{bmatrix}$

21.7. Let

$$\mathcal{B} = \left\{ \begin{bmatrix} 1 \\ 0 \\ 2 \\ -1 \end{bmatrix}, \begin{bmatrix} 0 \\ 2 \\ 1 \\ 1 \end{bmatrix}, \begin{bmatrix} 2 \\ 1 \\ -1 \\ 0 \end{bmatrix} \right\}.$$

(a) Write each vector $\mathbf{v}$ in standard coordinates.

    i. $[\mathbf{v}]_{\mathcal{B}} = \begin{bmatrix} 3 \\ -1 \\ 0 \end{bmatrix}$

    ii. $[\mathbf{v}]_{\mathcal{B}} = \begin{bmatrix} 4 \\ -2 \\ 1 \end{bmatrix}$

(b) Find $[\mathbf{v}]_{\mathcal{B}}$ for each vector $\mathbf{v}$.

    i. $\mathbf{v} = \begin{bmatrix} -4 \\ 5 \\ 0 \\ 5 \end{bmatrix}$

    ii. $\mathbf{v} = \begin{bmatrix} 8 \\ -5 \\ -3 \\ -6 \end{bmatrix}$

21.8. Let $\mathcal{B}$ be the basis $\{\mathbf{v}_1, \mathbf{v}_2, \mathbf{v}_3\}$ of $\mathbf{R}^3$ where

$$\mathbf{v}_1 = \begin{bmatrix} 1 \\ 1 \\ 1 \end{bmatrix} \qquad \mathbf{v}_2 = \begin{bmatrix} 2 \\ 3 \\ 0 \end{bmatrix} \qquad \mathbf{v}_3 = \begin{bmatrix} -1 \\ 2 \\ -6 \end{bmatrix}.$$

(a) Let $\mathbf{T} : \mathbf{R}^3 \to \mathbf{R}^3$ be the linear transformation which satisfies

$$\mathbf{T}(\mathbf{v}_1) = \mathbf{v}_2 \qquad \mathbf{T}(\mathbf{v}_2) = \mathbf{v}_3 \qquad \mathbf{T}(\mathbf{v}_3) = \mathbf{v}_1.$$

Write down the matrix B for $\mathbf{T}$ with respect to the basis $\mathcal{B}$ and use this to find the matrix A for $\mathbf{T}$ with respect to the standard basis.

(b) Compute B^3 and use this to calculate A^3.

(c) Use the result in part (b) to find A^{2000}.

21.9. Let $\mathcal{B}$ be the basis $\{\mathbf{v}_1, \mathbf{v}_2, \mathbf{v}_3\}$ of $\mathbf{R}^3$ where

$$\mathbf{v}_1 = \begin{bmatrix} 2 \\ 1 \\ 0 \end{bmatrix} \qquad \mathbf{v}_2 = \begin{bmatrix} 0 \\ 4 \\ 1 \end{bmatrix} \qquad \mathbf{v}_3 = \begin{bmatrix} -3 \\ 0 \\ 2 \end{bmatrix}.$$

159

Let $\mathbf{T} : \mathbf{R}^3 \to \mathbf{R}^3$ be the linear transformation which satisfies

$$\mathbf{T}(\mathbf{v}_1) = 2\mathbf{v}_1 - 3\mathbf{v}_2 \qquad \mathbf{T}(\mathbf{v}_2) = \mathbf{v}_1 + 2\mathbf{v}_2 - 4\mathbf{v}_3 \qquad \mathbf{T}(\mathbf{v}_3) = -\mathbf{v}_1 + 5\mathbf{v}_3.$$

Write down the matrix B for $\mathbf{T}$ with respect to the basis $\mathcal{B}$ and use this to find the matrix A for $\mathbf{T}$ with respect to the standard basis in $\mathbf{R}^3$.

21.10. Let $\mathbf{Proj}_L : \mathbf{R}^2 \to \mathbf{R}^2$ be projection onto the line L spanned by $\mathbf{v} = \begin{bmatrix} 2 \\ 3 \end{bmatrix}$. Let

$$\mathcal{B} = \left\{ \begin{bmatrix} 2 \\ 3 \end{bmatrix}, \begin{bmatrix} -3 \\ 2 \end{bmatrix} \right\}.$$

Find the matrix B for $\mathbf{Proj}_L$ with respect to $\mathcal{B}$. Use this to find the matrix A for $\mathbf{Proj}_L$ with respect to the standard basis in $\mathbf{R}^2$.

21.11. Let $\mathbf{Ref}_L : \mathbf{R}^2 \to \mathbf{R}^2$ be reflection across the line L spanned by $\mathbf{v} = \begin{bmatrix} 1 \\ -2 \end{bmatrix}$. Let

$$\mathcal{B} = \left\{ \begin{bmatrix} 1 \\ -2 \end{bmatrix}, \begin{bmatrix} 2 \\ 1 \end{bmatrix} \right\}.$$

Find the matrix B for $\mathbf{Ref}_L$ with respect to $\mathcal{B}$. Use this to find the matrix A for $\mathbf{Ref}_L$ with respect to the standard basis in $\mathbf{R}^2$.

21.12. Let L be the line in $\mathbf{R}^3$ spanned by

$$\mathbf{v}_1 = \begin{bmatrix} 1 \\ 1 \\ 1 \end{bmatrix}$$

(a) Find a basis $\{\mathbf{v}_2, \mathbf{v}_3\}$ for the plane perpendicular to L, and verify that $\mathcal{B} = \{\mathbf{v}_1, \mathbf{v}_2, \mathbf{v}_3\}$ is a basis for $\mathbf{R}^3$.

(b) Let $\mathbf{Proj}_L$ denote the projection onto the line L. Find the matrix B for $\mathbf{Proj}_L$ with respect to the basis $\mathcal{B}$.

(c) Use your answer to part (b) to find the matrix A for $\mathbf{Proj}_L$ with respect to the standard basis for $\mathbf{R}^3$.

21.13. Let $\mathbf{v}_1, \mathbf{v}_2$ be two linearly independent vectors in $\mathbf{R}^3$. Let $\mathbf{Proj}_P : \mathbf{R}^3 \to \mathbf{R}^3$ be projection onto the plane P spanned by $\{\mathbf{v}_1, \mathbf{v}_2\}$. Let $\mathbf{v}_3$ be a normal vector to this plane. Let

$$\mathcal{B} = \{\mathbf{v}_1, \mathbf{v}_2, \mathbf{v}_3\}.$$

(a) Find the matrix B for $\mathbf{Proj}_P$ with respect to $\mathcal{B}$.

(b) Let

$$\mathbf{v}_1 = \begin{bmatrix} 1 \\ 0 \\ 2 \end{bmatrix} \qquad \mathbf{v}_2 = \begin{bmatrix} -2 \\ 1 \\ 0 \end{bmatrix} \qquad \mathbf{v}_3 = \begin{bmatrix} 2 \\ 4 \\ -1 \end{bmatrix}.$$

Use your answer to part (a) to find the matrix A for $\mathbf{Proj}_P$ with respect to the standard basis for $\mathbf{R}^3$.

21.14. Let $\mathbf{v}_1, \mathbf{v}_2$ be two linearly independent vectors in $\mathbf{R}^3$. Let $\mathbf{Ref}_P : \mathbf{R}^3 \to \mathbf{R}^3$ be reflection across the plane P spanned by $\{\mathbf{v}_1, \mathbf{v}_2\}$. Let $\mathbf{v}_3$ be a normal vector to this plane. Let

$$\mathcal{B} = \{\mathbf{v}_1, \mathbf{v}_2, \mathbf{v}_3\}.$$

(a) Find the matrix B for $\mathbf{Ref}_P$ with respect to $\mathcal{B}$.

(b) Let

$$\mathbf{v}_1 = \begin{bmatrix} -1 \\ 1 \\ 0 \end{bmatrix} \qquad \mathbf{v}_2 = \begin{bmatrix} 1 \\ 0 \\ 2 \end{bmatrix} \qquad \mathbf{v}_3 = \begin{bmatrix} 2 \\ 2 \\ -1 \end{bmatrix}.$$

Use your answer to part (a) to find the matrix A for $\mathbf{Ref}_P$ with respect to the standard basis for $\mathbf{R}^3$.

21.15. Let $\mathbf{v}_1 = \begin{bmatrix} 1 \\ 3 \\ 2 \end{bmatrix}$. Let L be the line in $\mathbf{R}^3$ spanned by $\mathbf{v}_1$. Let P be the plane in $\mathbf{R}^3$ which satisfies $4x_1 - 2x_2 + x_3 = 0$. Let $\mathbf{T} : P \to P$ be the linear transformation which projects vectors in P onto L.

(a) Find a vector $\mathbf{v}_2$ in P orthogonal to $\mathbf{v}_1$.

(b) Let $\mathcal{B} = \{\mathbf{v}_1, \mathbf{v}_2\}$. Find the matrix for $\mathbf{T}$ with respect to $\mathcal{B}$.

21.16. Prove Proposition 21.1,

(a) Part 1.

(b) Part 2.

(c) Part 3.

(d) Part 4.

(e) Part 5.

(f) Part 6.

21.17. *True/False*

(a) If A is similar to B, then A^T is similar to B^T.

(b) If A is similar to B and C is similar to D, then AC is similar to BD.

(c) Let $\mathbf{T} : \mathbf{R}^n \to \mathbf{R}^n$ be a linear transformation. If B_1 is the matrix for $\mathbf{T}$ with respect to a basis $\mathcal{B}_1$ and B_2 is the matrix for $\mathbf{T}$ with respect to a basis $\mathcal{B}_2$, then B_1 is similar to B_2.

22   Orthonormal Bases

A set $\{\mathbf{v}_1, \dots, \mathbf{v}_k\}$ consisting of mutually orthogonal unit vectors is called an **orthonormal** set. In terms of dot products, we have

$$\mathbf{v}_i \cdot \mathbf{v}_j = \begin{cases} 0 & i \neq j \\ 1 & i = j \end{cases}$$

for $1 \leq i \leq k$ and $1 \leq j \leq k$. A basis for a subspace V of $\mathbf{R}^n$ consisting of mutually orthogonal unit vectors is called an **orthonormal basis** for V.

Example 22.1. The standard basis $\{\mathbf{e}_1, \dots, \mathbf{e}_n\}$ is an orthonormal basis for $\mathbf{R}^n$. $\diamond$

Example 22.2. Let

$$\mathbf{v}_1 = \begin{bmatrix} 1/3 \\ 2/3 \\ 2/3 \end{bmatrix} \qquad \text{and} \qquad \mathbf{v}_2 = \begin{bmatrix} 2/3 \\ 1/3 \\ -2/3 \end{bmatrix}.$$

Since $\mathbf{v}_1 \cdot \mathbf{v}_2 = 0$ and $\mathbf{v}_1 \cdot \mathbf{v}_1 = \mathbf{v}_2 \cdot \mathbf{v}_2 = 1$, the set $\{\mathbf{v}_1, \mathbf{v}_2\}$ is an orthonormal set. It is an orthonormal basis for the plane V that it spans. $\diamond$

We next illustrate some of the advantages of orthonormal bases. The first is that it is very easy to determine the coordinates of any given vector with respect to an orthonormal basis. To see this, suppose $\{\mathbf{v}_1, \dots, \mathbf{v}_k\}$ is an orthonormal basis for V and let $\mathbf{v}$ be any vector in V. Then

$$\mathbf{v} = c_1 \mathbf{v}_1 + c_2 \mathbf{v}_2 + \cdots + c_k \mathbf{v}_k$$

for some coefficients c_1 through c_k. Taking the dot product of both sides with one of the basis vectors $\mathbf{v}_i$ yields

$$\mathbf{v} \cdot \mathbf{v}_i = c_1 \mathbf{v}_1 \cdot \mathbf{v}_i + c_2 \mathbf{v}_2 \cdot \mathbf{v}_i + \cdots + c_k \mathbf{v}_k \cdot \mathbf{v}_i.$$

All of the dot products on the right hand side vanish, except $\mathbf{v}_i \cdot \mathbf{v}_i$ which equals 1, so the right hand side simplifies to just c_i. Thus $c_i = \mathbf{v} \cdot \mathbf{v}_i$, so the coefficient of $\mathbf{v}_i$ is simply the dot product of $\mathbf{v}$ with $\mathbf{v}_i$. This proves the following result.

Proposition 22.1. Let $\{\mathbf{v}_1, \dots, \mathbf{v}_k\}$ be an orthonormal basis for V. Then

$$\mathbf{v} = (\mathbf{v} \cdot \mathbf{v}_1)\mathbf{v}_1 + (\mathbf{v} \cdot \mathbf{v}_2)\mathbf{v}_2 + \cdots + (\mathbf{v} \cdot \mathbf{v}_k)\mathbf{v}_k$$

for all $\mathbf{v}$ in V.

Example 22.3. Let

$$\mathbf{v}_1 = \begin{bmatrix} 3/5 \\ 4/5 \end{bmatrix} \quad \text{and} \quad \mathbf{v}_2 = \begin{bmatrix} -4/5 \\ 3/5 \end{bmatrix}.$$

Then $\mathcal{B} = \{\mathbf{v}_1, \mathbf{v}_2\}$ is an orthonormal basis for $\mathbf{R}^2$. Let

$$\mathbf{v} = \begin{bmatrix} 7 \\ -4 \end{bmatrix}.$$

Since $\mathbf{v} \cdot \mathbf{v}_1 = 1$ and $\mathbf{v} \cdot \mathbf{v}_2 = -8$, we have $\mathbf{v} = \mathbf{v}_1 - 8\mathbf{v}_2$, so the $\mathcal{B}$ coordinates of $\mathbf{v}$ are

$$[\mathbf{v}]_{\mathcal{B}} = \begin{bmatrix} 1 \\ -8 \end{bmatrix}.$$

$\diamond$

Another benefit of having an orthonormal basis for V is that the formula for the orthogonal projection onto V is simplified. Recall once again that any vector $\mathbf{x}$ can be expressed uniquely as $\mathbf{v} + \mathbf{w}$, where $\mathbf{v}$ is the projection of $\mathbf{x}$ onto V and $\mathbf{w}$ is in $V^\perp$. In terms of the orthonormal basis for V, this implies

$$\mathbf{x} = \underbrace{c_1\mathbf{v}_1 + c_2\mathbf{v}_2 + \cdots + c_k\mathbf{v}_k}_{\mathbf{v} = \mathbf{Proj}_V(\mathbf{x})} + \mathbf{w}.$$

As above, if we take the dot product of both sides with $\mathbf{v}_i$, all terms on the right hand side vanish, except $c_i\mathbf{v}_i \cdot \mathbf{v}_i = c_i$, and thus $c_i = \mathbf{x} \cdot \mathbf{v}_i$. This proves the following.

Proposition 22.2. Let $\{\mathbf{v}_1, \mathbf{v}_2, \ldots, \mathbf{v}_k\}$ be an orthonormal basis for a subspace V of $\mathbf{R}^n$. Then

$$\mathbf{Proj}_V(\mathbf{x}) = (\mathbf{x} \cdot \mathbf{v}_1)\mathbf{v}_1 + (\mathbf{x} \cdot \mathbf{v}_2)\mathbf{v}_2 + \cdots + (\mathbf{x} \cdot \mathbf{v}_k)\mathbf{v}_k$$

for all $\mathbf{x}$ in $\mathbf{R}^n$.

Now let A be the matrix whose columns are the basis vectors. Then

$$A^T A = \begin{bmatrix} \text{---} & \mathbf{v}_1^T & \text{---} \\ \text{---} & \mathbf{v}_2^T & \text{---} \\ & \vdots & \\ \text{---} & \mathbf{v}_k^T & \text{---} \end{bmatrix} \begin{bmatrix} | & | & & | \\ \mathbf{v}_1 & \mathbf{v}_2 & \cdots & \mathbf{v}_k \\ | & | & & | \end{bmatrix} = \begin{bmatrix} 1 & 0 & \cdots & 0 \\ 0 & 1 & \cdots & 0 \\ \vdots & \vdots & \ddots & \vdots \\ 0 & 0 & \cdots & 1 \end{bmatrix} = I_k$$

since the ij^{th} entry of $A^T A$ is the dot product of $\mathbf{v}_i$ with $\mathbf{v}_j$. As a consequence, the formula $A(A^T A)^{-1}A^T$ simplifies to AA^T.

163

Proposition 22.3. Let A be a matrix whose columns form an orthonormal basis for V. Then AA^T is the matrix for $\mathbf{Proj}_V$, the orthogonal projection onto V.

Example 22.4. Let $\{\mathbf{v}_1, \mathbf{v}_2\}$ be the orthonormal set from Example 22.2. The matrix for the orthogonal projection onto the plane spanned by these vectors is

$$AA^T = \begin{bmatrix} 1/3 & 2/3 \\ 2/3 & 1/3 \\ 2/3 & -2/3 \end{bmatrix} \begin{bmatrix} 1/3 & 2/3 & 2/3 \\ 2/3 & 1/3 & -2/3 \end{bmatrix} = \frac{1}{9} \begin{bmatrix} 5 & 4 & -2 \\ 4 & 5 & 2 \\ -2 & 2 & 8 \end{bmatrix}.$$

$\diamond$

Orthogonal Matrices

Suppose $\mathcal{B} = \{\mathbf{v}_1, \ldots, \mathbf{v}_n\}$ is an orthonormal basis for $\mathbf{R}^n$. Its change of basis matrix

$$C = \begin{bmatrix} | & | & & | \\ \mathbf{v}_1 & \mathbf{v}_2 & \cdots & \mathbf{v}_n \\ | & | & & | \end{bmatrix}$$

has columns which are mutually orthogonal unit vectors. So, just as above, we have

$$C^T C = I_n$$

and since C is a square matrix, this implies that C is invertible and

$$\boxed{C^{-1} = C^T.}$$

A matrix with this property is called an **orthogonal matrix**. This property simplifies many calculations since it is clearly easier in general to take a transpose than an inverse. In particular, suppose the matrices for a linear transformation $\mathbf{T}$ with respect to the standard basis and $\mathcal{B}$ are A and B, respectively. Then the relationship between A and B becomes

$$B = C^T A C$$
$$A = C B C^T.$$

Example 22.5. Let

$$\mathbf{v}_1 = \begin{bmatrix} 2/3 \\ -2/3 \\ 1/3 \end{bmatrix}, \qquad \mathbf{v}_2 = \begin{bmatrix} 2/3 \\ 1/3 \\ -2/3 \end{bmatrix} \qquad \text{and} \qquad \mathbf{v}_3 = \begin{bmatrix} 1/3 \\ 2/3 \\ 2/3 \end{bmatrix}.$$

Then $\mathcal{B} = \{\mathbf{v}_1, \mathbf{v}_2, \mathbf{v}_3\}$ is an orthonormal basis for $\mathbf{R}^3$. Let V be the plane spanned by $\mathbf{v}_1$ and $\mathbf{v}_2$, and let $\mathbf{T} : \mathbf{R}^3 \to \mathbf{R}^3$ be the reflection through the plane V, which sends vectors in $\mathbf{R}^3$ to their mirror image on the opposite side of V. Then

$$\mathbf{T}(\mathbf{v}_1) = \mathbf{v}_1 = 1\mathbf{v}_1 + 0\mathbf{v}_2 + 0\mathbf{v}_3$$
$$\mathbf{T}(\mathbf{v}_2) = \mathbf{v}_2 = 0\mathbf{v}_1 + 1\mathbf{v}_2 + 0\mathbf{v}_3$$
$$\mathbf{T}(\mathbf{v}_3) = -\mathbf{v}_3 = 0\mathbf{v}_1 + 0\mathbf{v}_2 - 1\mathbf{v}_3$$

so the matrix for $\mathbf{T}$ with respect to $\mathcal{B}$ is

$$B = \begin{bmatrix} 1 & 0 & 0 \\ 0 & 1 & 0 \\ 0 & 0 & -1 \end{bmatrix}.$$

Therefore

$$A = CBC^T = \begin{bmatrix} 2/3 & 2/3 & 1/3 \\ -2/3 & 1/3 & 2/3 \\ 1/3 & -2/3 & 2/3 \end{bmatrix} \begin{bmatrix} 1 & 0 & 0 \\ 0 & 1 & 0 \\ 0 & 0 & -1 \end{bmatrix} \begin{bmatrix} 2/3 & -2/3 & 1/3 \\ 2/3 & 1/3 & -2/3 \\ 1/3 & 2/3 & 2/3 \end{bmatrix} = \frac{1}{9} \begin{bmatrix} 7 & -4 & -4 \\ -4 & 1 & -8 \\ -4 & -8 & 1 \end{bmatrix}$$

is the matrix for $\mathbf{T}$ in standard coordinates. $\diamond$

One very important property of orthogonal matrices is that they preserve lengths and angles. This fact is a consequence of the following result.

Proposition 22.4. Let C be any $n \times n$ orthogonal matrix. Then

$$C\mathbf{v} \cdot C\mathbf{w} = \mathbf{v} \cdot \mathbf{w}$$

for all $\mathbf{v}$ and $\mathbf{w}$ in $\mathbf{R}^n$.

Proof. By Proposition 18.2 and the fact that $C^T C = I_n$, we have $C\mathbf{v} \cdot C\mathbf{w} = \mathbf{v} \cdot C^T C\mathbf{w} = \mathbf{v} \cdot \mathbf{w}$ for all $\mathbf{v}$ and $\mathbf{w}$ in $\mathbf{R}^n$. $\square$

Now, since

$$\|C\mathbf{v}\|^2 = C\mathbf{v} \cdot C\mathbf{v} = \mathbf{v} \cdot \mathbf{v} = \|\mathbf{v}\|^2$$

we have $\|C\mathbf{v}\| = \|\mathbf{v}\|$, so C preserves length. To see that C preserves angle, recall that $\mathbf{v} \cdot \mathbf{w} = \|\mathbf{v}\|\|\mathbf{w}\| \cos\theta$, where θ is the angle between $\mathbf{v}$ and $\mathbf{w}$. Thus

$$\cos\theta = \frac{\mathbf{v} \cdot \mathbf{w}}{\|\mathbf{v}\|\|\mathbf{w}\|} = \frac{C\mathbf{v} \cdot C\mathbf{w}}{\|C\mathbf{v}\|\|C\mathbf{w}\|} = \cos\phi,$$

where ϕ is the angle between $C\mathbf{v}$ and $C\mathbf{w}$. Hence $\theta = \phi$.

Gram-Schmidt Process

We next outline a procedure for producing an orthonormal basis from any given basis $\{\mathbf{v}_1, \mathbf{v}_2, \ldots, \mathbf{v}_k\}$ for a subspace V. We first define

$$V_1 = \operatorname{span}(\mathbf{v}_1)$$
$$V_2 = \operatorname{span}(\mathbf{v}_1, \mathbf{v}_2)$$
$$\vdots$$
$$V_k = \operatorname{span}(\mathbf{v}_1, \mathbf{v}_2, \ldots, \mathbf{v}_k) = V.$$

Next, let

$$\mathbf{w}_1 = \frac{\mathbf{v}_1}{\|\mathbf{v}_1\|}.$$

It is clear that $\{\mathbf{w}_1\}$ is an orthonormal basis for V_1. If V is a one-dimensional subspace, then $V = V_1$ and we are done. Otherwise the process continues by letting

$$\mathbf{y}_2 = \mathbf{v}_2 - \mathbf{Proj}_{V_1}(\mathbf{v}_2).$$

By definition, the difference of $\mathbf{v}_2$ and its projection onto V_1 is in $V_1^\perp$, and is therefore orthogonal to $\mathbf{w}_1$.

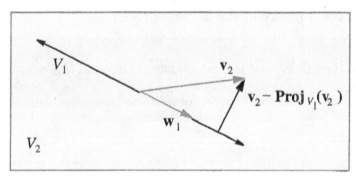

Now since $\mathbf{w}_1$ forms an orthonormal basis for V_1, the projection onto V_1 is given by equation Proposition 22.2. Thus

$$\mathbf{y}_2 = \mathbf{v}_2 - (\mathbf{v}_2 \cdot \mathbf{w}_1)\mathbf{w}_1.$$

By the linear independence of $\mathbf{v}_1$ and $\mathbf{v}_2$, $\mathbf{v}_2$ is not a scalar multiple of $\mathbf{w}_1$, so $\mathbf{y}_2$ is nonzero and we may define

$$\mathbf{w}_2 = \frac{\mathbf{y}_2}{\|\mathbf{y}_2\|}.$$

Then $\{\mathbf{w}_1, \mathbf{w}_2\}$ is an orthonormal basis for V_2. If V is two-dimensional, then $V = V_2$ and we are done. Otherwise we continue as above by letting

$$\mathbf{y}_3 = \mathbf{v}_3 - \mathbf{Proj}_{V_2}(\mathbf{v}_3).$$

166

The vector $\mathbf{y}_3$ is in $V_2^\perp$ and is therefore orthogonal to both $\mathbf{w}_1$ and $\mathbf{w}_2$. Since $\{\mathbf{w}_1, \mathbf{w}_2\}$ is an orthonormal basis for V_2, Proposition 22.2 again implies

$$\mathbf{y}_3 = \mathbf{v}_3 - (\mathbf{v}_3 \cdot \mathbf{w}_1)\mathbf{w}_1 - (\mathbf{v}_3 \cdot \mathbf{w}_2)\mathbf{w}_2.$$

By the linear independence of $\{\mathbf{v}_1, \mathbf{v}_2, \mathbf{v}_3\}$, $\mathbf{v}_3$ is not a linear combination of $\mathbf{w}_1$ and $\mathbf{w}_2$, so $\mathbf{y}_3$ is nonzero, and we may define

$$\mathbf{w}_3 = \frac{\mathbf{y}_3}{\|\mathbf{y}_3\|}.$$

Then $\{\mathbf{w}_1, \mathbf{w}_2, \mathbf{w}_3\}$ is an orthonormal basis for V_3. If V is three-dimensional, then $V = V_3$ and we are done. Otherwise the process continues in the same manner until we have constructed an orthonormal basis for $V_k = V$. The process is summarized as follows.

Gram-Schmidt Process

Let $\{\mathbf{v}_1, \mathbf{v}_2, \ldots, \mathbf{v}_k\}$ be a basis for a subspace V of $\mathbf{R}^n$.

1. Let $\mathbf{w}_1 = \mathbf{v}_1/\|\mathbf{v}_1\|$.

2. Having constructed the orthonormal basis $\{\mathbf{w}_1, \ldots, \mathbf{w}_j\}$ for V_j, to construct $\mathbf{w}_{j+1}$ define

$$\begin{aligned}
\mathbf{y}_{j+1} &= \mathbf{v}_{j+1} - \mathbf{Proj}_{V_j}(\mathbf{v}_{j+1}) \\
&= \mathbf{v}_{j+1} - (\mathbf{v}_{j+1} \cdot \mathbf{w}_1)\mathbf{w}_1 - (\mathbf{v}_{j+1} \cdot \mathbf{w}_2)\mathbf{w}_2 - \cdots - (\mathbf{v}_{j+1} \cdot \mathbf{w}_j)\mathbf{w}_j
\end{aligned}$$

and let $\mathbf{w}_{j+1} = \mathbf{y}_{j+1}/\|\mathbf{y}_{j+1}\|$.

Then $\{\mathbf{w}_1, \mathbf{w}_2, \ldots, \mathbf{w}_k\}$ is an orthonormal basis for V.

Example 22.6. Find an orthonormal basis for the plane $x_1 + x_2 + x_3 = 0$.
Solution. First, solving the equation yields the basis vectors

$$\mathbf{v}_1 = \begin{bmatrix} -1 \\ 1 \\ 0 \end{bmatrix} \qquad \text{and} \qquad \mathbf{v}_2 = \begin{bmatrix} -1 \\ 0 \\ 1 \end{bmatrix}$$

for the plane. Applying the Gram-Schmidt process we first have

$$\mathbf{w}_1 = \mathbf{v}_1/\|\mathbf{v}_1\| = \frac{1}{\sqrt{2}} \begin{bmatrix} -1 \\ 1 \\ 0 \end{bmatrix}.$$

Next we let

$$\mathbf{y}_2 = \mathbf{v}_2 - (\mathbf{v}_2 \cdot \mathbf{w}_1)\mathbf{w}_1 = \begin{bmatrix} -1 \\ 0 \\ 1 \end{bmatrix} - \frac{1}{\sqrt{2}}\frac{1}{\sqrt{2}} \begin{bmatrix} -1 \\ 1 \\ 0 \end{bmatrix} = \begin{bmatrix} -1/2 \\ -1/2 \\ 1 \end{bmatrix}$$

and finally

$$\mathbf{w}_2 = \mathbf{y}_2 / \|\mathbf{y}_2\| = \frac{1}{\sqrt{6}} \begin{bmatrix} -1 \\ -1 \\ 2 \end{bmatrix}.$$

So

$$\left\{ \frac{1}{\sqrt{2}} \begin{bmatrix} -1 \\ 1 \\ 0 \end{bmatrix}, \frac{1}{\sqrt{6}} \begin{bmatrix} -1 \\ -1 \\ 2 \end{bmatrix} \right\}$$

is an orthonormal basis for the plane.   ◇

Example 22.7. Find an orthonormal basis for the subspace

$$V = \text{span}\left(\begin{bmatrix} 1 \\ 1 \\ 0 \\ 0 \end{bmatrix}, \begin{bmatrix} 0 \\ 1 \\ 1 \\ 0 \end{bmatrix}, \begin{bmatrix} 0 \\ 0 \\ 1 \\ 1 \end{bmatrix} \right)$$

of $\mathbf{R}^4$.

Solution. The order in which we write the basis vectors is arbitrary, so to make the first step easier let

$$\mathbf{v}_1 = \begin{bmatrix} 1 \\ 1 \\ 0 \\ 0 \end{bmatrix}, \quad \mathbf{v}_2 = \begin{bmatrix} 0 \\ 0 \\ 1 \\ 1 \end{bmatrix}, \quad \text{and} \quad \mathbf{v}_3 = \begin{bmatrix} 0 \\ 1 \\ 1 \\ 0 \end{bmatrix}.$$

Then

$$\mathbf{w}_1 = \mathbf{v}_1 / \|\mathbf{v}_1\| = \frac{1}{\sqrt{2}} \begin{bmatrix} 1 \\ 1 \\ 0 \\ 0 \end{bmatrix}$$

and since $\mathbf{v}_2$ and $\mathbf{w}_1$ are orthogonal,

$$\mathbf{y}_2 = \mathbf{v}_2 - (\mathbf{v}_2 \cdot \mathbf{w}_1)\mathbf{w}_1 = \mathbf{v}_2$$

so

$$\mathbf{w}_2 = \mathbf{y}_2 / \|\mathbf{y}_2\| = \frac{1}{\sqrt{2}} \begin{bmatrix} 0 \\ 0 \\ 1 \\ 1 \end{bmatrix}.$$

Finally

$$\mathbf{y}_3 = \mathbf{v}_3 - (\mathbf{v}_3 \cdot \mathbf{w}_1)\mathbf{w}_1 - (\mathbf{v}_3 \cdot \mathbf{w}_2)\mathbf{w}_2 = \begin{bmatrix} 0 \\ 1 \\ 1 \\ 0 \end{bmatrix} - \frac{1}{2}\begin{bmatrix} 1 \\ 1 \\ 0 \\ 0 \end{bmatrix} - \frac{1}{2}\begin{bmatrix} 0 \\ 0 \\ 1 \\ 1 \end{bmatrix} = \begin{bmatrix} -1/2 \\ 1/2 \\ 1/2 \\ -1/2 \end{bmatrix}$$

and thus

$$\mathbf{w}_3 = \mathbf{y}_3/\|\mathbf{y}_3\| = \begin{bmatrix} -1/2 \\ 1/2 \\ 1/2 \\ -1/2 \end{bmatrix}.$$

$\diamond$

As a final example we consider the rather difficult problem of finding the matrix for the rotation about an axis in $\mathbf{R}^3$ which is not one of the coordinate axes.

Example 22.8. Let

$$\mathbf{v}_1 = \begin{bmatrix} 1 \\ 1 \\ 1 \end{bmatrix},$$

and let L be the line spanned by $\mathbf{v}_1$. Define $\mathbf{T}$ to be the rotation through angle θ about the axis L, where the direction of rotation is counterclockwise as viewed from the head of $\mathbf{v}_1$ looking toward the origin. To find the matrix for $\mathbf{T}$ we first construct an appropriate basis for $\mathbf{R}^3$. Vectors in L are fixed by this rotation, so we choose $\mathbf{u}_1 = \mathbf{v}_1/\|\mathbf{v}_1\|$ as the first basis vector. In the plane P perpendicular to L, the rotation behaves like an ordinary rotation in $\mathbf{R}^2$, so we should find a basis for P. The plane P is given by $x_1 + x_2 + x_3 = 0$, so the vectors

$$\mathbf{u}_2 = \frac{1}{\sqrt{2}}\begin{bmatrix} -1 \\ 1 \\ 0 \end{bmatrix} \qquad \text{and} \qquad \mathbf{u}_3 = \frac{1}{\sqrt{6}}\begin{bmatrix} -1 \\ -1 \\ 2 \end{bmatrix}$$

found in Example 22.6 form an orthonormal basis for P. Thus $\mathcal{B} = \{\mathbf{u}_1, \mathbf{u}_2, \mathbf{u}_3\}$ is an orthonormal basis for $\mathbf{R}^3$. To determine the orientation of $\mathbf{u}_2$ and $\mathbf{u}_3$ in the plane P we take their cross product. Since

$$\mathbf{u}_2 \times \mathbf{u}_3 = \frac{1}{\sqrt{12}}\begin{bmatrix} 2 \\ 2 \\ 2 \end{bmatrix} = +\mathbf{u}_1,$$

looking down on P from the head of $\mathbf{v}_1$ we see the following.

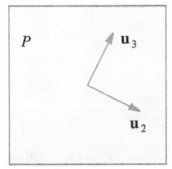

169

So the rotation is such that $\mathbf{u}_2$ is rotated toward $\mathbf{u}_3$. Thus we have

$$\mathbf{T}(\mathbf{u}_1) = \mathbf{u}_1 = 1\mathbf{u}_1 + 0\mathbf{u}_2 + 0\mathbf{u}_3$$
$$\mathbf{T}(\mathbf{u}_2) = (\cos\theta)\mathbf{u}_2 + (\sin\theta)\mathbf{u}_3 = 0\mathbf{u}_1 + (\cos\theta)\mathbf{u}_2 + (\sin\theta)\mathbf{u}_3$$
$$\mathbf{T}(\mathbf{u}_3) = (-\sin\theta)\mathbf{u}_2 + (\cos\theta)\mathbf{u}_3 = 0\mathbf{u}_1 + (-\sin\theta)\mathbf{u}_2 + (\cos\theta)\mathbf{u}_3$$

so the matrix for $\mathbf{T}$ with respect to $\mathcal{B}$ is

$$B = \begin{bmatrix} 1 & 0 & 0 \\ 0 & \cos\theta & -\sin\theta \\ 0 & \sin\theta & \cos\theta \end{bmatrix}.$$

The change of basis matrix for $\mathcal{B}$ is

$$C = \begin{bmatrix} 1/\sqrt{3} & -1/\sqrt{2} & -1/\sqrt{6} \\ 1/\sqrt{3} & 1/\sqrt{2} & -1/\sqrt{6} \\ 1/\sqrt{3} & 0 & 2/\sqrt{6} \end{bmatrix}$$

Since C is an orthogonal matrix, $C^{-1} = C^T$ and the matrix for $\mathbf{T}$ in standard coordinates is

$$A = CBC^T$$

$$= \begin{bmatrix} 1/\sqrt{3} & -1/\sqrt{2} & -1/\sqrt{6} \\ 1/\sqrt{3} & 1/\sqrt{2} & -1/\sqrt{6} \\ 1/\sqrt{3} & 0 & 2/\sqrt{6} \end{bmatrix} \begin{bmatrix} 1 & 0 & 0 \\ 0 & \cos\theta & -\sin\theta \\ 0 & \sin\theta & \cos\theta \end{bmatrix} \begin{bmatrix} 1/\sqrt{3} & 1/\sqrt{3} & 1/\sqrt{3} \\ -1/\sqrt{2} & 1/\sqrt{2} & 0 \\ -1/\sqrt{6} & -1/\sqrt{6} & 2/\sqrt{6} \end{bmatrix}$$

$$= \begin{bmatrix} 1/\sqrt{3} & -1/\sqrt{2} & -1/\sqrt{6} \\ 1/\sqrt{3} & 1/\sqrt{2} & -1/\sqrt{6} \\ 1/\sqrt{3} & 0 & 2/\sqrt{6} \end{bmatrix} \begin{bmatrix} 1/\sqrt{3} & 1/\sqrt{3} & 1/\sqrt{3} \\ -\frac{1}{\sqrt{2}}\cos\theta + \frac{1}{\sqrt{6}}\sin\theta & \frac{1}{\sqrt{2}}\cos\theta + \frac{1}{\sqrt{6}}\sin\theta & -\frac{2}{\sqrt{6}}\sin\theta \\ -\frac{1}{\sqrt{2}}\sin\theta - \frac{1}{\sqrt{6}}\cos\theta & \frac{1}{\sqrt{2}}\sin\theta - \frac{1}{\sqrt{6}}\cos\theta & \frac{2}{\sqrt{6}}\cos\theta \end{bmatrix}$$

$$= \begin{bmatrix} \frac{1}{3} + \frac{2}{3}\cos\theta & \frac{1}{3} - \frac{1}{\sqrt{3}}\sin\theta - \frac{1}{3}\cos\theta & \frac{1}{3} + \frac{1}{\sqrt{3}}\sin\theta - \frac{1}{3}\cos\theta \\ \frac{1}{3} + \frac{1}{\sqrt{3}}\sin\theta - \frac{1}{3}\cos\theta & \frac{1}{3} + \frac{2}{3}\cos\theta & \frac{1}{3} - \frac{1}{\sqrt{3}}\sin\theta - \frac{1}{3}\cos\theta \\ \frac{1}{3} - \frac{1}{\sqrt{3}}\sin\theta - \frac{1}{3}\cos\theta & \frac{1}{3} + \frac{1}{\sqrt{3}}\sin\theta - \frac{1}{3}\cos\theta & \frac{1}{3} + \frac{2}{3}\cos\theta \end{bmatrix}.$$

For instance, the matrix for a $30°$ ($\pi/6$ radian) rotation about L is

$$\begin{bmatrix} \frac{1}{3} + \frac{1}{\sqrt{3}} & \frac{1}{3} - \frac{1}{\sqrt{3}} & \frac{1}{3} \\ \frac{1}{3} & \frac{1}{3} + \frac{1}{\sqrt{3}} & \frac{1}{3} - \frac{1}{\sqrt{3}} \\ \frac{1}{3} - \frac{1}{\sqrt{3}} & \frac{1}{3} & \frac{1}{3} + \frac{1}{\sqrt{3}} \end{bmatrix}.$$

$\diamond$

Exercises

22.1. Let $\mathbf{v}_1 = \begin{bmatrix} 1/\sqrt{5} \\ 2/\sqrt{5} \end{bmatrix}$, $\mathbf{v}_2 = \begin{bmatrix} -2/\sqrt{5} \\ 1/\sqrt{5} \end{bmatrix}$.

(a) Verify that $\mathcal{B} = \{\mathbf{v}_1, \mathbf{v}_2\}$ is an orthonormal basis for $\mathbf{R}^2$.

(b) Write the following vectors in $\mathcal{B}$ coordinates.

    i. $\mathbf{v} = \begin{bmatrix} 1 \\ 3 \end{bmatrix}$

    ii. $\mathbf{v} = \begin{bmatrix} -2 \\ 4 \end{bmatrix}$

22.2. Let $\mathbf{v}_1 = \begin{bmatrix} 1/3 \\ 2/3 \\ 2/3 \end{bmatrix}$, $\mathbf{v}_2 = \begin{bmatrix} 2/3 \\ 1/3 \\ -2/3 \end{bmatrix}$, $\mathbf{v}_3 = \begin{bmatrix} 2/3 \\ -2/3 \\ 1/3 \end{bmatrix}$.

(a) Verify that $\mathcal{B} = \{\mathbf{v}_1, \mathbf{v}_2, \mathbf{v}_3\}$ is an orthonormal basis for $\mathbf{R}^3$.

(b) Write the following vectors in $\mathcal{B}$ coordinates.

    i. $\mathbf{v} = \begin{bmatrix} 0 \\ 1 \\ 0 \end{bmatrix}$

    ii. $\mathbf{v} = \begin{bmatrix} 2 \\ -2 \\ 2 \end{bmatrix}$

22.3. Let $\mathbf{v}_1 = \begin{bmatrix} 1/2 \\ 1/2 \\ 1/2 \\ 1/2 \end{bmatrix}$, $\mathbf{v}_2 = \begin{bmatrix} 1/2 \\ -1/2 \\ -1/2 \\ 1/2 \end{bmatrix}$. Let $V = \mathrm{span}(\mathbf{v}_1, \mathbf{v}_2)$. Let $\mathbf{Proj}_V : \mathbf{R}^4 \to \mathbf{R}^4$ be orthogonal projection onto V. Using the fact that $\{\mathbf{v}_1, \mathbf{v}_2\}$ is an orthonormal basis for V, find the matrix for $\mathbf{Proj}_V$.

22.4. Let $\mathbf{v}_1 = \begin{bmatrix} 1/\sqrt{3} \\ -1/\sqrt{3} \\ 1/\sqrt{3} \end{bmatrix}$, $\mathbf{v}_2 = \begin{bmatrix} 1/\sqrt{5} \\ 2/\sqrt{5} \\ 1/\sqrt{5} \end{bmatrix}$. Let $V = \mathrm{span}(\mathbf{v}_1, \mathbf{v}_2)$. Let $\mathbf{Proj}_V : \mathbf{R}^3 \to \mathbf{R}^3$ be orthogonal projection onto V. Using the fact that $\{\mathbf{v}_1, \mathbf{v}_2\}$ is an orthonormal basis for V, find the matrix for $\mathbf{Proj}_V$.

22.5. Let P be the plane in $\mathbf{R}^3$ which satisfies the equation $-3x_1 + x_2 + 2x_3 = 0$. Let $\mathbf{v}_1 = \begin{bmatrix} 1/\sqrt{3} \\ 1/\sqrt{3} \\ 1/\sqrt{3} \end{bmatrix}$. Notice that $\mathbf{v}_1$ is a unit vector in P.

(a) Find a unit vector $\mathbf{v}_2$ in P perpendicular to $\mathbf{v}_1$.

(b) Notice that $\{\mathbf{v}_1, \mathbf{v}_2\}$ forms an orthonormal basis for P. Find the matrix for $\mathbf{Proj}_P : \mathbf{R}^3 \to \mathbf{R}^3$, the orthogonal projection onto P.

22.6. Let L be the line spanned by $\mathbf{v}_1 = \begin{bmatrix} 1 \\ 2 \\ 2 \end{bmatrix}$, and let $\mathbf{T} : \mathbf{R}^3 \to \mathbf{R}^3$ be the rotation through angle θ about the axis L, where the direction of rotation is counterclockwise as viewed from the head of $\mathbf{v}_1$ looking toward the origin.

(a) Find an orthonormal basis $\{\mathbf{v}_2, \mathbf{v}_3\}$ for the plane $P = L^\perp$.

(b) Find the matrix for $\mathbf{T}$ with respect to the basis $\mathcal{B} = \{\mathbf{v}_1, \mathbf{v}_2, \mathbf{v}_3\}$ for $\mathbf{R}^3$.

(c) Use the answer to part (b) to find the matrix for $\mathbf{T}$ in standard coordinates.

In Exercises 7 through 10 find an orthonormal basis for the subspace V.

22.7. $V = \text{span}\left(\begin{bmatrix} 1 \\ 1 \\ 0 \end{bmatrix}, \begin{bmatrix} 5 \\ -1 \\ 3 \end{bmatrix} \right)$

22.8. $V = \text{span}\left(\begin{bmatrix} -1 \\ -1 \\ 1 \end{bmatrix}, \begin{bmatrix} 2 \\ -2 \\ 3 \end{bmatrix} \right)$

22.9. $V = \text{span}\left(\begin{bmatrix} 1 \\ 1 \\ 1 \\ 0 \end{bmatrix}, \begin{bmatrix} 1 \\ 0 \\ 2 \\ 1 \end{bmatrix}, \begin{bmatrix} 3 \\ -1 \\ 4 \\ 4 \end{bmatrix} \right)$

22.10. $V = \text{span}\left(\begin{bmatrix} 1 \\ 2 \\ 3 \\ 4 \end{bmatrix}, \begin{bmatrix} 1 \\ 1 \\ 0 \\ 0 \end{bmatrix}, \begin{bmatrix} 0 \\ 0 \\ 1 \\ 1 \end{bmatrix} \right)$

23   Eigenvectors

Given a linear transformation $\mathbf{T}$, a *good* basis $\mathcal{B}$ for $\mathbf{R}^n$ is one such that the matrix B for $\mathbf{T}$ with respect to $\mathcal{B}$ is a diagonal matrix. Suppose that such a basis $\mathcal{B} = \{\mathbf{v}_1, \mathbf{v}_2, \ldots, \mathbf{v}_n\}$ exists and that the matrix for $\mathbf{T}$ with respect to $\mathcal{B}$ is

$$B = \begin{bmatrix} \lambda_1 & 0 & \cdots & 0 \\ 0 & \lambda_2 & \cdots & 0 \\ \vdots & \vdots & \ddots & \vdots \\ 0 & 0 & \cdots & \lambda_n \end{bmatrix}.$$

Then

$$[\mathbf{T}(\mathbf{v}_1)]_\mathcal{B} = B[\mathbf{v}_1]_\mathcal{B} = B\mathbf{e}_1 = \begin{bmatrix} \lambda_1 \\ 0 \\ \vdots \\ 0 \end{bmatrix}$$

which means

$$\mathbf{T}(\mathbf{v}_1) = \lambda_1 \mathbf{v}_1.$$

172

Likewise

$$\mathbf{T}(\mathbf{v}_2) = \lambda_2 \mathbf{v}_2$$

$$\vdots$$

$$\mathbf{T}(\mathbf{v}_n) = \lambda_n \mathbf{v}_n.$$

So when $\mathbf{T}$ is applied to each basis vector, the result is a scalar multiple of that vector. An **eigenvector** of a linear transformation $\mathbf{T} : \mathbf{R}^n \to \mathbf{R}^n$ is a nonzero vector $\mathbf{v}$ such that

$$\boxed{\mathbf{T}(\mathbf{v}) = \lambda \mathbf{v}}$$

for some scalar λ. The number λ is called the **eigenvalue** associated with the eigenvector $\mathbf{v}$. If A is the matrix (in standard coordinates) for $\mathbf{T}$, then $A\mathbf{v} = \lambda\mathbf{v}$, and we say that $\mathbf{v}$ is an eigenvector of A and λ is an eigenvalue of A.

We exclude the zero vector from this definition for two reasons. First, since $\mathbf{T}(\mathbf{0}) = \mathbf{0} = \lambda\mathbf{0}$ for *every* scalar λ, it is unclear what eigenvalue to associate with the zero vector. Also, for the purposes of constructing a basis of $\mathbf{R}^n$, the zero vector is not very useful.

Note however that the number zero could be an eigenvalue. If A is a matrix with nontrivial null space, then any nonzero vector $\mathbf{v}$ in $N(A)$ satisfies $A\mathbf{v} = \mathbf{0} = 0\mathbf{v}$, and is therefore an eigenvector with eigenvalue zero.

Example 23.1. Let

$$A = \begin{bmatrix} 3 & -2 \\ 2 & -2 \end{bmatrix}, \qquad \mathbf{v}_1 = \begin{bmatrix} 2 \\ 1 \end{bmatrix} \qquad \text{and} \qquad \mathbf{v}_2 = \begin{bmatrix} 1 \\ 2 \end{bmatrix}.$$

Then

$$A\mathbf{v}_1 = 2\mathbf{v}_1 \qquad \text{and} \qquad A\mathbf{v}_2 = -\mathbf{v}_2.$$

Thus $\mathbf{v}_1$ is an eigenvector with eigenvalue 2 and $\mathbf{v}_2$ is an eigenvector with eigenvalue -1.

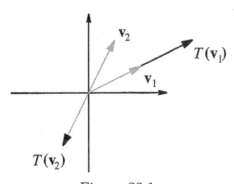

Figure 23.1.

This explains the choice of basis in Example 21.8. Notice that these vectors had to be chosen carefully. Given an arbitrary vector, chances are it is not an eigenvector. For example

$$\mathbf{v} = \begin{bmatrix} 1 \\ 1 \end{bmatrix} \qquad \Longrightarrow \qquad A\mathbf{v} = \begin{bmatrix} 1 \\ 0 \end{bmatrix}$$

so $\mathbf{v}$ is not an eigenvector. $\diamond$

This brings up the question of how to find eigenvectors and eigenvalues. We begin with the eigenvalues.

Finding Eigenvalues

Suppose λ is an eigenvalue of a matrix A. Then for some nonzero vector $\mathbf{v}$,

$$A\mathbf{v} = \lambda\mathbf{v}.$$

Putting both terms on the same side we get

$$\lambda\mathbf{v} - A\mathbf{v} = \mathbf{0}.$$

Since $\mathbf{v} = I_n\mathbf{v}$ this becomes

$$(\lambda I_n - A)\mathbf{v} = \mathbf{0}.$$

Since $\mathbf{v}$ is nonzero, this means that the matrix $\lambda I_n - A$ has a nontrivial null space and is therefore not invertible. Thus

$$\det(\lambda I_n - A) = 0.$$

Observe that each step in this chain of implications can be reversed, so we have the following test for eigenvalues.

> **Proposition 23.1.** Let A be an $n \times n$ matrix. Then λ is an eigenvalue of A if and only if $\det(\lambda I_n - A) = 0$.

Example 23.2. Let

$$A = \begin{bmatrix} 1 & 2 \\ 4 & 3 \end{bmatrix}.$$

Then

$$\lambda I_2 - A = \begin{bmatrix} \lambda & 0 \\ 0 & \lambda \end{bmatrix} - \begin{bmatrix} 1 & 2 \\ 4 & 3 \end{bmatrix} = \begin{bmatrix} \lambda - 1 & -2 \\ -4 & \lambda - 3 \end{bmatrix}$$

so

$$\det(\lambda I_2 - A) = (\lambda - 1)(\lambda - 3) - 8 = \lambda^2 - 4\lambda - 5 = (\lambda - 5)(\lambda + 1).$$

This expression is zero when $\lambda = 5$ or $\lambda = -1$, so these are the only eigenvalues of A. $\diamond$

The expression

$$\boxed{p(\lambda) = \det(\lambda I_n - A)}$$

174

is in general a polynomial of degree n, called the **characteristic polynomial** of A. The eigenvalues of A are the roots of this polynomial. If the characteristic polynomial has no real roots then A has no real eigenvalues or eigenvectors.

Example 23.3. The characteristic polynomial of

$$A = \begin{bmatrix} 0 & -1 \\ 1 & 0 \end{bmatrix}$$

is $\lambda^2 + 1$, which has no real roots, so A has no real eigenvalues or eigenvectors. This makes sense since A is the matrix for a rotation (with angle $\pi/2$) which does not send any vectors to multiples of themselves.

$\diamond$

The matrix A does have *complex* eigenvalues. The roots of $\lambda^2 + 1 = 0$ are $\lambda = \pm i$, where $i = \sqrt{-1}$ is an **imaginary number**. A **complex number** is a number of the form $a + bi$ where a and b are real numbers. We will discuss complex eigenvalues in the next section. Next we consider the task of finding the eigenvectors.

Finding Eigenvectors

Once an eigenvalue λ of a matrix A is known, the associated eigenvectors are the nonzero solutions of $A\mathbf{v} = \lambda\mathbf{v}$. Equivalently, they are the nonzero elements of the null space of $\lambda I_n - A$. We call

$$\boxed{E_\lambda = N(\lambda I_n - A)}$$

the **eigenspace** associated with the eigenvalue λ.

Example 23.4. Let $\mathbf{T} : \mathbf{R}^2 \rightarrow \mathbf{R}^2$ be the linear transformation with matrix

$$A = \begin{bmatrix} 1 & 2 \\ 4 & 3 \end{bmatrix}.$$

In Example 23.2 we found that the eigenvalues of A were 5 and -1. For $\lambda = 5$,

$$5I_2 - A = \begin{bmatrix} 4 & -2 \\ -4 & 2 \end{bmatrix} \qquad \Longrightarrow \qquad E_5 = N(5I_2 - A) = \text{span}\left(\begin{bmatrix} 1 \\ 2 \end{bmatrix}\right).$$

For $\lambda = -1$,

$$-1I_2 - A = \begin{bmatrix} -2 & -2 \\ -4 & -4 \end{bmatrix} \qquad \Longrightarrow \qquad E_{-1} = N(-1I_2 - A) = \text{span}\left(\begin{bmatrix} -1 \\ 1 \end{bmatrix}\right).$$

Now if we let

$$\mathbf{v}_1 = \begin{bmatrix} 1 \\ 2 \end{bmatrix} \qquad \mathbf{v}_2 = \begin{bmatrix} -1 \\ 1 \end{bmatrix}$$

then $\mathcal{B} = \{\mathbf{v}_1, \mathbf{v}_2\}$ is a basis for $\mathbf{R}^2$ and the matrix for $\mathbf{T}$ with respect to $\mathcal{B}$ is

$$B = C^{-1}AC = \frac{1}{3}\begin{bmatrix} 1 & 1 \\ -2 & 1 \end{bmatrix}\begin{bmatrix} 1 & 2 \\ 4 & 3 \end{bmatrix}\begin{bmatrix} 1 & -1 \\ 2 & 1 \end{bmatrix} = \begin{bmatrix} 5 & 0 \\ 0 & -1 \end{bmatrix}.$$

Notice that the eigenvalues appear on the diagonal.

$\diamond$

Example 23.5. The characteristic polynomial of

$$A = \begin{bmatrix} -1 & 2 & 2 \\ 2 & 2 & -1 \\ 2 & -1 & 2 \end{bmatrix}$$

is

$$p(\lambda) = (\lambda - 3)^2(\lambda + 3),$$

so the eigenvalues are $\lambda = 3$ and $\lambda = -3$. Since

$$3I_3 - A = \begin{bmatrix} 4 & -2 & -2 \\ -2 & 1 & 1 \\ -2 & 1 & 1 \end{bmatrix}$$

the eigenspace associated with $\lambda = 3$ is

$$E_3 = N(3I_3 - A) = \text{span}\left(\begin{bmatrix} 1 \\ 2 \\ 0 \end{bmatrix}, \begin{bmatrix} 1 \\ 0 \\ 2 \end{bmatrix} \right),$$

and since

$$-3I_3 - A = \begin{bmatrix} -2 & -2 & -2 \\ -2 & -5 & 1 \\ -2 & 1 & -5 \end{bmatrix} \implies \text{rref}(-3I_3 - A) = \begin{bmatrix} 1 & 0 & 2 \\ 0 & 1 & -1 \\ 0 & 0 & 0 \end{bmatrix},$$

the eigenspace associated with $\lambda = -3$ is

$$E_{-3} = N(-3I_3 - A) = \text{span}\left(\begin{bmatrix} -2 \\ 1 \\ 1 \end{bmatrix} \right).$$

Letting

$$C = \begin{bmatrix} 1 & 1 & -2 \\ 2 & 0 & 1 \\ 0 & 2 & 1 \end{bmatrix}$$

be the matrix consisting of the basis vectors for the two eigenspaces, we have

$$C^{-1}AC = \begin{bmatrix} 3 & 0 & 0 \\ 0 & 3 & 0 \\ 0 & 0 & -3 \end{bmatrix}.$$

$\diamond$

Diagonalizability

A matrix A is called **diagonalizable** if there exists a matrix C such that $C^{-1}AC$ is a diagonal matrix. That is, A is diagonalizable if A is similar to a diagonal matrix. The matrices in Examples 23.4 and 23.4 are diagonalizable because in both cases consisting of eigenvectors of A.

Proposition 23.2. A real $n \times n$ matrix A is diagonalizable over $\mathbf{R}$ if and only if there exists a basis of $\mathbf{R}^n$ consisting of eigenvectors of A. Such a basis is called an **eigenbasis**.

Proof. First suppose A is diagonalizable, so that $C^{-1}AC = D$ for some diagonal matrix. Since C is invertible, its columns form a basis for $\mathbf{R}^n$. We claim that these columns are all eigenvectors of A. Multiplying both sides by C gives $AC = CD$. Now write

$$C = \begin{bmatrix} | & | & & | \\ \mathbf{v}_1 & \mathbf{v}_2 & \cdots & \mathbf{v}_n \\ | & | & & | \end{bmatrix} \quad \text{and} \quad D = \begin{bmatrix} \lambda_1 & 0 & \cdots & 0 \\ 0 & \lambda_2 & \cdots & 0 \\ \vdots & \vdots & \ddots & \vdots \\ 0 & 0 & \cdots & \lambda_n \end{bmatrix}.$$

Recall that the columns of a product AB are A times the columns of B, so

$$AC = \begin{bmatrix} | & | & & | \\ A\mathbf{v}_1 & A\mathbf{v}_2 & \cdots & A\mathbf{v}_n \\ | & | & & | \end{bmatrix}$$

and

$$CD = \begin{bmatrix} | & | & & | \\ \lambda_1\mathbf{v}_1 & \lambda_2\mathbf{v}_2 & \cdots & \lambda_n\mathbf{v}_n \\ | & | & & | \end{bmatrix}$$

and thus $A\mathbf{v}_i = \lambda_i \mathbf{v}_i$ for $1 \le i \le n$.

Now suppose that $\{\mathbf{v}_1, \ldots, \mathbf{v}_n\}$ is a basis for $\mathbf{R}^n$ consisting of eigenvectors for A, and let C be the matrix whose columns are these eigenvectors. Then, by the same calculations, $AC = CD$, where D is the diagonal matrix whose diagonal entries are the associated eigenvalues. Since the columns of C form a basis for $\mathbf{R}^n$, C is invertible, and we can solve to get $C^{-1}AC = D$, so A is diagonalizable. $\square$

Example 23.6. The characteristic polynomial of

$$A = \begin{bmatrix} 3 & 0 \\ 2 & 3 \end{bmatrix}$$

is $p(\lambda) = (\lambda - 3)^2$, so $\lambda = 3$ is the only eigenvalue. Since

$$\text{rref}(3I_2 - A) = \begin{bmatrix} 1 & 0 \\ 0 & 0 \end{bmatrix}$$

we have

$$E_3 = \mathrm{span}\left(\begin{bmatrix} 0 \\ 1 \end{bmatrix}\right).$$

Since A has no other eigenvectors, A does not have an eigenbasis, and is therefore not diagonalizable. $\diamond$

The problem in the previous example was caused by the fact that $\lambda = 3$ was a repeated root of the characteristic polynomial. In the case that we do not have repeated roots, the eigenvalues are all different, and it turns out that this implies diagonalizability.

Proposition 23.3. Let A be an $n \times n$ matrix with n different eigenvalues $\lambda_1, \ldots, \lambda_n$. Then A is diagonalizable.

Proof. Choose eigenvector $\mathbf{v}_1, \ldots, \mathbf{v}_n$ with eigenvalues $\lambda_1 \ldots, \lambda_n$, respectively. We claim that these eigenvectors are linearly independent. Suppose

$$c_1\mathbf{v}_1 + c_2\mathbf{v}_2 + \cdots + c_n\mathbf{v}_n = \mathbf{0}.$$

Since $\mathbf{v}_i$ is in the null space of $\lambda_i I_n - A$, we have $(\lambda_i I_n - A)\mathbf{v}_i = \mathbf{0}$. On the other hand $(\lambda_i I_n - A)\mathbf{v}_j = (\lambda_i - \lambda_j)\mathbf{v}_j$ for $j \neq i$. So if we apply the product

$$(\lambda_2 I_n - A) \cdot (\lambda_3 I_n - A) \cdots (\lambda_n I_n - A)$$

to both sides, every term but the $\mathbf{v}_1$ term vanishes, and we are left with

$$(\lambda_2 - \lambda_1)(\lambda_3 - \lambda_1) \cdots (\lambda_n - \lambda_1)c_1\mathbf{v}_1 = \mathbf{0}.$$

Since $\mathbf{v}_1$ is an eigenvector, it is nonzero, and by assumption the eigenvalues are different, so each term in parentheses is nonzero. Hence c_1 must equal zero. Now we are left with

$$c_2\mathbf{v}_2 + \cdots + c_n\mathbf{v}_n = \mathbf{0},$$

and proceeding in the same way we find that $c_2 = 0$, and so on, until $c_n = 0$, so the eigenvectors are linearly independent. Since there are n of them, they form a basis for $\mathbf{R}^n$. $\square$

Example 23.7. The characteristic polynomial of

$$A = \begin{bmatrix} 3 & 8 & 3 \\ 0 & -4 & 5 \\ 0 & 0 & 7 \end{bmatrix}$$

is $p(\lambda) = (\lambda - 3)(\lambda + 4)(\lambda - 7)$, so the eigenvalues are 3, -4 and 7. Since these are different, Proposition 23.3 implies that A is diagonalizable. $\diamond$

Note that Proposition 23.3 provides a sufficient condition for diagonalizability. It is certainly not necessary that the eigenvalues be different. For instance, consider any scalar multiple of the identity, $A = \alpha I_n$. Its characteristic polynomial is $(\lambda - \alpha)^n$, so α is the only eigenvalue, but A is a diagonal matrix, and hence trivially diagonalizable. In Section 25 we will consider another condition which guarantees diagonalizability.

Exercises

23.1. Show that a square matrix A is invertible if and only if zero is not an eigenvalue of A.

23.2. Let A be an invertible matrix, and suppose that $\mathbf{v}$ is an eigenvector of A with eigenvalue λ. Show that $\mathbf{v}$ is an eigenvector of A^{-1}. What is the associated eigenvalue?

23.3. Let V be a subspace of $\mathbf{R}^n$, and let A be a matrix whose columns form a basis for V. Recall that $P = A(A^T A)^{-1} A^T$ is the matrix for the orthogonal projection onto V.

   (a) Show that $P^2 = P$.

   (b) Show that the only eigenvalues of P are 0 and 1.

   (c) What are the associated eigenspaces?

For each matrix A in Exercises 4 through 9, find the eigenvalues and a basis for each corresponding eigenspaces.

23.4. $A = \begin{bmatrix} 1 & 2 \\ 3 & 4 \end{bmatrix}$

23.5. $A = \begin{bmatrix} 1 & 1 \\ 1 & 1 \end{bmatrix}$

23.6. $A = \begin{bmatrix} 0 & 4 \\ 9 & 0 \end{bmatrix}$

23.7. $A = \begin{bmatrix} 2 & 1 & -1 \\ 0 & -1 & 3 \\ 0 & 0 & 3 \end{bmatrix}$

23.8. $A = \begin{bmatrix} 1 & -1 & -1 \\ -1 & 1 & -1 \\ -1 & -1 & 1 \end{bmatrix}$

23.9. $A = \begin{bmatrix} 1 & 1 \\ 1 & 0 \end{bmatrix}$

23.10. Suppose A and B are similar matrices. That is, $B = C^{-1}AC$ for some matrix C.

   (a) Show that A and B have the same characteristic polynomial, and therefore the same eigenvectors.

(b) Show that if **v** is an eigenvector of B with eigenvalue λ, then $C\mathbf{v}$ is an eigenvector of A with eigenvalue λ.

23.11. Show that the product of two diagonalizable matrices is diagonalizable.

23.12. Find two diagonalizable matrices whose sum is not diagonalizable.

24   Complex Eigenvalues and Eigenvectors

Recall that the eigenvalues of a matrix A are the roots of its characteristic polynomial $p(\lambda) = \det(\lambda I_n - A)$. As we have seen, not every polynomial has real roots. The polynomial $p(\lambda) = \lambda^2 + 1$, for instance, has roots $\pm i$, where $i = \sqrt{-1}$. Any number of the form bi for some nonzero real number b is called an **imaginary number**. A **complex number** is any number of the form $a + bi$ where a and b are real numbers. We denote by $\mathbf{C}$ the set of all complex numbers. That is,

$$\mathbf{C} = \{a + bi \mid a, b \in \mathbf{R}\}.$$

The complex number $z = a + bi$ is said to have **real part** $\Re(z) = a$ and **imaginary part** $\Im(z) = b$. Thus a real number is simply a complex number with zero imaginary part. A complex number $z = a + bi$ is usually represented by the point (a, b) in the **complex plane**, where the horizontal axis represents the real part and the vertical axis the imaginary part.

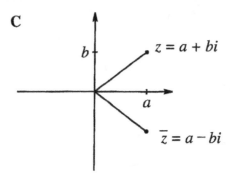

The **complex conjugate** of a complex number $z = a + bi$ is the number

$$\bar{z} = a - bi$$

which, in the complex plane, is the reflection of z across the real axis. Conjugating twice thus does nothing: $\bar{\bar{z}} = z$. A number z is real if and only if $\bar{z} = z$.

Example 24.1. $\overline{2 - 3i} = 2 + 3i$, $\overline{4i} = -4i$, and $\overline{7} = 7$.   ◇

The sum of two complex numbers $z_1 = a + bi$ and $z_2 = c + di$ are given by

$$z_1 + z_2 = (a + bi) + (c + di) = (a + b) + (c + d)i$$

and their product is

$$z_1 z_2 = (a + bi)(c + di) = (ac - bd) + (ad + bc)i$$

where in the second formula the fact that $i^2 = -1$ is used.

Example 24.2. $(2 + 3i) + (3 - 4i) = 5 - i$, $(2 + 3i)(3 + 2i) = 13i$, and $(2 + 3i)^2 = -5 + 12i$.
◇

It is easy to check that, for any two complex numbers z_1 and z_2,

$$\overline{z_1 + z_2} = \overline{z_1} + \overline{z_2}$$

and

$$\overline{z_1 z_2} = \overline{z_1}\ \overline{z_2}.$$

The **modulus** of a complex number $z = a + bi$ is $|z| = \sqrt{a^2 + b^2}$, the distance from z to 0 in the complex plane. Notice that the modulus squared can be expressed as

$$|z|^2 = z\bar{z},$$

the product of z and its complex conjugate $\bar{z}$. It is also fairly easy to see that

$$|z_1 z_2| = |z_1||z_2|$$

for any two complex numbers z_1 and z_2.

The formula

$$e^{i\theta} = \cos\theta + i\sin\theta$$

is often useful in simplifying expressions involving complex numbers.

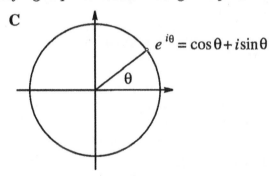

Formally, this comes from the Taylor series expansions of e^x, $\cos x$ and $\sin x$. See the exercises. Any complex number $z = a + bi$ can be expressed as $z = re^{i\theta} = r(\cos\theta + i\sin\theta)$ for some positive real number r, and some angle θ. Taking the modulus of both sides gives

$$r = \sqrt{a^2 + b^2} = |z|$$

The angle θ is determined by looking at a and b. For instance, if $a \neq 0$, then $b/a = (r\sin\theta)/(r\cos\theta) = \tan\theta$.

181

Example 24.3. Let $z = 1 + i$. Then $|z| = \sqrt{2}$, and $\tan\theta = 1$, so $\theta = \pi/4$. Thus $z = \sqrt{2}(\cos(\pi/4) + i\sin(\pi/4)) = \sqrt{2}e^{i\pi/4}$. Suppose we want to know z^{17}. Then

$$
\begin{aligned}
z^{17} &= (\sqrt{2})^{17}e^{17i\pi/4} \\
&= 2^8\sqrt{2}(\cos(17\pi/4) + i\sin(17\pi/4)) \\
&= 256\sqrt{2}(\cos(\pi/4) + i\sin(\pi/4)) \\
&= 256\sqrt{2}(\sqrt{2}/2 + i\sqrt{2}/2) \\
&= 256(1 + i).
\end{aligned}
$$

$\diamond$

For our purposes the most important fact regarding complex numbers is that any polynomial with complex coefficients factors completely. The proof of this fact requires techniques from complex analysis, and is beyond the scope of this text.

Proposition 24.1. (Fundamental Theorem of Algebra) Let

$$
p(z) = a_n z^n + a_{n-1}z^{n-1} + \cdots + a_1 z + a_0
$$

be any n^{th} degree polynomial with complex coefficients a_0 through a_n ($a_n \neq 0$). Then

$$
p_n(z) = a_n(z - r_1)(z - r_2)\cdots(z - r_n)
$$

for some complex numbers r_1 through r_n.

Thus any polynomial with complex coefficients has n complex roots r_1 through r_n. The roots may or may not be distinct. The number of times a root appears in the factorization is called the **multiplicity** of the root. We remark that, since real numbers are complex numbers (with zero imaginary part), this result applies to polynomials with real coefficients as well.

Example 24.4. By the quadratic formula, the polynomial $p(z) = z^2 - 2z + 2$ has roots $1 + i$ and $1 - i$, so $p(z) = (z - 1 - i)(z - 1 + i)$. $\diamond$

Example 24.5. By inspection, the polynomial $p(z) = z^4 - 2z^3 + 2z^2 - 2z + 1$ has a root $z = 1$, so we can factor out $z - 1$ to get $p(z) = (z - 1)(z^3 - z^2 + z - 1)$. Again, by inspection, $z = 1$ is a root of the cubic term, so $p(z) = (z - 1)^2(z^2 + 1)$. Finally, the roots of $z^2 + 1$ are $\pm i$, so $p(z) = (z - 1)^2(z - i)(z + i)$. Thus the roots of $p(z)$ are $z = 1$, with multiplicity 2, $z = i$ and $z = -i$, each with multiplicity 1. $\diamond$

Example 24.6. Let $p(z) = z^2 + i$. The roots are the square roots of $-i$. The number $-i$ lies on the unit circle in the complex plane, at angle $3\pi/2$, so $-i = e^{3\pi i/2}$. Note that if $z = re^{i\theta}$, then $z^2 = r^2 e^{2i\theta}$, so if we choose $r = 1$ and $\theta = 3\pi/4$, then $z^2 = -i$. Thus

$$
z_1 = e^{3\pi i/4} = \cos(3\pi/4) + i\sin(3\pi/4) = -\frac{\sqrt{2}}{2} + \frac{\sqrt{2}}{2}i
$$

is one root. Clearly $-z_1$ must be the other, so $p(z) = \left(z + \frac{\sqrt{2}}{2} - \frac{\sqrt{2}}{2}i\right)\left(z - \frac{\sqrt{2}}{2} + \frac{\sqrt{2}}{2}i\right)$. $\diamond$

In polynomials with real coefficients the non-real roots appear in complex conjugate pairs.

Proposition 24.2. Let $p(z) = a_n z^n + a_{n-1} z^{n-1} + \cdots + a_1 z + a_0$ be a polynomial with *real* coefficients a_0 through a_n, and suppose z_0 is any root of p. Then $\bar{z}_0$ is a root of p.

Proof. Since z_0 is a root,

$$p(z_0) = a_n z_0^n + a_{n-1} z_0^{n-1} + \cdots + a_1 z_0 + a_0 = 0.$$

Taking the conjugate of both sides, and using the fact that conjugation commutes with addition and multiplication, and the fact that all of the coefficients are real, we have

$$
\begin{aligned}
0 &= \overline{a_n z_0^n + a_{n-1} z_0^{n-1} + \cdots + a_1 z_0 + a_0} \\
&= \overline{a_n z_0^n} + \overline{a_{n-1} z_0^{n-1}} + \cdots + \overline{a_1 z_0} + \overline{a_0} \\
&= a_n \bar{z}_0^n + a_{n-1} \bar{z}_0^{n-1} + \cdots + a_1 \bar{z}_0 + a_0 \\
&= p(\bar{z}_0)
\end{aligned}
$$

and thus $\bar{z}_0$ is a root. $\square$

Note that this statement is of interest only in the case that z_0 is not a real number, since if z_0 is real, $\bar{z}_0 = z_0$.

Complex Vectors and Matrices

By analogy with our definition of $\mathbf{R}^n$, we define $\mathbf{C}^n$ to be the set of ordered n-tuples of complex numbers. Vectors in $\mathbf{C}^n$ take the form

$$
\mathbf{v} = \begin{bmatrix} v_1 \\ v_2 \\ \vdots \\ v_n \end{bmatrix} = \begin{bmatrix} a_1 + b_1 i \\ a_2 + b_2 i \\ \vdots \\ a_n + b_n i \end{bmatrix}.
$$

Addition and scalar multiplication are defined componentwise as in $\mathbf{R}^n$, but now the scalars may be complex numbers as well.

Example 24.7. The vectors

$$
\mathbf{v} = \begin{bmatrix} 2 - i \\ -1 + 2i \\ 3 + 3i \end{bmatrix} \quad \text{and} \quad \mathbf{w} = \begin{bmatrix} -1 + 3i \\ 4 + 5i \\ 2 - 5i \end{bmatrix}
$$

are elements of $\mathbf{C}^3$. Their sum is

$$
\mathbf{v} + \mathbf{w} = \begin{bmatrix} 1 + 2i \\ 3 + 7i \\ 5 - 2i \end{bmatrix}
$$

and if we let $c = i + 1$, then

$$c\mathbf{v} = \begin{bmatrix} 3 + i \\ -3 + i \\ 6i \end{bmatrix}.$$

$\diamond$

With these definitions, the notions of linear combinations, spans, linear independence, subspaces, and linear transformations are defined in the same manner as in $\mathbf{R}^n$. The matrix for a linear transformation $\mathbf{T} : \mathbf{C}^n \to \mathbf{C}^m$ is an $m \times n$ matrix with complex entries. The operations of addition and multiplication of matrices are defined as for real matrices.

Example 24.8. Let

$$A = \begin{bmatrix} 3 + i & 5i \\ -2 & 2 - 2i \end{bmatrix}, \qquad B = \begin{bmatrix} 3 & 1 - 3i \\ 4 + i & 0 \end{bmatrix}, \qquad \text{and} \qquad \mathbf{v} = \begin{bmatrix} 3 + 4i \\ 1 - i \end{bmatrix}.$$

Then

$$A + B = \begin{bmatrix} 6 + i & 1 + 2i \\ 2 + i & 2 - 2i \end{bmatrix}, \qquad AB = \begin{bmatrix} 4 + 23i & 6 - 8i \\ 4 - 6i & -2 + 6i \end{bmatrix}, \qquad \text{and} \qquad A\mathbf{v} = \begin{bmatrix} 10 + 20i \\ -6 - 12i \end{bmatrix}.$$

$\diamond$

We define the complex conjugate of a vector in $\mathbf{C}^n$ componentwise by

$$\overline{\mathbf{v}} = \begin{bmatrix} \overline{v_1} \\ \overline{v_2} \\ \vdots \\ \overline{v_n} \end{bmatrix} = \begin{bmatrix} a_1 - b_1 i \\ a_2 - b_2 i \\ \vdots \\ a_n - b_n i \end{bmatrix}.$$

Likewise the conjugate of a complex matrix is defined by taking the conjugate of each entry.

$$\overline{\begin{bmatrix} a_{11} & a_{12} & \cdots & a_{1n} \\ a_{21} & a_{22} & \cdots & a_{2n} \\ \vdots & \vdots & \ddots & \vdots \\ a_{m1} & a_{m2} & \cdots & a_{mn} \end{bmatrix}} = \begin{bmatrix} \overline{a_{11}} & \overline{a_{12}} & \cdots & \overline{a_{1n}} \\ \overline{a_{21}} & \overline{a_{22}} & \cdots & \overline{a_{2n}} \\ \vdots & \vdots & \ddots & \vdots \\ \overline{a_{m1}} & \overline{a_{m2}} & \cdots & \overline{a_{mn}} \end{bmatrix}$$

Example 24.9.

$$\overline{\begin{bmatrix} 2 - i \\ -1 + 2i \\ 3 + 3i \end{bmatrix}} = \begin{bmatrix} 2 + i \\ -1 - 2i \\ 3 - 3i \end{bmatrix} \qquad \text{and} \qquad \overline{\begin{bmatrix} 4 + 7i & 2 - 3i \\ -5 + 2i & 6 + 5i \end{bmatrix}} = \begin{bmatrix} 4 - 7i & 2 + 3i \\ -5 - 2i & 6 - 5i \end{bmatrix}$$

$\diamond$

Since the conjugate of a product of complex numbers is the product of the conjugates, and likewise for sums, and since the entries in the product matrix AB are sums of products of entries of A and B, it follows that

$$\overline{AB} = \overline{A}\,\overline{B}.$$

The same property holds for matrix-vector products and dot products, since both are special cases of matrix products. The one major difference between $\mathbf{C}^n$ and $\mathbf{R}^n$ is that the length of a complex vector in $\mathbf{C}^n$ is defined to be

$$\|\mathbf{v}\| = \sqrt{|v_1|^2 + |v_2|^2 + \cdots + |v_n|^2}.$$

where, in place of v_i^2 which could be negative for complex v_i, we have $|v_i|^2$ which is always nonnegative.

Example 24.10. The vector

$$\mathbf{v} = \begin{bmatrix} 5 - 2i \\ 1 + 2i \\ -1 + i \end{bmatrix}$$

has length $\|\mathbf{v}\| = \sqrt{(25 + 4) + (1 + 4) + (1 + 1)} = 6.$ ◇

With this definition, lengths have the same properties as lengths of real vectors, with one important exception. The relation between dot product and length is

$$\|\mathbf{v}\|^2 = \mathbf{v} \cdot \overline{\mathbf{v}}.$$

Eigenvalues and Eigenvectors

Applying Proposition 24.1 to the characteristic polynomial $p(\lambda) = (\lambda I_n - A)$ of some $n \times n$ matrix A, we see that

$$p(\lambda) = (\lambda - \lambda_1)(\lambda - \lambda_2) \cdots (\lambda - \lambda_n) \tag{24.1}$$

for some complex numbers $\lambda_1, \cdots, \lambda_n$, which are the eigenvalues of A. The corresponding eigenspaces are defined in the same way as before, only now they may consist of vectors in $\mathbf{C}^n$

Example 24.11. The characteristic polynomial of

$$A = \begin{bmatrix} 0 & -1 \\ 1 & 0 \end{bmatrix}$$

is $p(\lambda) = \lambda^2 + 1$, so the eigenvalues of A are $\lambda = \pm i$. Since

$$\text{rref}(iI_2 - A) = \begin{bmatrix} 1 & -i \\ 0 & 0 \end{bmatrix},$$

the eigenspace associated with $\lambda = i$ is

$$E_i = \text{span}\left(\begin{bmatrix} i \\ 1 \end{bmatrix}\right)$$

and since

$$\text{rref}(-iI_2 - A) = \begin{bmatrix} 1 & i \\ 0 & 0 \end{bmatrix},$$

the eigenspace associated with $\lambda = -i$ is

$$E_{-i} = \text{span}\left(\begin{bmatrix} -i \\ 1 \end{bmatrix}\right).$$

$\diamond$

Notice that the two eigenvectors in this example are conjugates of one another. In general, if A is a matrix with real entries, then the conjugate of an eigenvector is also an eigenvector.

Proposition 24.3. Let A be an $n \times n$ matrix with real entries, and suppose $\mathbf{v}$ is an eigenvector of A with eigenvalue λ. Then $\overline{\mathbf{v}}$ is an eigenvector of A with eigenvalue $\overline{\lambda}$.

Proof. Suppose $\mathbf{v}$ is an eigenvector with eigenvalue λ, so that $A\mathbf{v} = \lambda\mathbf{v}$. Taking the complex conjugate of both sides gives $\overline{A\mathbf{v}} = \overline{\lambda\mathbf{v}} = \overline{\lambda}\,\overline{\mathbf{v}}$. Since A has real entries $\overline{A\mathbf{v}} = \overline{A}\,\overline{\mathbf{v}} = A\,\overline{\mathbf{v}}$. Thus we have $A\,\overline{\mathbf{v}} = \overline{\lambda}\,\overline{\mathbf{v}}$, as claimed. $\square$

We next establish an important relationship between the eigenvalues of a matrix A and the determinant of A. By (24.1), evaluating the characteristic polynomial at $\lambda = 0$ gives

$$p(0) = (-\lambda_1)(-\lambda_2)\cdots(-\lambda_n) = (-1)^n \lambda_1 \cdot \lambda_2 \cdots \lambda_n.$$

On the other hand

$$p(0) = \det(-A) = (-1)^n \det(A),$$

and therefore

$$\det(A) = \lambda_1 \cdot \lambda_2 \cdots \lambda_n.$$

Proposition 24.4. Let A be a square matrix. The determinant of A equals the product of the eigenvalues of A.

Another important quantity associated with a square matrix A is its **trace**, defined by

$$\text{tr}(A) = \sum_{i=1}^{n} a_{ii}.$$

That is, the trace of A is the sum of the diagonal entries of A. In the case that A is a diagonal matrix, the eigenvalues are on the diagonal, so the sum of the eigenvalues equals the trace. This relationship turns out to be true generally.

Proposition 24.5. Let A be a square matrix. The trace of A equals the sum of the eigenvalues of A.

Proof. First we observe that

$$p(\lambda) = (\lambda - \lambda_1)(\lambda - \lambda_2) \cdots (\lambda - \lambda_n)$$
$$= \lambda^n - (\lambda_1 + \lambda_2 + \cdots + \lambda_n)\lambda^{n-1} + \text{ lower degree terms}$$

so the coefficient of λ^{n-1} in $p(\lambda)$ is minus the sum of the eigenvalues. We next find this coefficient in terms of A using the fact that $p(\lambda) = \det(\lambda I_n - A)$. First notice that

$$\lambda I_n - A = \begin{bmatrix} \lambda - a_{11} & -a_{12} & \cdots & -a_{1n} \\ -a_{21} & \lambda - a_{22} & \cdots & -a_{2n} \\ \vdots & \vdots & \ddots & \vdots \\ -a_{n1} & -a_{n2} & \cdots & \lambda - a_{nn} \end{bmatrix}.$$

Expanding the determinant across the first row we claim that the term

$$(\lambda - a_{11}) \begin{vmatrix} \lambda - a_{22} & \cdots & -a_{2n} \\ \vdots & \ddots & \vdots \\ -a_{n2} & \cdots & \lambda - a_{nn} \end{vmatrix}$$

is the only term which contributes to the λ^{n-1} term. To see this, observe that all other terms involve determinants of $(n-1) \times (n-1)$ submatrices obtained by removing the first row and a column other than the first column, and therefore have only $n-2$ entries which contain a λ. Thus these terms contribute only to the terms of degree $n-2$ or less. Now, expanding the remaining determinant across the first row, the same reasoning implies that only the first term will lead to a contribution to λ^{n-1}. Repeating these arguments, we see that

$$\det(\lambda I_n - A) = (\lambda - a_{11})(\lambda - a_{22}) \cdots (\lambda - a_{nn}) + \text{ terms of degree } n-2 \text{ or less.}$$

Thus, expanding the first term, we have

$$p(\lambda) = \lambda^n - (a_{11} + a_{22} + \cdots + a_{nn})\lambda^{n-1} + \text{ terms of degree } n-2 \text{ or less,}$$

so the coefficient of λ^{n-1} in $p(\lambda)$ is minus the trace of A. Comparison with the previous calculation proves the result. $\square$

Exercises

In Exercises 1 through 9, compute the given expression.

24.1. $\begin{bmatrix} 4 - 5i \\ 7 + 8i \end{bmatrix} + \begin{bmatrix} 7i \\ 1 + 6i \end{bmatrix}$

24.2. $i \begin{bmatrix} 1 + 2i \\ 3 + 4i \end{bmatrix}$

24.3. $\begin{bmatrix} 2 + 5i \\ 4 + 2i \\ -1 + 8i \end{bmatrix} + \begin{bmatrix} -2 + i \\ 4i \\ 1 - 7i \end{bmatrix}$

24.4. $(i + 3) \begin{bmatrix} 3 + i \\ 2 - 3i \\ -i \end{bmatrix}$

24.5. $\begin{bmatrix} 2 & 1 + i \\ i - 1 & i \\ 0 & 3 \end{bmatrix} \begin{bmatrix} -1 + 2i \\ 3i \end{bmatrix}$

24.6. $\begin{bmatrix} 2 & 1 + i & 0 \\ 1 + i & i + 4 & 1 + 3i \end{bmatrix} \begin{bmatrix} -1 + 2i \\ 3i \\ 1 \end{bmatrix}$

24.7. $\begin{bmatrix} 2 & 1 + i \\ i - 1 & i \\ 0 & 3 \end{bmatrix} \begin{bmatrix} 2 & 1 + i & 0 \\ 1 + i & i + 4 & 1 + 3i \end{bmatrix}$

24.8. $\begin{bmatrix} 2 & 1 + i & 0 \\ 1 + i & i + 4 & 1 + 3i \end{bmatrix} \begin{bmatrix} 2 & 1 + i \\ i - 1 & i \\ 0 & 3 \end{bmatrix}$

24.9. $\overline{\begin{bmatrix} 5 - 2i & 3 + i \\ -2 + 4i & -1 - 7i \end{bmatrix}}^{T}$

24.10. Let

$$\mathbf{v} = \begin{bmatrix} 1 + 5i \\ 5 + 7i \end{bmatrix},$$

and compute the following.

(a) $\mathbf{v} + \overline{\mathbf{v}}$

(b) $\mathbf{v} - \overline{\mathbf{v}}$

(c) $\mathbf{v} \cdot \mathbf{v}$

(d) $\mathbf{v} \cdot \overline{\mathbf{v}}$

(e) $\|\mathbf{v}\|$

24.11. Let

$$\mathbf{v} = \begin{bmatrix} 1 + 2i \\ 1 - 5i \\ 2 + i \end{bmatrix},$$

and compute the following.

(a) $\mathbf{v} + \overline{\mathbf{v}}$

(b) $\mathbf{v} - \overline{\mathbf{v}}$

(c) $\mathbf{v} \cdot \mathbf{v}$

(d) $\mathbf{v} \cdot \overline{\mathbf{v}}$

(e) $\|\mathbf{v}\|$

24.12. Consider the following Taylor series expansions.

$$e^x = 1 + x + \frac{x^2}{2!} + \frac{x^3}{3!} + \frac{x^4}{4!} + \cdots$$

$$\cos x = 1 - \frac{x^2}{2!} + \frac{x^4}{4!} - \frac{x^6}{6!} + \cdots$$

$$\sin x = x - \frac{x^3}{3!} + \frac{x^5}{5!} - \frac{x^7}{7!} + \cdots$$

Evaluate the first expansion at $x = i\theta$, and simplify using the other two expansions to deduce the formula $e^{i\theta} = \cos\theta + i\sin\theta$.

24.13. Let z_1 and z_2 be any complex numbers.

(a) Show that $\overline{z_1 + z_2} = \overline{z_1} + \overline{z_2}$.

(b) Show that $\overline{z_1 z_2} = \overline{z_1}\, \overline{z_2}$.

(c) Show that $|z_1 z_2| = |z_1|\,|z_2|$.

Find all roots of the following polynomials, and determine the multiplicity of each root.

24.14. $z^2 + 6$

24.15. $z^2 + 2z + 5$

24.16. $z^3 - z^2 + z - 1$

24.17. $z^4 + 2z^2 + 1$

24.18. $z^4 + z^3 + z^2$

24.19. $z^4 + 4$

24.20. $z^2 - 1 - i$

25 Symmetric Matrices

A square matrix A is called **symmetric** if $A^T = A$.

Example 25.1. Let

$$A = \begin{bmatrix} 1 & 2 & -1 \\ 2 & 3 & 4 \\ -1 & 4 & 7 \end{bmatrix} \quad \text{and} \quad B = \begin{bmatrix} 1 & 2 & 3 \\ 4 & 5 & 2 \\ 6 & 4 & 1 \end{bmatrix}.$$

Then

$$A^T = \begin{bmatrix} 1 & 2 & -1 \\ 2 & 3 & 4 \\ -1 & 4 & 7 \end{bmatrix} = A$$

so A is symmetric, but

$$B^T = \begin{bmatrix} 1 & 4 & 6 \\ 2 & 5 & 4 \\ 3 & 2 & 1 \end{bmatrix} \neq B$$

so B is not symmetric. $\diamond$

It turns out that real symmetric matrices are always diagonalizable. Before we can prove this we need the following result about the eigenvalues of a symmetric matrix.

Proposition 25.1. All the eigenvalues of a real symmetric matrix A are real numbers.

Proof. Let λ be an eigenvalue of A, and let $\mathbf{v}$ be an eigenvector with eigenvalue λ. Then by Proposition 24.3 the vector $\overline{\mathbf{v}}$ is also an eigenvector, with eigenvalue $\overline{\lambda}$. We now evaluate the expression $A\mathbf{v} \cdot \overline{\mathbf{v}}$. First, using the fact that $\mathbf{v}$ is an eigenvector, we get

$$A\mathbf{v} \cdot \overline{\mathbf{v}} = \lambda \mathbf{v} \cdot \overline{\mathbf{v}} = \lambda \|\mathbf{v}\|^2.$$

Next, using Proposition 18.2, the symmetry of A and the fact the $\overline{\mathbf{v}}$ is an eigenvector, we have

$$A\mathbf{v} \cdot \overline{\mathbf{v}} = \mathbf{v} \cdot A^T \overline{\mathbf{v}} = \mathbf{v} \cdot A\overline{\mathbf{v}} = \mathbf{v} \cdot \overline{\lambda}\overline{\mathbf{v}} = \overline{\lambda}\mathbf{v} \cdot \overline{\mathbf{v}} = \overline{\lambda}\|\mathbf{v}\|^2.$$

Since $\mathbf{v}$ is an eigenvector, $\mathbf{v}$ is nonzero, and therefore we have $\lambda = \overline{\lambda}$, so λ is real. $\square$

Proposition 25.2. (Spectral Theorem) Let A be an $n \times n$ real symmetric matrix. Then there exists an orthonormal basis $\mathcal{B} = \{\mathbf{v}_1, \ldots, \mathbf{v}_n\}$ of $\mathbf{R}^n$ consisting of eigenvectors of A.

So not only is A diagonalizable, but the eigenvectors can be chosen to be *orthonormal*. If we let C be the matrix whose columns are the basis vectors, then C is an orthogonal matrix, so $C^{-1} = C^T$. It then follows from Proposition 23.2 that

$$C^T A C = D$$

where D is the diagonal matrix whose diagonal entries are the eigenvalues.

Proof. We use induction on the size n of the matrix A. (See Appendix A.) For the case $n = 1$, suppose A is a 1×1 matrix $[\lambda]$, so the vector $[1]$ is a unit eigenvector of A with eigenvalue λ, and forms an orthonormal eigenbasis for $\mathbf{R}^1$. Now suppose the result holds for all $k \times k$ real symmetric matrices. That is, suppose that every $k \times k$ real symmetric matrix has an orthonormal eigenbasis. We must now show that the same holds for any $(k+1) \times (k+1)$ real symmetric matrix. So suppose A is a $(k+1) \times (k+1)$ real symmetric matrix. By Proposition 25.1, the eigenvalues of A are real, so let λ be a real eigenvalue of A, and let $\mathbf{v}$ be a real unit eigenvector with eigenvalue λ. Let $V = \operatorname{span}(\mathbf{v})$ and let $\mathbf{T} : \mathbf{R}^n \to \mathbf{R}^n$ be the linear transformation defined by $\mathbf{T}(\mathbf{x}) = A\mathbf{x}$. We claim that $\mathbf{T}$ sends vectors from $V^\perp$ to $V^\perp$. To see this, suppose $\mathbf{w}$ is in $V^\perp$, so that $\mathbf{w} \cdot \mathbf{v} = 0$. Then, by Proposition 18.2

$$\mathbf{T}(\mathbf{w}) \cdot \mathbf{v} = A\mathbf{w} \cdot \mathbf{v} = \mathbf{w} \cdot A\mathbf{v} = \mathbf{w} \cdot \lambda\mathbf{v} = \lambda \mathbf{w} \cdot \mathbf{v} = 0,$$

so $\mathbf{T}(\mathbf{w})$ is orthogonal to $\mathbf{v}$, and hence orthogonal to any scalar multiple of $\mathbf{v}$. Thus $\mathbf{T}(\mathbf{w})$ is in $V^\perp$. Thus we may regard $\mathbf{T}$ as a linear transformation from $V^\perp$ to $V^\perp$. Since V has dimension 1, $V^\perp$ has dimension k. Let $\mathcal{B} = \{\mathbf{w}_1, \dots, \mathbf{w}_k\}$ be any orthonormal basis for $V^\perp$ and let B be the matrix for $\mathbf{T} : V^\perp \to V^\perp$ with respect to $\mathcal{B}$. That is, B is the $k \times k$ matrix such that

$$[\mathbf{T}(\mathbf{w})]_{\mathcal{B}} = B[\mathbf{w}]_{\mathcal{B}}$$

for all $\mathbf{w}$ in $V^\perp$. Observe that B is a real matrix. We will now show that B is symmetric. Let C denote the matrix whose columns are $\mathbf{w}_1$ through $\mathbf{w}_k$. Since $\mathbf{w} = C[\mathbf{w}]_{\mathcal{B}}$ for all $\mathbf{w}$ in $V^\perp$, using Proposition 18.2 and the fact that $C^T C = I_k$, we have

$$\mathbf{w} \cdot \mathbf{x} = C[\mathbf{w}]_{\mathcal{B}} \cdot C[\mathbf{x}]_{\mathcal{B}} = [\mathbf{w}]_{\mathcal{B}} \cdot C^T C[\mathbf{x}]_{\mathcal{B}} = [\mathbf{w}]_{\mathcal{B}} \cdot [\mathbf{x}]_{\mathcal{B}}$$

for any $\mathbf{w}$ and $\mathbf{x}$ in $V^\perp$. Using Proposition 18.2 again, along with the symmetry of A, we have

$$\mathbf{T}(\mathbf{w}) \cdot \mathbf{x} = A\mathbf{w} \cdot \mathbf{x} = \mathbf{w} \cdot A\mathbf{x} = \mathbf{w} \cdot \mathbf{T}(\mathbf{x})$$

and thus

$$B[\mathbf{w}]_{\mathcal{B}} \cdot [\mathbf{x}]_{\mathcal{B}} = [\mathbf{T}(\mathbf{w})]_{\mathcal{B}} \cdot [\mathbf{x}]_{\mathcal{B}} = \mathbf{T}(\mathbf{w}) \cdot \mathbf{x} = \mathbf{w} \cdot \mathbf{T}(\mathbf{x}) = [\mathbf{w}]_{\mathcal{B}} \cdot [\mathbf{T}(\mathbf{x})]_{\mathcal{B}} = [\mathbf{w}]_{\mathcal{B}} \cdot B[\mathbf{x}]_{\mathcal{B}}$$

for every $\mathbf{w}$ and $\mathbf{x}$ in $V^\perp$. Applying this to the basis vectors in $\mathcal{B}$, we find that

$$B\mathbf{e}_i \cdot \mathbf{e}_j = B[\mathbf{v}_i]_{\mathcal{B}} \cdot [\mathbf{v}_j]_{\mathcal{B}} = [\mathbf{v}_i]_{\mathcal{B}} \cdot B[\mathbf{v}_j]_{\mathcal{B}} = \mathbf{e}_i \cdot B\mathbf{e}_j$$

191

for $1 \leq i \leq k$ and $1 \leq j \leq k$. Since $B\mathbf{e}_i$ is column i of B, $B\mathbf{e}_i \cdot \mathbf{e}_j$ is the entry in row j, column i of B. Likewise, $\mathbf{e}_i \cdot B\mathbf{e}_j$ is the entry in row i, column j of B. Since these are equal, B must be symmetric. Since B is $k \times k$, the induction hypothesis implies that there exists an orthonormal basis $\{\mathbf{y}_1, \ldots, \mathbf{y}_k\}$ of $\mathbf{R}^k$ consisting of eigenvectors of B. Call the corresponding eigenvectors λ_1 through λ_k and define

$$\mathbf{v}_1 = C\mathbf{y}_1, \qquad \cdots \qquad , \mathbf{v}_k = C\mathbf{y}_k.$$

Observing that this implies $[\mathbf{v}_i]_{\mathcal{B}} = \mathbf{y}_i$ for $1 \leq i \leq k$, we have

$$A\mathbf{v}_i = \mathbf{T}(\mathbf{v}_i) = C[\mathbf{T}(\mathbf{v}_i)]_{\mathcal{B}} = CB[\mathbf{v}_i]_{\mathcal{B}} = CB\mathbf{y}_i = C(\lambda_i \mathbf{y}_i) = \lambda_i C\mathbf{y}_i = \lambda_i \mathbf{v}_i$$

so each $\mathbf{v}_i$ is an eigenvector of A. We now claim that $\{\mathbf{v}, \mathbf{v}_1, \ldots, \mathbf{v}_k\}$ is an orthonormal basis for $\mathbf{R}^{k+1}$. To see this, we first observe that, since $\{\mathbf{y}_1, \ldots, \mathbf{y}_k\}$ is an orthonormal set, the relation

$$\mathbf{v}_i \cdot \mathbf{v}_j = C\mathbf{y}_i \cdot C\mathbf{y}_j = \mathbf{y}_i \cdot C^T C \mathbf{y}_j = \mathbf{y}_i \cdot \mathbf{y}_j$$

implies that $\{\mathbf{v}_1, \ldots, \mathbf{v}_k\}$ is an orthonormal set. Next, since the columns of C are in $V^{\perp}$, each vector $\mathbf{v}_i = C\mathbf{y}_i$ is in $V^{\perp}$, and therefore orthogonal to $\mathbf{v}$. Hence, since $\mathbf{v}$ is a unit eigenvector of A, $\{\mathbf{v}, \mathbf{v}_1, \ldots, \mathbf{v}_k\}$ is an orthonormal basis for $\mathbf{R}^{k+1}$ consisting of eigenvectors of A. By the principle of induction this completes the proof. $\square$

Geometrically, the Spectral Theorem says that any symmetric matrix represents a transformation which stretches or contracts vectors along some set of perpendicular axes.

Example 25.2. Let

$$A = \begin{bmatrix} 1 & 2 \\ 2 & -2 \end{bmatrix}.$$

The characteristic polynomial of A is

$$\lambda^2 + \lambda - 6 = (\lambda + 3)(\lambda - 2)$$

so the eigenvalues of A are $\lambda = -3$ and $\lambda = 2$. Since

$$-3I_2 - A = \begin{bmatrix} -4 & -2 \\ -2 & -1 \end{bmatrix}$$

the eigenspace associated with $\lambda = 4$ is

$$E_{-3} = \mathrm{span}\left(\begin{bmatrix} 1 \\ -2 \end{bmatrix} \right)$$

and since

$$2I_2 - A = \begin{bmatrix} 1 & -2 \\ -2 & 4 \end{bmatrix}$$

the eigenspace associated with $\lambda = 2$ is

$$E_2 = \text{span}\left(\begin{bmatrix} 2 \\ 1 \end{bmatrix}\right).$$

Thus if we let

$$\mathbf{v}_1 = \frac{1}{\sqrt{5}}\begin{bmatrix} 1 \\ -2 \end{bmatrix} \qquad \mathbf{v}_2 = \frac{1}{\sqrt{5}}\begin{bmatrix} 2 \\ 1 \end{bmatrix}$$

then $\mathcal{B} = \{\mathbf{v}_1, \mathbf{v}_2\}$ is an orthonormal eigenbasis for A. The change of basis matrix is

$$C = \frac{1}{\sqrt{5}}\begin{bmatrix} 1 & 2 \\ -2 & 1 \end{bmatrix}$$

and we have

$$C^T A C = \begin{bmatrix} -3 & 0 \\ 0 & 2 \end{bmatrix}.$$

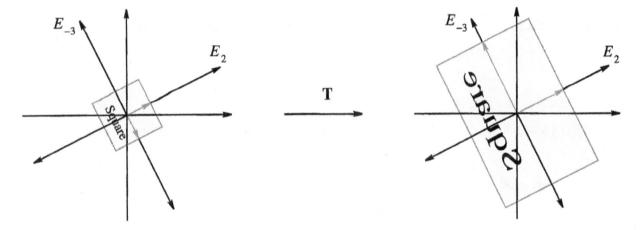

As shown above, the image under the linear transformation defined by A of a square whose sides are parallel to the eigenspaces is a rectangle whose sides are parallel to the eigenspaces. The square is stretched by a factor of 2 parallel to E_2, stretched by a factor of 3 parallel to E_{-3}, and reflected across E_2 (the orthogonal complement of E_{-3}) because of the sign of the eigenvalue -3. $\diamond$

The Spectral Theorem only guarantees the *existence* of an orthonormal basis of eigenvectors. In many cases, however, finding an orthonormal basis can be tricky. The following result simplifies matters somewhat.

Proposition 25.3. Let A be a real symmetric matrix and suppose that $\mathbf{v}_1$ and $\mathbf{v}_2$ are eigenvectors with different eigenvalues $\lambda_1 \neq \lambda_2$. Then $\mathbf{v}_1$ and $\mathbf{v}_2$ are orthogonal.

Proof. Since A is symmetric, the eigenvalues and associated eigenvectors are real. To prove the result we calculate the dot product $A\mathbf{v}_1 \cdot \mathbf{v}_2$ in two ways. First, since $\mathbf{v}_1$ is an eigenvector,

$$A\mathbf{v}_1 \cdot \mathbf{v}_2 = \lambda_1 \mathbf{v}_1 \cdot \mathbf{v}_2.$$

On the other hand, since $\mathbf{v}_2$ is an eigenvector, and A is symmetric, using Proposition 18.2 gives

$$A\mathbf{v}_1 \cdot \mathbf{v}_2 = \mathbf{v}_1 \cdot A^T\mathbf{v}_2 = \mathbf{v}_1 \cdot A\mathbf{v}_2 = \lambda_2 \mathbf{v}_1 \cdot \mathbf{v}_2.$$

Thus, subtracting the two displayed equations results in

$$(\lambda_1 - \lambda_2)\mathbf{v}_1 \cdot \mathbf{v}_2 = 0,$$

and since $\lambda_1 \neq \lambda_2$ by assumption, $\mathbf{v}_1 \cdot \mathbf{v}_2 = 0$, so $\mathbf{v}_1$ and $\mathbf{v}_2$ are orthogonal. $\square$

So eigenvectors with different eigenvalues are automatically orthogonal. The difficulty arises when one or more of the eigenspaces has dimension greater than one. Eigenvectors in the same eigenspace are not necessarily orthogonal. However, by applying the Gram-Schmidt process it is always possible to find an orthonormal basis for each eigenspace.

Example 25.3. The characteristic polynomial of the symmetric matrix

$$A = \begin{bmatrix} 2 & 1 & 1 \\ 1 & 2 & 1 \\ 1 & 1 & 2 \end{bmatrix}$$

is $p(\lambda) = (\lambda - 1)^2(\lambda - 4)$, so the eigenvalues are $\lambda = 1$, with multiplicity 2, and $\lambda = 4$. Since

$$4I_3 - A = \begin{bmatrix} 2 & -1 & -1 \\ -1 & 2 & -1 \\ -1 & -1 & 2 \end{bmatrix} \quad \Longrightarrow \quad \mathrm{rref}(I_3 - A) = \begin{bmatrix} 1 & 0 & -1 \\ 0 & 1 & -1 \\ 0 & 0 & 0 \end{bmatrix},$$

the vector

$$\mathbf{u}_1 = \frac{1}{\sqrt{3}}\begin{bmatrix} 1 \\ 1 \\ 1 \end{bmatrix}$$

forms an orthonormal basis for E_4. Next, since

$$1I_3 - A = \begin{bmatrix} -1 & -1 & -1 \\ -1 & -1 & -1 \\ -1 & -1 & -1 \end{bmatrix} \quad \Longrightarrow \quad \mathrm{rref}(1I_3 - A) = \begin{bmatrix} 1 & 1 & 1 \\ 0 & 0 & 0 \\ 0 & 0 & 0 \end{bmatrix},$$

the vectors

$$\mathbf{v}_2 = \begin{bmatrix} -1 \\ 1 \\ 0 \end{bmatrix} \quad \text{and} \quad \mathbf{v}_3 = \begin{bmatrix} -1 \\ 0 \\ 1 \end{bmatrix}$$

form a basis for E_1. Notice that $\mathbf{v}_1$ and $\mathbf{v}_2$ are both orthogonal to $\mathbf{u}_1$ as guaranteed by Proposition 25.3. However $\mathbf{v}_1$ and $\mathbf{v}_2$ are not orthogonal to one another. In Example 22.6, we found via the Gram-Schmidt process that the vectors

$$\mathbf{u}_2 = \frac{1}{\sqrt{2}} \begin{bmatrix} -1 \\ 1 \\ 0 \end{bmatrix} \qquad \text{and} \qquad \mathbf{u}_3 = \frac{1}{\sqrt{6}} \begin{bmatrix} -1 \\ -1 \\ 2 \end{bmatrix}$$

form a basis for the plane spanned by $\mathbf{v}_1$ and $\mathbf{v}_2$. Therefore $\{\mathbf{u}_2, \mathbf{u}_3\}$ is an orthonormal basis for the eigenspace E_1, and consequently, $\{\mathbf{u}_1, \mathbf{u}_2, \mathbf{u}_3\}$ is an orthonormal eigenbasis for A. $\diamond$

Exercises

25.1. Suppose A and B are $n \times n$ symmetric matrices.

(a) Show that $A + B$ is symmetric.

(b) Show that cA is symmetric for any scalar c in $\mathbf{R}$.

(c) Show by example that AB need not be symmetric.

25.2. Let A be any $m \times n$ matrix. Show that $A^T A$ and AA^T are symmetric.

25.3. Show that if A is an invertible symmetric matrix, then A^{-1} is symmetric.

25.4. A square matrix A is called **skew symmetric** if $A^T = -A$. Show that the only real eigenvalue of a skew symmetric matrix is zero.

25.5. Let A be any square matrix. Show that $A + A^T$ is symmetric.

25.6. Show that for all $n \times n$ symmetric matrices A, the matrix $A^2 + I_n$ is invertible.

Find an orthonormal eigenbasis for each symmetric matrix A in Exercises 7 through 17.

25.7. $A = \begin{bmatrix} 2 & 0 \\ 0 & 5 \end{bmatrix}$

25.8. $A = \begin{bmatrix} 0 & 0 \\ 0 & 0 \end{bmatrix}$

25.9. $A = \begin{bmatrix} 0 & 2 \\ 2 & 0 \end{bmatrix}$

25.10. $A = \begin{bmatrix} 1 & -2 \\ -2 & 4 \end{bmatrix}$

25.11. $A = \begin{bmatrix} 3 & 0 \\ 0 & 3 \end{bmatrix}$

25.12. $A = \begin{bmatrix} 3 & 2 \\ 2 & 1 \end{bmatrix}$

25.13. $A = \begin{bmatrix} 1 & 0 & 0 \\ 0 & 2 & 0 \\ 0 & 0 & 3 \end{bmatrix}$

25.14. $A = \begin{bmatrix} 1 & 0 & 0 \\ 0 & 2 & 0 \\ 0 & 0 & 1 \end{bmatrix}$

25.15. $A = \begin{bmatrix} 0 & 0 & 1 \\ 0 & 2 & 0 \\ 1 & 0 & 0 \end{bmatrix}$

25.16. $A = \begin{bmatrix} 0 & 0 & 0 \\ 0 & 2 & 0 \\ 0 & 0 & 0 \end{bmatrix}$

25.17. $A = \begin{bmatrix} 1 & 0 & 0 & 1 \\ 0 & 0 & 0 & 0 \\ 0 & 0 & 0 & 0 \\ 1 & 0 & 0 & 1 \end{bmatrix}$

26 Quadratic Forms

A **quadratic form** is a function $Q : \mathbf{R}^n \rightarrow \mathbf{R}$ given by

$$Q(\mathbf{x}) = \mathbf{x}^T A \mathbf{x}$$

where A is a symmetric matrix.

Example 26.1. Let

$$A = \begin{bmatrix} a & b \\ b & c \end{bmatrix}$$

Then

$$Q(x, y) = \begin{bmatrix} x & y \end{bmatrix} \begin{bmatrix} a & b \\ b & c \end{bmatrix} \begin{bmatrix} x \\ y \end{bmatrix} = \begin{bmatrix} x & y \end{bmatrix} \begin{bmatrix} ax + by \\ bx + cy \end{bmatrix} = ax^2 + 2bxy + cy^2$$

is the quadratic form with matrix A. $\diamond$

Example 26.2. Let

$$A = \begin{bmatrix} a & b & c \\ b & d & e \\ c & e & f \end{bmatrix}$$

196

Then

$$Q(x,y,z) = \begin{bmatrix} x & y & z \end{bmatrix} \begin{bmatrix} a & b & c \\ b & d & e \\ c & e & f \end{bmatrix} \begin{bmatrix} x \\ y \\ z \end{bmatrix} = ax^2 + dy^2 + fz^2 + 2bxy + 2cxz + 2eyz$$

is the quadratic form with matrix A. ◇

Every quadratic form is a polynomial consisting only of second degree terms, where the entry a_{ij} in row i column j of A gives rise to the term $a_{ij}x_ix_j$ in the quadratic form. The symmetry of A implies that for $i \neq j$ this is the same as $a_{ji}x_jx_i$, and thus these terms combine to give $2a_{ij}x_ix_j$. Conversely, any polynomial consisting solely of second degree terms is a quadratic form. The ij^{th} entry a_{ij} of the associated matrix A is half the coefficient of x_ix_j for $i \neq j$, while each diagonal entries a_{ii} is the coefficient of x_i^2.

Example 26.3. The polynomial

$$Q(x_1, x_2, x_3, x_4) = x_1^2 - 2x_1x_4 + x_2x_3 + 2x_3^2 - 6x_3x_4 - 7x_4^2$$

is the quadratic form with matrix

$$A = \begin{bmatrix} 1 & 0 & 0 & -1 \\ 0 & 0 & 1/2 & 0 \\ 0 & 1/2 & 2 & -3 \\ -1 & 0 & -3 & -7 \end{bmatrix}.$$

◇

Definiteness

A quadratic form Q is called **positive definite** if $Q(\mathbf{x}) > 0$ for all $\mathbf{x} \neq \mathbf{0}$, **negative definite** if $Q(\mathbf{x}) < 0$ for all $\mathbf{x} \neq \mathbf{0}$, **positive semidefinite** if $Q(\mathbf{x}) \geq 0$ for all $\mathbf{x}$, **negative semidefinite** if $Q(\mathbf{x}) \leq 0$ for all $\mathbf{x}$, and **indefinite** if there exist $\mathbf{x}_1$ and $\mathbf{x}_2$ such that $Q(\mathbf{x}_1) > 0$ and $Q(\mathbf{x}_2) < 0$.

Example 26.4.

$$A = \begin{bmatrix} 1 & 0 \\ 0 & 2 \end{bmatrix} \qquad \Longrightarrow \qquad Q(x,y) = x^2 + 2y^2$$

It is clear that $Q(x,y) > 0$ for all $(x,y) \neq (0,0)$, so Q is positive definite. The graph of the function Q is shown below.

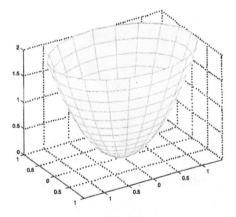

197

Example 26.5.

$$B = \begin{bmatrix} -1 & 0 \\ 0 & -2 \end{bmatrix} \qquad \Longrightarrow \qquad Q(x,y) = -x^2 - 2y^2$$

In this case $Q(x,y) < 0$ for all $(x,y) \neq (0,0)$, so Q is negative definite.

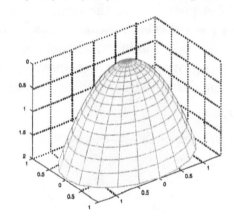

Example 26.6.

$$C = \begin{bmatrix} 1 & 0 \\ 0 & -2 \end{bmatrix} \qquad \Longrightarrow \qquad Q(x,y) = x^2 - 2y^2$$

Since $Q(1,0) > 0$ and $Q(0,1) < 0$, Q is indefinite.

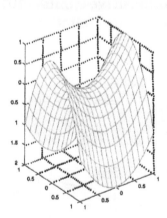

Example 26.7.

$$D = \begin{bmatrix} 1 & 0 \\ 0 & 0 \end{bmatrix} \qquad \Longrightarrow \qquad Q(x,y) = x^2$$

Since $Q(\mathbf{x}) \geq 0$ for all $\mathbf{x}$, Q is positive semidefinite. Q is not positive definite since $Q(1,0) = 0$.

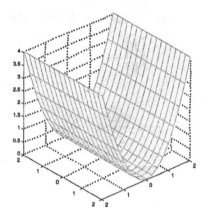

The matrix $-D$ gives rise to a form which is negative semidefinite. $\diamond$

Eigenvalues and Quadratic Forms

There is a beautiful relationship between the eigenvalues of a symmetric matrix and the definiteness of the quadratic form it generates. This is illustrated in the following example.

Example 26.8.

$$A = \begin{bmatrix} 1 & 4 \\ 4 & 1 \end{bmatrix} \qquad \Longrightarrow \qquad Q(x,y) = x^2 + 8xy + y^2$$

At first glance it is not obvious whether this form is positive definite, negative definite, or indefinite. In all the previous examples, the matrices were diagonal matrices, so there was no xy term. By finding the eigenvalues and eigenvectors of A we can make a change of coordinates which will eliminate this cross term. First we find the eigenvalues. Since

$$\det(\lambda I_2 - A) = (\lambda - 1)^2 - 16 = \lambda^2 - 2\lambda - 15 = (\lambda - 5)(\lambda + 3)$$

the eigenvalues are 5 and -3. Next, we find the corresponding eigenspaces.

$$5I_2 - A = \begin{bmatrix} 4 & -4 \\ -4 & 4 \end{bmatrix} \xrightarrow[\text{rref}]{} \begin{bmatrix} 1 & -1 \\ 0 & 0 \end{bmatrix} \qquad \Longrightarrow \qquad E_5 = \text{span}\left(\begin{bmatrix} 1 \\ 1 \end{bmatrix}\right)$$

$$-3I_2 - A = \begin{bmatrix} -4 & -4 \\ -4 & -4 \end{bmatrix} \xrightarrow[\text{rref}]{} \begin{bmatrix} 1 & 1 \\ 0 & 0 \end{bmatrix} \qquad \Longrightarrow \qquad E_{-3} = \text{span}\left(\begin{bmatrix} -1 \\ 1 \end{bmatrix}\right)$$

Now consider a basis consisting of **unit** eigenvectors of A,

$$\left\{ \begin{bmatrix} \frac{\sqrt{2}}{2} \\ \frac{\sqrt{2}}{2} \end{bmatrix}, \begin{bmatrix} -\frac{\sqrt{2}}{2} \\ \frac{\sqrt{2}}{2} \end{bmatrix} \right\}$$

and let

$$C = \begin{bmatrix} \frac{\sqrt{2}}{2} & -\frac{\sqrt{2}}{2} \\ \frac{\sqrt{2}}{2} & \frac{\sqrt{2}}{2} \end{bmatrix}$$

199

denote the change of basis matrix for this basis. If we make the change of variable

$$\begin{bmatrix} x \\ y \end{bmatrix} = C \begin{bmatrix} u \\ v \end{bmatrix}$$

then

$$x = \frac{\sqrt{2}}{2}u - \frac{\sqrt{2}}{2}v$$
$$y = \frac{\sqrt{2}}{2}u + \frac{\sqrt{2}}{2}v.$$

So

$$Q(x,y) = \left(\frac{\sqrt{2}}{2}u - \frac{\sqrt{2}}{2}v\right)^2 + 8\left(\frac{\sqrt{2}}{2}u - \frac{\sqrt{2}}{2}v\right)\left(\frac{\sqrt{2}}{2}u + \frac{\sqrt{2}}{2}v\right) + \left(\frac{\sqrt{2}}{2}u + \frac{\sqrt{2}}{2}v\right)^2$$
$$= 5u^2 - 3v^2.$$

In (u, v) coordinates it is clear that Q is indefinite, since the coefficients have opposite sign. For instance Q is positive when $(u, v) = (1, 0)$, and Q is negative when $(u, v) = (0, 1)$. Since

$$C(1,0) = (\sqrt{2}/2, \sqrt{2}/2) \qquad \text{and} \qquad C(0,1) = (-\sqrt{2}/2, \sqrt{2}/2)$$

we know the (x, y) coordinates at which Q is positive and negative.

$$Q(\sqrt{2}/2, \sqrt{2}/2) = 5 \qquad Q(-\sqrt{2}/2, \sqrt{2}/2) = -3$$

Notice that the coefficients of u^2 and v^2 are exactly the eigenvalues of A. This is not a coincidence. ◇

Proposition 26.1. Let $Q(\mathbf{x}) = \mathbf{x}^T A \mathbf{x}$ be the quadratic form generated by an $n \times n$ symmetric matrix A.

1. If all of the eigenvalues of A are positive then Q is positive definite.

2. If all of the eigenvalues of A are negative then Q is negative definite.

3. If all of the eigenvalues of A are nonnegative then Q is positive semidefinite.

4. If all of the eigenvalues of A are nonpositive then Q is negative semidefinite.

5. If A has both positive and negative eigenvalues then Q is indefinite.

Proof. By the Spectral Theorem, there exists an orthonormal basis $\{\mathbf{u}_1, \mathbf{u}_2, \ldots, \mathbf{u}_n\}$ of $\mathbf{R}^n$ consisting of eigenvectors of A. Let

$$C = \begin{bmatrix} | & | & & | \\ \mathbf{u}_1 & \mathbf{u}_2 & \cdots & \mathbf{u}_n \\ | & | & & | \end{bmatrix}$$

200

be the change of basis matrix for this basis. Then we have

$$C^T A C = D = \begin{bmatrix} \lambda_1 & 0 & \cdots & 0 \\ 0 & \lambda_2 & \cdots & 0 \\ \vdots & \vdots & \ddots & \vdots \\ 0 & 0 & \cdots & \lambda_n \end{bmatrix}$$

where $\lambda_1, \lambda_2, \ldots, \lambda_n$ are the eigenvalues of A. If we make the change of variable $\mathbf{x} = C\mathbf{y}$ then

$$\begin{aligned} Q(\mathbf{x}) &= \mathbf{x}^T A \mathbf{x} \\ &= (C\mathbf{y})^T A C\mathbf{y} \\ &= \mathbf{y}^T C^T A C\mathbf{y} \\ &= \mathbf{y}^T D\mathbf{y} \\ &= \lambda_1 y_1^2 + \lambda_2 y_2^2 + \cdots + \lambda_n y_n^2. \end{aligned}$$

It is clear from this expression that $Q(\mathbf{x}) \geq 0$ for all $\mathbf{x}$ if all of the eigenvalues are nonnegative, and that $Q(\mathbf{x}) \leq 0$ for all $\mathbf{x}$ if all of the eigenvalues are nonpositive. This proves statements 3 and 4 in the theorem.

Next suppose that all of the eigenvalues of A are positive. Then $Q(\mathbf{x})$ is positive unless $y_1 = y_2 = \cdots = y_n = 0$, in which case $\mathbf{y} = \mathbf{0}$, which implies $\mathbf{x} = C\mathbf{0} = \mathbf{0}$. Thus Q is positive definite. Similarly, if all of the eigenvalues of A are negative, then Q is negative definite.

Finally, suppose that A has both positive and negative eigenvalues. If $\lambda_i > 0$ and $\lambda_j < 0$, let $\mathbf{y}_1 = \mathbf{e}_i$ and $\mathbf{y}_2 = \mathbf{e}_j$, and let

$$\mathbf{x}_1 = C\mathbf{y}_1 = C\mathbf{e}_i \qquad \text{and} \qquad \mathbf{x}_2 = C\mathbf{y}_2 = C\mathbf{e}_j.$$

Then

$$Q(\mathbf{x}_1) = \lambda_i > 0 \qquad \text{and} \qquad Q(\mathbf{x}_2) = \lambda_j < 0$$

so Q is indefinite. $\qquad\qquad\square$

Example 26.9. Let

$$A = \begin{bmatrix} 1 & 2 & 2 \\ 2 & 1 & 2 \\ 2 & 2 & 1 \end{bmatrix}.$$

The characteristic polynomial of A is

$$\begin{aligned} p(\lambda) &= (\lambda - 1)[(\lambda - 1)^2 - 4] + 2[(-2)(\lambda - 1) - 4] - 2[4 + 2(\lambda - 1)] \\ &= (\lambda - 1)^3 - 12\lambda - 4 \\ &= \lambda^3 - 3\lambda^2 - 9\lambda - 5 \\ &= (\lambda + 1)^2(\lambda - 5). \end{aligned}$$

The eigenvalues are therefore -1, with multiplicity 2, and 5, so the quadratic form with matrix A is indefinite. $\qquad\qquad\diamond$

Example 26.10. Let

$$A = \begin{bmatrix} 2 & 2 & 2 \\ 2 & 2 & 2 \\ 2 & 2 & 2 \end{bmatrix}.$$

The characteristic polynomial of A is

$$p(\lambda) = \lambda^3 - 6\lambda^2 = \lambda^2(\lambda - 6)$$

so the eigenvalues are 0, with multiplicity 2, and 6, and the associated quadratic form is positive semidefinite. ◇

Example 26.11. Let

$$A = \begin{bmatrix} 3 & 2 & 2 \\ 2 & 3 & 2 \\ 2 & 2 & 3 \end{bmatrix}.$$

The characteristic polynomial of A is

$$p(\lambda) = (\lambda - 1)^2(\lambda - 7)$$

so the eigenvalues are 1 (with multiplicity 2) and 7, and the associated quadratic form is positive definite. ◇

For a 2×2 symmetric matrix A, we can easily determine the signs of the eigenvalues in terms of the trace and determinant of A.

Proposition 26.2. Let

$$A = \begin{bmatrix} a & b \\ b & c \end{bmatrix}$$

be a 2×2 symmetric matrix, and let Q be the associated quadratic form.

1. If $\det(A) > 0$ and $\mathrm{tr}(A) > 0$ then the eigenvalues of A are both positive, so Q is positive definite.

2. If $\det(A) > 0$ and $\mathrm{tr}(A) < 0$ then the eigenvalues of A are both negative, so Q is negative definite.

3. If $\det(A) = 0$ and $\mathrm{tr}(A) \geq 0$ then the eigenvalues of A are both nonnegative, so Q is positive semidefinite.

4. If $\det(A) = 0$ and $\mathrm{tr}(A) \leq 0$ then the eigenvalues of A are both nonpositive, so Q is negative semidefinite.

5. If $\det(A) < 0$ then the eigenvalues of A have opposite signs, so Q is indefinite.

Proof. If $\det(A) > 0$ then, since $\det(A)$ is the product of the eigenvalues, the eigenvalues are nonzero and have the same sign. Since $\text{tr}(A)$ is the sum of the eigenvalues, this sign is positive if $\text{tr}(A) > 0$ and negative if $\text{tr}(A) < 0$.

If $\det(A) = 0$, at least one of the eigenvalues is zero, and therefore $\text{tr}(A)$ equals the other eigenvalue. So if $\text{tr}(A) \geq 0$ they are both nonnegative, and if $\text{tr}(A) \leq 0$ they are both nonpositive.

Finally, if $\det(M) < 0$ then the product of the eigenvalues is negative, so the eigenvalues have opposite signs. $\square$

Exercises

In Exercises 1 through 8, find the matrix for the given quadratic form, and determine the definiteness of the form.

26.1. $Q(x,y) = x^2 + 2xy + y^2$

26.2. $Q(x,y,z) = 2xy + 2xz + 2yz$

26.3. $Q(x,y) = 3x^2 - 2xy + 2y^2$

26.4. $Q(x,y,z) = x^2 + y^2$

26.5. $Q(x,y,z) = -2x^2 - 3y^2 - z^2$

26.6. $Q(w,x,y,z) = -2x^2 - 3y^2 - z^2$

26.7. $Q(w,x,y,z) = x^2 + 4yz$

26.8. $Q(w,x,y,z) = 4x^2 + xz$

In Exercises 9 through 18, determine the definiteness of the quadratic form Q with the given matrix A.

26.9. $A = \begin{bmatrix} 5 & 6 \\ 6 & 8 \end{bmatrix}$

26.10. $A = \begin{bmatrix} -1 & -2 \\ -2 & -3 \end{bmatrix}$

26.11. $A = \begin{bmatrix} -1 & -1 \\ -1 & -3 \end{bmatrix}$

26.12. $A = \begin{bmatrix} 1 & -2 \\ -2 & 4 \end{bmatrix}$

26.13. $A = \begin{bmatrix} -1 & 3 \\ 3 & -9 \end{bmatrix}$

26.14. $A = \begin{bmatrix} 2 & -1 \\ -1 & 1 \end{bmatrix}$

26.15. $A = \begin{bmatrix} 1 & 0 & 1 \\ 0 & 1 & 0 \\ 1 & 0 & 1 \end{bmatrix}$

26.16. $A = \begin{bmatrix} 1 & 1 & 1 \\ 1 & 1 & 1 \\ 1 & 1 & 1 \end{bmatrix}$

26.17. $A = \begin{bmatrix} 1 & 0 & 2 \\ 0 & 1 & 0 \\ 2 & 0 & 1 \end{bmatrix}$

26.18. $A = \begin{bmatrix} 1 & -2 & 8 & 3 \\ -2 & 3 & 4 & 7 \\ 8 & 4 & -1 & 2 \\ 3 & 7 & 2 & 5 \end{bmatrix}$ Hint: You do not need to find the eigenvalues.

26.19. Show that if $Q_1 : \mathbf{R}^n \to \mathbf{R}$ and $Q_2 : \mathbf{R}^n \to \mathbf{R}$ are quadratic forms with matrices A_1 and A_2, respectively, then $Q_1 + Q_2$ is a quadratic form with matrix $A_1 + A_2$.

26.20. Let A_1 and A_2 be $n \times n$ symmetric matrices, both of which have only positive eigenvalues. Use the result of the previous exercise to show that all the eigenvalues of $A_1 + A_2$ are positive.

A   Principle of Mathematical Induction

In this section we briefly explain the method of proof by mathematical induction. This method of proof applies to sequences of statements S_n, which are indexed by the positive integers n. The idea of induction is simple. We first prove that S_1 is true, and then that the truth of each statement S_k implies the truth of the next statement S_{k+1}. Having done this, since S_1 is true and S_1 implies S_2, it follows that S_2 is true. Since S_2 is now true and S_2 implies S_3, S_3 must also be true, an so on.

To make this argument somewhat more rigorous we need to use one of the axioms of the positive integers, called the Well Ordering Principle.

Well Ordering Principle.
Every nonempty set of positive integers contains a smallest element.

The well ordering principle is an axiom, so it does not make sense to speak of proving it. We can however prove the principle of induction using the Well Ordering Principle.

Proposition A.1. (Principle of Mathematical Induction) Let $\{S_n\}_{n=1}^{\infty}$ be a sequence of statements and suppose the following two conditions are satisfied.

1. S_1 is true.

2. For all positive integers k, if S_k is true then S_{k+1} is true.

Then S_n is true for all positive integers n.

Proof. Let $\{S_n\}_{n=1}^{\infty}$ be a sequence of statements which satisfies the two properties above, and let F be the set of positive integers k for which the statement S_k is false. We intend to show that F is the empty set, and therefore S_n is true for all positive integers n. To do so, we suppose to the contrary that F is nonempty. Then by the Well Ordering Principle, F has a smallest element. Call this positive integer m. By property 1, S_1 is true, so 1 is not an element of F, and thus $m > 1$. Since m is the smallest element of F, $m - 1$ is a positive integer which is not in F, and therefore S_{m-1} is true. By property 2, however, this implies that S_m is true, and therefore m is not in F. Thus we have a contradiction, which means that our assumption that F is nonempty is false. $\square$

Example A.1. Let S_n be the following formula for the sum of the first n positive integers.

$$\sum_{i=1}^{n} i = \frac{n(n+1)}{2}$$

We will use induction to prove this for all positive integers n. First we must establish the base case S_1. Since

$$\sum_{i=1}^{1} i = 1 = \frac{1(1+1)}{2}$$

the statement S_1 is true. Next we must show for all positive integers k that *if* S_k is true then S_{k+1} is true. So we suppose S_k is true. That is we suppose

$$\sum_{i=1}^{k} i = \frac{k(k+1)}{2}$$

for some positive integer k. From this we need to conclude that S_{k+1} is true, i.e. that

$$\sum_{i=1}^{k+1} i = \frac{(k+1)(k+2)}{2}.$$

To do so we notice that

$$\sum_{i=1}^{k+1} i = \sum_{i=1}^{k} i + (k+1),$$

so using the hypothesis that S_k is true this becomes

$$\sum_{i=1}^{k+1} i = \frac{k(k+1)}{2} + (k+1) = \frac{1}{2}(k^2 + 3k + 2) = \frac{(k+1)(k+2)}{2},$$

which is what we were trying to show. $\diamond$

B Existence of Bases

Proposition B.1. Let V be a nontrivial subspace of $\mathbf{R}^n$. Then there exists a basis for V.

Proof. We first make the following claim. For any set of k linearly independent vectors $\{\mathbf{v}_1, \ldots, \mathbf{v}_k\}$ in V, either

1. these vectors form a basis for V, or

2. there exists a vector $\mathbf{v}_{k+1}$ in V such that $\{\mathbf{v}_1, \ldots, \mathbf{v}_k, \mathbf{v}_{k+1}\}$ is a linearly independent set.

Before proving the claim, we use it to prove the Proposition. Since V is nontrivial, there exists a nonzero vector $\mathbf{v}_1$ in V. The set $\{\mathbf{v}_1\}$ is linearly independent. If this set is not a basis for V, then by the claim, there exists a vector $\mathbf{v}_2$ in V, such that the set $\{\mathbf{v}_1, \mathbf{v}_2\}$ is linearly independent. Now if this set is not a basis for V, then by the claim, there exists a vector $\mathbf{v}_3$ in V, such that the set $\{\mathbf{v}_1, \mathbf{v}_2, \mathbf{v}_3\}$ is linearly independent. This process must eventually terminate in a basis for V, since otherwise, we could find a set of more than n linearly independent vectors in $\mathbf{R}^n$, and this contradicts Proposition 8.4.

Now we prove the claim. Suppose $\{\mathbf{v}_1, \ldots, \mathbf{v}_k\}$ is a linearly independent set, and let $V_k = \text{span}(\mathbf{v}_1, \ldots, \mathbf{v}_k)$. If $V_k = V$, then $\{\mathbf{v}_1, \ldots, \mathbf{v}_k\}$ is a basis for V. Otherwise, there exists a vector $\mathbf{v}_{k+1}$ in V which is not in V_k. Now suppose

$$c_1 \mathbf{v}_1 + \cdots + c_k \mathbf{v}_k + c_{k+1} \mathbf{v}_{k+1} = \mathbf{0}.$$

If $c_{k+1} \neq 0$, then solving for $\mathbf{v}_{k+1}$ gives

$$\mathbf{v}_{k+1} = -\frac{c_1}{c_{k+1}} \mathbf{v}_1 - \cdots - \frac{c_k}{c_{k+1}} \mathbf{v}_k$$

which implies $\mathbf{v}_{k+1}$ is in V_k, a contradiction. Hence c_{k+1} must equal zero. But this implies

$$c_1 \mathbf{v}_1 + \cdots + c_k \mathbf{v}_k = \mathbf{0}$$

and the linear independence of $\{\mathbf{v}_1, \ldots, \mathbf{v}_k\}$ implies that $c_1 = \cdots = c_k = 0$. Thus the set $\{\mathbf{v}_1, \ldots, \mathbf{v}_k, \mathbf{v}_{k+1}\}$ is linearly independent. This proves the claim. $\square$

C Uniqueness of Reduced Row Echelon Form

Proposition C.1. Let A be any $m \times n$ matrix. Then A is row equivalent to exactly one reduced row echelon form matrix. This matrix is called the reduced row echelon form of A and is denoted rref(A).

Proof of Uniqueness. If a matrix A is row equivalent to two reduced row echelon form matrices R_1 and R_2, then R_1 and R_2 are row equivalent to each other. Thus, to prove uniqueness it suffices to show that if two reduced row echelon form matrices are row equivalent, then they must be equal.

We prove this by induction on the number of columns n. For the base case $n = 1$, there are only two possible reduced row echelon form matrices with one column,

$$\begin{bmatrix} 1 \\ 0 \\ \vdots \\ 0 \end{bmatrix} \quad \text{or} \quad \begin{bmatrix} 0 \\ 0 \\ \vdots \\ 0 \end{bmatrix},$$

and it is clear that they are not row equivalent. For our inductive hypothesis, we assume that any two row equivalent, reduced row echelon form matrices with k columns are equal. We now need to show that any two row equivalent, reduced row echelon form matrices R_1 and R_2 with $k + 1$ columns are equal. If we write

$$R_1 = \begin{bmatrix} A & \mathbf{b}_1 \end{bmatrix} \quad \text{and} \quad R_2 = \begin{bmatrix} B & \mathbf{b}_2 \end{bmatrix},$$

where A and B are matrices with k columns and $\mathbf{b}_1$ and $\mathbf{b}_2$ are column vectors, then A and B are in reduced row echelon form, and row equivalent via the same row operations which take R_1 to R_2. So by the induction hypothesis, $A = B$, and we have

$$R_1 = \begin{bmatrix} A & \mathbf{b}_1 \end{bmatrix} \quad \text{and} \quad R_2 = \begin{bmatrix} A & \mathbf{b}_2 \end{bmatrix}.$$

Now these matrices can be regarded as the augmented matrices for the systems $A\mathbf{x} = \mathbf{b}_1$ and $A\mathbf{x} = \mathbf{b}_2$, respectively. Since R_1 and R_2 are row equivalent, the solution sets of these systems are the same. If this common solution set is nonempty, we may consider any such solution $\mathbf{x}_0$. Then $\mathbf{b}_1 = A\mathbf{x}_0 = \mathbf{b}_2$, and therefore $R_1 = R_2$. On the other hand, if neither system has a solution, then by Proposition 6.2, both systems contain the equation $0 = 1$, and therefore have a pivot in the final column. Thus both $\mathbf{b}_1$ and $\mathbf{b}_2$ have a 1 in one component, and a zero in all others. But by definition of reduced row echelon form, the 1 must be in the row immediately below the last pivot of A. This again implies $\mathbf{b}_1 = \mathbf{b}_2$ and thus $R_1 = R_2$. By induction it follows that any two row equivalent reduced row echelon form matrices are equal. $\qquad\square$

Index

PART 2

VECTOR CALCULUS, *Fourth Edition*

by Susan Jane Colley

2 | Differentiation in Several Variables

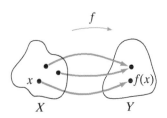

Figure 2.1 The mapping nature of a function.

2.1 Functions of Several Variables; Graphing Surfaces

The volume and surface area of a sphere depend on its radius, the formulas describing their relationships being $V = \frac{4}{3}\pi r^3$ and $S = 4\pi r^2$. (Here V and S are, respectively, the volume and surface area of the sphere and r its radius.) These equations define the volume and surface area as **functions** of the radius. The essential characteristic of a function is that the so-called independent variable (in this case the radius) determines a *unique* value of the dependent variable (V or S). No doubt you can think of many quantities that are determined uniquely not by one variable (as the volume of a sphere is determined by its radius) but by several: the area of a rectangle, the volume of a cylinder or cone, the average annual rainfall in Cleveland, or the national debt. Realistic modeling of the world requires that we understand the concept of a function of more than one variable and how to find meaningful ways to visualize such functions.

Definitions, Notation, and Examples

A function, *any* function, has three features: (1) a **domain** set X, (2) a **codomain** set Y, and (3) a **rule of assignment** that associates to each element x in the domain X a unique element, usually denoted $f(x)$, in the codomain Y. We will frequently use the notation $f: X \to Y$ for a function. Such notation indicates all the ingredients of a particular function, although it does not make the nature of the rule of assignment explicit. This notation also suggests the "mapping" nature of a function, indicated by Figure 2.1.

EXAMPLE 1 Abstract definitions are necessary, but it is just as important that you understand functions as they actually occur. Consider the act of assigning to each U.S. citizen his or her social security number. This pairing defines a function: Each citizen is assigned one social security number. The domain is the set of U.S. citizens and the codomain is the set of all nine-digit strings of numbers.

On the other hand, when a university assigns students to dormitory rooms, it is unlikely that it is creating a function from the set of available rooms to the set of students. This is because some rooms may have more than one student assigned to them, so that a particular room does not necessarily determine a unique student occupant. ◆

> **DEFINITION 1.1**   The **range** of a function $f: X \to Y$ is the set of those elements of Y that are actual values of f. That is, the range of f consists of those y in Y such that $y = f(x)$ for some x in X.
>
> Using set notation, we find that
>
> $$\text{Range } f = \{y \in Y \mid y = f(x) \text{ for some } x \in X\}.$$

In the social security function of Example 1, the range consists of those nine-digit numbers actually used as social security numbers. For example, the number 000-00-0000 is *not* in the range, since no one is actually assigned this number.

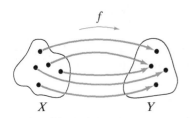

Figure 2.2 Every $y \in Y$ is "hit" by at least one $x \in X$.

> **DEFINITION 1.2**   A function $f: X \to Y$ is said to be **onto** (or **surjective**) if every element of Y is the image of some element of X, that is, if range $f = Y$.

The social security function is *not* onto, since 000-00-0000 is in the codomain but not in the range. Pictorially, an onto function is suggested by Figure 2.2. A function that is *not* onto looks instead like Figure 2.3. You may find it helpful to think of the codomain of a function f as the set of *possible* (or allowable) values of f, and the range of f as the set of *actual* values attained. Then an onto function is one whose possible and actual values are the same.

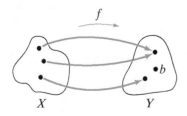

Figure 2.3 The element $b \in Y$ is not the image of any $x \in X$.

> **DEFINITION 1.3**   A function $f: X \to Y$ is called **one-one** (or **injective**) if no two distinct elements of the domain have the same image under f. That is, f is one-one if whenever $x_1, x_2 \in X$ and $x_1 \neq x_2$, then $f(x_1) \neq f(x_2)$. (See Figure 2.4.)

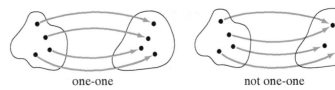

one-one   not one-one

Figure 2.4 The figure on the left depicts a one-one mapping; the one on the right shows a function that is not one-one.

One would expect the social security function to be one-one, but we have heard of cases of two people being assigned the same number so that, alas, apparently it is not.

When you studied single-variable calculus, the functions of interest were those whose domains and codomains were subsets of **R** (the real numbers). It was probably the case that only the rule of assignment was made explicit; it is generally assumed that the domain is the largest possible subset of **R** for which the function makes sense. The codomain is generally taken to be all of **R**.

EXAMPLE 2   Suppose $f: \mathbf{R} \to \mathbf{R}$ is given by $f(x) = x^2$. Then the domain and codomain are, explicitly, all of $\mathbf{R}$, but the range of f is the interval $[0, \infty)$. Thus f is not onto, since the codomain is strictly larger than the range. Note that f is not one-one, since $f(2) = f(-2) = 4$, but $2 \neq -2$.   ◆

EXAMPLE 3   Suppose g is a function such that $g(x) = \sqrt{x-1}$. Then if we take the codomain to be all of $\mathbf{R}$, the domain cannot be any larger than $[1, \infty)$. If the domain included any values less than one, the radicand would be negative and, hence, g would not be real-valued.   ◆

Now we're ready to think about functions of more than one real variable. In the most general terms, these are the functions whose domains are subsets X of $\mathbf{R}^n$ and whose codomains are subsets of $\mathbf{R}^m$, for some positive integers n and m. (For simplicity of notation, we'll take the codomains to be all of $\mathbf{R}^m$, except when specified otherwise.) That is, such a function is a mapping $\mathbf{f}: X \subseteq \mathbf{R}^n \to \mathbf{R}^m$ that associates to a vector (or point) $\mathbf{x}$ in X a unique vector (point) $\mathbf{f}(\mathbf{x})$ in $\mathbf{R}^m$.

EXAMPLE 4   Let $T: \mathbf{R}^3 \to \mathbf{R}$ be defined by $T(x, y, z) = xy + xz + yz$. We can think of T as a sort of "temperature function." Given a point $\mathbf{x} = (x, y, z)$ in $\mathbf{R}^3$, $T(\mathbf{x})$ calculates the temperature at that point.   ◆

EXAMPLE 5   Let $L: \mathbf{R}^n \to \mathbf{R}$ be given by $L(\mathbf{x}) = \|\mathbf{x}\|$. This is a "length function" in that it computes the length of any vector $\mathbf{x}$ in $\mathbf{R}^n$. Note that L is not one-one, since $L(\mathbf{e}_i) = L(\mathbf{e}_j) = 1$, where $\mathbf{e}_i$ and $\mathbf{e}_j$ are any two of the standard basis vectors for $\mathbf{R}^n$. L also fails to be onto, since the length of a vector is always nonnegative.   ◆

EXAMPLE 6   Consider the function given by $\mathbf{N}(\mathbf{x}) = \mathbf{x}/\|\mathbf{x}\|$ where $\mathbf{x}$ is a vector in $\mathbf{R}^3$. Note that $\mathbf{N}$ is not defined if $\mathbf{x} = \mathbf{0}$, so the largest possible domain for $\mathbf{N}$ is $\mathbf{R}^3 - \{\mathbf{0}\}$. The range of $\mathbf{N}$ consists of all unit vectors in $\mathbf{R}^3$. The function $\mathbf{N}$ is the "normalization function," that is, the function that takes a nonzero vector in $\mathbf{R}^3$ and returns the unit vector that points in the same direction.   ◆

EXAMPLE 7   Sometimes a function may be given numerically by a table. One such example is the notion of **windchill**—the apparent temperature one feels when taking into account both the actual air temperature and the speed of the wind. A standard table of windchill values is shown in Figure 2.5.[1] From it we see that if the air temperature is $20\,°F$ and the windspeed is 25 mph, the windchill temperature ("how cold it feels") is $3\,°F$. Similarly, if the air temperature is $35\,°F$ and the windspeed is 10 mph, then the windchill is $27\,°F$. In other words, if s denotes windspeed and t air temperature, then the windchill is a function $W(s, t)$.   ◆

The functions described in Examples 4, 5, and 7 are **scalar-valued** functions, that is, functions whose codomains are $\mathbf{R}$ or subsets of $\mathbf{R}$. Scalar-valued functions are our main concern for this chapter. Nonetheless, let's look at a few examples of functions whose codomains are $\mathbf{R}^m$ where $m > 1$.

---

[1] NOAA, National Weather Service, Office of Climate, Water, and Weather Services, "NWS Wind Chill Temperature Index." February 26, 2004. <http://www.nws.noaa.gov/om/windchill> (July 31, 2010).

Air Temp (deg F)	Windspeed (mph)											
	5	10	15	20	25	30	35	40	45	50	55	60
40	36	34	32	30	29	28	28	27	26	26	25	25
35	31	27	25	24	23	22	21	20	19	19	18	17
30	25	21	19	17	16	15	14	13	12	12	11	10
25	19	15	13	11	9	8	7	6	5	4	4	3
20	13	9	6	4	3	1	0	−1	−2	−3	−3	−4
15	7	3	0	−2	−4	−5	−7	−8	−9	−10	−11	−11
10	1	−4	−7	−9	−11	−12	−14	−15	−16	−17	−18	−19
5	−5	−10	−13	−15	−17	−19	−21	−22	−23	−24	−25	−26
0	−11	−16	−19	−22	−24	−26	−27	−29	−30	−31	−32	−33
−5	−16	−22	−26	−29	−31	−33	−34	−36	−37	−38	−39	−40
−10	−22	−28	−32	−35	−37	−39	−41	−43	−44	−45	−46	−48
−15	−28	−35	−39	−42	−44	−46	−48	−50	−51	−52	−54	−55
−20	−34	−41	−45	−48	−51	−53	−55	−57	−58	−60	−61	−62
−25	−40	−47	−51	−55	−58	−60	−62	−64	−65	−67	−68	−69
−30	−46	−53	−58	−61	−64	−67	−69	−71	−72	−74	−75	−76
−35	−52	−59	−64	−68	−71	−73	−76	−78	−79	−81	−82	−84
−40	−57	−66	−71	−74	−78	−80	−82	−84	−86	−88	−89	−91
−45	−63	−72	−77	−81	−84	−87	−89	−91	−93	−95	−97	−98

Figure 2.5 Table of windchill values in English units.

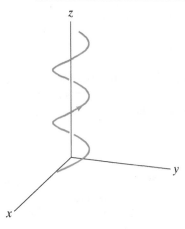

Figure 2.6 The helix of Example 8. The arrow shows the direction of increasing t.

Figure 2.7 A water pitcher. The velocity $\mathbf{v}$ of the water is a function from a subset of $\mathbf{R}^4$ to $\mathbf{R}^3$.

EXAMPLE 8 Define $\mathbf{f}: \mathbf{R} \to \mathbf{R}^3$ by $\mathbf{f}(t) = (\cos t, \sin t, t)$. The range of f is the curve in $\mathbf{R}^3$ with parametric equations $x = \cos t$, $y = \sin t$, $z = t$. If we think of t as a time parameter, then this function traces out the corkscrew curve (called a **helix**) shown in Figure 2.6. ◆

EXAMPLE 9 We can think of the velocity of a fluid as a vector in $\mathbf{R}^3$. This vector depends on (at least) the point at which one measures the velocity and also the time at which one makes the measurement. In other words, velocity may be considered to be a function $\mathbf{v}: X \subseteq \mathbf{R}^4 \to \mathbf{R}^3$. The domain X is a subset of $\mathbf{R}^4$ because three variables x, y, z are required to describe a point in the fluid and a fourth variable t is needed to keep track of time. (See Figure 2.7.) For instance, such a function $\mathbf{v}$ might be given by the expression

$$\mathbf{v}(x, y, z, t) = xyzt\mathbf{i} + (x^2 - y^2)\mathbf{j} + (3z + t)\mathbf{k}.$$ ◆

You may have noted that the expression for $\mathbf{v}$ in Example 9 is considerably more complicated than those for the functions given in Examples 4–8. This is because all the variables and vector components have been written out explicitly. In general, if we have a function $\mathbf{f}: X \subseteq \mathbf{R}^n \to \mathbf{R}^m$, then $\mathbf{x} \in X$ can be written as $\mathbf{x} = (x_1, x_2, \ldots, x_n)$ and $\mathbf{f}$ can be written in terms of its **component functions** $f_1, f_2, \ldots, f_m$. The component functions are **scalar-valued** functions of $\mathbf{x} \in X$ that define the components of the vector $\mathbf{f}(\mathbf{x}) \in \mathbf{R}^m$. What results is a morass of symbols:

$$\mathbf{f}(\mathbf{x}) = \mathbf{f}(x_1, x_2, \ldots, x_n) \qquad \text{(emphasizing the variables)}$$

$$= (f_1(\mathbf{x}), f_2(\mathbf{x}), \ldots, f_m(\mathbf{x})) \qquad \text{(emphasizing the component functions)}$$

$$= (f_1(x_1, x_2, \ldots, x_n), f_2(x_1, x_2, \ldots, x_n), \ldots, f_m(x_1, x_2, \ldots, x_n))$$

$$\text{(writing out all components)}.$$

For example, the function L of Example 5, when expanded, becomes

$$L(\mathbf{x}) = L(x_1, x_2, \ldots, x_n) = \sqrt{x_1^2 + x_2^2 + \cdots + x_n^2}.$$

The function $\mathbf{N}$ of Example 6 becomes

$$\mathbf{N}(\mathbf{x}) = \frac{\mathbf{x}}{\|\mathbf{x}\|} = \frac{(x_1, x_2, x_3)}{\sqrt{x_1^2 + x_2^2 + x_3^2}}$$

$$= \left(\frac{x_1}{\sqrt{x_1^2 + x_2^2 + x_3^2}}, \frac{x_2}{\sqrt{x_1^2 + x_2^2 + x_3^2}}, \frac{x_3}{\sqrt{x_1^2 + x_2^2 + x_3^2}} \right),$$

and, hence, the three component functions of $\mathbf{N}$ are

$$N_1(x_1, x_2, x_3) = \frac{x_1}{\sqrt{x_1^2 + x_2^2 + x_3^2}}, \quad N_2(x_1, x_2, x_3) = \frac{x_2}{\sqrt{x_1^2 + x_2^2 + x_3^2}},$$

$$N_3(x_1, x_2, x_3) = \frac{x_3}{\sqrt{x_1^2 + x_2^2 + x_3^2}}.$$

Although writing a function in terms of all its variables and components has the advantage of being explicit, quite a lot of paper and ink are used in the process. The use of vector notation not only saves space and trees but also helps to make the meaning of a function clear by emphasizing that a function maps points in $\mathbf{R}^n$ to points in $\mathbf{R}^m$. Vector notation makes a function of 300 variables look "just like" a function of one variable. Try to avoid writing out components as much as you can (except when you want to impress your friends).

Visualizing Functions

No doubt you have been graphing scalar-valued functions of one variable for so long that you give the matter little thought. Let's scrutinize what you've been doing, however. A function $f: X \subseteq \mathbf{R} \to \mathbf{R}$ takes a real number and returns another real number as suggested by Figure 2.8. The **graph** of f is something that "lives" in $\mathbf{R}^2$. (See Figure 2.9.) It consists of points (x, y) such that $y = f(x)$. That is,

$$\text{Graph } f = \{(x, f(x)) \mid x \in X\} = \{(x, y) \mid x \in X, y = f(x)\}.$$

The important fact is that, in general, the graph of a scalar-valued function of a single variable is a curve—a one-dimensional object—sitting inside two-dimensional space.

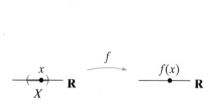

Figure 2.8 A function $f: X \subseteq \mathbf{R} \to \mathbf{R}$.

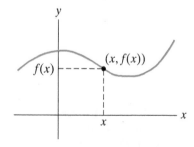

Figure 2.9 The graph of f.

Now suppose we have a function $f: X \subseteq \mathbf{R}^2 \to \mathbf{R}$, that is, a function of two variables. We make essentially the same definition for the graph:

$$\text{Graph } f = \{(\mathbf{x}, f(\mathbf{x})) \mid \mathbf{x} \in X\}. \tag{1}$$

Of course, $\mathbf{x} = (x, y)$ is a point of $\mathbf{R}^2$. Thus, $\{(\mathbf{x}, f(\mathbf{x}))\}$ may also be written as

$$\{(x, y, f(x, y))\}, \quad \text{or as} \quad \{(x, y, z) \mid (x, y) \in X, z = f(x, y)\}.$$

Hence, the graph of a scalar-valued function of two variables is something that sits in $\mathbf{R}^3$. Generally speaking, the graph will be a surface.

EXAMPLE 10   The graph of the function

$$f: \mathbf{R}^2 \to \mathbf{R}, \qquad f(x, y) = \frac{1}{12}y^3 - y - \frac{1}{4}x^2 + \frac{7}{2}$$

is shown in Figure 2.10. For each point $\mathbf{x} = (x, y)$ in $\mathbf{R}^2$, the point in $\mathbf{R}^3$ with coordinates $\left(x, y, \frac{1}{12}y^3 - y - \frac{1}{4}x^2 + \frac{7}{2}\right)$ is graphed.   ◆

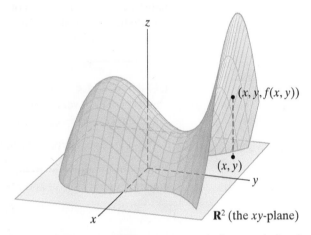

Figure 2.10 The graph of $f(x, y) = \frac{1}{12}y^3 - y - \frac{1}{4}x^2 + \frac{7}{2}$.

Graphing functions of two variables is a much more difficult task than graphing functions of one variable. Of course, one method is to let a computer do the work. Nonetheless, if you want to get a feeling for functions of more than one variable, being able to sketch a rough graph by hand is still a valuable skill. The trick to putting together a reasonable graph is to find a way to cut down on the dimensions involved. One way this can be achieved is by drawing certain special curves that lie on the surface $z = f(x, y)$. These special curves, called **contour curves,** are the ones obtained by intersecting the surface with horizontal planes $z = c$ for various values of the constant c. Some contour curves drawn on the surface of Example 10 are shown in Figure 2.11. If we compress all the contour curves onto the xy-plane (in essence, if we look down along the positive z-axis), then we create a "topographic map" of the surface that is shown in Figure 2.12. These curves in the xy-plane are called the **level curves** of the original function f.

The point of the preceding discussion is that we can reverse the process in order to sketch systematically the graph of a function f of two variables: We

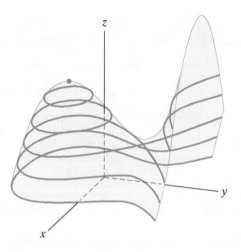

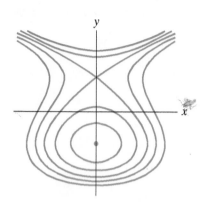

Figure 2.11 Some contour curves of the function in Example 10.

Figure 2.12 Some level curves of the function in Example 10.

first construct a topographic map in $\mathbf{R}^2$ by finding the level curves of f, then situate these curves in $\mathbf{R}^3$ as contour curves at the appropriate heights, and finally complete the graph of the function. Before we give an example, let's restate our terminology with greater precision.

DEFINITION 1.4 Let $f: X \subseteq \mathbf{R}^2 \to \mathbf{R}$ be a scalar-valued function of two variables. The **level curve at height** c **of** f is the curve in $\mathbf{R}^2$ defined by the equation $f(x, y) = c$, where c is a constant. In mathematical notation,

$$\text{Level curve at height } c = \left\{(x, y) \in \mathbf{R}^2 \mid f(x, y) = c\right\}.$$

The **contour curve at height** c **of** f is the curve in $\mathbf{R}^3$ defined by the two equations $z = f(x, y)$ and $z = c$. Symbolized,

$$\text{Contour curve at height } c = \left\{(x, y, z) \in \mathbf{R}^3 \mid z = f(x, y) = c\right\}.$$

In addition to level and contour curves, consideration of the **sections** of a surface by the planes where x or y is held constant is also helpful. A **section** of a surface by a plane is just the intersection of the surface with that plane. Formally, we have the following definition:

DEFINITION 1.5 Let $f: X \subseteq \mathbf{R}^2 \to \mathbf{R}$ be a scalar-valued function of two variables. The **section of the graph of** f **by the plane** $x = c$ (where c is a constant) is the set of points (x, y, z), where $z = f(x, y)$ and $x = c$. Symbolized,

$$\text{Section by } x = c \text{ is } \left\{(x, y, z) \in \mathbf{R}^3 \mid z = f(x, y), x = c\right\}.$$

Similarly, the **section of the graph of** f **by the plane** $y = c$ is the set of points described as follows:

$$\text{Section by } y = c \text{ is } \left\{(x, y, z) \in \mathbf{R}^3 \mid z = f(x, y), y = c\right\}.$$

EXAMPLE 11   We'll use level and contour curves to construct the graph of the function

$$f: \mathbf{R}^2 \to \mathbf{R}, \qquad f(x, y) = 4 - x^2 - y^2.$$

By Definition 1.4, the level curve at height c is

$$\left\{ (x, y) \in \mathbf{R}^2 \mid 4 - x^2 - y^2 = c \right\} = \left\{ (x, y) \mid x^2 + y^2 = 4 - c \right\}.$$

Thus, we see that the level curves for $c < 4$ are circles centered at the origin of radius $\sqrt{4 - c}$. The level "curve" at height $c = 4$ is not a curve at all but just a single point (the origin). Finally, there are no level curves at heights larger than 4 since the equation $x^2 + y^2 = 4 - c$ has no real solutions in x and y. (Why not?) These remarks are summarized in the following table:

c	Level curve $x^2 + y^2 = 4 - c$
-5	$x^2 + y^2 = 9$
-1	$x^2 + y^2 = 5$
0	$x^2 + y^2 = 4$
1	$x^2 + y^2 = 3$
3	$x^2 + y^2 = 1$
4	$x^2 + y^2 = 0 \iff x = y = 0$
c, where $c > 4$	empty

Thus, the family of level curves, the "topographic map" of the surface $z = 4 - x^2 - y^2$, is shown in Figure 2.13. Some contour curves, *which sit in* $\mathbf{R}^3$, are shown in Figure 2.14, where we can get a feeling for the complete graph of $z = 4 - x^2 - y^2$. It is a surface that looks like an inverted dish and is called a **paraboloid**. (See Figure 2.15.) To make the picture clearer, we have also sketched in the sections of the surface by the planes $x = 0$ and $y = 0$. The section by $x = 0$ is given analytically by the set

$$\left\{ (x, y, z) \in \mathbf{R}^3 \mid z = 4 - x^2 - y^2, x = 0 \right\} = \left\{ (0, y, z) \mid z = 4 - y^2 \right\}.$$

Similarly, the section by $y = 0$ is

$$\left\{ (x, y, z) \in \mathbf{R}^3 \mid z = 4 - x^2 - y^2, y = 0 \right\} = \left\{ (x, 0, z) \mid z = 4 - x^2 \right\}.$$

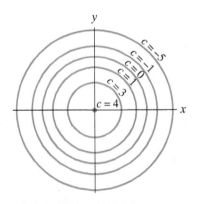

Figure 2.13 The topographic map of $z = 4 - x^2 - y^2$ (i.e., several of its level curves).

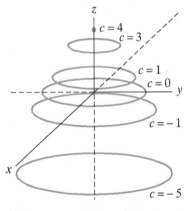

Figure 2.14 Some contour curves of $z = 4 - x^2 - y^2$.

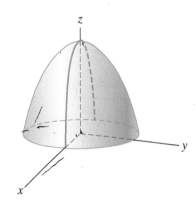

Figure 2.15 The graph of $f(x, y) = 4 - x^2 - y^2$.

Since these sections are parabolas, it is easy to see how this surface obtained its name.   ◆

EXAMPLE 12   We'll graph the function $g: \mathbf{R}^2 \to \mathbf{R}$, $g(x, y) = y^2 - x^2$. The level curves are all hyperbolas, with the exception of the level curve at height 0, which is a pair of intersecting lines.

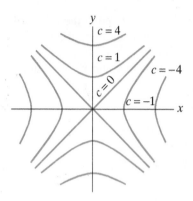

Figure 2.16 Some level curves of $g(x, y) = y^2 - x^2$.

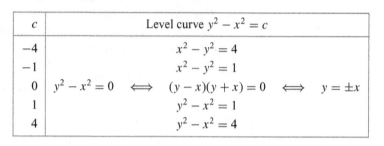

c	Level curve $y^2 - x^2 = c$
-4	$x^2 - y^2 = 4$
-1	$x^2 - y^2 = 1$
0	$y^2 - x^2 = 0 \iff (y - x)(y + x) = 0 \iff y = \pm x$
1	$y^2 - x^2 = 1$
4	$y^2 - x^2 = 4$

The collection of level curves is graphed in Figure 2.16. The sections by $x = c$ are

$$\{(x, y, z) \mid z = y^2 - x^2, x = c\} = \{(c, y, z) \mid z = y^2 - c^2\}.$$

These are clearly parabolas in the planes $x = c$. The sections by $y = c$ are

$$\{(x, y, z) \mid z = y^2 - x^2, y = c\} = \{(c, y, z) \mid z = c^2 - x^2\},$$

which are again parabolas. The level curves and sections generate the contour curves and surface depicted in Figure 2.17. Perhaps understandably, this surface is called a **hyperbolic paraboloid**.   ◆

EXAMPLE 13   We compare the graphs of the function $f(x, y) = 4 - x^2 - y^2$ of Example 11 with that of

$$h: \mathbf{R}^2 - \{(0, 0)\} \to \mathbf{R}, \qquad h(x, y) = \ln(x^2 + y^2).$$

The level curve of h at height c is

$$\left\{(x, y) \in \mathbf{R}^2 \mid \ln(x^2 + y^2) = c\right\} = \left\{(x, y) \mid x^2 + y^2 = e^c\right\}.$$

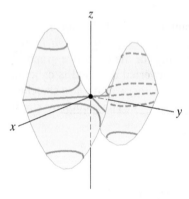

Figure 2.17 The contour curves and graph of $g(x, y) = y^2 - x^2$.

Since $e^c > 0$ for all $c \in \mathbf{R}$, we see that the level curve exists for any c and is a circle of radius $\sqrt{e^c} = e^{c/2}$.

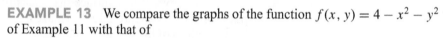

c	Level curve $x^2 + y^2 = e^c$
-5	$x^2 + y^2 = e^{-5}$
-1	$x^2 + y^2 = e^{-1}$
0	$x^2 + y^2 = 1$
1	$x^2 + y^2 = e$
3	$x^2 + y^2 = e^3$
4	$x^2 + y^2 = e^4$

The collection of level curves is shown in Figure 2.18 and the graph in Figure 2.19. Note that the section of the graph by $x = 0$ is

$$\left\{(x, y, z) \in \mathbf{R}^3 \mid z = \ln(x^2 + y^2), x = 0\right\} = \left\{(0, y, z) \mid z = \ln(y^2) = 2\ln|y|\right\}.$$

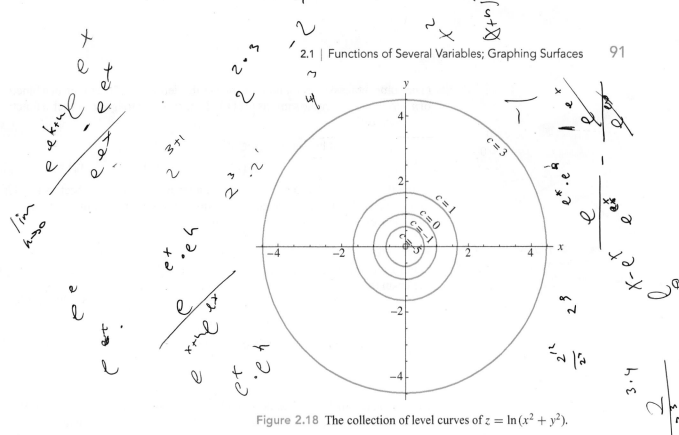

Figure 2.18 The collection of level curves of $z = \ln(x^2 + y^2)$.

The section by $y = 0$ is entirely similar:

$$\left\{(x, y, z) \in \mathbf{R}^3 \mid z = \ln(x^2 + y^2), y = 0\right\} = \left\{(x, 0, z) \mid z = \ln(x^2) = 2\ln|x|\right\}.$$

◆

In fact, if we switch from Cartesian to cylindrical coordinates, it is quite easy to understand the surfaces in both Examples 11 and 13. In view of the Cartesian/cylindrical relation $x^2 + y^2 = r^2$, we see that for the function f of Example 11,

$$z = 4 - x^2 - y^2 = 4 - (x^2 + y^2) = 4 - r^2.$$

For the function h of Example 13, we have

$$z = \ln(x^2 + y^2) = \ln(r^2) = 2\ln r,$$

where we assume the usual convention that the cylindrical coordinate r is non-negative. Thus both of the graphs in Figures 2.15 and 2.19 are of surfaces of revolution obtained by revolving different curves about the z-axis. As a result, the level curves are, in general, circular.

The preceding discussion has been devoted entirely to graphing scalar-valued functions of just two variables. However, all the ideas can be extended to more variables and higher dimensions. If $f: X \subseteq \mathbf{R}^n \to \mathbf{R}$ is a (scalar-valued) function of n variables, then the **graph** of f is the subset of $\mathbf{R}^{n+1}$ given by

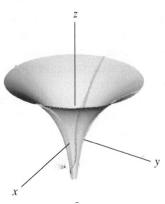

Figure 2.19 The graph of $z = \ln(x^2 + y^2)$, shown with sections by $x = 0$ and $y = 0$.

$$
\begin{aligned}
\text{Graph } f &= \{(\mathbf{x}, f(\mathbf{x})) \mid \mathbf{x} \in X\} \\
&= \{(x_1, \ldots, x_n, x_{n+1}) \mid (x_1, \ldots, x_n) \in X, \\
&\qquad\qquad x_{n+1} = f(x_1, \ldots, x_n)\}.
\end{aligned}
\tag{2}
$$

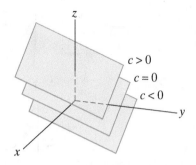

Figure 2.20 The level sets of the function $F(x, y, z) = x + y + z$ are planes in $\mathbf{R}^3$.

(The compactness of vector notation makes the definition of the graph of a function of n variables *exactly* the same as in (1).) The **level set at height** c of such a function is defined by

$$\text{Level set at height } c = \{\mathbf{x} \in \mathbf{R}^n \mid f(\mathbf{x}) = c\}$$
$$= \{(x_1, x_2, \ldots, x_n) \mid f(x_1, x_2, \ldots, x_n) = c\}.$$

While the graph of f is a subset of $\mathbf{R}^{n+1}$, a level set of f is a subset of $\mathbf{R}^n$. This makes it possible to get some geometric insight into graphs of functions of *three* variables, even though we cannot actually visualize them.

EXAMPLE 14   Let $F: \mathbf{R}^3 \to \mathbf{R}$ be given by $F(x, y, z) = x + y + z$. Then the graph of F is the set $\{(x, y, z, w) \mid w = x + y + z\}$ and is a subset (called a **hypersurface**) of $\mathbf{R}^4$, which we cannot depict adequately. Nonetheless, we can look at the level sets of F, which are surfaces in $\mathbf{R}^3$. (See Figure 2.20.) We have

$$\text{Level set at height } c = \{(x, y, z) \mid x + y + z = c\}.$$

Thus, the level sets form a family of parallel planes with normal vector $\mathbf{i} + \mathbf{j} + \mathbf{k}$.

◆

Surfaces in General

Not all curves in $\mathbf{R}^2$ can be described as the graph of a single function of one variable. Perhaps the most familiar example is the unit circle shown in Figure 2.21. Its graph *cannot* be determined by a single equation of the form $y = f(x)$ (or, for that matter, by one of the form $x = g(y)$). As we know, the graph of the circle may be described analytically by the equation $x^2 + y^2 = 1$. In general, a curve in $\mathbf{R}^2$ is determined by an arbitrary equation in x and y, not necessarily one that isolates y alone on one side. In other words, this means that a general curve is given by an equation of the form $F(x, y) = c$ (i.e., a level set of a function of *two* variables).

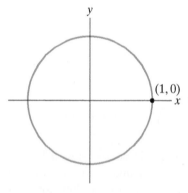

Figure 2.21 The unit circle $x^2 + y^2 = 1$.

The analogous situation occurs with surfaces in $\mathbf{R}^3$. Frequently a surface is determined by an equation of the form $F(x, y, z) = c$ (i.e., as a level set of a function of three variables), *not* necessarily one of the form $z = f(x, y)$.

EXAMPLE 15   A **sphere** is a surface in $\mathbf{R}^3$ whose points are all equidistant from a fixed point. If this fixed point is the origin, then the equation for the sphere is

$$\|\mathbf{x} - \mathbf{0}\| = \|\mathbf{x}\| = a, \tag{3}$$

where a is a positive constant and $\mathbf{x} = (x, y, z)$ is a point on the sphere. If we square both sides of equation (3) and expand the (implicit) dot product, then we obtain perhaps the familiar equation of a sphere of radius a centered at the origin:

$$x^2 + y^2 + z^2 = a^2. \tag{4}$$

If the center of the sphere is at the point $\mathbf{x}_0 = (x_0, y_0, z_0)$, rather than the origin, then equation (3) should be modified to

$$\|\mathbf{x} - \mathbf{x}_0\| = a. \tag{5}$$

(See Figure 2.22.)

When equation (5) is expanded, the following general equation for a sphere is obtained:

$$(x - x_0)^2 + (y - y_0)^2 + (z - z_0)^2 = a^2 \tag{6}$$

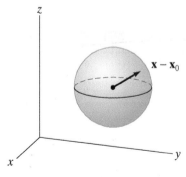

Figure 2.22 The sphere of radius a, centered at (x_0, y_0, z_0).

sin(x+h) − sin(x)

x^2

$$\frac{(x+h)^2 - x^2}{x^2}$$

$$\frac{x^2 + 2xh + h^2}{2xh + h^2}$$
$$\frac{2xh + h^2}{x^2}$$

In the equation for a sphere, there is no way to solve for z *uniquely* in terms of x and y. Indeed, if we try to isolate z in equation (4), then

$$z^2 = a^2 - x^2 - y^2,$$

so we are forced to make a *choice* of positive or negative square roots in order to solve for z:

$$z = \sqrt{a^2 - x^2 - y^2} \quad \text{or} \quad z = -\sqrt{a^2 - x^2 - y^2}.$$

The positive square root corresponds to the upper hemisphere and the negative square root to the lower one. In any case, the entire sphere *cannot* be the graph of a single function of two variables. ◆

Of course, the graph of a function of two variables does describe a surface in the "level set" sense. If a surface happens to be given by an equation of the form

$$z = f(x, y)$$

for some appropriate function $f: X \subseteq \mathbf{R}^2 \to \mathbf{R}$, then we can move z to the opposite side, obtaining

$$f(x, y) - z = 0.$$

If we define a new function F of *three* variables by

$$F(x, y, z) = f(x, y) - z,$$

then the graph of f is precisely the level set at height 0 of F. We reiterate this point since it is all too often forgotten: *The graph of a function of two variables is a surface in $\mathbf{R}^3$ and is a level set of a function of three variables. However, not all level sets of functions of three variables are graphs of functions of two variables.* We urge you to understand this distinction.

Quadric Surfaces

Conic sections, those curves obtained from the intersection of a cone with various planes, are among the simplest, yet also the most interesting, of plane curves: They are the circle, the ellipse, the parabola, and the hyperbola. Besides being produced in a similar geometric manner, conic sections have an elegant algebraic connection: Every conic section is described analytically by a polynomial equation of degree two in two variables. That is, every conic can be described by an equation that looks like

$$Ax^2 + Bxy + Cy^2 + Dx + Ey + F = 0$$

for suitable constants $A, \ldots, F$.

In $\mathbf{R}^3$, the analytic analogue of the conic section is called a **quadric surface**. Quadric surfaces are those defined by equations that are polynomials of degree two in three variables:

$$Ax^2 + Bxy + Cxz + Dy^2 + Eyz + Fz^2 + Gx + Hy + Iz + J = 0.$$

To pass from this equation to the appropriate graph is, in general, a cumbersome process without the aid of either a computer or more linear algebra than we currently have at our disposal. So, instead, we offer examples of those quadric surfaces whose axes of symmetry lie along the coordinate axes in $\mathbf{R}^3$ and whose corresponding analytic equations are relatively simple. In the discussion that follows, a, b, and c are constants, which, for convenience, we take to be positive.

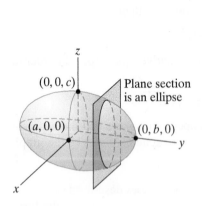

Figure 2.23 The ellipsoid
$$\frac{x^2}{a^2} + \frac{y^2}{b^2} + \frac{z^2}{c^2} = 1.$$

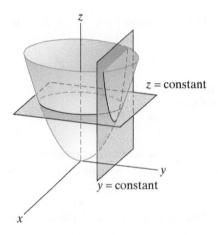

Figure 2.24 The elliptic paraboloid
$$\frac{z}{c} = \frac{x^2}{a^2} + \frac{y^2}{b^2}.$$

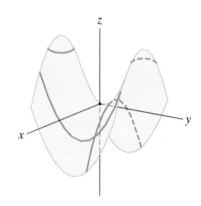

Figure 2.25 The hyperbolic
paraboloid $\dfrac{z}{c} = \dfrac{y^2}{b^2} - \dfrac{x^2}{a^2}.$

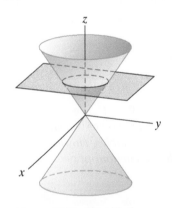

Figure 2.26 The elliptic
cone $\dfrac{z^2}{c^2} = \dfrac{x^2}{a^2} + \dfrac{y^2}{b^2}.$

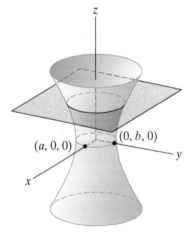

Figure 2.27 The graph of the
equation $\dfrac{x^2}{a^2} + \dfrac{y^2}{b^2} - \dfrac{z^2}{c^2} = 1$ is a
hyperboloid of one sheet.

Ellipsoid (Figure 2.23.) $x^2/a^2 + y^2/b^2 + z^2/c^2 = 1$.
This is the three-dimensional analogue of an ellipse in the plane. The sections
of the ellipsoid by planes perpendicular to the coordinate axes are all ellipses.
For example, if the ellipsoid is intersected with the plane $z = 0$, one obtains the
standard ellipse $x^2/a^2 + y^2/b^2 = 1$, $z = 0$. If $a = b = c$, then the ellipsoid is a
sphere of radius a.

Elliptic paraboloid (Figure 2.24.) $z/c = x^2/a^2 + y^2/b^2$.
(The roles of x, y, and z may be interchanged.) This surface is the graph of
a function of x and y. The paraboloid has elliptical (or single-point or empty)
sections by the planes "$z =$ constant" and parabolic sections by "$x =$ constant" or
"$y =$ constant" planes. The constants a and b affect the aspect ratio of the elliptical
cross sections, and the constant c affects the steepness of the dish. (Larger values
of c produce steeper paraboloids.)

Hyperbolic paraboloid (Figure 2.25.) $z/c = y^2/b^2 - x^2/a^2$.
(Again the roles of x, y, and z may be interchanged.) We saw the graph of this
surface earlier in Example 12 of this section. It is shaped like a saddle whose "$x =$
constant" or "$y =$ constant" sections are parabolas and "$z =$ constant" sections
are hyperbolas.

Elliptic cone (Figure 2.26.) $z^2/c^2 = x^2/a^2 + y^2/b^2$.
The sections by "$z =$ constant" planes are ellipses. The sections by $x = 0$ or
$y = 0$ are each a pair of intersecting lines.

Hyperboloid of one sheet (Figure 2.27.) $x^2/a^2 + y^2/b^2 - z^2/c^2 = 1$.
The term "one sheet" signifies that the surface is *connected* (i.e., that you can
travel between any two points on the surface without having to leave the surface).
The sections by "$z =$ constant" planes are ellipses and those by "$x =$ constant"
or "$y =$ constant" planes are hyperbolas, hence, this surface's name.

Hyperboloid of two sheets (Figure 2.28.) $z^2/c^2 - x^2/a^2 - y^2/b^2 = 1$.
The fact that the left-hand side of the defining equation is the opposite of the left
side of the equation for the previous hyperboloid is what causes this surface to
consist of two pieces instead of one. More precisely, consider the sections of the

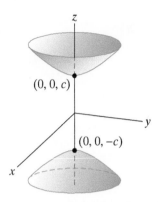

Figure 2.28 The graph of the equation
$$\frac{z^2}{c^2} - \frac{x^2}{a^2} - \frac{y^2}{b^2} = 1 \text{ is a}$$
hyperboloid of two sheets.

Figure 2.29 The hyperboloids
$$\frac{z^2}{c^2} = \frac{x^2}{a^2} + \frac{y^2}{b^2} \pm 1 \text{ are}$$
asymptotic to the cone
$$\frac{z^2}{c^2} = \frac{x^2}{a^2} + \frac{y^2}{b^2}.$$

surface by planes of the form $z = k$ for different constants k. These sections are thus given by

$$\frac{k^2}{c^2} - \frac{x^2}{a^2} - \frac{y^2}{b^2} = 1, \quad z = k$$

or, equivalently, by

$$\frac{x^2}{a^2} + \frac{y^2}{b^2} = \frac{k^2}{c^2} - 1, \quad z = k.$$

If $-c < k < c$, then $0 \le k^2/c^2 < 1$. Thus, $k^2/c^2 - 1 < 0$, and so the preceding equation has no solution in x and y. Hence, the section by $z = k$, where $|k| < c$, is empty. If $|k| > c$, then the section is an ellipse. The sections by "$x = $ constant" or "$y = $ constant" planes are hyperbolas.

In the same way that the hyperbolas

$$\frac{x^2}{a^2} - \frac{y^2}{b^2} = \pm 1$$

are asymptotic to the lines $y = \pm(b/a)x$, the hyperboloids

$$\frac{z^2}{c^2} = \frac{x^2}{a^2} + \frac{y^2}{b^2} \pm 1$$

are asymptotic to the cone

$$\frac{z^2}{c^2} = \frac{x^2}{a^2} + \frac{y^2}{b^2}.$$

This is perhaps intuitively clear from Figure 2.29, but let's see how to prove it rigorously. In our present context, to say that the hyperboloids are asymptotic to the cones means that they look more and more like the cones as $|z|$ becomes (arbitrarily) large. Analytically, this should mean that the equations for the hyperboloids should approximate the equation for the cone for sufficiently large $|z|$. The equations of the hyperboloids can be written as follows:

$$\frac{x^2}{a^2} + \frac{y^2}{b^2} = \frac{z^2}{c^2} \pm 1 = \frac{z^2}{c^2}\left(1 \pm \frac{c^2}{z^2}\right).$$

As $|z| \to \infty$, $c^2/z^2 \to 0$, so the right side of the equation for the hyperboloids approaches z^2/c^2. Hence, the equations for the hyperboloids approximate that of the cone, as desired.

2.1 Exercises

---

1. Let $f: \mathbf{R} \to \mathbf{R}$ be given by $f(x) = 2x^2 + 1$.
  (a) Find the domain and range of f.
  (b) Is f one-one?
  (c) Is f onto?

2. Let $g: \mathbf{R}^2 \to \mathbf{R}$ be given by $g(x, y) = 2x^2 + 3y^2 - 7$.
  (a) Find the domain and range of g.
  (b) Find a way to restrict the domain to make a new function with the same rule of assignment as g that is one-one.

  (c) Find a way to restrict the codomain to make a new function with the same rule of assignment as g that is onto.

Find the domain and range of each of the functions given in Exercises 3–7.

3. $f(x, y) = \dfrac{x}{y}$

4. $f(x, y) = \ln(x + y)$

5. $g(x, y, z) = \sqrt{x^2 + (y - 2)^2 + (z + 1)^2}$

6. $g(x, y, z) = \dfrac{1}{\sqrt{4 - x^2 - y^2 - z^2}}$

7. $\mathbf{f}(x, y) = \left(x + y, \dfrac{1}{y - 1}, x^2 + y^2\right)$

8. Let $\mathbf{f}: \mathbf{R}^2 \to \mathbf{R}^3$ be defined by $\mathbf{f}(x, y) = (x + y, ye^x, x^2y + 7)$. Determine the component functions of $\mathbf{f}$.

9. Determine the component functions of the function $\mathbf{v}$ in Example 9.

10. Let $\mathbf{f}: \mathbf{R}^3 \to \mathbf{R}^3$ be defined by $\mathbf{f}(\mathbf{x}) = \mathbf{x} + 3\mathbf{j}$. Write out the component functions of $\mathbf{f}$ in terms of the components of the vector $\mathbf{x}$.

11. Consider the mapping that assigns to a nonzero vector $\mathbf{x}$ in $\mathbf{R}^3$ the vector of length 2 that points in the direction opposite to $\mathbf{x}$.
 (a) Give an analytic (symbolic) description of this mapping.
 (b) If $\mathbf{x} = (x, y, z)$, determine the component functions of this mapping.

12. Consider the function $\mathbf{f}: \mathbf{R}^2 \to \mathbf{R}^3$ given by $\mathbf{f}(\mathbf{x}) = A\mathbf{x}$, where $A = \begin{bmatrix} 2 & -1 \\ 5 & 0 \\ -6 & 3 \end{bmatrix}$ and the vector $\mathbf{x}$ in $\mathbf{R}^2$ is written as the 2×1 column matrix $\mathbf{x} = \begin{bmatrix} x_1 \\ x_2 \end{bmatrix}$.
 (a) Explicitly determine the component functions of $\mathbf{f}$ in terms of the components x_1, x_2 of the vector (i.e., column matrix) $\mathbf{x}$.
 (b) Describe the range of $\mathbf{f}$.

13. Consider the function $\mathbf{f}: \mathbf{R}^4 \to \mathbf{R}^3$ given by $\mathbf{f}(\mathbf{x}) = A\mathbf{x}$, where $A = \begin{bmatrix} 2 & 0 & -1 & 1 \\ 0 & 3 & 0 & 0 \\ 2 & 0 & -1 & 1 \end{bmatrix}$ and the vector $\mathbf{x}$ in $\mathbf{R}^4$ is written as the 4×1 column matrix $\mathbf{x} = \begin{bmatrix} x_1 \\ x_2 \\ x_3 \\ x_4 \end{bmatrix}$.
 (a) Determine the component functions of $\mathbf{f}$ in terms of the components x_1, x_2, x_3, x_4 of the vector (i.e., column matrix) $\mathbf{x}$.
 (b) Describe the range of $\mathbf{f}$.

In each of Exercises 14–23, (a) determine several level curves of the given function f (make sure to indicate the height c of each curve); (b) use the information obtained in part (a) to sketch the graph of f.

14. $f(x, y) = 3$

15. $f(x, y) = x^2 + y^2$

16. $f(x, y) = x^2 + y^2 - 9$

17. $f(x, y) = \sqrt{x^2 + y^2}$

18. $f(x, y) = 4x^2 + 9y^2$

19. $f(x, y) = xy$

20. $f(x, y) = \dfrac{y}{x}$

21. $f(x, y) = \dfrac{x}{y}$

22. $f(x, y) = 3 - 2x - y$

23. $f(x, y) = |x|$

In Exercises 24–27, use a computer to provide a portrait of the given function $g(x, y)$. To do this, (a) use the computer to help you understand some of the level curves of the function, and (b) use the computer to graph (a portion of) the surface $z = g(x, y)$. In addition, mark on your surface some of the contour curves corresponding to the level curves you obtained in part (a). (See Figures 2.10 and 2.11.)

24. $g(x, y) = ye^x$

25. $g(x, y) = x^2 - xy$

26. $g(x, y) = (x^2 + 3y^2)e^{1 - x^2 - y^2}$

27. $g(x, y) = \dfrac{\sin(2 - x^2 - y^2)}{x^2 + y^2 + 1}$

28. The **ideal gas law** is the equation $PV = kT$, where P denotes the pressure of the gas, V the volume, T the temperature, and k is a positive constant.
 (a) Describe the temperature T of the gas as a function of volume and pressure. Sketch some level curves for this function.
 (b) Describe the volume V of the gas as a function of pressure and temperature. Sketch some level curves.

29. (a) Graph the surfaces $z = x^2$ and $z = y^2$.
 (b) Explain how one can understand the graph of the surfaces $z = f(x)$ and $z = f(y)$ by considering the *curve* in the uv-plane given by $v = f(u)$.
 (c) Graph the surface in $\mathbf{R}^3$ with equation $y = x^2$.

30. Use a computer to graph the family of level curves for the functions in Exercises 20 and 21 and compare your results with those obtained by hand sketching. How do you account for any differences?

31. Given a function $f(x, y)$, can two different level curves of f intersect? Why or why not?

In Exercises 32–36, describe the graph of $g(x, y, z)$ by computing some level surfaces. (If you prefer, use a computer to assist you.)

32. $g(x, y, z) = x - 2y + 3z$

33. $g(x, y, z) = x^2 + y^2 - z$

34. $g(x, y, z) = x^2 + y^2 + z^2$

35. $g(x, y, z) = x^2 + 9y^2 + 4z^2$

36. $g(x, y, z) = xy - yz$

37. (a) Describe the graph of $g(x, y, z) = x^2 + y^2$ by computing some level surfaces.

    (b) Suppose g is a function such that the expression for $g(x, y, z)$ involves only x and y (i.e., $g(x, y, z) = h(x, y)$). What can you say about the level surfaces of g?

    (c) Suppose g is a function such that the expression for $g(x, y, z)$ involves only x and z. What can you say about the level surfaces of g?

    (d) Suppose g is a function such that the expression for $g(x, y, z)$ involves only x. What can you say about the level surfaces of g?

38. This problem concerns the surface determined by the graph of the equation $x^2 + xy - xz = 2$.

    (a) Find a function $F(x, y, z)$ of three variables so that this surface may be considered to be a level set of F.

    (b) Find a function $f(x, y)$ of two variables so that this surface may be considered to be the graph of $z = f(x, y)$.

39. Graph the ellipsoid

$$\frac{x^2}{4} + \frac{y^2}{9} + z^2 = 1.$$

Is it possible to find a function $f(x, y)$ so that this ellipsoid may be considered to be the graph of $z = f(x, y)$? Explain.

Sketch or describe the surfaces in $\mathbf{R}^3$ determined by the equations in Exercises 40–46.

40. $z = \dfrac{x^2}{4} - y^2$

41. $z^2 = \dfrac{x^2}{4} - y^2$

42. $x = \dfrac{y^2}{4} - \dfrac{z^2}{9}$

43. $x^2 + \dfrac{y^2}{9} - \dfrac{z^2}{16} = 0$

44. $\dfrac{x^2}{4} - \dfrac{y^2}{16} + \dfrac{z^2}{9} = 1$

45. $\dfrac{x^2}{25} + \dfrac{y^2}{16} = z^2 - 1$

46. $z = y^2 + 2$

We can look at examples of quadric surfaces with centers or vertices at points other than the origin by employing a change of coordinates of the form $\bar{x} = x - x_0$, $\bar{y} = y - y_0$, and $\bar{z} = z - z_0$. This coordinate change simply puts the point (x_0, y_0, z_0) of the xyz-coordinate system at the origin of the $\bar{x}\bar{y}\bar{z}$-coordinate system by a translation of axes. Then, for example, the surface having equation

$$\frac{(x-1)^2}{4} + \frac{(y+2)^2}{9} + (z-5)^2 = 1$$

can be identified by setting $\bar{x} = x - 1$, $\bar{y} = y + 2$, and $\bar{z} = z - 5$, so that we obtain

$$\frac{\bar{x}^2}{4} + \frac{\bar{y}^2}{9} + \bar{z}^2 = 1,$$

which is readily seen to be an ellipsoid centered at $(1, -2, 5)$ of the xyz-coordinate system. By completing the square in x, y, or z as necessary, identify and sketch the quadric surfaces in Exercises 47–52.

47. $(x-1)^2 + (y+1)^2 = (z+3)^2$

48. $z = 4x^2 + (y+2)^2$

49. $4x^2 + y^2 + z^2 + 8x = 0$

50. $4x^2 + y^2 - 4z^2 + 8x - 4y + 4 = 0$

51. $x^2 + 2y^2 - 6x - z + 10 = 0$

52. $9x^2 + 4y^2 - 36z^2 - 8y - 144z = 104$

2.2 Limits

As you may recall, limit processes are central to the development of calculus. The mathematical and philosophical debate in the 18th and 19th centuries surrounding the meaning and soundness of techniques of taking limits was intense, questioning the very foundations of calculus. By the middle of the 19th century, the infamous "$\epsilon - \delta$" definition of limits had been devised, chiefly by Karl Weierstrass and Augustin Cauchy, much to the chagrin of many 20th (and 21st) century students of calculus. In the ensuing discussion, we study both the intuitive and rigorous meanings of the limit of a function $\mathbf{f}: X \subseteq \mathbf{R}^n \to \mathbf{R}^m$ and how limits lead to the notion of a continuous function, our main object of study for the remainder of this text.

The Notion of a Limit

For a scalar-valued function of a single variable, $f: X \subseteq \mathbf{R} \to \mathbf{R}$, you have seen the statement

$$\lim_{x \to a} f(x) = L$$

and perhaps have an intuitive understanding of its meaning. In imprecise terms, the preceding equation (read "The limit of $f(x)$ as x approaches a is L.") means that you can make the numerical value of $f(x)$ arbitrarily close to L by keeping x sufficiently close (but not equal) to a. This idea generalizes immediately to functions $\mathbf{f}: X \subseteq \mathbf{R}^n \to \mathbf{R}^m$. In particular, by writing the equation

$$\lim_{\mathbf{x} \to \mathbf{a}} \mathbf{f}(\mathbf{x}) = \mathbf{L},$$

where $\mathbf{f}: X \subseteq \mathbf{R}^n \to \mathbf{R}^m$, we mean that we can make the vector $\mathbf{f}(\mathbf{x})$ arbitrarily close to the **limit vector** $\mathbf{L}$ by keeping the vector $\mathbf{x} \in X$ sufficiently close (but not equal) to $\mathbf{a}$.

The word "close" means that the distance (in the sense of §1.6) between $\mathbf{f}(\mathbf{x})$ and $\mathbf{L}$ is small. Thus, we offer a first definition of limit using the notation for distance.

DEFINITION 2.1   (INTUITIVE DEFINITION OF LIMIT)   The equation

$$\lim_{\mathbf{x} \to \mathbf{a}} \mathbf{f}(\mathbf{x}) = \mathbf{L},$$

where $\mathbf{f}: X \subseteq \mathbf{R}^n \to \mathbf{R}^m$, means that we can make $\|\mathbf{f}(\mathbf{x}) - \mathbf{L}\|$ arbitrarily small (i.e., near zero) by keeping $\|\mathbf{x} - \mathbf{a}\|$ sufficiently small (but nonzero).

In the case of a scalar-valued function $f: X \subseteq \mathbf{R}^n \to \mathbf{R}$, the vector length $\|\mathbf{f}(\mathbf{x}) - \mathbf{L}\|$ can be replaced by the absolute value $|f(\mathbf{x}) - L|$. Similarly, if f is a function of just one variable, then $\|\mathbf{x} - \mathbf{a}\|$ can be replaced by $|x - a|$.

EXAMPLE 1   Suppose that $f: \mathbf{R} \to \mathbf{R}$ is given by

$$f(x) = \begin{cases} 0 & \text{if } x < 1 \\ 2 & \text{if } x \geq 1 \end{cases}.$$

The graph of f is shown in Figure 2.30. What should $\lim_{x \to 1} f(x)$ be? The limit can't be 0, because no matter how near we make x to 1 (i.e., no matter how small we take $|x - 1|$), the values of x can be both slightly larger and slightly smaller than 1. The values of f corresponding to those values of x larger than 1 will be 2. Thus, for such values of x, we cannot make $|f(x) - 0|$ arbitrarily small, since, for $x \geq 1$, $|f(x) - 0| = |2 - 0| = 2$. Similarly, the limit can't be 2, since no matter how small we take $|x - 1|$, x can be slightly smaller than 1. For $x < 1$, $f(x) = 0$ and, therefore, we cannot make $|f(x) - 2| = |0 - 2| = 2$ arbitrarily small. Indeed, it should now be clear that the limit can't be L for *any* $L \in \mathbf{R}$. Hence, $\lim_{x \to 1} f(x)$ *does not exist* for this function.   ◆

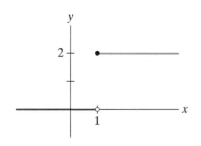

Figure 2.30 The graph of f of Example 1.

EXAMPLE 2   Let $\mathbf{f}: \mathbf{R}^2 \to \mathbf{R}^2$ be defined by $\mathbf{f}(\mathbf{x}) = 5\mathbf{x}$. (That is, $\mathbf{f}$ is five times the **identity function**.) Then it should be obvious intuitively that

$$\lim_{\mathbf{x} \to \mathbf{i}+\mathbf{j}} \mathbf{f}(\mathbf{x}) = \lim_{\mathbf{x} \to \mathbf{i}+\mathbf{j}} 5\mathbf{x} = 5\mathbf{i} + 5\mathbf{j}.$$

Indeed, if we write $\mathbf{x} = x\mathbf{i} + y\mathbf{j}$, then

$$\|\mathbf{f}(\mathbf{x}) - (5\mathbf{i} + 5\mathbf{j})\| = \|(5x\mathbf{i} + 5y\mathbf{j}) - (5\mathbf{i} + 5\mathbf{j})\|$$
$$= \|5(x-1)\mathbf{i} + 5(y-1)\mathbf{j}\| = \sqrt{25(x-1)^2 + 25(y-1)^2}$$
$$= 5\sqrt{(x-1)^2 + (y-1)^2}.$$

This last quantity can be made as small as we wish by keeping

$$\|\mathbf{x} - (\mathbf{i} + \mathbf{j})\| = \sqrt{(x-1)^2 + (y-1)^2}$$

sufficiently small.   ◆

EXAMPLE 3   Now suppose that $\mathbf{g}: \mathbf{R}^n \to \mathbf{R}^n$ is defined by $\mathbf{g}(\mathbf{x}) = 3\mathbf{x}$. We claim that, for any $\mathbf{a} \in \mathbf{R}^n$,

$$\lim_{\mathbf{x} \to \mathbf{a}} 3\mathbf{x} = 3\mathbf{a}.$$

In other words, we claim that $\|3\mathbf{x} - 3\mathbf{a}\|$ can be made as small as we like by keeping $\|\mathbf{x} - \mathbf{a}\|$ sufficiently small. Note that

$$\|3\mathbf{x} - 3\mathbf{a}\| = \|3(\mathbf{x} - \mathbf{a})\| = 3\|\mathbf{x} - \mathbf{a}\|.$$

This means that if we wish to make $\|3\mathbf{x} - 3\mathbf{a}\|$ no more than, say, 0.003, then we may do so by making sure that $\|\mathbf{x} - \mathbf{a}\|$ is no more than 0.001. If, instead, we want $\|3\mathbf{x} - 3\mathbf{a}\|$ to be no more than 0.0003, we can achieve this by keeping $\|\mathbf{x} - \mathbf{a}\|$ no more than 0.0001. Indeed, if we want $\|3\mathbf{x} - 3\mathbf{a}\|$ to be no more than *any* specified amount (no matter how small), then we can achieve this by making sure that $\|\mathbf{x} - \mathbf{a}\|$ is no more than one-third of that amount.

More generally, if $\mathbf{h}: \mathbf{R}^n \to \mathbf{R}^n$ is any constant k times the identity function (i.e., $\mathbf{h}(\mathbf{x}) = k\mathbf{x}$) and $\mathbf{a} \in \mathbf{R}^n$ is *any* vector, then

$$\lim_{\mathbf{x} \to \mathbf{a}} \mathbf{h}(\mathbf{x}) = \lim_{\mathbf{x} \to \mathbf{a}} k\mathbf{x} = k\mathbf{a}. \qquad ◆$$

The main difficulty with Definition 2.1 lies in the terms "arbitrarily small" and "sufficiently small." They are simply too vague. We can add some precision to our intuition as follows: Think of applying the function $\mathbf{f}: X \subseteq \mathbf{R}^n \to \mathbf{R}^m$ as performing some sort of scientific experiment. Letting the variable $\mathbf{x}$ take on a particular value in X amounts to making certain measurements of the input variables to the experiment, and the resulting value $\mathbf{f}(\mathbf{x})$ can be considered to be the outcome of the experiment. Experiments are designed to test theories, so suppose that this hypothetical experiment is designed to test the theory that as the input is closer and closer to $\mathbf{a}$, then the outcome gets closer and closer to $\mathbf{L}$. To verify this theory, you should establish some acceptable (absolute) experimental error for the outcome, say, 0.05. That is, you want $\|\mathbf{f}(\mathbf{x}) - \mathbf{L}\| < 0.05$, if $\|\mathbf{x} - \mathbf{a}\|$ is sufficiently small. Then just how small does $\|\mathbf{x} - \mathbf{a}\|$ need to be? Perhaps it turns out that you must have $\|\mathbf{x} - \mathbf{a}\| < 0.02$, and that if you do take $\|\mathbf{x} - \mathbf{a}\| < 0.02$, then indeed $\|\mathbf{f}(\mathbf{x}) - \mathbf{L}\| < 0.05$. Does this mean that your theory is correct? Not yet. Now, suppose that you decide to be more exacting and will only accept an experimental error of 0.005 instead of 0.05. In other words, you desire $\|\mathbf{f}(\mathbf{x}) - \mathbf{L}\| < 0.005$. Perhaps you find that if you take $\|\mathbf{x} - \mathbf{a}\| < 0.001$, then this new goal can be achieved. Is your theory correct? Well, there's nothing sacred about the number 0.005, so perhaps you should insist that $\|\mathbf{f}(\mathbf{x}) - \mathbf{L}\| < 0.001$, or that $\|\mathbf{f}(\mathbf{x}) - \mathbf{L}\| < 0.00001$. The point is that if your theory really is correct, then *no matter what* (absolute) experimental error ϵ you choose for your outcome, you should be able to find a "tolerance level" δ for your input $\mathbf{x}$ so that if $\|\mathbf{x} - \mathbf{a}\| < \delta$, then

$\|\mathbf{f}(\mathbf{x}) - \mathbf{L}\| < \epsilon$. It is this heuristic approach that motivates the technical definition of the limit.

DEFINITION 2.2   (RIGOROUS DEFINITION OF LIMIT) Let $\mathbf{f}: X \subseteq \mathbf{R}^n \to \mathbf{R}^m$ be a function. Then to say

$$\lim_{\mathbf{x} \to \mathbf{a}} \mathbf{f}(\mathbf{x}) = \mathbf{L}$$

means that given any $\epsilon > 0$, you can find a $\delta > 0$ (which will, in general, depend on ϵ) such that if $\mathbf{x} \in X$ and $0 < \|\mathbf{x} - \mathbf{a}\| < \delta$, then $\|\mathbf{f}(\mathbf{x}) - \mathbf{L}\| < \epsilon$.

The condition $0 < \|\mathbf{x} - \mathbf{a}\|$ simply means that we care only about values $\mathbf{f}(\mathbf{x})$ when $\mathbf{x}$ is *near* $\mathbf{a}$, but *not* equal to $\mathbf{a}$. Definition 2.2 is not easy to use in practice (and we will not use it frequently). Moreover, it is of little value insofar as actually *evaluating* limits of functions is concerned. (The evaluation of the limit of a function of more than one variable is, in general, a difficult task.)

EXAMPLE 4   So that you have some feeling for working with Definition 2.2, let's see rigorously that

$$\lim_{(x,y,z) \to (1,-1,2)} (3x - 5y + 2z) = 12$$

(as should be "obvious"). This means that given any number $\epsilon > 0$, we can find a corresponding $\delta > 0$ such that

if $0 < \|(x, y, z) - (1, -1, 2)\| < \delta$,   then $|3x - 5y + 2z - 12| < \epsilon$.

(Note the uses of vector lengths and absolute values.) We'll present a formal proof in the next paragraph, but for now we'll do the necessary background calculations in order to provide such a proof. First, we need to rewrite the two inequalities in such a way as to make it more plausible that the ϵ-inequality could arise algebraically from the δ-inequality. From the definition of vector length, the δ-inequality becomes

$$0 < \sqrt{(x-1)^2 + (y+1)^2 + (z-2)^2} < \delta.$$

If this is true, then we certainly have the three inequalities

$$\sqrt{(x-1)^2} = |x-1| < \delta,$$
$$\sqrt{(y+1)^2} = |y+1| < \delta,$$
$$\sqrt{(z-2)^2} = |z-2| < \delta.$$

Now, rewrite the left side of the ϵ-inequality and use the triangle inequality (2) of §1.6:

$$|3x - 5y + 2z - 12| = |3(x-1) - 5(y+1) + 2(z-2)|$$
$$\leq |3(x-1)| + |5(y+1)| + |2(z-2)|$$
$$= 3|x-1| + 5|y+1| + 2|z-2|.$$

Thus, if

$$0 < \|(x, y, z) - (1, -1, 2)\| < \delta,$$

then

$$|x-1| < \delta, \quad |y+1| < \delta, \quad \text{and} \quad |z-2| < \delta,$$

so that

$$|3x - 5y + 2z - 12| \leq 3|x-1| + 5|y+1| + 2|z-2|$$
$$< 3\delta + 5\delta + 2\delta = 10\delta.$$

If we think of δ as a positive quantity that we can make as small as desired, then 10δ can also be made small. In fact, it is 10δ that plays the role of ϵ.

Now for a formal, "textbook" proof: Given any $\epsilon > 0$, choose $\delta > 0$ so that $\delta \leq \epsilon/10$. Then, if

$$0 < \|(x, y, z) - (1, -1, 2)\| < \delta,$$

it follows that

$$|x - 1| < \delta, \quad |y + 1| < \delta, \quad \text{and} \quad |z - 2| < \delta,$$

so that

$$|3x - 5y + 2z - 12| \leq 3|x - 1| + 5|y + 1| + 2|z - 2|$$
$$< 3\delta + 5\delta + 2\delta$$
$$= 10\delta \leq 10\frac{\epsilon}{10} = \epsilon.$$

Thus, $\lim_{(x,y,z)\to(1,-1,2)}(3x - 5y + 2z) = 12$, as desired. ◆

Using the same methods as in Example 4, you can show that

$$\lim_{\mathbf{x}\to\mathbf{b}}(a_1 x_1 + a_2 x_2 + \cdots + a_n x_n) = a_1 b_1 + a_2 b_2 + \cdots + a_n b_n$$

for any a_i, $i = 1, 2, \ldots, n$.

Some Topological Terminology

Before discussing the geometric meaning of the limit of a function, we need to introduce some standard terminology regarding sets of points in $\mathbf{R}^n$. The underlying geometry of point sets of a space is known as the **topology** of that space.

Recall from §2.1 that the vector equation $\|\mathbf{x} - \mathbf{a}\| = r$, where $\mathbf{x}$ and $\mathbf{a}$ are in $\mathbf{R}^3$ and $r > 0$, defines a sphere of radius r centered at $\mathbf{a}$. If we modify this equation so that it becomes the inequality

$$\|\mathbf{x} - \mathbf{a}\| \leq r, \tag{1}$$

then the points $\mathbf{x} \in \mathbf{R}^3$ that satisfy it fill out what is called a **closed ball** shown in Figure 2.31. Similarly, the *strict* inequality

$$\|\mathbf{x} - \mathbf{a}\| < r \tag{2}$$

describes points $\mathbf{x} \in \mathbf{R}^3$ that are a distance of less than r from $\mathbf{a}$. Such points determine an **open ball** of radius r centered at $\mathbf{a}$, that is, a solid ball *without* the boundary sphere.

There is nothing about the inequalities (1) and (2) that tie them to $\mathbf{R}^3$. In fact, if we take $\mathbf{x}$ and $\mathbf{a}$ to be points of $\mathbf{R}^n$, then (1) and (2) define, respectively, closed and open n-dimensional balls of radius r centered at $\mathbf{a}$. While we cannot draw sketches when $n > 3$, we can see what (1) and (2) mean when n is 1 or 2. (See Figures 2.32 and 2.33.)

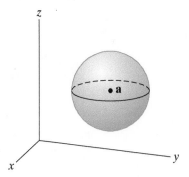

Figure 2.31 A closed ball centered at $\mathbf{a}$.

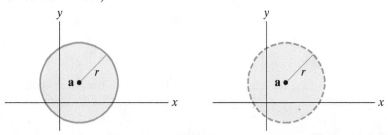

Figure 2.32 The closed and open balls (disks) in $\mathbf{R}^2$ defined by $\|\mathbf{x} - \mathbf{a}\| \leq r$ and $\|\mathbf{x} - \mathbf{a}\| < r$.

Figure 2.33 The closed and open balls (intervals) in **R** defined by $|x - a| \leq r$ and $|x - a| < r$.

DEFINITION 2.3   A set $X \subseteq \mathbf{R}^n$ is said to be **open** in $\mathbf{R}^n$ if, for each point $\mathbf{x} \in X$, there is some open ball centered at $\mathbf{x}$ that lies entirely within X. A point $\mathbf{x} \in \mathbf{R}^n$ is said to be in the **boundary** of a set $X \subseteq \mathbf{R}^n$ if every open ball centered at $\mathbf{x}$, no matter how small, contains some points that are in X and also some points that are not in X. A set $X \subseteq \mathbf{R}^n$ is said to be **closed** in $\mathbf{R}^n$ if it contains all of its boundary points. Finally, a **neighborhood** of a point $\mathbf{x} \in X$ is an open set containing $\mathbf{x}$ and contained in X.

It is an easy consequence of Definition 2.3 that a set X is closed in $\mathbf{R}^n$ precisely if its complement $\mathbf{R}^n - X$ is open.

EXAMPLE 5   The rectangular region

$$X = \{(x, y) \in \mathbf{R}^2 \mid -1 < x < 1, -1 < y < 2\}$$

is open in $\mathbf{R}^2$. (See Figure 2.34.) Each point in X has an open disk around it contained entirely in the rectangle. The boundary of X consists of the four sides of the rectangle. (See Figure 2.35.)   ◆

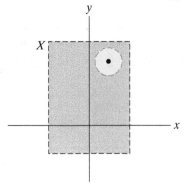

Figure 2.34 The graph of X.

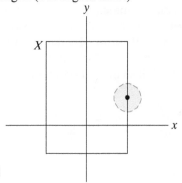

Figure 2.35 Every open disk about a point on a side of rectangle X of Example 5 contains points in both X and $\mathbf{R}^2 - X$.

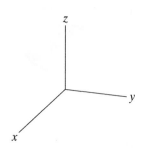

Figure 2.36 The set X of Example 6 consists of the nonnegative coordinate axes.

EXAMPLE 6   The set X consisting of the nonnegative coordinate axes in $\mathbf{R}^3$ in Figure 2.36 is closed since the boundary of X is just X itself.   ◆

EXAMPLE 7   Don't be fooled into thinking that sets are always either open or closed. (That is, a set is not a door.) The set

$$X = \{(x, y) \in \mathbf{R}^2 \mid 0 \leq x < 1, 0 \leq y < 1\}$$

shown in Figure 2.37 is neither open nor closed. It's not open since, for example, the point $\left(\frac{1}{2}, 0\right)$ that lies along the bottom edge of X has no open disk around it that lies completely in X. Furthermore, X is not closed, since the boundary of X includes points of the form $(x, 1)$ for $0 \leq x \leq 1$ (why?), which are not part of X.   ◆

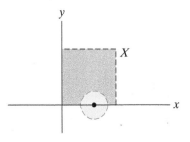

Figure 2.37 The set X of Example 7.

The Geometric Interpretation of a Limit

Suppose that $\mathbf{f}: X \subseteq \mathbf{R}^n \to \mathbf{R}^m$. Then the geometric meaning of the statement

$$\lim_{\mathbf{x} \to \mathbf{a}} \mathbf{f}(\mathbf{x}) = \mathbf{L}$$

is as follows: Given any $\epsilon > 0$, you can find a corresponding $\delta > 0$ such that if points $\mathbf{x} \in X$ are inside an open ball of radius δ centered at $\mathbf{a}$, then the corresponding points $\mathbf{f}(\mathbf{x})$ will remain inside an open ball of radius ϵ centered at $\mathbf{L}$. (See Figure 2.38.)

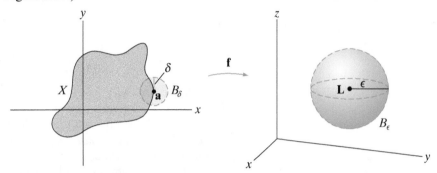

Figure 2.38 Definition of a limit: Given an open ball B_ϵ centered at $\mathbf{L}$ (right), you can always find a corresponding ball B_δ centered at $\mathbf{a}$ (left), so that points in $B_\delta \cap X$ are mapped by $\mathbf{f}$ to points in B_ϵ.

We remark that for this definition to make sense, the point $\mathbf{a}$ must be such that every neighborhood of it in $\mathbf{R}^n$ contains points $\mathbf{x} \in X$ distinct from $\mathbf{a}$. Such a point $\mathbf{a}$ is called an **accumulation point** of X. (Technically, this assumption should also be made in Definition 2.2.) A point $\mathbf{a} \in X$ is called an **isolated point** of X if it is not an accumulation point, that is, if there is some neighborhood of $\mathbf{a}$ in $\mathbf{R}^n$ containing no points of X other than $\mathbf{a}$.

From these considerations, we see that the statement $\lim_{\mathbf{x} \to \mathbf{a}} \mathbf{f}(\mathbf{x}) = \mathbf{L}$ really does mean that as $\mathbf{x}$ moves toward $\mathbf{a}$, $\mathbf{f}(\mathbf{x})$ moves toward $\mathbf{L}$. The significance of the "open ball" geometry is that entirely arbitrary motion is allowed.

EXAMPLE 8   Let $f: \mathbf{R}^2 - \{(0, 0)\} \to \mathbf{R}$ be defined by

$$f(x, y) = \frac{x^2 - y^2}{x^2 + y^2}.$$

Let's see what happens to f as $\mathbf{x} = (x, y)$ approaches $\mathbf{0} = (0, 0)$. (Note that f is undefined at the origin, although this is of no consequence insofar as evaluating limits is concerned.) Along the x-axis (i.e., the line $y = 0$), we calculate the value of f to be

$$f(x, 0) = \frac{x^2 - 0}{x^2 + 0} = 1.$$

Thus, as $\mathbf{x}$ approaches $\mathbf{0}$ *along the line* $y = 0$, the values of f remain constant, and so

$$\lim_{\mathbf{x} \to \mathbf{0} \text{ along } y=0} f(\mathbf{x}) = 1.$$

Along the y-axis, however, the value of f is

$$f(0, y) = \frac{0 - y^2}{0 + y^2} = -1.$$

Hence,

$$\lim_{\substack{\mathbf{x}\to\mathbf{0} \\ \text{along } x=0}} f(\mathbf{x}) = -1.$$

Indeed, the value of f is constant along each line through the origin. Along the line $y = mx$, m constant, we have

$$f(x, mx) = \frac{x^2 - m^2 x^2}{x^2 + m^2 x^2} = \frac{x^2(1 - m^2)}{x^2(1 + m^2)} = \frac{1 - m^2}{1 + m^2}.$$

Therefore,

$$\lim_{\substack{\mathbf{x}\to\mathbf{0} \\ \text{along } y=mx}} f(\mathbf{x}) = \frac{1 - m^2}{1 + m^2}.$$

As a result, the limit of f as $\mathbf{x}$ approaches $\mathbf{0}$ *does not exist,* since f has different "limiting values" depending on which direction we approach the origin. (See Figure 2.39.) That is, no matter how close we come to the origin, we can find points $\mathbf{x}$ such that $f(\mathbf{x})$ is *not* near any number $L \in \mathbf{R}$. (In other words, every open disk centered at $(0, 0)$, no matter how small, is mapped onto the interval $[-1, 1]$.) If we graph the surface having equation

$$z = \frac{x^2 - y^2}{x^2 + y^2}$$

(Figure 2.40), we can see quite clearly that there is no limiting value as x approaches the origin. ◆

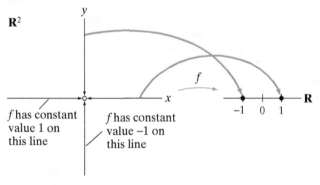

Figure 2.39 The function $f(x, y) = (x^2 - y^2)/(x^2 + y^2)$ of Example 8 has value 1 along the x-axis and value -1 along the y-axis (except at the origin).

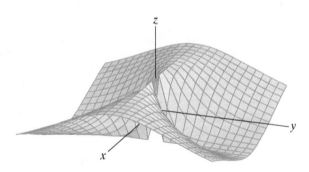

Figure 2.40 The graph of $f(x, y) = (x^2 - y^2)/(x^2 + y^2)$ of Example 8.

WARNING Example 8 might lead you to think you can establish that $\lim_{\mathbf{x}\to\mathbf{a}} \mathbf{f}(\mathbf{x}) = \mathbf{L}$ by showing that the values of $\mathbf{f}$ as $\mathbf{x}$ approaches $\mathbf{a}$ along straight-line paths all tend toward the same value $\mathbf{L}$. Although this is certainly good evidence that the limit should be $\mathbf{L}$, it is by no means conclusive. See Exercise 23 for an example that shows what can happen.

EXAMPLE 9   Another way we might work with the function $f(x, y) = (x^2 - y^2)/(x^2 + y^2)$ of Example 8 is to rewrite it in terms of polar coordinates. Thus, let $x = r \cos\theta$, $y = r \sin\theta$. Using the Pythagorean identity and the double angle formula for cosine, we obtain, for $r \neq 0$, that

$$\frac{x^2 - y^2}{x^2 + y^2} = \frac{r^2 \cos^2 \theta - r^2 \sin^2 \theta}{r^2 \cos^2 \theta + r^2 \sin^2 \theta} = \frac{r^2(\cos^2 \theta - \sin^2 \theta)}{r^2(\cos^2 \theta + \sin^2 \theta)} = \frac{\cos 2\theta}{1} = \cos 2\theta.$$

That is, for $r \neq 0$,

$$f(x, y) = f(r \cos \theta, r \sin \theta) = \cos 2\theta.$$

Moreover, to evaluate the limit of f as (x, y) approaches $(0, 0)$, we only must have r approach 0; there need be no restriction on θ. Therefore, we have

$$\lim_{(x,y)\to(0,0)} f(x, y) = \lim_{r\to 0} \cos 2\theta = \cos 2\theta.$$

This result clearly depends on θ. For example, if $\theta = 0$ (which defines the x-axis), then

$$\lim_{r\to 0 \text{ along } \theta = 0} \cos 2\theta = 1,$$

while if $\theta = \pi/4$ (which defines the line $y = x$), then

$$\lim_{r\to 0 \text{ along } \theta = \pi/4} \cos 2\theta = 0.$$

Thus, as in Example 8, we see that $\lim_{(x,y)\to(0,0)} f(x, y)$ fails to exist.   ◆

EXAMPLE 10 We use polar coordinates to investigate $\lim_{(x,y)\to(0,0)} f(x, y)$, where $f(x, y) = (x^3 + x^5)/(x^2 + y^2)$.

We first rewrite the expression $(x^3 + x^5)/(x^2 + y^2)$ using polar coordinates:

$$\frac{x^3 + x^5}{x^2 + y^2} = \frac{r^3 \cos^3 \theta + r^5 \cos^5 \theta}{r^2 \cos^2 \theta + r^2 \sin^2 \theta} = r(\cos^3 \theta + r^2 \cos^5 \theta).$$

Now $-1 \leq \cos \theta \leq 1$, which implies that

$$-1 - r^2 \leq \cos^3 \theta + r^2 \cos^5 \theta \leq 1 + r^2.$$

Hence,

$$-r(1 + r^2) \leq f(x, y) \leq r(1 + r^2).$$

As $r \to 0$, both the expressions $-r(1 + r^2)$ and $r(1 + r^2)$ approach zero. Hence, we conclude that $\lim_{(x,y)\to(0,0)} f(x, y) = 0$, since f is squeezed between two expressions with the same limit.   ◆

Properties of Limits

One of the biggest drawbacks to Definition 2.2 is that it is not at all useful for determining the value of a limit. You must already have a "candidate limit" in mind and must also be prepared to confront some delicate work with inequalities to use Definition 2.2. The results that follow (which are proved in the addendum to this section), plus a little faith, can be quite helpful for establishing limits, as the subsequent examples demonstrate.

THEOREM 2.4 (UNIQUENESS OF LIMITS)   If a limit exists, it is unique. That is, let $\mathbf{f}\colon X \subseteq \mathbf{R}^n \to \mathbf{R}^m$. If $\lim_{\mathbf{x}\to\mathbf{a}} \mathbf{f}(\mathbf{x}) = \mathbf{L}$ and $\lim_{\mathbf{x}\to\mathbf{a}} \mathbf{f}(\mathbf{x}) = \mathbf{M}$, then $\mathbf{L} = \mathbf{M}$.

THEOREM 2.5 (ALGEBRAIC PROPERTIES)   Let $\mathbf{F}, \mathbf{G}\colon X \subseteq \mathbf{R}^n \to \mathbf{R}^m$ be vector-valued functions, $f, g\colon X \subseteq \mathbf{R}^n \to \mathbf{R}$ be scalar-valued functions, and let $k \in \mathbf{R}$ be a scalar.

1. If $\lim_{\mathbf{x}\to\mathbf{a}} \mathbf{F}(\mathbf{x}) = \mathbf{L}$ and $\lim_{\mathbf{x}\to\mathbf{a}} \mathbf{G}(\mathbf{x}) = \mathbf{M}$,
   then $\lim_{\mathbf{x}\to\mathbf{a}}(\mathbf{F} + \mathbf{G})(\mathbf{x}) = \mathbf{L} + \mathbf{M}$.
2. If $\lim_{\mathbf{x}\to\mathbf{a}} \mathbf{F}(\mathbf{x}) = \mathbf{L}$, then $\lim_{\mathbf{x}\to\mathbf{a}} k\mathbf{F}(\mathbf{x}) = k\mathbf{L}$.
3. If $\lim_{\mathbf{x}\to\mathbf{a}} f(\mathbf{x}) = L$ and $\lim_{\mathbf{x}\to\mathbf{a}} g(\mathbf{x}) = M$, then $\lim_{\mathbf{x}\to\mathbf{a}}(fg)(\mathbf{x}) = LM$.
4. If $\lim_{\mathbf{x}\to\mathbf{a}} f(\mathbf{x}) = L$, $g(\mathbf{x}) \neq 0$ for $\mathbf{x} \in X$, and $\lim_{\mathbf{x}\to\mathbf{a}} g(\mathbf{x}) = M \neq 0$, then $\lim_{\mathbf{x}\to\mathbf{a}}(f/g)(\mathbf{x}) = L/M$.

There is nothing surprising about these theorems—they are exactly the same as the corresponding results for scalar-valued functions of a single variable. Moreover, Theorem 2.5 renders the evaluation of many limits relatively straightforward.

EXAMPLE 11   Either from rigorous considerations or blind faith, you should find it plausible that

$$\lim_{(x,y)\to(a,b)} x = a \quad \text{and} \quad \lim_{(x,y)\to(a,b)} y = b.$$

From these facts, it follows from Theorem 2.5 parts 1, 2, and 3 that

$$\lim_{(x,y)\to(a,b)} (x^2 + 2xy - y^3) = a^2 + 2ab - b^3,$$

because, by part 1 of Theorem 2.5,

$$\lim_{(x,y)\to(a,b)} (x^2 + 2xy - y^3) = \lim x^2 + \lim 2xy + \lim(-y^3)$$

and, by parts 2 and 3,

$$\lim_{(x,y)\to(a,b)} (x^2 + 2xy - y^3) = (\lim x)^2 + 2(\lim x)(\lim y) - (\lim y)^3$$

so that, from the facts just cited,

$$\lim_{(x,y)\to(a,b)} (x^2 + 2xy - y^3) = a^2 + 2ab - b^3. \qquad \blacklozenge$$

EXAMPLE 12   More generally, a **polynomial** in two variables x and y is any expression of the form

$$p(x, y) = \sum_{k=0}^{d} \sum_{l=0}^{d} c_{kl} x^k y^l,$$

where d is some nonnegative integer and $c_{kl} \in \mathbf{R}$ for $k, l = 0, \ldots, d$. That is, $p(x, y)$ is an expression consisting of a (finite) sum of terms that are real number coefficients times powers of x and y. For instance, the expression $x^2 + 2xy - y^3$ in Example 11 is a polynomial. For any $(a, b) \in \mathbf{R}^2$, we have, by part 1 of

Theorem 2.5,

$$\lim_{(x,y)\to(a,b)} p(x,y) = \sum_{k=0}^{d}\sum_{l=0}^{d} \lim_{(x,y)\to(a,b)} (c_{kl}x^k y^l),$$

so that, from part 2,

$$\lim_{(x,y)\to(a,b)} p(x,y) = \sum_{k=0}^{d}\sum_{l=0}^{d} c_{kl} \lim_{(x,y)\to(a,b)} x^k y^l$$

and, from part 3,

$$\lim_{(x,y)\to(a,b)} p(x,y) = \sum_{k=0}^{d}\sum_{l=0}^{d} c_{kl}(\lim x^k)(\lim y^l)$$

$$= \sum_{k=0}^{d}\sum_{l=0}^{d} c_{kl}a^k b^l.$$

Similarly, a **polynomial** in n variables $x_1, x_2, \ldots, x_n$ is an expression of the form

$$p(x_1, x_2, \ldots, x_n) = \sum_{k_1,\ldots,k_n=0}^{d} c_{k_1\cdots k_n} x_1^{k_1} x_2^{k_2} \cdots x_n^{k_n},$$

where d is some nonnegative integer and $c_{k_1\cdots k_n} \in \mathbf{R}$ for $k_1, \ldots, k_n = 0, \ldots, d$. For example, a polynomial in four variables might look like this:

$$p(x_1, \ldots, x_4) = 3x_1^2 x_2 + x_1 x_2 x_3 x_4 - 7x_3^8 x_4^2.$$

Theorem 2.5 implies readily that

$$\lim_{x\to a} \sum c_{k_1\cdots k_n} x_1^{k_1} x_2^{k_2} \cdots x_n^{k_n} = \sum c_{k_1\cdots k_n} a_1^{k_1} a_2^{k_2} \cdots a_n^{k_n}. \qquad \blacklozenge$$

EXAMPLE 13   We evaluate $\displaystyle\lim_{(x,y)\to(-1,0)} \frac{x^2+xy+3}{x^2 y - 5xy + y^2 + 1}$.

Using Example 12, we see that

$$\lim_{(x,y)\to(-1,0)} x^2 + xy + 3 = 4,$$

and

$$\lim_{(x,y)\to(-1,0)} x^2 y - 5xy + y^2 + 1 = 1(\neq 0).$$

Thus, from part 4 of Theorem 2.5, we conclude that

$$\lim_{(x,y)\to(-1,0)} \frac{x^2+xy+3}{x^2 y - 5xy + y^2 + 1} = \frac{4}{1} = 4. \qquad \blacklozenge$$

EXAMPLE 14   Of course, not all limits of quotient expressions are as simple to evaluate as that of Example 13. For instance, we cannot use Theorem 2.5 to evaluate

$$\lim_{(x,y)\to(0,0)} \frac{x^2-y^4}{x^2+y^4} \tag{3}$$

since $\lim_{(x,y)\to(0,0)}(x^2+y^4) = 0$. Indeed, since $\lim_{(x,y)\to(0,0)}(x^2-y^4) = 0$ as well, the expression $(x^2-y^4)/(x^2+y^4)$ becomes indeterminate as $(x,y) \to (0,0)$. To see what happens to the expression, we note that

$$\lim_{x\to 0 \text{ along } y=0} \frac{x^2-y^4}{x^2+y^4} = \lim_{x\to 0} \frac{x^2}{x^2} = 1,$$

while

$$\lim_{y\to 0 \text{ along } x=0} \frac{x^2 - y^4}{x^2 + y^4} = \lim_{y\to 0} \frac{-y^4}{y^4} = -1.$$

Thus, the limit in (3) does not exist. (Compare this with Example 8.)   ◆

The following result shows that evaluating the limit of a function $\mathbf{f}: X \subseteq \mathbf{R}^n \to \mathbf{R}^m$ is equivalent to evaluating the limits of its (scalar-valued) component functions. First recall from §2.1 that $\mathbf{f}(\mathbf{x})$ may be rewritten as $(f_1(\mathbf{x}), f_2(\mathbf{x}), \ldots, f_m(\mathbf{x}))$.

THEOREM 2.6 Suppose $\mathbf{f}: X \subseteq \mathbf{R}^n \to \mathbf{R}^m$ is a vector-valued function. Then $\lim_{\mathbf{x}\to\mathbf{a}} \mathbf{f}(\mathbf{x}) = \mathbf{L}$, where $\mathbf{L} = (L_1, \ldots, L_m)$, if and only if $\lim_{\mathbf{x}\to\mathbf{a}} f_i(\mathbf{x}) = L_i$ for $i = 1, \ldots, m$.

EXAMPLE 15 Consider the linear mapping $\mathbf{f}: \mathbf{R}^n \to \mathbf{R}^m$ defined by $\mathbf{f}(\mathbf{x}) = A\mathbf{x}$, where $A = (a_{ij})$ is an $m \times n$ matrix of real numbers. (See Example 5 of §1.6.) Theorem 2.6 shows us that

$$\lim_{\mathbf{x}\to\mathbf{b}} \mathbf{f}(\mathbf{x}) = A\mathbf{b}$$

for any $\mathbf{b} = (b_1, \ldots, b_n)$ in $\mathbf{R}^n$. If we write out the matrix multiplication, we have

$$\mathbf{f}(\mathbf{x}) = A\mathbf{x} = \begin{bmatrix} a_{11} & \cdots & a_{1n} \\ a_{21} & \cdots & a_{2n} \\ \vdots & \ddots & \vdots \\ a_{m1} & \cdots & a_{mn} \end{bmatrix} \begin{bmatrix} x_1 \\ x_2 \\ \vdots \\ x_n \end{bmatrix}$$

$$= \begin{bmatrix} a_{11}x_1 + a_{12}x_2 + \cdots + a_{1n}x_n \\ a_{21}x_1 + a_{22}x_2 + \cdots + a_{2n}x_n \\ \vdots \\ a_{m1}x_1 + a_{m2}x_2 + \cdots + a_{mn}x_n \end{bmatrix}.$$

Therefore, the ith component function of $\mathbf{f}$ is

$$f_i(x) = a_{i1}x_1 + a_{i2}x_2 + \cdots + a_{in}x_n.$$

From Example 4, we have that

$$\lim_{\mathbf{x}\to\mathbf{b}} f_i(\mathbf{x}) = a_{i1}b_1 + a_{i2}b_2 + \cdots + a_{in}b_n$$

for each i. Hence, Theorem 2.6 tells us that the limits of the component functions fit together to form a limit vector. We can, therefore, conclude that

$$\lim_{\mathbf{x}\to\mathbf{b}} \mathbf{f}(\mathbf{x}) = (\lim_{\mathbf{x}\to\mathbf{b}} f_1(\mathbf{x}), \ldots, \lim_{\mathbf{x}\to\mathbf{b}} f_m(\mathbf{x}))$$
$$= (a_{11}b_1 + \cdots + a_{1n}b_n, \ldots, a_{m1}b_1 + \cdots + a_{mn}b_n)$$
$$= \begin{bmatrix} a_{11}b_1 + \cdots + a_{1n}b_n \\ a_{21}b_1 + \cdots + a_{2n}b_n \\ \vdots \\ a_{m1}b_1 + \cdots + a_{mn}b_n \end{bmatrix} = A\mathbf{b},$$

once we take advantage of matrix notation.   ◆

Continuous Functions

For scalar-valued functions of a single variable, one often adopts the following attitude toward the notion of continuity: A function $f: X \subseteq \mathbf{R} \to \mathbf{R}$ is **continuous** if its graph can be drawn without taking the pen off the paper. By this criterion, Figure 2.41 describes a continuous function $y = f(x)$, while Figure 2.42 does not.

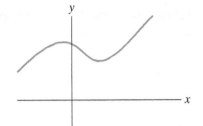

Figure 2.41 The graph of a continuous function.

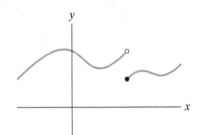

Figure 2.42 The graph of a function that is not continuous.

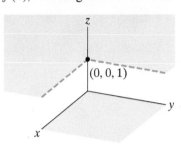

Figure 2.43 The graph of f where $f(x, y) = 0$ if both $x \geq 0$ and $y \geq 0$, and where $f(x, y) = 1$ otherwise.

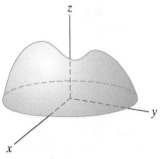

Figure 2.44 The graph of a continuous function $f(x, y)$.

We can try to extend this idea to scalar-valued functions of two variables: A function $f: X \subseteq \mathbf{R}^2 \to \mathbf{R}$ is **continuous** if its graph (in $\mathbf{R}^3$) has no breaks in it. Then the function shown in Figure 2.43 fails to be continuous, but Figure 2.44 depicts a continuous function. Although this graphical approach to continuity is pleasantly geometric and intuitive, it does have real and fatal flaws. For one thing, we can't visualize graphs of functions of more than two variables, so how will we be able to tell in general if a function $f: X \subseteq \mathbf{R}^n \to \mathbf{R}^m$ is continuous? Moreover, it is not always so easy to produce a graph of a function of two variables that is sufficient to make a visual determination of continuity. This said, we now give a rigorous definition of continuity of functions of several variables.

DEFINITION 2.7   Let $\mathbf{f}: X \subseteq \mathbf{R}^n \to \mathbf{R}^m$ and let $\mathbf{a} \in X$. Then $\mathbf{f}$ is said to be **continuous at a** if either $\mathbf{a}$ is an isolated point of X or if

$$\lim_{\mathbf{x} \to \mathbf{a}} \mathbf{f}(\mathbf{x}) = \mathbf{f}(\mathbf{a}).$$

If $\mathbf{f}$ is continuous at all points of its domain X, then we simply say that $\mathbf{f}$ is **continuous**.

EXAMPLE 16   Consider the function $f: \mathbf{R}^2 \to \mathbf{R}$ defined by

$$f(x, y) = \begin{cases} \dfrac{x^2 + xy - 2y^2}{x^2 + y^2} & \text{if } (x, y) \neq (0, 0) \\ 0 & \text{if } (x, y) = (0, 0) \end{cases}.$$

Therefore, $f(0, 0) = 0$, but $\lim_{(x, y) \to (0,0)} f(x, y)$ does not exist. (To see this, check what happens as (x, y) approaches $(0,0)$ first along $y = 0$ and then along $x = 0$.) Hence, f is not continuous at $(0,0)$.   ◆

It is worth noting that Definition 2.7 is nothing more than the "vectorized" version of the usual definition of continuity of a (scalar-valued) function of one variable. This definition thus provides another example of the power of our vector notation: Continuity looks the same no matter what the context.

One way of thinking about continuous functions is that they are the ones whose limits are easy to evaluate: When **f** is continuous, the *limit* of **f** as **x** approaches **a** is just the *value* of **f** at **a**. It's all too tempting to get into the habit of behaving as if all functions are continuous, especially since the functions that will be of primary interest to us will be continuous. Try to avoid such an impulse.

EXAMPLE 17   Polynomial functions in n variables are continuous. Example 12 gives a sketch of the fact that

$$\lim_{\mathbf{x} \to \mathbf{a}} \sum c_{k_1 \cdots k_n} x_1^{k_1} \cdots x_n^{k_n} = \sum c_{k_1 \cdots k_n} a_1^{k_1} \cdots a_n^{k_n},$$

where $\mathbf{x} = (x_1, \ldots, x_n)$ and $\mathbf{a} = (a_1, \ldots, a_n)$ are in $\mathbf{R}^n$. If $f \colon \mathbf{R}^n \to \mathbf{R}$ is defined by

$$f(\mathbf{x}) = \sum c_{k_1 \cdots k_n} x_1^{k_1} \cdots x_n^{k_n},$$

then the preceding limit statement says precisely that f is continuous at $\mathbf{a}$.   ◆

EXAMPLE 18   Linear mappings are continuous. If $\mathbf{f} \colon \mathbf{R}^n \to \mathbf{R}^m$ is defined by $\mathbf{f}(\mathbf{x}) = A\mathbf{x}$, where A is an $m \times n$ matrix, then Example 15 establishes that

$$\lim_{\mathbf{x} \to \mathbf{b}} \mathbf{f}(\mathbf{x}) = A\mathbf{b} = \mathbf{f}(\mathbf{b})$$

for all $\mathbf{b} \in \mathbf{R}^n$. Thus, **f** is continuous.   ◆

The geometric interpretation of the $\epsilon - \delta$ definition of a limit gives rise to a similar interpretation of continuity at a point: $\mathbf{f} \colon X \subseteq \mathbf{R}^n \to \mathbf{R}^m$ is continuous at a point $\mathbf{a} \in X$ if, for every open ball B_ϵ in $\mathbf{R}^m$ of radius ϵ centered at $\mathbf{f}(\mathbf{a})$, there is a corresponding open ball B_δ in $\mathbf{R}^n$ of radius δ centered at $\mathbf{a}$ such that points $\mathbf{x} \in X$ inside B_δ are mapped by **f** to points inside B_ϵ. (See Figure 2.45.) Roughly speaking, continuity of **f** means that "close" points in $X \subseteq \mathbf{R}^n$ are mapped to "close" points in $\mathbf{R}^m$.

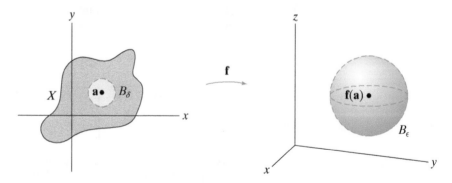

Figure 2.45 Given an open ball B_ϵ about $\mathbf{f}(\mathbf{a})$ (right), you can always find a corresponding open ball B_δ so that points in $B_\delta \cap X$ are mapped to points in B_ϵ.

In practice, we usually establish continuity of a function through the use of Theorems 2.5 and 2.6. These theorems, when interpreted in the context of continuity, tell us the following:

- The sum $\mathbf{F} + \mathbf{G}$ of two functions $\mathbf{F}, \mathbf{G} \colon X \subseteq \mathbf{R}^n \to \mathbf{R}^m$ that are continuous at $\mathbf{a} \in X$ is continuous at $\mathbf{a}$.
- For all $k \in \mathbf{R}$, the scalar multiple $k\mathbf{F}$ of a function $\mathbf{F} \colon X \subseteq \mathbf{R}^n \to \mathbf{R}^m$ that is continuous at $\mathbf{a} \in X$ is continuous at $\mathbf{a}$.
- The product fg and the quotient f/g ($g \neq 0$) of two scalar-valued functions $f, g \colon X \subseteq \mathbf{R}^n \to \mathbf{R}$ that are continuous at $\mathbf{a} \in X$ are continuous at $\mathbf{a}$.
- $\mathbf{F} \colon X \subseteq \mathbf{R}^n \to \mathbf{R}^m$ is continuous at $\mathbf{a} \in X$ if and only if its component functions $F_i \colon X \subseteq \mathbf{R}^n \to \mathbf{R}$, $i = 1, \dots, m$ are all continuous at $\mathbf{a}$.

EXAMPLE 19   The function $\mathbf{f} \colon \mathbf{R}^2 \to \mathbf{R}^3$ defined by

$$\mathbf{f}(x, y) = (x + y, x^2 y, y \sin(xy))$$

is continuous. In view of the remarks above, we can see this by checking that the three component functions

$$f_1(x, y) = x + y, \quad f_2(x, y) = x^2 y, \quad \text{and} \quad f_3(x, y) = y \sin(xy)$$

are each continuous (as scalar-valued functions). Now f_1 and f_2 are continuous, since they are polynomials in the two variables x and y. (See Example 17.) The function f_3 is the product of two further functions; that is,

$$f_3(x, y) = g(x, y)h(x, y),$$

where $g(x, y) = y$ and $h(x, y) = \sin(xy)$. The function g is clearly continuous. (It's a polynomial in two variables—one variable doesn't appear explicitly!) The function h is a *composite* of the sine function (which is continuous as a function of one variable) and the continuous function $p(x, y) = xy$. From these remarks, it's not difficult to see that

$$\lim_{(x,y)\to(a,b)} h(x, y) = \lim_{(x,y)\to(a,b)} \sin(p(x, y))$$

$$= \sin\left(\lim_{(x,y)\to(a,b)} p(x, y)\right),$$

since the sine function is continuous. Thus,

$$\lim_{(x,y)\to(a,b)} h(x, y) = \sin p(a, b) = h(a, b),$$

because p is continuous. Thus, h, hence f_3, and, consequently, $\mathbf{f}$ are all continuous on all of $\mathbf{R}^2$.   ◆

The discussion in Example 19 leads us to the following general result, whose proof we omit:

THEOREM 2.8   If $\mathbf{f} \colon X \subseteq \mathbf{R}^n \to \mathbf{R}^m$ and $\mathbf{g} \colon Y \subseteq \mathbf{R}^m \to \mathbf{R}^p$ are continuous functions such that range $\mathbf{f} \subseteq Y$, then the composite function $\mathbf{g} \circ \mathbf{f} \colon X \subseteq \mathbf{R}^n \to \mathbf{R}^p$ is defined and is also continuous.

Addendum: Proofs of Theorems 2.4, 2.5, 2.6, and 2.8

For the interested reader, we establish the various results regarding limits of functions that we used earlier in this section.

Proof of Theorem 2.4 The statement $\lim_{\mathbf{x}\to\mathbf{a}} \mathbf{f}(\mathbf{x}) = \mathbf{L}$ means that, given any $\epsilon > 0$, we can find some $\delta_1 > 0$ such that if $\mathbf{x} \in X$ and $0 < \|\mathbf{x} - \mathbf{a}\| < \delta_1$, then $\|\mathbf{f}(\mathbf{x}) - \mathbf{L}\| < \epsilon/2$. (The reason for writing $\epsilon/2$ rather than ϵ will become clear in a moment.) Similarly, $\lim_{\mathbf{x}\to\mathbf{a}} \mathbf{f}(\mathbf{x}) = \mathbf{M}$ means that, given any $\epsilon > 0$, we can find some $\delta_2 > 0$ such that if $\mathbf{x} \in X$ and $0 < \|\mathbf{x} - \mathbf{a}\| < \delta_2$, then $\|\mathbf{f}(\mathbf{x}) - \mathbf{M}\| < \epsilon/2$.

Now let $\delta = \min(\delta_1, \delta_2)$; that is, we set δ to be the smaller of δ_1 and δ_2. If $\mathbf{x} \in X$ and $0 < \|\mathbf{x} - \mathbf{a}\| < \delta$, then *both* $\|\mathbf{f}(\mathbf{x}) - \mathbf{L}\|$ and $\|\mathbf{f}(\mathbf{x}) - \mathbf{M}\|$ are less than $\epsilon/2$ so that, using the triangle inequality, we have

$$\|\mathbf{L} - \mathbf{M}\| = \|(\mathbf{L} - \mathbf{f}(\mathbf{x})) + (\mathbf{f}(\mathbf{x}) - \mathbf{M})\|$$
$$\leq \|\mathbf{L} - \mathbf{f}(\mathbf{x})\| + \|\mathbf{f}(\mathbf{x}) - \mathbf{M}\| < \frac{\epsilon}{2} + \frac{\epsilon}{2} = \epsilon.$$

This shows that the quantity $\|\mathbf{L} - \mathbf{M}\|$ can be made arbitrarily small; thus, it follows that $\mathbf{L} - \mathbf{M} = \mathbf{0}$. Hence, $\mathbf{L} = \mathbf{M}$. ∎

Proof of Theorem 2.5 To establish part 1, note that if $\lim_{\mathbf{x}\to\mathbf{a}} \mathbf{F}(\mathbf{x}) = \mathbf{L}$, then given any $\epsilon > 0$, we can find a $\delta_1 > 0$ such that if $\mathbf{x} \in X$ and $0 < \|\mathbf{x} - \mathbf{a}\| < \delta_1$, then $\|\mathbf{F}(\mathbf{x}) - \mathbf{L}\| < \epsilon/2$. Similarly, if $\lim_{\mathbf{x}\to\mathbf{a}} \mathbf{G}(\mathbf{x}) = \mathbf{M}$, then we can find a $\delta_2 > 0$ such that if $\mathbf{x} \in X$ and $0 < \|\mathbf{x} - \mathbf{a}\| < \delta_2$, then $\|\mathbf{G}(\mathbf{x}) - \mathbf{M}\| < \epsilon/2$. Now let $\delta = \min(\delta_1, \delta_2)$. Then if $\mathbf{x} \in X$ and $0 < \|\mathbf{x} - \mathbf{a}\| < \delta$, the triangle inequality implies that

$$\|(\mathbf{F}(\mathbf{x}) + \mathbf{G}(\mathbf{x})) - (\mathbf{L} + \mathbf{M})\| \leq \|\mathbf{F}(\mathbf{x}) - \mathbf{L}\| + \|\mathbf{G}(\mathbf{x}) - \mathbf{M}\| < \frac{\epsilon}{2} + \frac{\epsilon}{2} = \epsilon.$$

Hence, $\lim_{\mathbf{x}\to\mathbf{a}} (\mathbf{F}(\mathbf{x}) + \mathbf{G}(\mathbf{x})) = \mathbf{L} + \mathbf{M}$.

To prove part 2, suppose that $\epsilon > 0$ is given. If $\lim_{\mathbf{x}\to\mathbf{a}} \mathbf{F}(\mathbf{x}) = \mathbf{L}$, then we can find a $\delta > 0$ such that if $\mathbf{x} \in X$ and $0 < \|\mathbf{x} - \mathbf{a}\| < \delta$, then $\|\mathbf{F}(\mathbf{x}) - \mathbf{L}\| < \epsilon/|k|$. Therefore,

$$\|k\mathbf{F}(\mathbf{x}) - k\mathbf{L}\| = |k| \, \|\mathbf{F}(\mathbf{x}) - \mathbf{L}\| < |k| \frac{\epsilon}{|k|} = \epsilon,$$

which means that $\lim_{\mathbf{x}\to\mathbf{a}} k\mathbf{F}(\mathbf{x}) = k\mathbf{L}$. (Note: If $k = 0$, then part 2 holds trivially.)

To establish the rule for the limit of a product of scalar-valued functions (part 3), we will use the following algebraic identity:

$$f(\mathbf{x})g(\mathbf{x}) - LM = (f(\mathbf{x}) - L)(g(\mathbf{x}) - M) + L(g(\mathbf{x}) - M) + M(f(\mathbf{x}) - L).$$
$$\tag{4}$$

If $\lim_{\mathbf{x}\to\mathbf{a}} f(\mathbf{x}) = L$, then, given any $\epsilon > 0$, we can find $\delta_1 > 0$ such that if $\mathbf{x} \in X$ and $0 < \|\mathbf{x} - \mathbf{a}\| < \delta_1$, then

$$|f(\mathbf{x}) - L| < \sqrt{\epsilon}.$$

Similarly, if $\lim_{\mathbf{x}\to\mathbf{a}} g(\mathbf{x}) = M$, we can find $\delta_2 > 0$ such that if $\mathbf{x} \in X$ and $0 < \|\mathbf{x} - \mathbf{a}\| < \delta_2$, then

$$|g(\mathbf{x}) - M| < \sqrt{\epsilon}.$$

Let $\delta = \min(\delta_1, \delta_2)$. If $\mathbf{x} \in X$ and $0 < \|\mathbf{x} - \mathbf{a}\| < \delta$, then

$$|(f(\mathbf{x}) - L)(g(\mathbf{x}) - M)| < \sqrt{\epsilon} \cdot \sqrt{\epsilon} = \epsilon.$$

This means that $\lim_{x \to a}(f(x) - L)(g(x) - M) = 0$. Therefore, using (4) and parts 1 and 2, we see that

$$\lim_{x \to a}(f(x)g(x) - LM) = \lim_{x \to a}(f(x) - L)(g(x) - M) + L \lim_{x \to a}(g(x) - M)$$
$$+ M \lim_{x \to a}(f(x) - L)$$
$$= 0 + 0 + 0 = 0.$$

Since $\lim_{x \to a} f(x)g(x) = \lim_{x \to a}((f(x)g(x) - LM) + LM)$, the desired result follows from part 1.

The crux of the proof of part 4 is to show that

$$\lim_{x \to a} \frac{1}{g(x)} = \frac{1}{M}.$$

Once we show this, the desired result follows directly from part 3:

$$\lim_{x \to a} \frac{f(x)}{g(x)} = \lim_{x \to a}\left(f(x) \cdot \frac{1}{g(x)}\right) = L \cdot \frac{1}{M} = \frac{L}{M}.$$

Note that

$$\left|\frac{1}{g(x)} - \frac{1}{M}\right| = \frac{|M - g(x)|}{|Mg(x)|}$$

and, by the triangle inequality, that

$$|M| = |M - g(x) + g(x)| \le |M - g(x)| + |g(x)|. \tag{5}$$

If $\lim_{x \to a} g(x) = M$, then, given any $\epsilon > 0$, we can find δ_1 such that if $\mathbf{x} \in X$ and $0 < \|\mathbf{x} - \mathbf{a}\| < \delta_1$, then

$$|g(x) - M| < \frac{M^2}{2}\epsilon.$$

We can also find δ_2 such that if $\mathbf{x} \in X$ and $0 < \|\mathbf{x} - \mathbf{a}\| < \delta_2$, then $|g(x) - M| < |M|/2$ and, hence, using (5), that

$$|M| < \frac{|M|}{2} + |g(x)| \iff |g(x)| > \frac{|M|}{2} \iff \frac{1}{|g(x)|} < \frac{2}{|M|}.$$

Now let $\delta = \min(\delta_1, \delta_2)$. If $\mathbf{x} \in X$ and $0 < \|\mathbf{x} - \mathbf{a}\| < \delta$, then

$$\left|\frac{1}{g(x)} - \frac{1}{M}\right| = \frac{|M - g(x)|}{|Mg(x)|} = \frac{1}{|M|}\frac{|M - g(x)|}{|g(x)|}$$
$$< \frac{1}{|M|}\frac{2}{|M|}\frac{M^2}{2}\epsilon = \epsilon. \qquad \blacksquare$$

Proof of Theorem 2.6 Note first that, for $i = 1, \ldots, m$,

$$|f_i(x) - L_i| \le \sqrt{(f_1(x) - L_1)^2 + \cdots + (f_m(x) - L_m)^2} = \|\mathbf{f}(x) - \mathbf{L}\|. \tag{6}$$

If $\lim_{x \to a} \mathbf{f}(x) = \mathbf{L}$, then given any $\epsilon > 0$, we can find a $\delta > 0$ such that if $\mathbf{x} \in X$ and $0 < \|\mathbf{x} - \mathbf{a}\| < \delta$, then $\|\mathbf{f}(x) - \mathbf{L}\| < \epsilon$. Hence, (6) implies that $|f_i(x) - L_i| < \epsilon$ for $i = 1, \ldots, m$, which means that $\lim_{x \to a} f_i(x) = L_i$.

Conversely, suppose that $\lim_{x \to a} f_i(x) = L_i$ for $i = 1, \ldots, m$. This means that, given any $\epsilon > 0$, we can find, for each i, a $\delta_i > 0$ such that if $\mathbf{x} \in X$ and

$0 < \|\mathbf{x} - \mathbf{a}\| < \delta_i$, then $|f_i(\mathbf{x}) - L_i| < \epsilon/\sqrt{m}$. Set $\delta = \min(\delta_1, \ldots, \delta_m)$. Then if $\mathbf{x} \in X$ and $0 < \|\mathbf{x} - \mathbf{a}\| < \delta$, we see that (6) implies

$$\|\mathbf{f}(\mathbf{x}) - \mathbf{L}\| < \sqrt{\frac{\epsilon^2}{m} + \cdots \frac{\epsilon^2}{m}} = \sqrt{m\frac{\epsilon^2}{m}} = \epsilon.$$

Thus, $\lim_{\mathbf{x} \to \mathbf{a}} \mathbf{f}(\mathbf{x}) = \mathbf{L}$.   ■

Proof of Theorem 2.8 We must show that the composite function $\mathbf{g} \circ \mathbf{f}$ is continuous at every point $\mathbf{a} \in X$. If $\mathbf{a}$ is an isolated point of X, there is nothing to show. Otherwise, we must show that $\lim_{\mathbf{x} \to \mathbf{a}}(\mathbf{g} \circ \mathbf{f})(\mathbf{x}) = (\mathbf{g} \circ \mathbf{f})(\mathbf{a})$.

Given any $\epsilon > 0$, continuity of $\mathbf{g}$ at $\mathbf{f}(\mathbf{a})$ implies that we can find some $\gamma > 0$ such that if $\mathbf{y} \in \text{range } \mathbf{f}$ and $0 < \|\mathbf{y} - \mathbf{f}(\mathbf{a})\| < \gamma$ then

$$\|\mathbf{g}(\mathbf{y}) - \mathbf{g}(\mathbf{f}(\mathbf{a}))\| < \epsilon.$$

Since $\mathbf{f}$ is continuous at $\mathbf{a}$, we can find some $\delta > 0$ such that if $\mathbf{x} \in X$ and $0 < \|\mathbf{x} - \mathbf{a}\| < \delta$, then

$$\|\mathbf{f}(\mathbf{x}) - \mathbf{f}(\mathbf{a})\| < \gamma.$$

Therefore, if $\mathbf{x} \in X$ and $0 < \|\mathbf{x} - \mathbf{a}\| < \delta$, then

$$\|\mathbf{g}(\mathbf{f}(\mathbf{x})) - \mathbf{g}(\mathbf{f}(\mathbf{a}))\| < \epsilon.$$ ■

2.2 Exercises

In Exercises 1–6, determine whether the given set is open or closed (or neither).

1. $\{(x, y) \in \mathbf{R}^2 \mid 1 < x^2 + y^2 < 4\}$

2. $\{(x, y) \in \mathbf{R}^2 \mid 1 \leq x^2 + y^2 \leq 4\}$

3. $\{(x, y) \in \mathbf{R}^2 \mid 1 \leq x^2 + y^2 < 4\}$

4. $\{(x, y, z) \in \mathbf{R}^3 \mid 1 \leq x^2 + y^2 + z^2 \leq 4\}$

5. $\{(x, y) \in \mathbf{R}^2 \mid -1 < x < 1\} \cup \{(x, y) \in \mathbf{R}^2 \mid x = 2\}$

6. $\{(x, y, z) \in \mathbf{R}^3 \mid 1 < x^2 + y^2 < 4\}$

Evaluate the limits in Exercises 7–21, or explain why the limit fails to exist.

7. $\displaystyle\lim_{(x,y,z) \to (0,0,0)} x^2 + 2xy + yz + z^3 + 2$

8. $\displaystyle\lim_{(x,y) \to (0,0)} \frac{|y|}{\sqrt{x^2 + y^2}}$

9. $\displaystyle\lim_{(x,y) \to (0,0)} \frac{(x+y)^2}{x^2 + y^2}$

10. $\displaystyle\lim_{(x,y) \to (0,0)} \frac{e^x e^y}{x + y + 2}$

11. $\displaystyle\lim_{(x,y) \to (0,0)} \frac{2x^2 + y^2}{x^2 + y^2}$

12. $\displaystyle\lim_{(x,y) \to (-1,2)} \frac{2x^2 + y^2}{x^2 + y^2}$

13. $\displaystyle\lim_{(x,y) \to (0,0)} \frac{x^2 + 2xy + y^2}{x + y}$

14. $\displaystyle\lim_{(x,y) \to (0,0)} \frac{xy}{x^2 + y^2}$

15. $\displaystyle\lim_{(x,y) \to (0,0)} \frac{x^4 - y^4}{x^2 + y^2}$

16. $\displaystyle\lim_{(x,y) \to (0,0)} \frac{x^2}{x^2 + y^2}$

17. $\displaystyle\lim_{(x,y) \to (0,0), x \neq y} \frac{x^2 - xy}{\sqrt{x} - \sqrt{y}}$

18. $\displaystyle\lim_{(x,y) \to (2,0)} \frac{x^2 - y^2 - 4x + 4}{x^2 + y^2 - 4x + 4}$

19. $\displaystyle\lim_{(x,y,z) \to (0,\sqrt{\pi},1)} e^{xz} \cos y^2 - x$

20. $\displaystyle\lim_{(x,y,z) \to (0,0,0)} \frac{2x^2 + 3y^2 + z^2}{x^2 + y^2 + z^2}$

21. $\displaystyle\lim_{(x,y,z) \to (0,0,0)} \frac{xy - xz + yz}{x^2 + y^2 + z^2}$

22. (a) What is $\displaystyle\lim_{\theta \to 0} \frac{\sin \theta}{\theta}$?

(b) What is $\displaystyle\lim_{(x,y) \to (0,0)} \frac{\sin(x+y)}{x+y}$?

(c) What is $\displaystyle\lim_{(x,y) \to (0,0)} \frac{\sin(xy)}{xy}$?

23. Examine the behavior of $f(x, y) = x^4 y^4/(x^2 + y^4)^3$ as (x, y) approaches $(0, 0)$ along various straight lines. From your observations, what might you conjecture $\lim_{(x,y)\to(0,0)} f(x, y)$ to be? Next, consider what happens when (x, y) approaches $(0, 0)$ along the curve $x = y^2$. Does $\lim_{(x,y)\to(0,0)} f(x, y)$ exist? Why or why not?

In Exercises 24–27, (a) use a computer to graph $z = f(x, y)$; (b) use your graph in part (a) to give a geometric discussion as to whether $\lim_{(x,y)\to(0,0)} f(x, y)$ exists; (c) give an analytic (i.e., nongraphical) argument for your answer in part (b).

24. $f(x, y) = \dfrac{4x^2 + 2xy + 5y^2}{3x^2 + 5y^2}$

25. $f(x, y) = \dfrac{x^2 - y}{x^2 + y^2}$

26. $f(x, y) = \dfrac{xy^5}{x^2 + y^{10}}$

27. $f(x, y) = \begin{cases} x \sin \dfrac{1}{y} & \text{if } y \neq 0 \\ 0 & \text{if } y = 0 \end{cases}$

Some limits become easier to identify if we switch to a different coordinate system. In Exercises 28–33 switch from Cartesian to polar coordinates to evaluate the given limits. In Exercises 34–37 switch to spherical coordinates.

28. $\lim_{(x,y)\to(0,0)} \dfrac{x^2 y}{x^2 + y^2}$

29. $\lim_{(x,y)\to(0,0)} \dfrac{x^2}{x^2 + y^2}$

30. $\lim_{(x,y)\to(0,0)} \dfrac{x^2 + xy + y^2}{x^2 + y^2}$

31. $\lim_{(x,y)\to(0,0)} \dfrac{x^5 + y^4 - 3x^3 y + 2x^2 + 2y^2}{x^2 + y^2}$

32. $\lim_{(x,y)\to(0,0)} \dfrac{x^2 - y^2}{\sqrt{x^2 + y^2}}$

33. $\lim_{(x,y)\to(0,0)} \dfrac{x + y}{\sqrt{x^2 + y^2}}$

34. $\lim_{(x,y,z)\to(0,0,0)} \dfrac{x^2 y}{x^2 + y^2 + z^2}$

35. $\lim_{(x,y,z)\to(0,0,0)} \dfrac{xyz}{x^2 + y^2 + z^2}$

36. $\lim_{(x,y,z)\to(0,0,0)} \dfrac{x^2 + y^2}{\sqrt{x^2 + y^2 + z^2}}$

37. $\lim_{(x,y,z)\to(0,0,0)} \dfrac{xz}{x^2 + y^2 + z^2}$

In Exercises 38–45, determine whether the functions are continuous throughout their domains:

38. $f(x, y) = x^2 + 2xy - y^7$

39. $f(x, y, z) = x^2 + 3xyz + yz^3 + 2$

40. $g(x, y) = \dfrac{x^2 - y^2}{x^2 + 1}$

41. $h(x, y) = \cos\left(\dfrac{x^2 - y^2}{x^2 + 1}\right)$

42. $f(x, y) = \cos^2 x - 2 \sin^2 xy$

43. $f(x, y) = \begin{cases} \dfrac{x^2 - y^2}{x^2 + y^2} & \text{if } (x, y) \neq (0, 0) \\ 0 & \text{if } (x, y) = (0, 0) \end{cases}$

44. $g(x, y) = \begin{cases} \dfrac{x^3 + x^2 + xy^2 + y^2}{x^2 + y^2} & \text{if } (x, y) \neq (0, 0) \\ 2 & \text{if } (x, y) = (0, 0) \end{cases}$

45. $F(x, y, z) = \left(x^2 + 3xy, \dfrac{e^x e^y}{2x^2 + y^4 + 3}, \sin\left(\dfrac{xy}{y^2 + 1}\right)\right)$

46. Determine the value of the constant c so that

$$g(x, y) = \begin{cases} \dfrac{x^3 + xy^2 + 2x^2 + 2y^2}{x^2 + y^2} & \text{if } (x, y) \neq (0, 0) \\ c & \text{if } (x, y) = (0, 0) \end{cases}$$

is continuous.

47. Show that the function $f: \mathbf{R}^3 \to \mathbf{R}$ given by $f(\mathbf{x}) = (2\mathbf{i} - 3\mathbf{j} + \mathbf{k}) \cdot \mathbf{x}$ is continuous.

48. Show that the function $\mathbf{f}: \mathbf{R}^3 \to \mathbf{R}^3$ given by $\mathbf{f}(\mathbf{x}) = (6\mathbf{i} - 5\mathbf{k}) \times \mathbf{x}$ is continuous.

Exercises 49–53 involve Definition 2.2 of the limit.

49. Consider the function $f(x) = 2x - 3$.
   (a) Show that if $|x - 5| < \delta$, then $|f(x) - 7| < 2\delta$.
   (b) Use part (a) to prove that $\lim_{x\to 5} f(x) = 7$.

50. Consider the function $f(x, y) = 2x - 10y + 3$.
   (a) Show that if $\|(x, y) - (5, 1)\| < \delta$, then $|x - 5| < \delta$ and $|y - 1| < \delta$.
   (b) Use part (a) to show that if $\|(x, y) - (5, 1)\| < \delta$, then $|f(x, y) - 3| < 12\delta$.
   (c) Show that $\lim_{(x,y)\to(5,1)} f(x, y) = 3$.

51. If $A, B,$ and C are constants and $f(x, y) = Ax + By + C$, show that

$$\lim_{(x,y)\to(x_0,y_0)} f(x, y) = f(x_0, y_0) = Ax_0 + By_0 + C.$$

52. In this problem, you will establish rigorously that

$$\lim_{(x,y)\to(0,0)} \frac{x^3 + y^3}{x^2 + y^2} = 0.$$

(a) Show that $|x| \le \|(x, y)\|$ and $|y| \le \|(x, y)\|$.

(b) Show that $|x^3 + y^3| \le 2(x^2 + y^2)^{3/2}$. (Hint: Begin with the triangle inequality, and then use part (a).)

(c) Show that if $0 < \|(x, y)\| < \delta$, then $|(x^3 + y^3)/(x^2 + y^2)| < 2\delta$.

(d) Now prove that $\lim_{(x,y)\to(0,0)}(x^3 + y^3)/(x^2 + y^2) = 0$.

53. (a) If a and b are any real numbers, show that $2|ab| \le a^2 + b^2$.

(b) Let

$$f(x, y) = xy\left(\frac{x^2 - y^2}{x^2 + y^2}\right).$$

Use part (a) to show that if $0 < \|(x, y)\| < \delta$, then $|f(x, y)| < \delta^2/2$.

(c) Prove that $\lim_{(x,y)\to(0,0)} f(x, y)$ exists, and find its value.

2.3 The Derivative

Our goal for this section is to define the derivative of a function $\mathbf{f}: X \subseteq \mathbf{R}^n \to \mathbf{R}^m$, where n and m are arbitrary positive integers. Predictably, the derivative of a vector-valued function of several variables is a more complicated object than the derivative of a scalar-valued function of a single variable. In addition, the notion of differentiability is quite subtle in the case of a function of more than one variable.

We first define the basic computational tool of partial derivatives. After doing so, we can begin to understand differentiability via the geometry of tangent planes to surfaces. Finally, we generalize these relatively concrete ideas to higher dimensions.

Partial Derivatives

Recall that if $F: X \subseteq \mathbf{R} \to \mathbf{R}$ is a scalar-valued function of one variable, then the **derivative** of F at a number $a \in X$ is

$$F'(a) = \lim_{h \to 0} \frac{F(a + h) - F(a)}{h}. \tag{1}$$

Moreover, F is said to be **differentiable at** a precisely when the limit in equation (1) exists.

DEFINITION 3.1 Suppose $f: X \subseteq \mathbf{R}^n \to \mathbf{R}$ is a scalar-valued function of n variables. Let $\mathbf{x} = (x_1, x_2, \ldots, x_n)$ denote a point of $\mathbf{R}^n$. A **partial function F with respect to the variable** x_i is a one-variable function obtained from f by holding all variables constant except x_i. That is, we set x_j equal to a constant a_j for $j \ne i$. Then the partial function in x_i is defined by

$$F(x_i) = f(a_1, a_2, \ldots, x_i, \ldots, a_n).$$

EXAMPLE 1 If $f(x, y) = (x^2 - y^2)/(x^2 + y^2)$, then the partial functions with respect to x are given by

$$F(x) = f(x, a_2) = \frac{x^2 - a_2^2}{x^2 + a_2^2},$$

where a_2 may be any constant. If, for example, $a_2 = 0$, then the partial function is

$$F(x) = f(x, 0) = \frac{x^2}{x^2} \equiv 1.$$

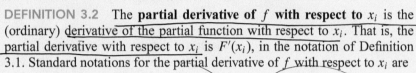

Geometrically, this partial function is nothing more than the restriction of f to the horizontal line $y = 0$. Note that since the origin is not in the domain of f, 0 should not be taken to be in the domain of F. (See Figure 2.46.) ◆

REMARK In practice, we usually do not go to the notational trouble of explicitly replacing the x_j's ($j \neq i$) by constants when working with partial functions. Instead, we make a mental note that the partial function is obtained by allowing only one variable to vary, while all the other variables are held fixed.

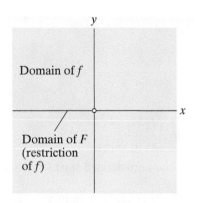

Figure 2.46 The function f of Example 1 is defined on $\mathbf{R}^2 - \{(0,0)\}$, while its partial function F along $y = 0$ is defined on the x-axis minus the origin.

DEFINITION 3.2 The **partial derivative of f with respect to** x_i is the (ordinary) derivative of the partial function with respect to x_i. That is, the partial derivative with respect to x_i is $F'(x_i)$, in the notation of Definition 3.1. Standard notations for the partial derivative of f with respect to x_i are

$$\frac{\partial f}{\partial x_i}, \quad D_{x_i} f(x_1, \ldots, x_n), \quad \text{and} \quad f_{x_i}(x_1, \ldots, x_n).$$

Symbolically, we have

$$\frac{\partial f}{\partial x_i} = \lim_{h \to 0} \frac{f(x_1, \ldots, x_i + h, \ldots, x_n) - f(x_1, \ldots, x_n)}{h}. \tag{2}$$

By definition, the partial derivative is the (instantaneous) rate of change of f when all variables, except the specified one, are held fixed. In the case where f is a (scalar-valued) function of two variables, we can understand

$$\frac{\partial f}{\partial x}(a, b)$$

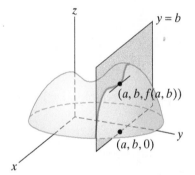

Figure 2.47 Visualizing the partial derivative $\frac{\partial f}{\partial x}(a, b)$.

geometrically as the slope at the point $(a, b, f(a, b))$ of the curve obtained by intersecting the surface $z = f(x, y)$ with the plane $y = b$, as shown in Figure 2.47. Similarly,

$$\frac{\partial f}{\partial y}(a, b)$$

is the slope at $(a, b, f(a, b))$ of the curve formed by the intersection of $z = f(x, y)$ and $x = a$, shown in Figure 2.48.

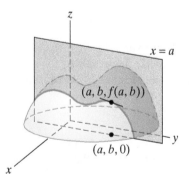

Figure 2.48 Visualizing the partial derivative $\frac{\partial f}{\partial y}(a, b)$.

EXAMPLE 2 For the most part, partial derivatives are quite easy to compute, once you become adept at treating variables like constants. If

$$f(x, y) = x^2 y + \cos(x + y),$$

then we have

$$\frac{\partial f}{\partial x} = 2xy - \sin(x + y).$$

(Imagine y to be a constant throughout the differentiation process.) Also

$$\frac{\partial f}{\partial y} = x^2 - \sin(x + y).$$

(Imagine x to be a constant.) Similarly, if $g(x, y) = xy/(x^2 + y^2)$, then, from the quotient rule of ordinary calculus, we have

$$g_x(x, y) = \frac{(x^2 + y^2)y - xy(2x)}{(x^2 + y^2)^2} = \frac{y(y^2 - x^2)}{(x^2 + y^2)^2},$$

and

$$g_y(x, y) = \frac{(x^2 + y^2)x - xy(2y)}{(x^2 + y^2)^2} = \frac{x(x^2 - y^2)}{(x^2 + y^2)^2}.$$

Note that, of course, neither g nor its partial derivatives are defined at $(0, 0)$. ◆

EXAMPLE 3   Occasionally, it is necessary to appeal explicitly to limits to evaluate partial derivatives. Suppose $f : \mathbf{R}^2 \to \mathbf{R}$ is defined by

$$f(x, y) = \begin{cases} \dfrac{3x^2 y - y^3}{x^2 + y^2} & \text{if } (x, y) \neq (0, 0) \\ 0 & \text{if } (x, y) = (0, 0) \end{cases}.$$

Then, for $(x, y) \neq (0, 0)$, we have

$$\frac{\partial f}{\partial x} = \frac{8xy^3}{(x^2 + y^2)^2} \quad \text{and} \quad \frac{\partial f}{\partial y} = \frac{3x^4 - 6x^2 y^2 - y^4}{(x^2 + y^2)^2}.$$

But what should $\dfrac{\partial f}{\partial x}(0, 0)$ and $\dfrac{\partial f}{\partial y}(0, 0)$ be? To find out, we return to Definition 3.2 of the partial derivatives:

$$\frac{\partial f}{\partial x}(0, 0) = \lim_{h \to 0} \frac{f(0 + h, 0) - f(0, 0)}{h} = \lim_{h \to 0} \frac{0 - 0}{h} = 0,$$

and

$$\frac{\partial f}{\partial y}(0, 0) = \lim_{h \to 0} \frac{f(0, 0 + h) - f(0, 0)}{h} = \lim_{h \to 0} \frac{-h - 0}{h} = \lim_{h \to 0} -1 = -1.$$ ◆

Tangency and Differentiability

If $F : X \subseteq \mathbf{R} \to \mathbf{R}$ is a scalar-valued function of one variable, then to have F differentiable at a number $a \in X$ means precisely that the graph of the curve $y = F(x)$ has a tangent line at the point $(a, F(a))$. (See Figure 2.49.) Moreover, this tangent line is given by the equation

$$y = F(a) + F'(a)(x - a). \tag{3}$$

If we define the function $H(x)$ to be $F(a) + F'(a)(x - a)$ (i.e., $H(x)$ is the right side of equation (3) that gives the equation for the tangent line), then H has two properties:

1. $H(a) = F(a)$
2. $H'(a) = F'(a)$.

In other words, the line defined by $y = H(x)$ passes through the point $(a, F(a))$ and has the same slope at $(a, F(a))$ as the curve defined by $y = F(x)$. (Hence, the term "tangent line.")

Now suppose $f : X \subseteq \mathbf{R}^2 \to \mathbf{R}$ is a scalar-valued function of two variables, where X is open in $\mathbf{R}^2$. Then the graph of f is a surface. What should the **tangent plane** to the graph of $z = f(x, y)$ at the point $(a, b, f(a, b))$ be? Geometrically,

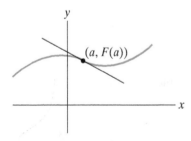

Figure 2.49 The tangent line to $y = F(x)$ at $x = a$ has equation $y = F(a) + F'(a)(x - a)$.

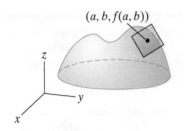

Figure 2.50 The plane tangent to $z = f(x, y)$ at $(a, b, f(a, b))$.

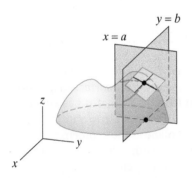

Figure 2.51 The tangent plane at $(a, b, f(a, b))$ contains the lines tangent to the curves formed by intersecting the surface $z = f(x, y)$ by the planes $x = a$ and $y = b$.

the situation is as depicted in Figure 2.50. From our earlier observations, we know that the partial derivative $f_x(a, b)$ is the slope of the line tangent at the point $(a, b, f(a, b))$ to the curve obtained by intersecting the surface $z = f(x, y)$ with the plane $y = b$. (See Figure 2.51.) This means that if we travel along this tangent line, then for every unit change in the positive x-direction, there's a change of $f_x(a, b)$ units in the z-direction. Hence, by using formula (1) of §1.2, the tangent line is given in vector parametric form as

$$\mathbf{l}_1(t) = (a, b, f(a, b)) + t(1, 0, f_x(a, b)).$$

Thus, a vector parallel to this tangent line is

$$\mathbf{u} = \mathbf{i} + f_x(a, b)\,\mathbf{k}.$$

Similarly, the partial derivative $f_y(a, b)$ is the slope of the line tangent at the point $(a, b, f(a, b))$ to the curve obtained by intersecting the surface $z = f(x, y)$ with the plane $x = a$. (Again see Figure 2.51.) Consequently, the tangent line is given by

$$\mathbf{l}_2(t) = (a, b, f(a, b)) + t(0, 1, f_y(a, b)),$$

so a vector parallel to this tangent line is

$$\mathbf{v} = \mathbf{j} + f_y(a, b)\,\mathbf{k}.$$

Both of the aforementioned tangent lines must be contained in the plane tangent to $z = f(x, y)$ at $(a, b, f(a, b))$, if one exists. Hence, a vector $\mathbf{n}$ *normal* to the tangent plane must be perpendicular to both $\mathbf{u}$ and $\mathbf{v}$. Therefore, we may take $\mathbf{n}$ to be

$$\mathbf{n} = \mathbf{u} \times \mathbf{v} = -f_x(a, b)\,\mathbf{i} - f_y(a, b)\,\mathbf{j} + \mathbf{k}.$$

Now, use equation (1) of §1.5 to find that the equation for the tangent plane—that is, the plane through $(a, b, f(a, b))$ with normal $\mathbf{n}$—is

$$(-f_x(a, b), -f_y(a, b), 1) \cdot (x - a, y - b, z - f(a, b)) = 0$$

or, equivalently,

$$-f_x(a, b)(x - a) - f_y(a, b)(y - b) + z - f(a, b) = 0.$$

By rewriting this last equation, we have shown the following result:

THEOREM 3.3 If the graph of $z = f(x, y)$ has a tangent plane at $(a, b, f(a, b))$, then that tangent plane has equation

$$z = f(a, b) + f_x(a, b)(x - a) + f_y(a, b)(y - b). \tag{4}$$

Note that if we define the function $h(x, y)$ to be equal to $f(a, b) + f_x(a, b)(x - a) + f_y(a, b)(y - b)$ (i.e., $h(x, y)$ is the right side of equation (4)), then h has the following properties:

1. $h(a, b) = f(a, b)$

2. $\dfrac{\partial h}{\partial x}(a, b) = \dfrac{\partial f}{\partial x}(a, b)$ and $\dfrac{\partial h}{\partial y}(a, b) = \dfrac{\partial f}{\partial y}(a, b)$.

In other words, h and its partial derivatives agree with those of f at (a, b).

It is tempting to think that the surface $z = f(x, y)$ has a tangent plane at $(a, b, f(a, b))$ as long as you can make sense of equation (4), that is, as long as the

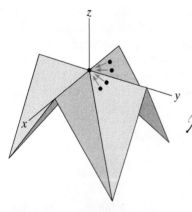

Figure 2.52 If two points approach $(0, 0, 0)$ while remaining on one face of the surface described in Example 4, the limiting plane they and $(0, 0, 0)$ determine is different from the one determined by letting the two points approach $(0, 0, 0)$ while remaining on another face.

partial derivatives $f_x(a, b)$ and $f_y(a, b)$ exist. Indeed, this would be analogous to the one-variable situation where the existence of the derivative and the existence of the tangent line mean exactly the same thing. However, it is possible for a function of two variables to have well-defined partial derivatives (so that equation (4) makes sense) yet *not* have a tangent plane.

EXAMPLE 4 Let $f(x, y) = ||x| - |y|| - |x| - |y|$ and consider the surface defined by the graph of $z = f(x, y)$ shown in Figure 2.52. The partial derivatives of f at the origin may be calculated from Definition 3.2 as

$$f_x(0, 0) = \lim_{h \to 0} \frac{f(0 + h, 0) - f(0, 0)}{h} = \lim_{h \to 0} \frac{||h|| - |h|}{h} = \lim_{h \to 0} 0 = 0$$

and

$$f_y(0, 0) = \lim_{h \to 0} \frac{f(0, 0 + h) - f(0, 0)}{h} = \lim_{h \to 0} \frac{|-|h|| - |h|}{h} = \lim_{h \to 0} 0 = 0.$$

(Indeed, the partial functions $F(x) = f(x, 0)$ and $G(y) = f(0, y)$ are both identically zero and, thus, have zero derivatives.) Consequently, *if* the surface in question has a tangent plane at the origin, then equation (4) tells us that it has equation $z = 0$. But there is no geometric sense in which the surface $z = f(x, y)$ has a tangent plane at the origin. If we think of a tangent plane as the geometric limit of planes that pass through the point of tangency and two other "moving" points on the surface as those two points approach the point of tangency, then Figure 2.52 shows that there is no uniquely determined limiting plane. ◆

Example 4 shows that the existence of a tangent plane to the graph of $z = f(x, y)$ is a stronger condition than the existence of partial derivatives. It turns out that such a stronger condition is more useful in that theorems from the calculus of functions of a single variable carry over to the context of functions of several variables. What we must do now is find a suitable analytic definition of differentiability that captures this idea. We begin by looking at the definition of the one-variable derivative with fresh eyes.

By replacing the quantity $a + h$ by the variable x, the limit equation in formula (1) may be rewritten as

$$F'(a) = \lim_{x \to a} \frac{F(x) - F(a)}{x - a}.$$

This is equivalent to the equation

$$\lim_{x \to a} \left(\frac{F(x) - F(a)}{x - a} \right) - F'(a) = 0.$$

The quantity $F'(a)$ does not depend on x and therefore may be brought inside the limit. We thus obtain the equation

$$\lim_{x \to a} \left\{ \frac{F(x) - F(a)}{x - a} - F'(a) \right\} = 0.$$

Finally, some easy algebra enables us to conclude that the function F is differentiable at a if there is a number $F'(a)$ such that

$$\lim_{x \to a} \frac{F(x) - [F(a) + F'(a)(x - a)]}{x - a} = 0. \tag{5}$$

What have we learned from writing equation (5)? Note that the expression in brackets in the numerator of the limit expression in equation (5) is the function

$H(x)$ that was used to define the tangent line to $y = F(x)$ at $(a, F(a))$. Thus, we may rewrite equation (5) as

$$\lim_{x \to a} \frac{F(x) - H(x)}{x - a} = 0.$$

For the limit above to be zero, we certainly must have that the limit of the numerator is zero. But since the limit of the denominator is also zero, we can say even more, namely, that the difference between the y-values of the graph of F and of its tangent line must approach zero faster than x approaches a. This is what is meant when we say that "H is a good linear approximation to F near a." (See Figure 2.53.) Geometrically, it means that, near the point of tangency, the graph of $y = F(x)$ is approximately straight like the graph of $y = H(x)$.

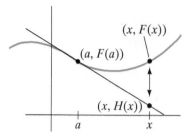

Figure 2.53 If F is differentiable at a, the vertical distance between $F(x)$ and $H(x)$ must approach zero faster than the horizontal distance between x and a does.

If we now pass to the case of a scalar-valued function $f(x, y)$ of two variables, then to say that $z = f(x, y)$ has a tangent plane at $(a, b, f(a, b))$ (i.e., that f is differentiable at (a, b)) should mean that the vertical distance between the graph of f and the "candidate" tangent plane given by

$$z = h(x, y) = f(a, b) + f_x(a, b)(x - a) + f_y(a, b)(y - b)$$

must approach zero faster than the point (x, y) approaches (a, b). (See Figure 2.54.) In other words, near the point of tangency, the graph of $z = f(x, y)$ is approximately flat just like the graph of $z = h(x, y)$. We can capture this geometric idea with the following formal definition of differentiability:

DEFINITION 3.4   Let X be open in $\mathbf{R}^2$ and $f: X \subseteq \mathbf{R}^2 \to \mathbf{R}$ be a scalar-valued function of two variables. We say that f is **differentiable at** $(a, b) \in X$ if the partial derivatives $f_x(a, b)$ and $f_y(a, b)$ exist and if the function

$$h(x, y) = f(a, b) + f_x(a, b)(x - a) + f_y(a, b)(y - b)$$

is a good linear approximation to f near (a, b)—that is, if

$$\lim_{(x, y) \to (a, b)} \frac{f(x, y) - h(x, y)}{\|(x, y) - (a, b)\|} = 0.$$

Moreover, if f is differentiable at (a, b), then the equation $z = h(x, y)$ defines the **tangent plane** to the graph of f at the point $(a, b, f(a, b))$. If f is differentiable at all points of its domain, then we simply say that f is **differentiable**.

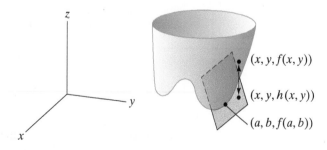

Figure 2.54 If f is differentiable at (a, b), the distance between $f(x, y)$ and $h(x, y)$ must approach zero faster than the distance between (x, y) and (a, b) does.

EXAMPLE 5 Let us return to the function $f(x, y) = ||x| - |y|| - |x| - |y|$ of Example 4. We already know that the partial derivatives $f_x(0, 0)$ and $f_y(0, 0)$ exist and equal zero. Thus, the function h of Definition 3.4 is the zero function. Consequently, f will be differentiable at (0,0) just in case

$$\lim_{(x,y) \to (0,0)} \frac{f(x, y) - h(x, y)}{||(x, y) - (0, 0)||} = \lim_{(x,y) \to (0,0)} \frac{f(x, y)}{||(x, y)||}$$

$$= \lim_{(x,y) \to (0,0)} \frac{||x| - |y|| - |x| - |y|}{\sqrt{x^2 + y^2}}$$

is zero. However, it is not hard to see that the limit in question fails to exist. Along the line $y = 0$, we have

$$\frac{f(x, y)}{||(x, y)||} = \frac{||x| - 0| - |x| - |0|}{\sqrt{x^2}} = \frac{0}{|x|} = 0,$$

but along the line $y = x$, we have

$$\frac{f(x, y)}{||(x, y)||} = \frac{||x| - |x|| - |x| - |x|}{\sqrt{x^2 + x^2}} = \frac{-2|x|}{\sqrt{2}|x|} = -\sqrt{2}.$$

Hence, f fails to be differentiable at $(0, 0)$ and has no tangent plane at $(0, 0, 0)$.◆

The limit condition in Definition 3.4 can be difficult to apply in practice. Fortunately, the following result, which we will not prove, simplifies matters in many instances. Recall from Definition 2.3 that the phrase "a **neighborhood** of a point P in a set X" just means an open set containing P and contained in X.

THEOREM 3.5 Suppose X is open in $\mathbf{R}^2$. If $f: X \to \mathbf{R}$ has continuous partial derivatives in a neighborhood of (a, b) in X, then f is differentiable at (a, b).

A proof of a more general result (Theorem 3.10) is provided in the addendum to this section.

EXAMPLE 6 Let $f(x, y) = x^2 + 2y^2$. Then $\partial f/\partial x = 2x$ and $\partial f/\partial y = 4y$, both of which are continuous functions on all of $\mathbf{R}^2$. Thus, Theorem 3.5 implies that f is differentiable everywhere. The surface $z = x^2 + 2y^2$ must therefore have a tangent plane at every point. At the point $(2, -1)$, for example, this tangent plane is given by the equation

$$z = 6 + 4(x - 2) - 4(y + 1)$$

(or, equivalently, by $4x - 4y - z = 6$).   ◆

While we're on the subject of continuity and differentiability, the next result is the multivariable analogue of a familiar theorem about functions of one variable.

THEOREM 3.6 If $f: X \subseteq \mathbf{R}^2 \to \mathbf{R}$ is differentiable at (a, b), then it is continuous at (a, b).

EXAMPLE 7 Let the function $f: \mathbf{R}^2 \to \mathbf{R}$ be defined by

$$f(x, y) = \begin{cases} \dfrac{x^2 y^2}{x^4 + y^4} & \text{if } (x, y) \neq (0, 0) \\ 0 & \text{if } (x, y) = (0, 0) \end{cases}.$$

The function f is not continuous at the origin, since $\lim_{(x,y)\to(0,0)} f(x, y)$ does not exist. (However, f is continuous everywhere else in $\mathbf{R}^2$.) By Theorem 3.6, f therefore cannot be differentiable at the origin. Nonetheless, the partial derivatives of f do exist at the origin, and we have

$$f(x, 0) = \frac{0}{x^4 + 0} \equiv 0 \quad \Longrightarrow \quad \frac{\partial f}{\partial x}(0, 0) = 0,$$

and

$$f(0, y) = \frac{0}{0 + y^4} \equiv 0 \quad \Longrightarrow \quad \frac{\partial f}{\partial y}(0, 0) = 0,$$

since the partial functions are constant. Thus, we see that if we want something like Theorem 3.6 to be true, the existence of partial derivatives alone is not enough. ◆

Differentiability in General

It is not difficult now to see how to generalize Definition 3.4 to three (or more) variables: For a scalar-valued function of three variables to be differentiable at a point (a, b, c), we must have that (i) the three partial derivatives exist at (a, b, c) and (ii) the function $h: \mathbf{R}^3 \to \mathbf{R}$ defined by

$$h(x, y, z) = f(a, b, c) + f_x(a, b, c)(x - a)$$
$$+ f_y(a, b, c)(y - b) + f_z(a, b, c)(z - c)$$

is a good linear approximation to f near (a, b, c). In other words, (ii) means that

$$\lim_{(x,y,z)\to(a,b,c)} \frac{f(x, y, z) - h(x, y, z)}{\|(x, y, z) - (a, b, c)\|} = 0.$$

The passage from three variables to arbitrarily many is now straightforward.

DEFINITION 3.7 Let X be open in $\mathbf{R}^n$ and $f: X \to \mathbf{R}$ be a scalar-valued function; let $\mathbf{a} = (a_1, a_2, \ldots, a_n) \in X$. We say that f is **differentiable at a** if all the partial derivatives $f_{x_i}(\mathbf{a})$, $i = 1, \ldots, n$, exist and if the function $h: \mathbf{R}^n \to \mathbf{R}$ defined by

$$h(\mathbf{x}) = f(\mathbf{a}) + f_{x_1}(\mathbf{a})(x_1 - a_1) + f_{x_2}(\mathbf{a})(x_2 - a_2)$$
$$+ \cdots + f_{x_n}(\mathbf{a})(x_n - a_n) \tag{6}$$

is a good linear approximation to f near $\mathbf{a}$, meaning that

$$\lim_{\mathbf{x}\to\mathbf{a}} \frac{f(\mathbf{x}) - h(\mathbf{x})}{\|\mathbf{x} - \mathbf{a}\|} = 0.$$

We can use vector and matrix notation to rewrite things a bit. Define the **gradient** of a scalar-valued function $f: X \subseteq \mathbf{R}^n \to \mathbf{R}$ to be the *vector*

$$\nabla f(\mathbf{x}) = \left(\frac{\partial f}{\partial x_1}, \frac{\partial f}{\partial x_2}, \ldots, \frac{\partial f}{\partial x_n} \right).$$

Consequently,

$$\nabla f(\mathbf{a}) = (f_{x_1}(\mathbf{a}), f_{x_2}(\mathbf{a}), \ldots, f_{x_n}(\mathbf{a})).$$

Alternatively, we can use matrix notation and define the **derivative** of f at $\mathbf{a}$, denoted $Df(\mathbf{a})$, to be the row matrix whose entries are the components of $\nabla f(\mathbf{a})$; that is,

$$Df(\mathbf{a}) = \begin{bmatrix} f_{x_1}(\mathbf{a}) & f_{x_2}(\mathbf{a}) & \cdots & f_{x_n}(\mathbf{a}) \end{bmatrix}.$$

Then, by identifying the vector $\mathbf{x} - \mathbf{a}$ with the $n \times 1$ column matrix whose entries are the components of $\mathbf{x} - \mathbf{a}$, we have

$$\nabla f(\mathbf{a}) \cdot (\mathbf{x} - \mathbf{a}) = Df(\mathbf{a})(\mathbf{x} - \mathbf{a}) = \begin{bmatrix} f_{x_1}(\mathbf{a}) & f_{x_2}(\mathbf{a}) & \cdots & f_{x_n}(\mathbf{a}) \end{bmatrix} \begin{bmatrix} x_1 - a_1 \\ x_2 - a_2 \\ \vdots \\ x_n - a_n \end{bmatrix}$$

$$= f_{x_1}(\mathbf{a})(x_1 - a_1) + f_{x_2}(\mathbf{a})(x_2 - a_2)$$

$$+ \cdots + f_{x_n}(\mathbf{a})(x_n - a_n).$$

Hence, vector notation allows us to rewrite equation (6) quite compactly as

$$h(\mathbf{x}) = f(\mathbf{a}) + \nabla f(\mathbf{a}) \cdot (\mathbf{x} - \mathbf{a}).$$

Thus, to say that h is a good linear approximation to f near $\mathbf{a}$ in equation (6) means that

$$\lim_{\mathbf{x} \to \mathbf{a}} \frac{f(\mathbf{x}) - [f(\mathbf{a}) + \nabla f(\mathbf{a}) \cdot (\mathbf{x} - \mathbf{a})]}{\|\mathbf{x} - \mathbf{a}\|} = 0. \tag{7}$$

Compare equation (7) with equation (5). Differentiability of functions of one and several variables should really look very much the same to you. It is worth noting that the analogues of Theorems 3.5 and 3.6 hold in the case of n variables.

The gradient of a function is an extremely important construction, and we consider it in greater detail in §2.6.

You may be wondering what, if any, geometry is embedded in this general notion of differentiability. Recall that the graph of the function $f: X \subseteq \mathbf{R}^n \to \mathbf{R}$ is the **hypersurface** in $\mathbf{R}^{n+1}$ given by the equation $x_{n+1} = f(x_1, x_2, \ldots, x_n)$. (See equation (2) of §2.1.) If f is differentiable at $\mathbf{a}$, then the hypersurface determined by the graph has a **tangent hyperplane** at $(\mathbf{a}, f(\mathbf{a}))$ given by the equation

$$x_{n+1} = h(x_1, x_2, \ldots, x_n) = f(\mathbf{a}) + \nabla f(\mathbf{a}) \cdot (\mathbf{x} - \mathbf{a})$$

$$= f(\mathbf{a}) + Df(\mathbf{a})(\mathbf{x} - \mathbf{a}). \tag{8}$$

Compare equation (8) with equation (3) for the tangent line to the curve $y = F(x)$ at $(\mathbf{a}, F(\mathbf{a}))$. Although we cannot visualize the graph of a function of more than two variables, nonetheless, we can use vector notation to lend real meaning to tangency in n dimensions.

EXAMPLE 8   Before we drown in a sea of abstraction and generalization, let's do some concrete computation. An example of an "n-dimensional paraboloid" in

$\mathbf{R}^{n+1}$ is given by the equation

$$x_{n+1} = x_1^2 + x_2^2 + \cdots + x_n^2,$$

that is, by the graph of the function $f(x_1, \ldots, x_n) = x_1^2 + x_2^2 + \cdots + x_n^2$. We have

$$\frac{\partial f}{\partial x_i} = 2x_i, \quad i = 1, 2, \ldots, n,$$

so that

$$\nabla f(x_1, \ldots, x_n) = (2x_1, 2x_2, \ldots, 2x_n).$$

Note that the partial derivatives of f are continuous everywhere. Hence, the n-dimensional version of Theorem 3.5 tells us that f is differentiable everywhere. In particular, f is differentiable at the point $(1, 2, \ldots, n)$,

$$\nabla f(1, 2, \ldots, n) = (2, 4, \ldots, 2n),$$

and

$$Df(1, 2, \ldots, n) = \begin{bmatrix} 2 & 4 & \cdots & 2n \end{bmatrix}.$$

Thus, the paraboloid has a tangent hyperplane at the point

$$(1, 2, \ldots, n, 1^2 + 2^2 + \cdots + n^2)$$

whose equation is given by equation (8):

$$x_{n+1} = (1^2 + 2^2 + \cdots + n^2) + \begin{bmatrix} 2 & 4 & \cdots & 2n \end{bmatrix} \begin{bmatrix} x_1 - 1 \\ x_2 - 2 \\ \vdots \\ x_n - n \end{bmatrix}$$

$$= (1^2 + 2^2 + \cdots + n^2) + 2(x_1 - 1) + 4(x_2 - 2) + \cdots + 2n(x_n - n)$$

$$= (1^2 + 2^2 + \cdots + n^2) + 2x_1 + 4x_2 + \cdots + 2nx_n$$

$$- (2 \cdot 1 + 4 \cdot 2 + \cdots + 2n \cdot n)$$

$$= 2x_1 + 4x_2 + \cdots + 2nx_n - (1^2 + 2^2 + \cdots + n^2)$$

$$= \sum_{i=1}^{n} 2ix_i - \frac{n(n+1)(2n+1)}{6}.$$

(The formula $1^2 + 2^2 + \cdots + n^2 = n(n+1)(2n+1)/6$ is a well-known identity, encountered when you first learned about the definite integral. It's straightforward to prove using mathematical induction.) ◆

At last we're ready to take a look at differentiability in the most general setting of all. Let X be open in $\mathbf{R}^n$ and let $\mathbf{f}: X \to \mathbf{R}^m$ be a vector-valued function of n variables. We define the **matrix of partial derivatives** of $\mathbf{f}$, denoted $D\mathbf{f}$, to be the $m \times n$ matrix whose ijth entry is $\partial f_i / \partial x_j$, where $f_i \colon X \subseteq \mathbf{R}^n \to \mathbf{R}$ is the ith component function of $\mathbf{f}$. That is,

$$
D\mathbf{f}(x_1, x_2, \ldots, x_n) =
\begin{bmatrix}
\dfrac{\partial f_1}{\partial x_1} & \dfrac{\partial f_1}{\partial x_2} & \cdots & \dfrac{\partial f_1}{\partial x_n} \\[2ex]
\dfrac{\partial f_2}{\partial x_1} & \dfrac{\partial f_2}{\partial x_2} & \cdots & \dfrac{\partial f_2}{\partial x_n} \\[2ex]
\vdots & \vdots & \ddots & \vdots \\[2ex]
\dfrac{\partial f_m}{\partial x_1} & \dfrac{\partial f_m}{\partial x_2} & \cdots & \dfrac{\partial f_m}{\partial x_n}
\end{bmatrix}.
$$

The ith row of $D\mathbf{f}$ is nothing more than Df_i—and the entries of Df_i are precisely the components of the gradient vector ∇f_i. (Indeed, in the case where $m = 1$, ∇f and Df mean exactly the same thing.)

EXAMPLE 9   Suppose $\mathbf{f} \colon \mathbf{R}^3 \to \mathbf{R}^2$ is given by $\mathbf{f}(x, y, z) = (x \cos y + z, xy)$. Then we have

$$
D\mathbf{f}(x, y, z) =
\begin{bmatrix}
\cos y & -x \sin y & 1 \\
y & x & 0
\end{bmatrix}.
$$ ◆

We generalize equation (7) and Definition 3.7 in an obvious way to make the following definition:

DEFINITION 3.8   (GRAND DEFINITION OF DIFFERENTIABILITY)   Let $X \subseteq \mathbf{R}^n$ be open, let $\mathbf{f} \colon X \to \mathbf{R}^m$, and let $\mathbf{a} \in X$. We say that $\mathbf{f}$ is **differentiable at a** if $D\mathbf{f}(\mathbf{a})$ exists and if the function $\mathbf{h} \colon \mathbf{R}^n \to \mathbf{R}^m$ defined by

$$
\mathbf{h}(\mathbf{x}) = \mathbf{f}(\mathbf{a}) + D\mathbf{f}(\mathbf{a})(\mathbf{x} - \mathbf{a})
$$

is a good linear approximation to $\mathbf{f}$ near $\mathbf{a}$. That is, we must have

$$
\lim_{\mathbf{x} \to \mathbf{a}} \frac{\|\mathbf{f}(\mathbf{x}) - \mathbf{h}(\mathbf{x})\|}{\|\mathbf{x} - \mathbf{a}\|} = \lim_{\mathbf{x} \to \mathbf{a}} \frac{\|\mathbf{f}(\mathbf{x}) - [\mathbf{f}(\mathbf{a}) + D\mathbf{f}(\mathbf{a})(\mathbf{x} - \mathbf{a})]\|}{\|\mathbf{x} - \mathbf{a}\|} = 0.
$$

Some remarks are in order. First, the reason for having the vector length appearing in the numerator in the limit equation in Definition 3.8 is so that there is a quotient of real numbers of which we can take a limit. (Definition 3.7 concerns scalar-valued functions only, so there is automatically a quotient of real numbers.) Second, the term $D\mathbf{f}(\mathbf{a})(\mathbf{x} - \mathbf{a})$ in the definition of $\mathbf{h}$ should be interpreted as the product of the $m \times n$ matrix $D\mathbf{f}(\mathbf{a})$ and the $n \times 1$ column matrix

$$
\begin{bmatrix}
x_1 - a_1 \\
x_2 - a_2 \\
\vdots \\
x_n - a_n
\end{bmatrix}.
$$

Because of the consistency of our definitions, the following results should not surprise you:

THEOREM 3.9   If $\mathbf{f}: X \subseteq \mathbf{R}^n \to \mathbf{R}^m$ is differentiable at $\mathbf{a}$, then it is continuous at $\mathbf{a}$.

THEOREM 3.10   If $\mathbf{f}: X \subseteq \mathbf{R}^n \to \mathbf{R}^m$ is such that, for $i = 1, \ldots, m$ and $j = 1, \ldots, n$, all $\partial f_i / \partial x_j$ exist and are continuous in a neighborhood of $\mathbf{a}$ in X, then $\mathbf{f}$ is differentiable at $\mathbf{a}$.

THEOREM 3.11   A function $\mathbf{f}: X \subseteq \mathbf{R}^n \to \mathbf{R}^m$ is differentiable at $\mathbf{a} \in X$ (in the sense of Definition 3.8) if and only if each of its component functions $f_i: X \subseteq \mathbf{R}^n \to \mathbf{R}$, $i = 1, \ldots, m$, is differentiable at $\mathbf{a}$ (in the sense of Definition 3.7).

The proofs of Theorems 3.9, 3.10, and 3.11 are provided in the addendum to this section. Note that Theorems 3.10 and 3.11 frequently make it a straight-forward matter to check that a function is differentiable: Just look at the partial derivatives of the component functions and verify that they are continuous. Thus, in many—but not all—circumstances, we can avoid working directly with the limit in Definition 3.8.

EXAMPLE 10   The function $\mathbf{g}: \mathbf{R}^3 - \{(0, 0, 0)\} \to \mathbf{R}^3$ given by

$$\mathbf{g}(x, y, z) = \left(\frac{3}{x^2 + y^2 + z^2}, xy, xz \right)$$

has

$$D\mathbf{g}(x, y, z) = \begin{bmatrix} \dfrac{-6x}{(x^2 + y^2 + z^2)^2} & \dfrac{-6y}{(x^2 + y^2 + z^2)^2} & \dfrac{-6z}{(x^2 + y^2 + z^2)^2} \\ y & x & 0 \\ z & 0 & x \end{bmatrix}.$$

Each of the entries of this matrix is continuous over $\mathbf{R}^3 - \{(0, 0, 0)\}$. Hence, by Theorem 3.10, $\mathbf{g}$ is differentiable over its entire domain. $\blacklozenge$

What Is a Derivative?

Although we have defined quite carefully what it means for a function to be differentiable, the derivative itself has really taken a "backseat" in the preceding discussion. It is time to get some perspective on the concept of the derivative.

In the case of a (differentiable) scalar-valued function of a single variable, $f: X \subseteq \mathbf{R} \to \mathbf{R}$, the derivative $f'(a)$ is simply a real number, the slope of the tangent line to the graph of f at the point $(a, f(a))$. From a more sophisticated (and slightly less geometric) point of view, the derivative $f'(a)$ is the number such that the function

$$h(x) = f(a) + f'(a)(x - a)$$

is a good linear approximation to $f(x)$ for x near a. (And, of course, $y = h(x)$ is the equation of the tangent line.)

If a function $f: X \subseteq \mathbf{R}^n \to \mathbf{R}$ of n variables is differentiable, there must exist n partial derivatives $\partial f / \partial x_1, \ldots, \partial f / \partial x_n$. These partial derivatives form the components of the gradient vector ∇f (or the entries of the $1 \times n$ matrix Df). It is the gradient that should properly be considered to be the derivative of f, but in the following sense: $\nabla f(\mathbf{a})$ is the vector such that the function $h \colon \mathbf{R}^n \to \mathbf{R}$ given by

$$h(\mathbf{x}) = f(\mathbf{a}) + \nabla f(\mathbf{a}) \cdot (\mathbf{x} - \mathbf{a})$$

is a good linear approximation to $f(\mathbf{x})$ for $\mathbf{x}$ near $\mathbf{a}$. Finally, the derivative of a differentiable vector-valued function $\mathbf{f} \colon X \subseteq \mathbf{R}^n \to \mathbf{R}^m$ may be taken to be the matrix $D\mathbf{f}$ of partial derivatives, but in the sense that the function $\mathbf{h} \colon \mathbf{R}^n \to \mathbf{R}^m$ given by

$$\mathbf{h}(\mathbf{x}) = \mathbf{f}(\mathbf{a}) + D\mathbf{f}(\mathbf{a})(\mathbf{x} - \mathbf{a})$$

is a good linear approximation to $\mathbf{f}(\mathbf{x})$ near $\mathbf{a}$. You should view the derivative $D\mathbf{f}(\mathbf{a})$ not as a "static" matrix of numbers, but rather as a matrix that defines a *linear mapping* from $\mathbf{R}^n$ to $\mathbf{R}^m$. (See Example 5 of §1.6.) This is embodied in the limit equation of Definition 3.8 and, though a subtle idea, is truly the heart of differential calculus of several variables.

In fact, we could have approached our discussion of differentiability much more abstractly right from the beginning. We could have defined a function $\mathbf{f} \colon X \subseteq \mathbf{R}^n \to \mathbf{R}^m$ to be differentiable at a point $\mathbf{a} \in X$ to mean that there exists some linear mapping $\mathbf{L} \colon \mathbf{R}^n \to \mathbf{R}^m$ such that

$$\lim_{\mathbf{x} \to \mathbf{a}} \frac{\|\mathbf{f}(\mathbf{x}) - [\mathbf{f}(\mathbf{a}) + \mathbf{L}(\mathbf{x} - \mathbf{a})]\|}{\|\mathbf{x} - \mathbf{a}\|} = 0.$$

Recall that any linear mapping $\mathbf{L} \colon \mathbf{R}^n \to \mathbf{R}^m$ is really nothing more than multiplication by a suitable $m \times n$ matrix A (i.e., that $\mathbf{L}(\mathbf{y}) = A\mathbf{y}$). It is possible to show that if there is a linear mapping that satisfies the aforementioned limit equation, then the matrix A that defines it is both uniquely determined and is precisely the matrix of partial derivatives $D\mathbf{f}(\mathbf{a})$. (See Exercises 60–62 where these facts are proved.) However, to begin with such a definition, though equivalent to Definition 3.8, strikes us as less well motivated than the approach we have taken. Hence, we have presented the notions of differentiability and the derivative from what we hope is a somewhat more concrete and geometric perspective.

Addendum: Proofs of Theorems 3.9, 3.10, and 3.11

Proof of Theorem 3.9 We begin by claiming the following: Let $\mathbf{x} \in \mathbf{R}^n$ and $B = (b_{ij})$ be an $m \times n$ matrix. If $\mathbf{y} = B\mathbf{x}$, (so $\mathbf{y} \in \mathbf{R}^m$), then

$$\|\mathbf{y}\| \leq K\|\mathbf{x}\|, \tag{9}$$

where $K = \left(\sum_{i,j} b_{ij}^2 \right)^{1/2}$. We postpone the proof of (9) until we establish the main theorem.

To show that $\mathbf{f}$ is continuous at $\mathbf{a}$, we will show that $\|\mathbf{f}(\mathbf{x}) - \mathbf{f}(\mathbf{a})\| \to 0$ as $\mathbf{x} \to \mathbf{a}$. We do so by using the fact that $\mathbf{f}$ is differentiable at $\mathbf{a}$ (Definition 3.8).

We have

$$\|\mathbf{f}(\mathbf{x}) - \mathbf{f}(\mathbf{a})\| = \|\mathbf{f}(\mathbf{x}) - \mathbf{f}(\mathbf{a}) - D\mathbf{f}(\mathbf{a})(\mathbf{x} - \mathbf{a}) + D\mathbf{f}(\mathbf{a})(\mathbf{x} - \mathbf{a})\|$$

$$\leq \|\mathbf{f}(\mathbf{x}) - \mathbf{f}(\mathbf{a}) - D\mathbf{f}(\mathbf{a})(\mathbf{x} - \mathbf{a})\| + \|D\mathbf{f}(\mathbf{a})(\mathbf{x} - \mathbf{a})\|, \tag{10}$$

using the triangle inequality. Note that the first term in the right side of inequality (10) is the numerator of the limit expression in Definition 3.8. Thus, since $\mathbf{f}$ is differentiable at $\mathbf{a}$, we can make $\|\mathbf{f}(\mathbf{x}) - \mathbf{f}(\mathbf{a}) - D\mathbf{f}(\mathbf{a})(\mathbf{x} - \mathbf{a})\|$ as small as we wish by keeping $\|\mathbf{x} - \mathbf{a}\|$ appropriately small. In particular,

$$\|\mathbf{f}(\mathbf{x}) - \mathbf{f}(\mathbf{a}) - D\mathbf{f}(\mathbf{a})(\mathbf{x} - \mathbf{a})\| \leq \|\mathbf{x} - \mathbf{a}\|$$

if $\|\mathbf{x} - \mathbf{a}\|$ is sufficiently small. To the second term in the right side of inequality (10), we may apply (9), since $D\mathbf{f}(\mathbf{a})$ is an $m \times n$ matrix. Therefore, we see that if $\|\mathbf{x} - \mathbf{a}\|$ is made sufficiently small,

$$\|\mathbf{f}(\mathbf{x}) - \mathbf{f}(\mathbf{a})\| \leq \|\mathbf{x} - \mathbf{a}\| + K\|\mathbf{x} - \mathbf{a}\| = (1 + K)\|\mathbf{x} - \mathbf{a}\|. \tag{11}$$

The constant K does not depend on $\mathbf{x}$. Thus, as $\mathbf{x} \to \mathbf{a}$, we have

$$\|\mathbf{f}(\mathbf{x}) - \mathbf{f}(\mathbf{a})\| \to 0,$$

as desired.

To complete the proof, we establish inequality (9). Writing out the matrix multiplication,

$$\mathbf{y} = B\mathbf{x} = \begin{bmatrix} b_{11}x_1 + b_{12}x_2 + \cdots + b_{1n}x_n \\ b_{21}x_1 + b_{22}x_2 + \cdots + b_{2n}x_n \\ \vdots \\ b_{m1}x_1 + b_{m2}x_2 + \cdots + b_{mn}x_n \end{bmatrix} = \begin{bmatrix} \mathbf{b}_1 \cdot \mathbf{x} \\ \mathbf{b}_2 \cdot \mathbf{x} \\ \vdots \\ \mathbf{b}_m \cdot \mathbf{x} \end{bmatrix},$$

where $\mathbf{b}_i$ denotes the ith row of B, considered as a vector in $\mathbf{R}^n$. Therefore, using the Cauchy–Schwarz inequality,

$$\begin{aligned} \|\mathbf{y}\| &= \left((\mathbf{b}_1 \cdot \mathbf{x})^2 + (\mathbf{b}_2 \cdot \mathbf{x})^2 + \cdots + (\mathbf{b}_m \cdot \mathbf{x})^2\right)^{1/2} \\ &\leq \left(\|\mathbf{b}_1\|^2\|\mathbf{x}\|^2 + \|\mathbf{b}_2\|^2\|\mathbf{x}\|^2 + \cdots + \|\mathbf{b}_m\|^2\|\mathbf{x}\|^2\right)^{1/2} \\ &= \left(\|\mathbf{b}_1\|^2 + \|\mathbf{b}_2\|^2 + \cdots + \|\mathbf{b}_m\|^2\right)^{1/2}\|\mathbf{x}\|. \end{aligned}$$

Now,

$$\|\mathbf{b}_i\|^2 = b_{i1}^2 + b_{i2}^2 + \cdots + b_{in}^2 = \sum_{j=1}^{n} b_{ij}^2.$$

Consequently,

$$\|\mathbf{b}_1\|^2 + \|\mathbf{b}_2\|^2 + \cdots + \|\mathbf{b}_m\|^2 = \sum_{i=1}^{m} \|\mathbf{b}_i\|^2 = \sum_{i=1}^{m}\sum_{j=1}^{n} b_{ij}^2 = K^2.$$

Thus, $\|\mathbf{y}\| \leq K\|\mathbf{x}\|$, and we have completed the proof of Theorem 3.9. ∎

Proof of Theorem 3.10 First, we prove Theorem 3.10 for the case where f is a scalar-valued function of two variables. We begin by writing

$$f(x_1, x_2) - f(a_1, a_2) = f(x_1, x_2) - f(a_1, x_2) + f(a_1, x_2) - f(a_1, a_2).$$

By the mean value theorem,[2] there exists a number c_1 between a_1 and x_1 such that

$$f(x_1, x_2) - f(a_1, x_2) = f_{x_1}(c_1, x_2)(x_1 - a_1)$$

---

[2] Recall that the mean value theorem says that if F is continuous on the closed interval $[a, b]$ and differentiable on the open interval (a, b), then there is a number c in (a, b) such that $F(b) - F(a) = F'(c)(b - a)$.

and a number c_2 between a_2 and x_2 such that

$$f(a_1, x_2) - f(a_1, a_2) = f_{x_2}(a_1, c_2)(x_2 - a_2).$$

(This works because in each case we hold all the variables in f constant except one, so that the mean value theorem applies.) Hence,

$$\left| f(x_1, x_2) - f(a_1, a_2) - f_{x_1}(a_1, a_2)(x_1 - a_1) - f_{x_2}(a_1, a_2)(x_2 - a_2) \right|$$

$$= \left| f_{x_1}(c_1, x_2)(x_1 - a_1) + f_{x_2}(a_1, c_2)(x_2 - a_2) - f_{x_1}(a_1, a_2)(x_1 - a_1) \right.$$

$$\left. - f_{x_2}(a_1, a_2)(x_2 - a_2) \right|$$

$$\leq \left| f_{x_1}(c_1, x_2)(x_1 - a_1) - f_{x_1}(a_1, a_2)(x_1 - a_1) \right|$$

$$+ \left| f_{x_2}(a_1, c_2)(x_2 - a_2) - f_{x_2}(a_1, a_2)(x_2 - a_2) \right|,$$

by the triangle inequality. Hence,

$$\left| f(x_1, x_2) - f(a_1, a_2) - f_{x_1}(a_1, a_2)(x_1 - a_1) - f_{x_2}(a_1, a_2)(x_2 - a_2) \right|$$

$$\leq \left| f_{x_1}(c_1, x_2) - f_{x_1}(a_1, a_2) \right| |x_1 - a_1|$$

$$+ \left| f_{x_2}(a_1, c_2) - f_{x_2}(a_1, a_2) \right| |x_2 - a_2|$$

$$\leq \left\{ \left| f_{x_1}(c_1, x_2) - f_{x_1}(a_1, a_2) \right| + \left| f_{x_2}(a_1, c_2) - f_{x_2}(a_1, a_2) \right| \right\} \|\mathbf{x} - \mathbf{a}\|,$$

since, for $i = 1, 2$,

$$|x_i - a_i| \leq \|\mathbf{x} - \mathbf{a}\| = ((x_1 - a_1)^2 + (x_2 - a_2)^2)^{1/2}.$$

Thus,

$$\frac{\left| f(x_1, x_2) - f(a_1, a_2) - f_{x_1}(a_1, a_2)(x_1 - a_1) - f_{x_2}(a_1, a_2)(x_2 - a_2) \right|}{\|\mathbf{x} - \mathbf{a}\|}$$

$$\leq \left| f_{x_1}(c_1, x_2) - f_{x_1}(a_1, a_2) \right| + \left| f_{x_2}(a_1, c_2) - f_{x_2}(a_1, a_2) \right|. \tag{12}$$

As $\mathbf{x} \to \mathbf{a}$, we must have that $c_i \to a_i$, for $i = 1, 2$, since c_i is between a_i and x_i. Consequently, by the continuity of the partial derivatives, both terms of the right side of (12) approach zero. Therefore,

$$\lim_{\mathbf{x} \to \mathbf{a}} \frac{\left| f(x_1, x_2) - f(a_1, a_2) - f_{x_1}(a_1, a_2)(x_1 - a_1) - f_{x_2}(a_1, a_2)(x_2 - a_2) \right|}{\|\mathbf{x} - \mathbf{a}\|} = 0$$

as desired.

Exactly the same kind of argument may be used in the case that f is a scalar-valued function of n variables—the details are only slightly more involved, so we omit them. Granting this, we consider the case of a vector-valued function $\mathbf{f} \colon \mathbf{R}^n \to \mathbf{R}^m$. According to Definition 3.8, we must show that

$$\lim_{\mathbf{x} \to \mathbf{a}} \frac{\|\mathbf{f}(\mathbf{x}) - \mathbf{f}(\mathbf{a}) - D\mathbf{f}(\mathbf{a})(\mathbf{x} - \mathbf{a})\|}{\|\mathbf{x} - \mathbf{a}\|} = 0. \tag{13}$$

The component functions of the expression appearing in the numerator may be written as

$$G_i = f_i(\mathbf{x}) - f_i(\mathbf{a}) - Df_i(\mathbf{a})(\mathbf{x} - \mathbf{a}), \tag{14}$$

where f_i, $i = 1, \ldots, m$, denotes the ith component function of $\mathbf{f}$. (Note that, by the cases of Theorem 3.10 already established, each scalar-valued function f_i is differentiable.) Now, we consider

$$\frac{\|\mathbf{f}(\mathbf{x}) - \mathbf{f}(\mathbf{a}) - D\mathbf{f}(\mathbf{a})(\mathbf{x} - \mathbf{a})\|}{\|\mathbf{x} - \mathbf{a}\|} = \frac{\|(G_1, G_2, \ldots, G_m)\|}{\|\mathbf{x} - \mathbf{a}\|}$$

$$= \frac{(G_1^2 + G_2^2 + \cdots + G_m^2)^{1/2}}{\|\mathbf{x} - \mathbf{a}\|}$$

$$\leq \frac{|G_1| + |G_2| + \cdots + |G_m|}{\|\mathbf{x} - \mathbf{a}\|}$$

$$= \frac{|G_1|}{\|\mathbf{x} - \mathbf{a}\|} + \frac{|G_2|}{\|\mathbf{x} - \mathbf{a}\|} + \cdots + \frac{|G_m|}{\|\mathbf{x} - \mathbf{a}\|}.$$

As $\mathbf{x} \to \mathbf{a}$, each term $|G_i|/\|\mathbf{x} - \mathbf{a}\| \to 0$, by definition of G_i in equation (14) and the differentiability of the component functions f_i of $\mathbf{f}$. Hence, equation (13) holds and $\mathbf{f}$ is differentiable at $\mathbf{a}$. (To see that $(G_1^2 + \cdots + G_m^2)^{1/2} \leq |G_1| + \cdots + |G_m|$, note that

$$(|G_1| + \cdots + |G_m|)^2 = |G_1|^2 + \cdots + |G_m|^2$$
$$+ 2|G_1||G_2| + 2|G_1||G_3| + \cdots + 2|G_{m-1}||G_m|$$
$$\geq |G_1|^2 + \cdots + |G_m|^2.$$

Then, taking square roots provides the inequality.) ∎

Proof of Theorem 3.11 In the final paragraph of the proof of Theorem 3.10, we showed that

$$\frac{\|\mathbf{f}(\mathbf{x}) - \mathbf{f}(\mathbf{a}) - D\mathbf{f}(\mathbf{a})(\mathbf{x} - \mathbf{a})\|}{\|\mathbf{x} - \mathbf{a}\|} \leq \frac{|G_1|}{\|\mathbf{x} - \mathbf{a}\|} + \frac{|G_2|}{\|\mathbf{x} - \mathbf{a}\|} + \cdots + \frac{|G_m|}{\|\mathbf{x} - \mathbf{a}\|},$$

where $G_i = f_i(\mathbf{x}) - f_i(\mathbf{a}) - Df_i(\mathbf{a})(\mathbf{x} - \mathbf{a})$ as in equation (14). From this, it follows immediately that differentiability of the component functions $f_1, \ldots, f_m$ at $\mathbf{a}$ implies differentiability of $\mathbf{f}$ at $\mathbf{a}$. Conversely, for $i = 1, \ldots, m$,

$$\frac{\|\mathbf{f}(\mathbf{x}) - \mathbf{f}(\mathbf{a}) - D\mathbf{f}(\mathbf{a})(\mathbf{x} - \mathbf{a})\|}{\|\mathbf{x} - \mathbf{a}\|} = \frac{\|(G_1, G_2, \ldots, G_m)\|}{\|\mathbf{x} - \mathbf{a}\|} \geq \frac{|G_i|}{\|\mathbf{x} - \mathbf{a}\|}.$$

Hence, differentiability of $\mathbf{f}$ at $\mathbf{a}$ forces differentiability of each component function. ∎

2.3 Exercises

In Exercises 1–9, calculate $\partial f/\partial x$ and $\partial f/\partial y$.

1. $f(x, y) = xy^2 + x^2y$

2. $f(x, y) = e^{x^2+y^2}$

3. $f(x, y) = \sin xy + \cos xy$

4. $f(x, y) = \dfrac{x^3 - y^2}{1 + x^2 + 3y^4}$

5. $f(x, y) = \dfrac{x^2 - y^2}{x^2 + y^2}$

6. $f(x, y) = \ln(x^2 + y^2)$

7. $f(x, y) = \cos x^3 y$

8. $f(x, y) = \ln\left(\dfrac{x}{y}\right)$

9. $f(x, y) = xe^y + y\sin(x^2 + y)$

In Exercises 10–17, evaluate the partial derivatives $\partial F/\partial x$, $\partial F/\partial y$, and $\partial F/\partial z$ for the given functions F.

10. $F(x, y, z) = x + 3y - 2z$

11. $F(x, y, z) = \dfrac{x - y}{y + z}$

12. $F(x, y, z) = xyz$

13. $F(x, y, z) = \sqrt{x^2 + y^2 + z^2}$

14. $F(x, y, z) = e^{ax} \cos by + e^{az} \sin bx$

15. $F(x, y, z) = \dfrac{x + y + z}{(1 + x^2 + y^2 + z^2)^{3/2}}$

16. $F(x, y, z) = \sin x^2 y^3 z^4$

17. $F(x, y, z) = \dfrac{x^3 + yz}{x^2 + z^2 + 1}$

Find the gradient $\nabla f(\mathbf{a})$, where f and $\mathbf{a}$ are given in Exercises 18–25.

18. $f(x, y) = x^2 y + e^{y/x}, \quad \mathbf{a} = (1, 0)$

19. $f(x, y) = \dfrac{x - y}{x^2 + y^2 + 1}, \quad \mathbf{a} = (2, -1)$

20. $f(x, y, z) = \sin xyz, \quad \mathbf{a} = (\pi, 0, \pi/2)$

21. $f(x, y, z) = xy + y \cos z - x \sin yz,$
$\mathbf{a} = (2, -1, \pi)$

22. $f(x, y) = e^{xy} + \ln(x - y), \quad \mathbf{a} = (2, 1)$

23. $f(x, y, z) = \dfrac{x + y}{e^z}, \quad \mathbf{a} = (3, -1, 0)$

24. $f(x, y, z) = \cos z \ln(x + y^2), \quad \mathbf{a} = (e, 0, \pi/4)$

25. $f(x, y, z) = \dfrac{xy^2 - x^2 z}{y^2 + z^2 + 1}, \quad \mathbf{a} = (-1, 2, 1)$

In Exercises 26–33, find the matrix $D\mathbf{f}(\mathbf{a})$ of partial derivatives, where $\mathbf{f}$ and $\mathbf{a}$ are as indicated.

26. $f(x, y) = \dfrac{x}{y}, \quad \mathbf{a} = (3, 2)$

27. $f(x, y, z) = x^2 + x \ln(yz), \quad \mathbf{a} = (-3, e, e)$

28. $\mathbf{f}(x, y, z) = (2x - 3y + 5z, x^2 + y, \ln(yz)),$
$\mathbf{a} = (3, -1, -2)$

29. $\mathbf{f}(x, y, z) = \left(xyz, \sqrt{x^2 + y^2 + z^2}\right),$

$\mathbf{a} = (1, 0, -2)$

30. $\mathbf{f}(t) = (t, \cos 2t, \sin 5t), \quad a = 0$

31. $\mathbf{f}(x, y, z, w) = (3x - 7y + z, 5x + 2z - 8w,$
$y - 17z + 3w), \quad \mathbf{a} = (1, 2, 3, 4)$

32. $\mathbf{f}(x, y) = (x^2 y, x + y^2, \cos \pi xy), \quad \mathbf{a} = (2, -1)$

33. $\mathbf{f}(s, t) = (s^2, st, t^2), \quad \mathbf{a} = (-1, 1)$

Explain why each of the functions given in Exercises 34–36 is differentiable at every point in its domain.

34. $f(x, y) = xy - 7x^8 y^2 + \cos x$

35. $f(x, y, z) = \dfrac{x + y + z}{x^2 + y^2 + z^2}$

36. $\mathbf{f}(x, y) = \left(\dfrac{xy^2}{x^2 + y^4}, \dfrac{x}{y} + \dfrac{y}{x}\right)$

37. (a) Explain why the graph of $z = x^3 - 7xy + e^y$ has a tangent plane at $(-1, 0, 0)$.

(b) Give an equation for this tangent plane.

38. Find an equation for the plane tangent to the graph of $z = 4 \cos xy$ at the point $(\pi/3, 1, 2)$.

39. Find an equation for the plane tangent to the graph of $z = e^{x+y} \cos xy$ at the point $(0, 1, e)$.

40. Find equations for the planes tangent to $z = x^2 - 6x + y^3$ that are parallel to the plane $4x - 12y + z = 7$.

41. Use formula (8) to find an equation for the hyperplane tangent to the 4-dimensional paraboloid $x_5 = 10 - (x_1^2 + 3x_2^2 + 2x_3^2 + x_4^2)$ at the point $(2, -1, 1, 3, -8)$.

42. Suppose that you have the following information concerning a differentiable function f:

$$f(2, 3) = 12, \quad f(1.98, 3) = 12.1, \quad f(2, 3.01) = 12.2.$$

(a) Give an approximate equation for the plane tangent to the graph of f at $(2, 3, 12)$.

(b) Use the result of part (a) to estimate $f(1.98, 2.98)$.

In Exercises 43–45, (a) use the linear function $h(\mathbf{x})$ in Definition 3.8 to approximate the indicated value of the given function f. (b) How accurate is the approximation determined in part (a)?

43. $f(x, y) = e^{x+y}, \ f(0.1, -0.1)$

44. $f(x, y) = 3 + \cos \pi xy, \ f(0.98, 0.51)$

45. $f(x, y, z) = x^2 + xyz + y^3 z, \ f(1.01, 1.95, 2.2)$

46. Calculate the partial derivatives of

$$f(x_1, x_2, \ldots, x_n) = \dfrac{x_1 + x_2 + \cdots + x_n}{\sqrt{x_1^2 + x_2^2 + \cdots + x_n^2}}.$$

47. Let

$$f(x, y) = \begin{cases} \dfrac{xy^2 - x^2 y + 3x^3 - y^3}{x^2 + y^2} & \text{if } (x, y) \neq (0, 0) \\ 0 & \text{if } (x, y) = (0, 0) \end{cases}.$$

(a) Calculate $\partial f/\partial x$ and $\partial f/\partial y$ for $(x, y) \neq (0, 0)$. (You may wish to use a computer algebra system for this part.)

(b) Find $f_x(0, 0)$ and $f_y(0, 0)$.

As mentioned in the text, if a function $F(x)$ of a single variable is differentiable at a, then, as we zoom in on the point $(a, F(a))$, the graph of $y = F(x)$ will "straighten out" and look like its tangent line at $(a, F(a))$. For the differentiable functions given *in Exercises 48–51, (a) calculate the tangent line at the indicated point, and (b) use a computer to graph the function and the tangent line on the same set of axes. Zoom in on the point of tangency to illustrate how the graph of $y = F(x)$ looks like its tangent line near $(a, F(a))$.*

48. $F(x) = x^3 - 2x + 3, \quad a = 1$

49. $F(x) = x + \sin x, \quad a = \dfrac{\pi}{4}$

50. $F(x) = \dfrac{x^3 - 3x^2 + x}{x^2 + 1}, \quad a = 0$

51. $F(x) = \ln(x^2 + 1), \quad a = -1$

52. (a) Use a computer to graph the function $F(x) = (x - 2)^{2/3}$.

(b) By zooming in near $x = 2$, offer a geometric discussion concerning the differentiability of F at $x = 2$.

As discussed in the text, a function $f(x, y)$ may have partial derivatives $f_x(a, b)$ and $f_y(a, b)$ yet fail to be differentiable at (a, b). Geometrically, if a function $f(x, y)$ is differentiable at (a, b), then, as we zoom in on the point $(a, b, f(a, b))$, the graph of $z = f(x, y)$ will "flatten out" and look like the plane given by equation (4) in this section. For the functions $f(x, y)$ given in Exercises 53–57, (a) calculate $f_x(a, b)$ and $f_y(a, b)$ at the indicated point (a, b) and write the equation for the plane given by formula (4) of this section, (b) use a computer to graph the equation $z = f(x, y)$ together with the plane calculated in part (a). Zoom in near the point $(a, b, f(a, b))$ and discuss whether or not $f(x, y)$ is differentiable at (a, b). (c) Give an analytic (i.e., nongraphical) argument for your answer in part (b).

53. $f(x, y) = x^3 - xy + y^2, \quad (a, b) = (2, 1)$

54. $f(x, y) = ((x - 1)y)^{2/3}, \quad (a, b) = (1, 0)$

55. $f(x, y) = \dfrac{xy}{x^2 + y^2 + 1}, \quad (a, b) = (0, 0)$

56. $f(x, y) = \sin x \cos y, \quad (a, b) = \left(\dfrac{\pi}{6}, \dfrac{3\pi}{4}\right)$

57. $f(x, y) = x^2 \sin y + y^2 \cos x, \quad (a, b) = \left(\dfrac{\pi}{3}, \dfrac{\pi}{4}\right)$

58. Let $g(x, y) = \sqrt[3]{xy}$.

(a) Is g continuous at $(0, 0)$?

(b) Calculate $\partial g / \partial x$ and $\partial g / \partial y$ when $xy \neq 0$.

(c) Show that $g_x(0, 0)$ and $g_y(0, 0)$ exist by supplying values for them.

(d) Are $\partial g / \partial x$ and $\partial g / \partial y$ continuous at $(0, 0)$?

(e) Does the graph of $z = g(x, y)$ have a tangent plane at $(0, 0)$? You might consider creating a graph of this surface.

(f) Is g differentiable at $(0, 0)$?

59. Suppose $\mathbf{f} \colon \mathbf{R}^n \to \mathbf{R}^m$ is a linear mapping; that is,

$$\mathbf{f(x)} = A\mathbf{x}, \quad \text{where } \mathbf{x} = (x_1, x_2, \ldots, x_n) \in \mathbf{R}^n$$

and A is an $m \times n$ matrix. Calculate $D\mathbf{f(x)}$ and relate your result to the derivative of the one-variable linear function $f(x) = ax$.

In Exercises 60–62 you will establish that the matrix $D\mathbf{f(a)}$ of partial derivatives of the component functions of $\mathbf{f}$ is uniquely determined by the limit equation in Definition 3.8.

60. Let X be an open set in $\mathbf{R}^n$, let $\mathbf{a} \in X$, and let $\mathbf{F} \colon X \subseteq \mathbf{R}^n \to \mathbf{R}^m$. Show that

$$\lim_{\mathbf{x} \to \mathbf{a}} \|\mathbf{F(x)}\| = 0 \iff \lim_{\mathbf{x} \to \mathbf{a}} \mathbf{F(x)} = \mathbf{0}.$$

61. Let X be an open set in $\mathbf{R}^n$, let $\mathbf{a} \in X$, and let $\mathbf{f} \colon X \subseteq \mathbf{R}^n \to \mathbf{R}^m$. Suppose that A and B are $m \times n$ matrices such that

$$\lim_{\mathbf{x} \to \mathbf{a}} \frac{\|\mathbf{f(x)} - [\mathbf{f(a)} + A(\mathbf{x} - \mathbf{a})]\|}{\|\mathbf{x} - \mathbf{a}\|} =$$
$$\lim_{\mathbf{x} \to \mathbf{a}} \frac{\|\mathbf{f(x)} - [\mathbf{f(a)} + B(\mathbf{x} - \mathbf{a})]\|}{\|\mathbf{x} - \mathbf{a}\|} = 0.$$

(a) Use Exercise 60 to show that

$$\lim_{\mathbf{x} \to \mathbf{a}} \frac{(B - A)(\mathbf{x} - \mathbf{a})}{\|\mathbf{x} - \mathbf{a}\|} = \mathbf{0}.$$

(b) Write $\mathbf{x} - \mathbf{a}$ as $t\mathbf{h}$, where $\mathbf{h}$ is a nonzero vector in $\mathbf{R}^n$. First argue that

$$\lim_{\mathbf{x} \to \mathbf{a}} \frac{(B - A)(\mathbf{x} - \mathbf{a})}{\|\mathbf{x} - \mathbf{a}\|} = \mathbf{0} \quad \text{implies}$$
$$\lim_{t \to 0} \frac{(B - A)(t\mathbf{h})}{\|t\mathbf{h}\|} = \mathbf{0},$$

and then use this result to conclude that $A = B$. (Hint: Break into cases where $t > 0$ and where $t < 0$.)

62. Let X be an open set in $\mathbf{R}^n$, let $\mathbf{a} \in X$, and let $\mathbf{f} \colon X \subseteq \mathbf{R}^n \to \mathbf{R}^m$. Suppose that A is an $m \times n$ matrix such that

$$\lim_{\mathbf{x} \to \mathbf{a}} \frac{\|\mathbf{f(x)} - [\mathbf{f(a)} + A(\mathbf{x} - \mathbf{a})]\|}{\|\mathbf{x} - \mathbf{a}\|} = 0.$$

In this problem you will establish that $A = D\mathbf{f(a)}$.

(a) Define $\mathbf{F} \colon X \subseteq \mathbf{R}^n \to \mathbf{R}^m$ by

$$\mathbf{F(x)} = \frac{\mathbf{f(x)} - \mathbf{f(a)} - A(\mathbf{x} - \mathbf{a})}{\|\mathbf{x} - \mathbf{a}\|}.$$

Identify the ith component function $F_i(\mathbf{x})$ using component functions of $\mathbf{f}$ and parts of the matrix A.

(b) Note that under the assumptions of this problem and Exercise 60, we have that $\lim_{\mathbf{x} \to \mathbf{a}} \mathbf{F(x)} = \mathbf{0}$.

First argue that, for $i = 1, \ldots, m$, we have $\lim_{\mathbf{x} \to \mathbf{a}} F_i(\mathbf{x}) = 0$. Next, argue that

$$\lim_{\mathbf{x} \to \mathbf{a}} F_i(\mathbf{x}) = 0 \quad \text{implies} \quad \lim_{h \to 0} F_i(\mathbf{a} + h\mathbf{e}_j) = 0,$$

where $\mathbf{e}_j$ denotes the standard basis vector $(0, \ldots, 1, \ldots, 0)$ for $\mathbf{R}^n$.

(c) Use parts (a) and (b) to show that $a_{ij} = \dfrac{\partial f_i}{\partial x_j}(\mathbf{a})$, where a_{ij} denotes the ijth entry of A. (Hint: Break into cases where $h > 0$ and where $h < 0$.)

2.4 Properties; Higher-order Partial Derivatives

Properties of the Derivative

From our work in the previous section, we know that the derivative of a function $\mathbf{f}: X \subseteq \mathbf{R}^n \to \mathbf{R}^m$ can be identified with its matrix of partial derivatives. We next note several properties that the derivative must satisfy. The proofs of these results involve Definition 3.8 of the derivative, properties of ordinary differentiation, and matrix algebra.

PROPOSITION 4.1 (LINEARITY OF DIFFERENTIATION) Let $\mathbf{f}, \mathbf{g}: X \subseteq \mathbf{R}^n \to \mathbf{R}^m$ be two functions that are both differentiable at a point $\mathbf{a} \in X$, and let $c \in \mathbf{R}$ be any scalar. Then

1. The function $\mathbf{h} = \mathbf{f} + \mathbf{g}$ is also differentiable at $\mathbf{a}$, and we have
$$D\mathbf{h}(\mathbf{a}) = D(\mathbf{f} + \mathbf{g})(\mathbf{a}) = D\mathbf{f}(\mathbf{a}) + D\mathbf{g}(\mathbf{a}).$$

2. The function $\mathbf{k} = c\mathbf{f}$ is differentiable at $\mathbf{a}$ and
$$D\mathbf{k}(\mathbf{a}) = D(c\mathbf{f})(\mathbf{a}) = c\,D\mathbf{f}(\mathbf{a}).$$

EXAMPLE 1 Let $\mathbf{f}$ and $\mathbf{g}$ be defined by $\mathbf{f}(x, y) = (x + y, xy \sin y, y/x)$ and $\mathbf{g}(x, y) = (x^2 + y^2, ye^{xy}, 2x^3 - 7y^5)$. We have

$$D\mathbf{f}(x, y) = \begin{bmatrix} 1 & 1 \\ y \sin y & x \sin y + xy \cos y \\ -y/x^2 & 1/x \end{bmatrix}$$

and

$$D\mathbf{g}(x, y) = \begin{bmatrix} 2x & 2y \\ y^2 e^{xy} & e^{xy} + xye^{xy} \\ 6x^2 & -35y^4 \end{bmatrix}.$$

Thus, by Theorem 3.10, $\mathbf{f}$ is differentiable on $\mathbf{R}^2 - \{y\text{-axis}\}$ and $\mathbf{g}$ is differentiable on all of $\mathbf{R}^2$. If we let $\mathbf{h} = \mathbf{f} + \mathbf{g}$, then part 1 of Proposition 4.1 tells us that $\mathbf{h}$ must be differentiable on all of its domain, and

$$D\mathbf{h}(x, y) = D\mathbf{f}(x, y) + D\mathbf{g}(x, y)$$

$$= \begin{bmatrix} 2x + 1 & 2y + 1 \\ y \sin y + y^2 e^{xy} & x \sin y + xy \cos y + e^{xy} + xye^{xy} \\ 6x^2 - y/x^2 & 1/x - 35y^4 \end{bmatrix}.$$

Note also that the function $\mathbf{k} = 3\mathbf{g}$ must be differentiable everywhere by part 2 of Proposition 4.1. We can readily check that $D\mathbf{k}(x, y) = 3D\mathbf{g}(x, y)$: We have

$$\mathbf{k}(x, y) = (3x^2 + 3y^2, 3ye^{xy}, 6x^3 - 21y^5).$$

Hence,

$$D\mathbf{k}(x, y) = \begin{bmatrix} 6x & 6y \\ 3y^2 e^{xy} & 3e^{xy} + 3xye^{xy} \\ 18x^2 & -105y^4 \end{bmatrix}$$

$$= 3 \begin{bmatrix} 2x & 2y \\ y^2 e^{xy} & e^{xy} + xye^{xy} \\ 6x^2 & -35y^4 \end{bmatrix}$$

$$= 3D\mathbf{g}(x, y). \qquad \blacklozenge$$

Due to the nature of matrix multiplication, general versions of the product and quotient rules do not exist in any particularly simple form. However, for scalar-valued functions, it is possible to prove the following:

PROPOSITION 4.2 Let $f, g: X \subseteq \mathbf{R}^n \to \mathbf{R}$ be differentiable at $\mathbf{a} \in X$. Then

1. The product function fg is also differentiable at $\mathbf{a}$, and

$$D(fg)(\mathbf{a}) = g(\mathbf{a})Df(\mathbf{a}) + f(\mathbf{a})Dg(\mathbf{a}).$$

2. If $g(\mathbf{a}) \neq 0$, then the quotient function f/g is differentiable at $\mathbf{a}$, and

$$D(f/g)(\mathbf{a}) = \frac{g(\mathbf{a})Df(\mathbf{a}) - f(\mathbf{a})Dg(\mathbf{a})}{g(\mathbf{a})^2}.$$

EXAMPLE 2   If $f(x, y, z) = ze^{xy}$ and $g(x, y, z) = xy + 2yz - xz$, then

$$(fg)(x, y, z) = (xyz + 2yz^2 - xz^2)e^{xy},$$

so that

$$D(fg)(x, y, z) = \begin{bmatrix} (yz - z^2)e^{xy} + (xyz + 2yz^2 - xz^2)ye^{xy} \\ (xz + 2z^2)e^{xy} + (xyz + 2yz^2 - xz^2)xe^{xy} \\ (xy + 4yz - 2xz)e^{xy} \end{bmatrix}^T.$$

Also, we have

$$Df(x, y, z) = \begin{bmatrix} yze^{xy} & xze^{xy} & e^{xy} \end{bmatrix}$$

and

$$Dg(x, y, z) = \begin{bmatrix} y - z & x + 2z & 2y - x \end{bmatrix},$$

so that

$$g(x, y, z)Df(x, y, z) + f(x, y, z)Dg(x, y, z)$$

$$= \begin{bmatrix} (xy^2z + 2y^2z^2 - xyz^2)e^{xy} \\ (x^2yz + 2xyz^2 - x^2z^2)e^{xy} \\ (xy + 2yz - xz)e^{xy} \end{bmatrix}^T + \begin{bmatrix} (yz - z^2)e^{xy} \\ (xz + 2z^2)e^{xy} \\ (2yz - xz)e^{xy} \end{bmatrix}^T$$

$$= e^{xy} \begin{bmatrix} xy^2z + 2y^2z^2 - xyz^2 + yz - z^2 \\ x^2yz + 2xyz^2 - x^2z^2 + xz + 2z^2 \\ xy + 4yz - 2xz \end{bmatrix}^T,$$

which checks with part 1 of Proposition 4.2. (Note: The matrix transpose is used simply to conserve space on the page.) ◆

The product rule in part 1 of Proposition 4.2 is not the most general result possible. Indeed, if $f: X \subseteq \mathbf{R}^n \to \mathbf{R}$ is a scalar-valued function and $\mathbf{g}: X \subseteq \mathbf{R}^n \to \mathbf{R}^m$ is a vector-valued function, then if f and $\mathbf{g}$ are both differentiable at $\mathbf{a} \in X$, so is $f\mathbf{g}$, and the following formula holds (where we view $\mathbf{g}(\mathbf{a})$ as an $m \times 1$ matrix):

$$D(f\mathbf{g})(\mathbf{a}) = \mathbf{g}(\mathbf{a})Df(\mathbf{a}) + f(\mathbf{a})D\mathbf{g}(\mathbf{a}).$$

Partial Derivatives of Higher Order

Thus far in our study of differentiation, we have been concerned only with partial derivatives of first order. Nonetheless, it is easy to imagine computing second- and third-order partials by iterating the process of differentiating with respect to one variable, while all others are held constant.

EXAMPLE 3   Let $f(x, y, z) = x^2y + y^2z$. Then the first-order partial derivatives are

$$\frac{\partial f}{\partial x} = 2xy, \quad \frac{\partial f}{\partial y} = x^2 + 2yz, \quad \text{and} \quad \frac{\partial f}{\partial z} = y^2.$$

The **second-order partial derivative** with respect to x, denoted by $\partial^2 f/\partial x^2$ or $f_{xx}(x, y, z)$, is

$$\frac{\partial^2 f}{\partial x^2} = \frac{\partial}{\partial x}\left(\frac{\partial f}{\partial x}\right) = \frac{\partial}{\partial x}(2xy) = 2y.$$

Similarly, the second-order partials with respect to y and z are, respectively,

$$\frac{\partial^2 f}{\partial y^2} = \frac{\partial}{\partial y}\left(\frac{\partial f}{\partial y}\right) = \frac{\partial}{\partial y}(x^2 + 2yz) = 2z,$$

and

$$\frac{\partial^2 f}{\partial z^2} = \frac{\partial}{\partial z}\left(\frac{\partial f}{\partial z}\right) = \frac{\partial}{\partial z}(y^2) \equiv 0.$$

There are more second-order partials, however. The **mixed partial derivative** with respect to first x and then y, denoted $\partial^2 f/\partial y\partial x$ or $f_{xy}(x, y, z)$, is

$$\frac{\partial^2 f}{\partial y\partial x} = \frac{\partial}{\partial y}\left(\frac{\partial f}{\partial x}\right) = \frac{\partial}{\partial y}(2xy) = 2x.$$

There are five more mixed partials for this particular function: $\partial^2 f/\partial x\partial y$, $\partial^2 f/\partial z\partial x$, $\partial^2 f/\partial x\partial z$, $\partial^2 f/\partial z\partial y$, and $\partial^2 f/\partial y\partial z$. Compute each of them to get a feeling for the process. ◆

In general, if $f: X \subseteq \mathbf{R}^n \to \mathbf{R}$ is a (scalar-valued) function of n variables, the **kth-order partial derivative** with respect to the variables $x_{i_1}, x_{i_2}, \ldots, x_{i_k}$ (in that order), where $i_1, i_2, \ldots, i_k$ are integers in the set $\{1, 2, \ldots, n\}$ (possibly repeated), is the iterated derivative

$$\frac{\partial^k f}{\partial x_{i_k} \cdots \partial x_{i_2} \partial x_{i_1}} = \frac{\partial}{\partial x_{i_k}} \cdots \frac{\partial}{\partial x_{i_2}} \frac{\partial}{\partial x_{i_1}} (f(x_1, x_2, \ldots, x_n)).$$

Equivalent (and frequently more manageable) notation for this kth-order partial is

$$f_{x_{i_1} x_{i_2} \cdots x_{i_k}}(x_1, x_2, \ldots, x_n).$$

Note that the order in which we write the variables with respect to which we differentiate is different in the two notations: In the subscript notation, we write the differentiation variables from left to right in the order we differentiate, while in the ∂-notation, we write those variables in the *opposite* order (i.e., from right to left).

EXAMPLE 4   Let $f(x, y, z, w) = xyz + xy^2 w - \cos(x + zw)$. We then have

$$f_{yw}(x, y, z, w) = \frac{\partial^2 f}{\partial w \partial y} = \frac{\partial}{\partial w} \frac{\partial}{\partial y}(xyz + xy^2 w - \cos(x + zw))$$

$$= \frac{\partial}{\partial w}(xz + 2xyw) = 2xy,$$

and

$$f_{wy}(x, y, z, w) = \frac{\partial^2 f}{\partial y \partial w} = \frac{\partial}{\partial y} \frac{\partial}{\partial w}(xyz + xy^2 w - \cos(x + zw))$$

$$= \frac{\partial}{\partial y}(xy^2 + z \sin(x + zw)) = 2xy. \qquad \blacklozenge$$

Although it is generally ill-advised to formulate conjectures based on a single piece of evidence, Example 4 suggests that there might be an outrageously simple relationship among the mixed second partials. Indeed, such is the case, as the next result, due to the 18th-century French mathematician Alexis Clairaut, indicates.

THEOREM 4.3   Suppose that X is open in $\mathbf{R}^n$ and $f \colon X \subseteq \mathbf{R}^n \to \mathbf{R}$ has continuous first- and second-order partial derivatives. Then the order in which we evaluate the mixed second-order partials is immaterial; that is, if i_1 and i_2 are any two integers between 1 and n, then

$$\frac{\partial^2 f}{\partial x_{i_1} \partial x_{i_2}} = \frac{\partial^2 f}{\partial x_{i_2} \partial x_{i_1}}.$$

A proof of Theorem 4.3 is provided in the addendum to this section. We also suggest a second proof (using integrals!) in Exercise 4 of the Miscellaneous Exercises for Chapter 5.

It is natural to speculate about the possibility of an analogue to Theorem 4.3 for kth-order mixed partials. Before we state what should be an easily anticipated result, we need some terminology.

DEFINITION 4.4   Assume X is open in $\mathbf{R}^n$. A scalar-valued function $f: X \subseteq \mathbf{R}^n \to \mathbf{R}$ whose partial derivatives up to (and including) order at least k exist and are continuous on X is said to be **of class C^k**. If f has continuous partial derivatives of all orders on X, then f is said to be **of class C^∞**, or **smooth**. A vector-valued function $\mathbf{f}: X \subseteq \mathbf{R}^n \to \mathbf{R}^m$ is of class C^k (respectively, of class C^∞) if and only if each of its component functions is of class C^k (respectively, C^∞).

THEOREM 4.5   Let $f: X \subseteq \mathbf{R}^n \to \mathbf{R}$ be a scalar-valued function of class C^k. Then the order in which we calculate any kth-order partial derivative does not matter: If $(i_1, \ldots, i_k)$ are any k integers (not necessarily distinct) between 1 and n, and if $(j_1, \ldots, j_k)$ is any permutation (rearrangement) of these integers, then

$$\frac{\partial^k f}{\partial x_{i_1} \cdots \partial x_{i_k}} = \frac{\partial^k f}{\partial x_{j_1} \cdots \partial x_{j_k}}.$$

EXAMPLE 5   If $f(x, y, z, w) = x^2 w e^{yz} - z e^{xw} + xyzw$, then you can check that

$$\frac{\partial^5 f}{\partial x \partial w \partial z \partial y \partial x} = 2e^{yz}(yz + 1) = \frac{\partial^5 f}{\partial z \partial y \partial w \partial^2 x},$$

verifying Theorem 4.5 in this case.   ◆

Addendum: Two Technical Proofs

Proof of Part 1 of Proposition 4.1

Step 1. We show that the matrix of partial derivatives of $\mathbf{h}$ is the sum of those of $\mathbf{f}$ and $\mathbf{g}$. If we write $\mathbf{h}(\mathbf{x})$ as $(h_1(\mathbf{x}), h_2(\mathbf{x}), \ldots, h_m(\mathbf{x}))$ (i.e., in terms of its component functions), then the ijth entry of $D\mathbf{h}(\mathbf{a})$ is $\partial h_i / \partial x_j$ evaluated at $\mathbf{a}$. But $h_i(\mathbf{x}) = f_i(\mathbf{x}) + g_i(\mathbf{x})$ by definition of $\mathbf{h}$. Hence,

$$\frac{\partial h_i}{\partial x_j} = \frac{\partial}{\partial x_j}(f_i(\mathbf{x}) + g_i(\mathbf{x})) = \frac{\partial f_i}{\partial x_j} + \frac{\partial g_i}{\partial x_j},$$

by properties of ordinary differentiation (since all variables except x_j are held constant). Thus,

$$\frac{\partial h_i}{\partial x_j}(\mathbf{a}) = \frac{\partial f_i}{\partial x_j}(\mathbf{a}) + \frac{\partial g_i}{\partial x_j}(\mathbf{a}),$$

and, therefore,

$$D\mathbf{h}(\mathbf{a}) = D\mathbf{f}(\mathbf{a}) + D\mathbf{g}(\mathbf{a}).$$

Step 2. Now that we know the desired matrix of partials exists, we must show that $\mathbf{h}$ really is differentiable; that is, we must establish that

$$\lim_{\mathbf{x} \to \mathbf{a}} \frac{\|\mathbf{h}(\mathbf{x}) - [\mathbf{h}(\mathbf{a}) + D\mathbf{h}(\mathbf{a})(\mathbf{x} - \mathbf{a})]\|}{\|\mathbf{x} - \mathbf{a}\|} = 0.$$

As preliminary background, we note that

$$\frac{\|\mathbf{h}(\mathbf{x}) - [\mathbf{h}(\mathbf{a}) + D\mathbf{h}(\mathbf{a})(\mathbf{x} - \mathbf{a})]\|}{\|\mathbf{x} - \mathbf{a}\|}$$

$$= \frac{\|\mathbf{f}(\mathbf{x}) + \mathbf{g}(\mathbf{x}) - [\mathbf{f}(\mathbf{a}) + \mathbf{g}(\mathbf{a}) + D\mathbf{f}(\mathbf{a})(\mathbf{x} - \mathbf{a}) + D\mathbf{g}(\mathbf{a})(\mathbf{x} - \mathbf{a})]\|}{\|\mathbf{x} - \mathbf{a}\|}$$

$$= \frac{\|(\mathbf{f}(\mathbf{x}) - [\mathbf{f}(\mathbf{a}) + D\mathbf{f}(\mathbf{a})(\mathbf{x} - \mathbf{a})]) + (\mathbf{g}(\mathbf{x}) - [\mathbf{g}(\mathbf{a}) + D\mathbf{g}(\mathbf{a})(\mathbf{x} - \mathbf{a})])\|}{\|\mathbf{x} - \mathbf{a}\|}$$

$$\leq \frac{\|\mathbf{f}(\mathbf{x}) - [\mathbf{f}(\mathbf{a}) + D\mathbf{f}(\mathbf{a})(\mathbf{x} - \mathbf{a})]\|}{\|\mathbf{x} - \mathbf{a}\|} + \frac{\|\mathbf{g}(\mathbf{x}) - [\mathbf{g}(\mathbf{a}) + D\mathbf{g}(\mathbf{a})(\mathbf{x} - \mathbf{a})]\|}{\|\mathbf{x} - \mathbf{a}\|},$$

by the triangle inequality, formula (2) of §1.6. To show that the desired limit equation for $\mathbf{h}$ follows from the definition of the limit, we must show that given any $\epsilon > 0$, we can find a number $\delta > 0$ such that

$$\text{if } 0 < \|\mathbf{x} - \mathbf{a}\| < \delta, \text{ then } \frac{\|\mathbf{h}(\mathbf{x}) - [\mathbf{h}(\mathbf{a}) + D\mathbf{h}(\mathbf{a})(\mathbf{x} - \mathbf{a})]\|}{\|\mathbf{x} - \mathbf{a}\|} < \epsilon. \tag{1}$$

Since $\mathbf{f}$ is given to be differentiable at $\mathbf{a}$, this means that given any $\epsilon_1 > 0$, we can find $\delta_1 > 0$ such that

$$\text{if } 0 < \|\mathbf{x} - \mathbf{a}\| < \delta_1, \text{ then } \frac{\|\mathbf{f}(\mathbf{x}) - [\mathbf{f}(\mathbf{a}) + D\mathbf{f}(\mathbf{a})(\mathbf{x} - \mathbf{a})]\|}{\|\mathbf{x} - \mathbf{a}\|} < \epsilon_1. \tag{2}$$

Similarly, differentiability of $\mathbf{g}$ means that given any $\epsilon_2 > 0$, we can find a $\delta_2 > 0$ such that

$$\text{if } 0 < \|\mathbf{x} - \mathbf{a}\| < \delta_2, \text{ then } \frac{\|\mathbf{g}(\mathbf{x}) - [\mathbf{g}(\mathbf{a}) + D\mathbf{g}(\mathbf{a})(\mathbf{x} - \mathbf{a})]\|}{\|\mathbf{x} - \mathbf{a}\|} < \epsilon_2. \tag{3}$$

Now we're ready to establish statement (1). Suppose $\epsilon > 0$ is given. Let δ_1 and δ_2 be such that (2) and (3) hold with $\epsilon_1 = \epsilon_2 = \epsilon/2$. Take δ to be the smaller of δ_1 and δ_2. Hence, if $0 < \|\mathbf{x} - \mathbf{a}\| < \delta$, then both statements (2) and (3) hold (with $\epsilon_1 = \epsilon_2 = \epsilon/2$) and, moreover,

$$\frac{\|\mathbf{h}(\mathbf{x}) - [\mathbf{h}(\mathbf{a}) + D\mathbf{h}(\mathbf{a})(\mathbf{x} - \mathbf{a})]\|}{\|\mathbf{x} - \mathbf{a}\|} \leq \frac{\|\mathbf{f}(\mathbf{x}) - [\mathbf{f}(\mathbf{a}) + D\mathbf{f}(\mathbf{a})(\mathbf{x} - \mathbf{a})]\|}{\|\mathbf{x} - \mathbf{a}\|}$$

$$+ \frac{\|\mathbf{g}(\mathbf{x}) - [\mathbf{g}(\mathbf{a}) + D\mathbf{g}(\mathbf{a})(\mathbf{x} - \mathbf{a})]\|}{\|\mathbf{x} - \mathbf{a}\|}$$

$$< \epsilon_1 + \epsilon_2$$

$$= \frac{\epsilon}{2} + \frac{\epsilon}{2} = \epsilon.$$

That is, statement (1) holds, as desired. ∎

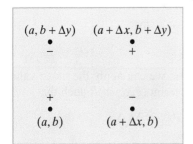

Figure 2.55 To construct the difference function D used in the proof of Theorem 4.3, evaluate f at the four points shown with the signs as indicated.

Proof of Theorem 4.3 For simplicity of notation only, we'll assume that f is a function of just two variables (x and y). Let the point $(a, b) \in \mathbf{R}^2$ be in the interior of some rectangle on which f_x, f_y, f_{xx}, f_{yy}, f_{xy}, and f_{yx} are all continuous. Consider the following "difference function." (See Figure 2.55.)

$$D(\Delta x, \Delta y) = f(a + \Delta x, b + \Delta y) - f(a + \Delta x, b)$$
$$- f(a, b + \Delta y) + f(a, b).$$

Our proof depends upon viewing this function in two ways. We first regard D as a difference of vertical differences in f:

$$D(\Delta x, \Delta y) = [f(a + \Delta x, b + \Delta y) - f(a + \Delta x, b)]$$
$$- [f(a, b + \Delta y) - f(a, b)]$$
$$= F(a + \Delta x) - F(a).$$

Here we define the one-variable function $F(x)$ to be $f(x, b + \Delta y) - f(x, b)$. As we will see, the mixed second partial of f can be found from two applications of the mean value theorem of one-variable calculus. Since f has continuous partials, it is differentiable. (See Theorem 3.10.) Hence, F is continuous and differentiable, and, thus, the mean value theorem implies that there is some number c between a and $a + \Delta x$ such that

$$D(\Delta x, \Delta y) = F(a + \Delta x) - F(a) = F'(c)\Delta x. \tag{4}$$

Now $F'(c) = f_x(c, b + \Delta y) - f_x(c, b)$. We again apply the mean value theorem, this time to the function $f_x(c, y)$. (Here, we think of c as constant and y as the variable.) By hypothesis f_x is differentiable since its partial derivatives, f_{xx} and f_{xy}, are assumed to be continuous. Consequently, the mean value theorem applies to give us a number d between b and $b + \Delta y$ such that

$$F'(c) = f_x(c, b + \Delta y) - f_x(c, b) = f_{xy}(c, d)\Delta y. \tag{5}$$

Using equation (5) in equation (4), we have

$$D(\Delta x, \Delta y) = F'(c)\Delta x = f_{xy}(c, d)\Delta y \Delta x.$$

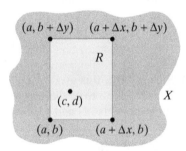

Figure 2.56 Applying the mean value theorem twice.

The point (c, d) lies somewhere in the interior of the rectangle R with vertices (a, b), $(a + \Delta x, b)$, $(a, b + \Delta y)$, $(a + \Delta x, b + \Delta y)$, as shown in Figure 2.56. Thus, as $(\Delta x, \Delta y) \to (0, 0)$, we have $(c, d) \to (a, b)$. Hence, it follows that

$$f_{xy}(c, d) \to f_{xy}(a, b) \quad \text{as} \quad (\Delta x, \Delta y) \to (0, 0),$$

since f_{xy} is assumed to be continuous. Therefore,

$$f_{xy}(a, b) = \lim_{(\Delta x, \Delta y) \to (0,0)} f_{xy}(c, d) = \lim_{(\Delta x, \Delta y) \to (0,0)} \frac{D(\Delta x, \Delta y)}{\Delta y \Delta x}.$$

On the other hand, we could just as well have written D as a difference of horizontal differences in f:

$$D(\Delta x, \Delta y) = [f(a + \Delta x, b + \Delta y) - f(a, b + \Delta y)]$$
$$- [f(a + \Delta x, b) - f(a, b)]$$
$$= G(b + \Delta y) - G(b).$$

Here $G(y) = f(a + \Delta x, y) - f(a, y)$. As before, we can apply the mean value theorem twice to find that there must be another point $(\bar{c}, \bar{d})$ in R such that

$$D(\Delta x, \Delta y) = G'(\bar{d})\Delta y = f_{yx}(\bar{c}, \bar{d})\Delta x \Delta y.$$

Therefore,

$$f_{yx}(a, b) = \lim_{(\Delta x, \Delta y) \to (0,0)} f_{yx}(\bar{c}, \bar{d}) = \lim_{(\Delta x, \Delta y) \to (0,0)} \frac{D(\Delta x, \Delta y)}{\Delta x \Delta y}.$$

Because this is the same limit as that for $f_{xy}(a, b)$ just given, we have established the desired result. ∎

2.4 Exercises

In Exercises 1–4, verify the sum rule for derivative matrices (i.e., part 1 of Proposition 4.1) for each of the given pairs of functions:

1. $f(x, y) = xy + \cos x$, $\quad g(x, y) = \sin(xy) + y^3$

2. $\mathbf{f}(x, y) = (e^{x+y}, xe^y)$, $\quad \mathbf{g}(x, y) = (\ln(xy), ye^x)$

3. $\mathbf{f}(x, y, z) = (x \sin y + z, ye^z - 3x^2)$, $\quad \mathbf{g}(x, y, z) = (x^3 \cos x, xyz)$

4. $\mathbf{f}(x, y, z) = (xyz^2, xe^{-y}, y \sin xz)$, $\quad \mathbf{g}(x, y, z) = (x - y, x^2 + y^2 + z^2, \ln(xz + 2))$

Verify the product and quotient rules (Proposition 4.2) for the pairs of functions given in Exercises 5–8.

5. $f(x, y) = x^2 y + y^3$, $\quad g(x, y) = \dfrac{x}{y}$

6. $f(x, y) = e^{xy}$, $\quad g(x, y) = x \sin 2y$

7. $f(x, y) = 3xy + y^5$, $\quad g(x, y) = x^3 - 2xy^2$

8. $f(x, y, z) = x \cos(yz)$,
$\quad g(x, y, z) = x^2 + x^9 y^2 + y^2 z^3 + 2$

For the functions given in Exercises 9–17 determine all second-order partial derivatives (including mixed partials).

9. $f(x, y) = x^3 y^7 + 3xy^2 - 7xy$

10. $f(x, y) = \cos(xy)$

11. $f(x, y) = e^{y/x} - ye^{-x}$

12. $f(x, y) = \sin\sqrt{x^2 + y^2}$

13. $f(x, y) = \dfrac{1}{\sin^2 x + 2e^y}$

14. $f(x, y) = e^{x^2 + y^2}$

15. $f(x, y) = y \sin x - x \cos y$

16. $f(x, y) = \ln\left(\dfrac{x}{y}\right)$

17. $f(x, y) = x^2 e^y + e^{2z}$

18. $f(x, y, z) = \dfrac{x - y}{y + z}$

19. $f(x, y, z) = x^2 yz + xy^2 z + xyz^2$

20. $f(x, y, z) = e^{xyz}$

21. $f(x, y, z) = e^{ax} \sin y + e^{bx} \cos z$

22. Consider the function $F(x, y, z) = 2x^3 y + xz^2 + y^3 z^5 - 7xyz$.
  (a) Find F_{xx}, F_{yy}, and F_{zz}.
  (b) Calculate the mixed second-order partials F_{xy}, F_{yx}, F_{xz}, F_{zx}, F_{yz}, and F_{zy}, and verify Theorem 4.3.

(c) Is $F_{xyx} = F_{xxy}$? Could you have known this without resorting to calculation?

(d) Is $F_{xyz} = F_{yzx}$?

23. Let $f(x, y) = ye^{3x}$. Give general formulas for $\partial^n f/\partial x^n$ and $\partial^n f/\partial y^n$, where $n \geq 2$.

24. Let $f(x, y, z) = xe^{2y} + ye^{3z} + ze^{-x}$. Give general formulas for $\partial^n f/\partial x^n$, $\partial^n f/\partial y^n$, and $\partial^n f/\partial z^n$, where $n \geq 1$.

25. Let $f(x, y, z) = \ln\left(\dfrac{xy}{z}\right)$. Give general formulas for $\partial^n f/\partial x^n$, $\partial^n f/\partial y^n$, and $\partial^n f/\partial z^n$, where $n \geq 1$. What can you say about the mixed partial derivatives?

26. Let $f(x, y, z) = x^7 y^2 z^3 - 2x^4 yz$.
  (a) What is $\partial^4 f/\partial x^2 \partial y \partial z$?
  (b) What is $\partial^5 f/\partial x^3 \partial y \partial z$?
  (c) What is $\partial^{15} f/\partial x^{13} \partial y \partial z$?

27. Recall from §2.2 that a polynomial in two variables x and y is an expression of the form

$$p(x, y) = \sum_{k,l=0}^{d} c_{kl} x^k y^l,$$

where c_{kl} can be any real number for $0 \leq k, l \leq d$. The **degree of the term** $c_{kl} x^k y^l$ when $c_{kl} \neq 0$ is $k + l$ and the **degree of the polynomial** p is the largest degree of any nonzero term of the polynomial (i.e., the largest degree of any term for which $c_{kl} \neq 0$). For example, the polynomial

$$p(x, y) = 7x^6 y^9 + 2x^2 y^3 - 3x^4 - 5xy^3 + 1$$

has five terms of degrees 15, 5, 4, 4, and 0. The degree of p is therefore 15. (Note: The degree of the **zero polynomial** $p(x, y) \equiv 0$ is undefined.)
  (a) If $p(x, y) = 8x^7 y^{10} - 9x^2 y + 2x$, what is the degree of $\partial p/\partial x$? $\partial p/\partial y$? $\partial^2 p/\partial x^2$? $\partial^2 p/\partial y^2$? $\partial^2 p/\partial x \partial y$?
  (b) If $p(x, y) = 8x^2 y + 2x^3 y$, what is the degree of $\partial p/\partial x$? $\partial p/\partial y$? $\partial^2 p/\partial x^2$? $\partial^2 p/\partial y^2$? $\partial^2 p/\partial x \partial y$?
  (c) Try to formulate and prove a conjecture relating the degree of a polynomial p to the degree of its partial derivatives.

28. The partial differential equation

$$\frac{\partial^2 f}{\partial x^2} + \frac{\partial^2 f}{\partial y^2} + \frac{\partial^2 f}{\partial z^2} = 0$$

is known as **Laplace's equation,** after Pierre Simon de Laplace (1749–1827). Any function f of class C^2

that satisfies Laplace's equation is called a **harmonic function**.[3]

(a) Is $f(x, y, z) = x^2 + y^2 - 2z^2$ harmonic? What about $f(x, y, z) = x^2 - y^2 + z^2$?

(b) We may generalize Laplace's equation to functions of n variables as

$$\frac{\partial^2 f}{\partial x_1^2} + \frac{\partial^2 f}{\partial x_2^2} + \cdots + \frac{\partial^2 f}{\partial x_n^2} = 0.$$

Give an example of a harmonic function of n variables, and verify that your example is correct.

29. The three-dimensional **heat equation** is the partial differential equation

$$k \left(\frac{\partial^2 T}{\partial x^2} + \frac{\partial^2 T}{\partial y^2} + \frac{\partial^2 T}{\partial z^2} \right) = \frac{\partial T}{\partial t},$$

where k is a positive constant. It models the temperature $T(x, y, z, t)$ at the point (x, y, z) and time t of a body in space.

(a) We examine a simplified version of the heat equation. Consider a straight wire "coordinatized" by x. Then the temperature $T(x, t)$ at time t and position x along the wire is modeled by the one-dimensional heat equation

$$k \frac{\partial^2 T}{\partial x^2} = \frac{\partial T}{\partial t}.$$

Show that the function $T(x, t) = e^{-kt} \cos x$ satisfies this equation. Note that if t is held constant at value t_0, then $T(x, t_0)$ shows how the temperature varies along the wire at time t_0. Graph the curves $z = T(x, t_0)$ for $t_0 = 0, 1, 10$, and use them to understand the graph of the surface $z = T(x, t)$ for $t \geq 0$. Explain what happens to the temperature of the wire after a long period of time.

(b) Show that $T(x, y, t) = e^{-kt}(\cos x + \cos y)$ satisfies the two-dimensional heat equation

$$k \left(\frac{\partial^2 T}{\partial x^2} + \frac{\partial^2 T}{\partial y^2} \right) = \frac{\partial T}{\partial t}.$$

Graph the surfaces given by $z = T(x, y, t_0)$, where $t_0 = 0, 1, 10$. If we view the function $T(x, y, t)$ as modeling the temperature at points (x, y) of a flat plate at time t, then describe what happens to the temperature of the plate after a long period of time.

(c) Now show that $T(x, y, z, t) = e^{-kt}(\cos x + \cos y + \cos z)$ satisfies the three-dimensional heat equation.

30. Let

$$f(x, y) = \begin{cases} xy \left(\dfrac{x^2 - y^2}{x^2 + y^2} \right) & \text{if } (x, y) \neq (0, 0) \\ 0 & \text{if } (x, y) = (0, 0) \end{cases}.$$

(a) Find $f_x(x, y)$ and $f_y(x, y)$ for $(x, y) \neq (0, 0)$. (You will find a computer algebra system helpful.)

(b) Either by hand (using limits) or by means of part (a), find the partial derivatives $f_x(0, y)$ and $f_y(x, 0)$.

(c) Find the values of $f_{xy}(0, 0)$ and $f_{yx}(0, 0)$. Reconcile your answer with Theorem 4.3.

A surface that has the least surface area among all surfaces with a given boundary is called a **minimal surface.** *Soap bubbles are naturally occurring examples of minimal surfaces. It is a fact that minimal surfaces having equations of the form $z = f(x, y)$ (where f is of class C^2) satisfy the partial differential equation*

$$\left(1 + z_y^2\right) z_{xx} + \left(1 + z_x^2\right) z_{yy} = 2 z_x z_y z_{xy}. \tag{6}$$

Exercises 31–33 concern minimal surfaces and equation (6).

31. Show that a plane is a minimal surface.

32. **Scherk's surface** is given by the equation $e^z \cos y = \cos x$.

(a) Use a computer to graph a portion of this surface.

(b) Verify that Scherk's surface is a minimal surface.

33. One way to describe the surface known as the **helicoid** is by the equation $x = y \tan z$.

(a) Use a computer to graph a portion of this surface.

(b) Verify that the helicoid is a minimal surface.

2.5 The Chain Rule

Among the various properties that the derivative satisfies, one that stands alone in both its usefulness and its subtlety is the derivative's behavior with respect to composition of functions. This behavior is described by a formula known as

---

[3] Laplace did fundamental and far-reaching work in both mathematical physics and probability theory. Laplace's equation and harmonic functions are part of the field of **potential theory**, a subject that Laplace can be credited as having developed. Potential theory has applications to such areas as gravitation, electricity and magnetism, and fluid mechanics, to name a few.

the **chain rule**. In this section, we review the chain rule of one-variable calculus and see how it generalizes to the cases of scalar- and vector-valued functions of several variables.

The Chain Rule for Functions of One Variable: A Review —

We begin with a typical example of the use of the chain rule from single-variable calculus.

EXAMPLE 1   Let $f(x) = \sin x$ and $x(t) = t^3 + t$. We may then construct the composite function $f(x(t)) = \sin(t^3 + t)$. The chain rule tells us how to find the derivative of $f \circ x$ with respect to t:

$$(f \circ x)'(t) = \frac{d}{dt}(\sin(t^3 + t)) = (\cos(t^3 + t))(3t^2 + 1).$$

Since $x = t^3 + t$, we have

$$(f \circ x)'(t) = \frac{d}{dx}(\sin x) \cdot \frac{d}{dt}(t^3 + t) = f'(x) \cdot x'(t). \qquad \blacklozenge$$

In general, suppose X and T are open subsets of $\mathbf{R}$ and $f \colon X \subseteq \mathbf{R} \to \mathbf{R}$ and $x \colon T \subseteq \mathbf{R} \to \mathbf{R}$ are functions defined so that the composite function $f \circ x \colon T \to \mathbf{R}$ makes sense. (See Figure 2.57.) In particular, this means that the range of the function x must be contained in X, the domain of f. The key result is the following:

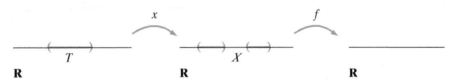

Figure 2.57 The range of the function x must be contained in the domain X of f in order for the composite $f \circ x$ to be defined.

THEOREM 5.1 (THE CHAIN RULE IN ONE VARIABLE)   Under the preceding assumptions, if x is differentiable at $t_0 \in T$ and f is differentiable at $x_0 = x(t_0) \in X$, then the composite $f \circ x$ is differentiable at t_0 and, moreover,

$$(f \circ x)'(t_0) = f'(x_0)x'(t_0). \tag{1}$$

A more common way to write the chain rule formula in Theorem 5.1 is

$$\frac{df}{dt}(t_0) = \frac{df}{dx}(x_0)\frac{dx}{dt}(t_0). \tag{2}$$

Although equation (2) is most useful in practice, it does represent an unfortunate abuse of notation in that the symbol f is used to denote both a function of x and one of t. It would be more appropriate to define a new function y by $y(t) = (f \circ x)(t)$ so that $dy/dt = (df/dx)(dx/dt)$. But our original abuse of notation is actually a convenient one, since it avoids the awkwardness of having too many variable names appearing in a single discussion. In the name of simplicity, we will therefore continue to commit such abuses and urge you to do likewise.

The formulas in equations (1) and (2) are so simple that little more needs to be said. We elaborate, nonetheless, because this will prove helpful when we generalize to the case of several variables. The chain rule tells us the following: To understand how f depends on t, we must know how f depends on the "intermediate variable" x and how this intermediate variable depends on the "final" independent variable t. The diagram in Figure 2.58 traces the hierarchy of the variable dependences. The "paths" indicate the derivatives involved in the chain rule formula.

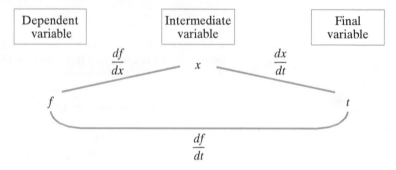

Figure 2.58 The chain rule for functions of a single variable.

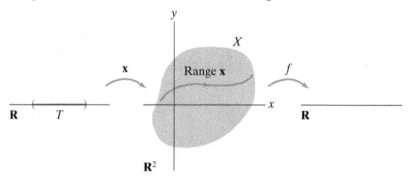

Figure 2.59 The composite function $f \circ \mathbf{x}$.

The Chain Rule in Several Variables

Now let's go a step further and assume $f: X \subseteq \mathbf{R}^2 \to \mathbf{R}$ is a C^1 function of two variables and $\mathbf{x}: T \subseteq \mathbf{R} \to \mathbf{R}^2$ is a differentiable vector-valued function of a single variable. If the range of $\mathbf{x}$ is contained in X, then the composite $f \circ \mathbf{x}: T \subseteq \mathbf{R} \to \mathbf{R}$ is defined. (See Figure 2.59.) It's good to think of $\mathbf{x}$ as describing a parametrized curve in $\mathbf{R}^2$ and f as a sort of "temperature function" on X. The composite $f \circ \mathbf{x}$ is then nothing more than the restriction of f to the curve (i.e., the function that measures the temperature along just the curve). The question is, how does f depend on t? We claim the following:

PROPOSITION 5.2 Suppose $\mathbf{x}: T \subseteq \mathbf{R} \to \mathbf{R}^2$ is differentiable at $t_0 \in T$, and $f: X \subseteq \mathbf{R}^2 \to \mathbf{R}$ is differentiable at $\mathbf{x}_0 = \mathbf{x}(t_0) = (x_0, y_0) \in X$, where T and X are open in $\mathbf{R}$ and $\mathbf{R}^2$, respectively, and range $\mathbf{x}$ is contained in X. If, in addition, f is of class C^1, then $f \circ \mathbf{x}: T \to \mathbf{R}$ is differentiable at t_0 and

$$\frac{df}{dt}(t_0) = \frac{\partial f}{\partial x}(\mathbf{x}_0)\frac{dx}{dt}(t_0) + \frac{\partial f}{\partial y}(\mathbf{x}_0)\frac{dy}{dt}(t_0).$$

Before we prove Proposition 5.2, some remarks are in order. First, notice the mixture of ordinary and partial derivatives appearing in the formula for the

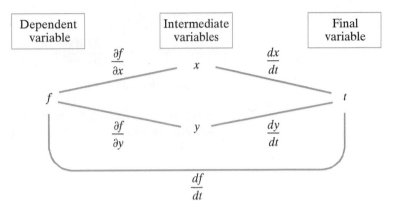

Figure 2.60 The chain rule of Proposition 5.2.

derivative. These terms make sense if we contruct an appropriate "variable hierarchy" diagram, as shown in Figure 2.60. At the intermediate level, f depends on two variables, x and y (or, equivalently, on the vector variable $\mathbf{x} = (x, y)$), so partial derivatives are in order. On the final or composite level, f depends on just a single independent variable t and, hence, the use of the ordinary derivative df/dt is warranted. Second, the formula in Proposition 5.2 is a generalization of equation (2): A product term appears for each of the two intermediate variables.

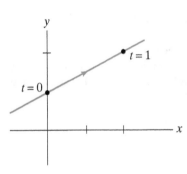

Figure 2.61 The graph of the function $\mathbf{x}$ of Example 2.

EXAMPLE 2 Suppose $f(x, y) = (x + y^2)/(2x^2 + 1)$ is a temperature function on $\mathbf{R}^2$ and $\mathbf{x}(t) = (2t, t + 1)$. The function $\mathbf{x}$ gives parametric equations for a line. (See Figure 2.61.) Then

$$(f \circ \mathbf{x})(t) = f(\mathbf{x}(t)) = \frac{2t + (t + 1)^2}{8t^2 + 1} = \frac{t^2 + 4t + 1}{8t^2 + 1}$$

is the temperature function along the line, and we have

$$\frac{df}{dt} = \frac{4 - 14t - 32t^2}{(8t^2 + 1)^2},$$

by the quotient rule. Thus, all the hypotheses of Proposition 5.2 are satisfied and so the derivative formula must hold. Indeed, we have

$$\frac{\partial f}{\partial x} = \frac{1 - 2x^2 - 4xy^2}{(2x^2 + 1)^2},$$

$$\frac{\partial f}{\partial y} = \frac{2y}{2x^2 + 1},$$

and

$$\mathbf{x}'(t) = \left(\frac{dx}{dt}, \frac{dy}{dt} \right) = (2, 1).$$

Therefore,

$$\frac{\partial f}{\partial x} \frac{dx}{dt} + \frac{\partial f}{\partial y} \frac{dy}{dt} = \frac{1 - 2x^2 - 4xy^2}{(2x^2 + 1)^2} \cdot 2 + \frac{2y}{2x^2 + 1} \cdot 1$$

$$= \frac{2(1 - 8t^2 - 8t(t + 1)^2)}{(8t^2 + 1)^2} + \frac{2(t + 1)}{8t^2 + 1},$$

after substitution of $2t$ for x and $t + 1$ for y. Hence,

$$\frac{\partial f}{\partial x}\frac{dx}{dt} + \frac{\partial f}{\partial y}\frac{dy}{dt} = \frac{2(2 - 7t - 16t^2)}{(8t^2 + 1)^2},$$

which checks with our previous result for df/dt. ◆

Proof of Proposition 5.2 Denote the composite function $f \circ \mathbf{x}$ by z. We want to establish a formula for dz/dt at t_0. Since z is just a scalar-valued function of one variable, differentiability and the existence of the derivative mean the same thing. Thus, we consider

$$\frac{dz}{dt}(t_0) = \lim_{t \to t_0} \frac{z(t) - z(t_0)}{t - t_0},$$

and see if this limit exists. We have

$$\frac{dz}{dt}(t_0) = \lim_{t \to t_0} \frac{f(x(t), y(t)) - f(x(t_0), y(t_0))}{t - t_0}.$$

The first step is to rewrite the numerator of the limit expression by subtracting and adding $f(x_0, y)$ and to apply a modicum of algebra. Thus,

$$\frac{dz}{dt}(t_0) = \lim_{t \to t_0} \frac{f(x, y) - f(x_0, y) + f(x_0, y) - f(x_0, y_0)}{t - t_0}$$

$$= \lim_{t \to t_0} \frac{f(x, y) - f(x_0, y)}{t - t_0} + \lim_{t \to t_0} \frac{f(x_0, y) - f(x_0, y_0)}{t - t_0}.$$

(Remember that $\mathbf{x}(t_0) = \mathbf{x}_0 = (x_0, y_0)$.) Now, for the main innovation of the proof. We apply the mean value theorem to the partial functions of f. This tells us that there must be a number c between x_0 and x and another number d between y_0 and y such that

$$f(x, y) - f(x_0, y) = f_x(c, y)(x - x_0)$$

and

$$f(x_0, y) - f(x_0, y_0) = f_y(x_0, d)(y - y_0).$$

Thus,

$$\frac{dz}{dt}(t_0) = \lim_{t \to t_0} f_x(c, y)\frac{x - x_0}{t - t_0} + \lim_{t \to t_0} f_y(x_0, d)\frac{y - y_0}{t - t_0}$$

$$= \lim_{t \to t_0} f_x(c, y)\frac{x(t) - x(t_0)}{t - t_0} + \lim_{t \to t_0} f_y(x_0, d)\frac{y(t) - y(t_0)}{t - t_0}$$

$$= f_x(x_0, y_0)\frac{dx}{dt}(t_0) + f_y(x_0, y_0)\frac{dy}{dt}(t_0),$$

by the definition of the derivatives

$$\frac{dx}{dt}(t_0) \quad \text{and} \quad \frac{dy}{dt}(t_0)$$

and the fact that $f_x(c, y)$ and $f_y(x_0, d)$ must approach $f_x(x_0, y_0)$ and $f_y(x_0, y_0)$, respectively, as t approaches t_0, by continuity of the partials. (Recall that f was assumed to be of class C^1.) This completes the proof. ■

Proposition 5.2 and its proof are easy to generalize to the case where f is a function of n variables (i.e., $f: X \subseteq \mathbf{R}^n \to \mathbf{R}$) and $\mathbf{x}: T \subseteq \mathbf{R} \to \mathbf{R}^n$. The appropriate chain rule formula in this case is

$$\frac{df}{dt}(t_0) = \frac{\partial f}{\partial x_1}(\mathbf{x}_0)\frac{dx_1}{dt}(t_0) + \frac{\partial f}{\partial x_2}(\mathbf{x}_0)\frac{dx_2}{dt}(t_0) + \cdots + \frac{\partial f}{\partial x_n}(\mathbf{x}_0)\frac{dx_n}{dt}(t_0). \qquad (3)$$

Note that the right side of equation (3) can also be written by using matrix notation so that

$$\frac{df}{dt}(t_0) = \begin{bmatrix} \dfrac{\partial f}{\partial x_1}(\mathbf{x}_0) & \dfrac{\partial f}{\partial x_2}(\mathbf{x}_0) & \cdots & \dfrac{\partial f}{\partial x_n}(\mathbf{x}_0) \end{bmatrix} \begin{bmatrix} \dfrac{dx_1}{dt}(t_0) \\[2ex] \dfrac{dx_2}{dt}(t_0) \\[1ex] \vdots \\[1ex] \dfrac{dx_n}{dt}(t_0) \end{bmatrix}.$$

Thus, we have shown

$$\frac{df}{dt}(t_0) = Df(\mathbf{x}_0)D\mathbf{x}(t_0) = \nabla f(\mathbf{x}_0) \cdot \mathbf{x}'(t_0), \qquad (4)$$

where we use $\mathbf{x}'(t_0)$ as a notational alternative to $D\mathbf{x}(t_0)$. The version of the chain rule given in formula (4) is particularly important and will be used a number of times in our subsequent work.

Let us consider further instances of composition of functions of many variables. For example, suppose X is open in $\mathbf{R}^3$, T is open in $\mathbf{R}^2$, and $f: X \subseteq \mathbf{R}^3 \to \mathbf{R}$ and $\mathbf{x}: T \subseteq \mathbf{R}^2 \to \mathbf{R}^3$ are such that the range of $\mathbf{x}$ is contained in X. Then the composite $f \circ \mathbf{x}: T \subseteq \mathbf{R}^2 \to \mathbf{R}$ can be formed, as shown in Figure 2.62. Note that the range of $\mathbf{x}$, that is, $\mathbf{x}(T)$, is just a surface in $\mathbf{R}^3$, so $f \circ \mathbf{x}$ can be thought of as an appropriate "temperature function" restricted to this surface. If we use $\mathbf{x} = (x, y, z)$ to denote the vector variable in $\mathbf{R}^3$ and $\mathbf{t} = (s, t)$ for the vector variable in $\mathbf{R}^2$, then we can write a plausible chain rule formula from an appropriate variable hierarchy diagram. (See Figure 2.63.) Thus, it is

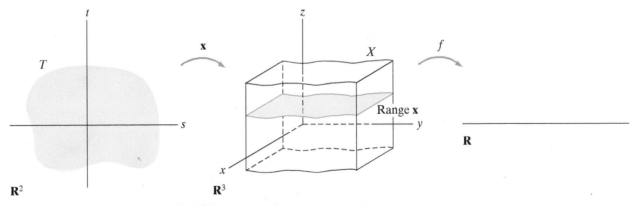

Figure 2.62 The composite $f \circ \mathbf{x}$ where $f: X \subseteq \mathbf{R}^3 \to \mathbf{R}$ and $\mathbf{x}: T \subseteq \mathbf{R}^2 \to \mathbf{R}^3$.

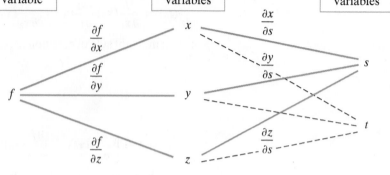

Figure 2.63 The chain rule for $f \circ \mathbf{x}$, where $f \colon X \subseteq \mathbf{R}^3 \to \mathbf{R}$ and $\mathbf{x} \colon T \subseteq \mathbf{R}^2 \to \mathbf{R}^3$.

reasonable to expect that the following formulas hold:

$$\frac{\partial f}{\partial s} = \frac{\partial f}{\partial x}\frac{\partial x}{\partial s} + \frac{\partial f}{\partial y}\frac{\partial y}{\partial s} + \frac{\partial f}{\partial z}\frac{\partial z}{\partial s}$$

and   (5)

$$\frac{\partial f}{\partial t} = \frac{\partial f}{\partial x}\frac{\partial x}{\partial t} + \frac{\partial f}{\partial y}\frac{\partial y}{\partial t} + \frac{\partial f}{\partial z}\frac{\partial z}{\partial t}.$$

(Again, we abuse notation by writing both $\partial f/\partial s$, $\partial f/\partial t$ and $\partial f/\partial x$, $\partial f/\partial y$, $\partial f/\partial z$.) Indeed, when f is a function of x, y, and z of class C^1, formula (3) with $n = 3$ applies once we realize that $\partial x/\partial s$, $\partial x/\partial t$, etc., represent ordinary differentiation of the partial functions in s or t.

EXAMPLE 3   Suppose

$$f(x, y, z) = x^2 + y^2 + z^2 \quad \text{and} \quad \mathbf{x}(s, t) = (s\cos t, e^{st}, s^2 - t^2).$$

Then $h(s, t) = f \circ \mathbf{x}(s, t) = s^2 \cos^2 t + e^{2st} + (s^2 - t^2)^2$, so that

$$\frac{\partial h}{\partial s} = \frac{\partial(f \circ \mathbf{x})}{\partial s} = 2s\cos^2 t + 2te^{2st} + 4s(s^2 - t^2)$$

$$\frac{\partial h}{\partial t} = \frac{\partial(f \circ \mathbf{x})}{\partial t} = -2s^2 \cos t \sin t + 2se^{2st} - 4t(s^2 - t^2).$$

We also have

$$\frac{\partial f}{\partial x} = 2x, \qquad \frac{\partial f}{\partial y} = 2y, \qquad \frac{\partial f}{\partial z} = 2z$$

and

$$\frac{\partial x}{\partial s} = \cos t, \qquad \frac{\partial x}{\partial t} = -s\sin t,$$

$$\frac{\partial y}{\partial s} = te^{st}, \qquad \frac{\partial y}{\partial t} = se^{st},$$

$$\frac{\partial z}{\partial s} = 2s, \qquad \frac{\partial z}{\partial t} = -2t.$$

Hence, we compute

$$\frac{\partial f}{\partial s} = \frac{\partial (f \circ \mathbf{x})}{\partial s} = \frac{\partial f}{\partial x}\frac{\partial x}{\partial s} + \frac{\partial f}{\partial y}\frac{\partial y}{\partial s} + \frac{\partial f}{\partial z}\frac{\partial z}{\partial s}$$

$$= 2x(\cos t) + 2y(te^{st}) + 2z(2s)$$

$$= 2s\cos t(\cos t) + 2e^{st}(te^{st}) + 2(s^2 - t^2)(2s)$$

$$= 2s\cos^2 t + 2te^{2st} + 4s(s^2 - t^2),$$

just as we saw earlier. We leave it to you to use the chain rule to calculate $\partial f / \partial t$ in a similar manner. ◆

Of course, there is no need for us to stop here. Suppose we have an open set X in $\mathbf{R}^m$, an open set T in $\mathbf{R}^n$, and functions $f: X \to \mathbf{R}$ and $\mathbf{x}: T \to \mathbf{R}^m$ such that $h = f \circ \mathbf{x}: T \to \mathbf{R}$ can be defined. If f is of class C^1 and $\mathbf{x}$ is differentiable, then, from the previous remarks, h must also be differentiable and, moreover,

$$\frac{\partial h}{\partial t_j} = \frac{\partial f}{\partial x_1}\frac{\partial x_1}{\partial t_j} + \frac{\partial f}{\partial x_2}\frac{\partial x_2}{\partial t_j} + \cdots + \frac{\partial f}{\partial x_m}\frac{\partial x_m}{\partial t_j}$$

$$= \sum_{k=1}^{m} \frac{\partial f}{\partial x_k}\frac{\partial x_k}{\partial t_j}, \quad j = 1, 2, \ldots, n.$$

Since the component functions of a vector-valued function are just scalar-valued functions, we can say even more. Suppose $\mathbf{f}: X \subseteq \mathbf{R}^m \to \mathbf{R}^p$ and $\mathbf{x}: T \subseteq \mathbf{R}^n \to \mathbf{R}^m$ are such that $\mathbf{h} = \mathbf{f} \circ \mathbf{x}: T \subseteq \mathbf{R}^n \to \mathbf{R}^p$ can be defined. (As always, we assume that X is open in $\mathbf{R}^m$ and T is open in $\mathbf{R}^n$.) See Figure 2.64 for a representation of the situation. If $\mathbf{f}$ is of class C^1 and $\mathbf{x}$ is differentiable, then the composite $\mathbf{h} = \mathbf{f} \circ \mathbf{x}$ is differentiable and the following general formula holds:

$$\frac{\partial h_i}{\partial t_j} = \sum_{k=1}^{m} \frac{\partial f_i}{\partial x_k}\frac{\partial x_k}{\partial t_j}, \quad i = 1, 2, \ldots, p; \quad j = 1, 2, \ldots, n. \tag{6}$$

The plausibility of formula (6) is immediate, given the variable hierarchy diagram shown in Figure 2.65.

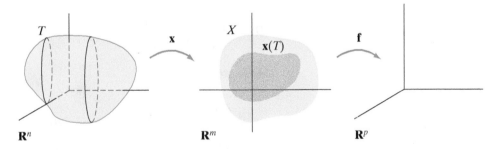

Figure 2.64 The composite $\mathbf{f} \circ \mathbf{x}$ where $\mathbf{f}: X \subseteq \mathbf{R}^m \to \mathbf{R}^p$ and $\mathbf{x}: T \subseteq \mathbf{R}^n \to \mathbf{R}^m$.

Now comes the real "magic." Recall that if A is a $p \times m$ matrix and B is an $m \times n$ matrix, then the product matrix $C = AB$ is defined and is a $p \times n$ matrix. Moreover, the ijth entry of C is given by

$$c_{ij} = \sum_{k=1}^{m} a_{ik}b_{kj}.$$

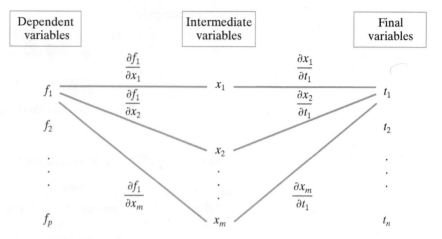

Figure 2.65 The chain rule diagram for $\mathbf{f} \circ \mathbf{x}$, where $\mathbf{f}: X \subseteq \mathbf{R}^m \to \mathbf{R}^p$ and $\mathbf{x}: T \subseteq \mathbf{R}^n \to \mathbf{R}^m$.

If we recall that the ijth entry of the matrix $D\mathbf{h}(\mathbf{t})$ is $\partial h_i / \partial t_j$, and similarly for $D\mathbf{f}(\mathbf{x})$ and $D\mathbf{x}(\mathbf{t})$, then we see that formula (6) expresses nothing more than the following equation of matrices:

$$D\mathbf{h}(\mathbf{t}) = D(\mathbf{f} \circ \mathbf{x})(\mathbf{t}) = D\mathbf{f}(\mathbf{x})D\mathbf{x}(\mathbf{t}). \tag{7}$$

The similarity between formulas (7) and (1) is striking. One of the reasons (perhaps the principal reason) for defining matrix multiplication as we have is precisely so that the chain rule in several variables can have the elegant appearance that it has in formula (7).

EXAMPLE 4 Suppose $\mathbf{f}: \mathbf{R}^3 \to \mathbf{R}^2$ is given by $\mathbf{f}(x_1, x_2, x_3) = (x_1 - x_2, x_1 x_2 x_3)$ and $\mathbf{x}: \mathbf{R}^2 \to \mathbf{R}^3$ is given by $\mathbf{x}(t_1, t_2) = (t_1 t_2, t_1^2, t_2^2)$. Then $\mathbf{f} \circ \mathbf{x}: \mathbf{R}^2 \to \mathbf{R}^2$ is given by $(\mathbf{f} \circ \mathbf{x})(t_1, t_2) = (t_1 t_2 - t_1^2, t_1^3 t_2^3)$, so that

$$D(\mathbf{f} \circ \mathbf{x})(\mathbf{t}) = \begin{bmatrix} t_2 - 2t_1 & t_1 \\ 3t_1^2 t_2^3 & 3t_1^3 t_2^2 \end{bmatrix}.$$

On the other hand,

$$D\mathbf{f}(\mathbf{x}) = \begin{bmatrix} 1 & -1 & 0 \\ x_2 x_3 & x_1 x_3 & x_1 x_2 \end{bmatrix} \quad \text{and} \quad D\mathbf{x}(t) = \begin{bmatrix} t_2 & t_1 \\ 2t_1 & 0 \\ 0 & 2t_2 \end{bmatrix},$$

so that the product matrix is

$$D\mathbf{f}(\mathbf{x})D\mathbf{x}(\mathbf{t}) = \begin{bmatrix} t_2 - 2t_1 & t_1 \\ x_2 x_3 t_2 + 2x_1 x_3 t_1 & x_2 x_3 t_1 + 2x_1 x_2 t_2 \end{bmatrix}$$

$$= \begin{bmatrix} t_2 - 2t_1 & t_1 \\ t_1^2 t_2^3 + 2t_1^2 t_2^3 & t_1^3 t_2^2 + 2t_1^3 t_2^2 \end{bmatrix},$$

after substituting for x_1, x_2, and x_3. Thus, $D(\mathbf{f} \circ \mathbf{x})(\mathbf{t}) = D\mathbf{f}(\mathbf{x})D\mathbf{x}(\mathbf{t})$, as expected.

Alternatively, we may use the variable hierarchy diagram shown in Figure 2.66 and compute any individual partial derivative we may desire. For example,

$$\frac{\partial f_2}{\partial t_1} = \frac{\partial f_2}{\partial x_1} \frac{\partial x_1}{\partial t_1} + \frac{\partial f_2}{\partial x_2} \frac{\partial x_2}{\partial t_1} + \frac{\partial f_2}{\partial x_3} \frac{\partial x_3}{\partial t_1}$$

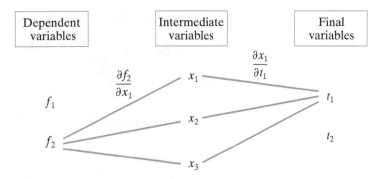

Figure 2.66 The variable hierarchy diagram for Example 4.

by formula (6). Then by abuse of notation,

$$\frac{\partial f_2}{\partial t_1} = (x_2 x_3)(t_2) + (x_1 x_3)(2t_1) + (x_1 x_2)(0)$$

$$= (t_1^2 t_2^2)(t_2) + (t_1 t_2)(t_2^2)(2t_1)$$

$$= 3t_1^2 t_2^3,$$

which is indeed the (2, 1) entry of the matrix product.   ◆

At last we state the most general version of the chain rule from a technical standpoint; a proof may be found in the addendum to this section.

THEOREM 5.3 (THE CHAIN RULE)   Suppose $X \subseteq \mathbf{R}^m$ and $T \subseteq \mathbf{R}^n$ are open and $\mathbf{f}: X \to \mathbf{R}^p$ and $\mathbf{x}: T \to \mathbf{R}^m$ are defined so that range $\mathbf{x} \subseteq X$. If $\mathbf{x}$ is differentiable at $\mathbf{t}_0 \in T$ and $\mathbf{f}$ is differentiable at $\mathbf{x}_0 = \mathbf{x}(\mathbf{t}_0)$, then the composite $\mathbf{f} \circ \mathbf{x}$ is differentiable at $\mathbf{t}_0$, and we have

$$D(\mathbf{f} \circ \mathbf{x})(\mathbf{t}_0) = D\mathbf{f}(\mathbf{x}_0)D\mathbf{x}(\mathbf{t}_0).$$

The advantage of Theorem 5.3 over the earlier versions of the chain rule we have been discussing is that it requires $\mathbf{f}$ only to be differentiable at the point in question, not to be of class C^1. Note that, of course, Theorem 5.3 includes all the special cases of the chain rule we have previously discussed. In particular, Theorem 5.3 includes the important case of formula (4).

EXAMPLE 5   Let $\mathbf{f}: \mathbf{R}^2 \to \mathbf{R}^2$ be defined by $\mathbf{f}(x, y) = (x - 2y + 7, 3xy^2)$. Suppose that $\mathbf{g}: \mathbf{R}^3 \to \mathbf{R}^2$ is differentiable at $(0, 0, 0)$ and we know that $\mathbf{g}(0, 0, 0) = (-2, 1)$ and

$$D\mathbf{g}(0, 0, 0) = \begin{bmatrix} 2 & 4 & 5 \\ -1 & 0 & 1 \end{bmatrix}.$$

We use this information to determine $D(\mathbf{f} \circ \mathbf{g})(0, 0, 0)$.

First, note that Theorem 5.3 tells us that $\mathbf{f} \circ \mathbf{g}$ must be differentiable at $(0, 0, 0)$ and, second, that

$$D(\mathbf{f} \circ \mathbf{g})(0, 0, 0) = D\mathbf{f}(\mathbf{g}(0, 0, 0)) \, D\mathbf{g}(0, 0, 0) = D\mathbf{f}(-2, 1)D\mathbf{g}(0, 0, 0).$$

Since we know **f** completely, it is easy to compute that

$$D\mathbf{f}(x, y) = \begin{bmatrix} 1 & -2 \\ 3y^2 & 6xy \end{bmatrix} \quad \text{so that} \quad D\mathbf{f}(-2, 1) = \begin{bmatrix} 1 & -2 \\ 3 & -12 \end{bmatrix}.$$

Thus,

$$D(\mathbf{f} \circ \mathbf{g})(0, 0, 0) = \begin{bmatrix} 1 & -2 \\ 3 & -12 \end{bmatrix} \begin{bmatrix} 2 & 4 & 5 \\ -1 & 0 & 1 \end{bmatrix} = \begin{bmatrix} 4 & 4 & 3 \\ 18 & 12 & 3 \end{bmatrix}.$$

We remark that we needed the full strength of Theorem 5.3, as we do not know anything about the differentiability of **g** other than at the point $(0, 0, 0)$.   ◆

EXAMPLE 6 (Polar/rectangular conversions)   Recall that in §1.7 we provided the basic equations relating polar and rectangular coordinates:

$$\begin{cases} x = r \cos\theta \\ y = r \sin\theta \end{cases}.$$

Now suppose you have an equation defining a quantity w as a function of x and y; that is,

$$w = f(x, y).$$

Then, of course, w may just as well be regarded as a function of r and θ by susbtituting $r \cos\theta$ for x and $r \sin\theta$ for y. That is,

$$w = g(r, \theta) = f(x(r, \theta), y(r, \theta)).$$

Our question is as follows: Assuming all functions involved are differentiable, how are the partial derivatives $\partial w / \partial r$, $\partial w / \partial\theta$ related to $\partial w / \partial x$, $\partial w / \partial y$?

In the situation just described, we have $w = g(r, \theta) = (f \circ \mathbf{x})(r, \theta)$, so that the chain rule implies

$$Dg(r, \theta) = Df(x, y)D\mathbf{x}(r, \theta).$$

Therefore,

$$\begin{bmatrix} \dfrac{\partial g}{\partial r} & \dfrac{\partial g}{\partial \theta} \end{bmatrix} = \begin{bmatrix} \dfrac{\partial f}{\partial x} & \dfrac{\partial f}{\partial y} \end{bmatrix} \begin{bmatrix} \dfrac{\partial x}{\partial r} & \dfrac{\partial x}{\partial \theta} \\ \dfrac{\partial y}{\partial r} & \dfrac{\partial y}{\partial \theta} \end{bmatrix}$$

$$= \begin{bmatrix} \dfrac{\partial f}{\partial x} & \dfrac{\partial f}{\partial y} \end{bmatrix} \begin{bmatrix} \cos\theta & -r \sin\theta \\ \sin\theta & r \cos\theta \end{bmatrix}.$$

By extracting entries, we see that the various partial derivatives of w are related by the following formulas:

$$\begin{cases} \dfrac{\partial w}{\partial r} = \cos\theta \, \dfrac{\partial w}{\partial x} + \sin\theta \, \dfrac{\partial w}{\partial y} \\ \dfrac{\partial w}{\partial \theta} = -r \sin\theta \, \dfrac{\partial w}{\partial x} + r \cos\theta \, \dfrac{\partial w}{\partial y} \end{cases}. \tag{8}$$

The significance of (8) is that it provides us with a relation of **differential operators**:

$$\begin{cases} \dfrac{\partial}{\partial r} = \cos\theta\,\dfrac{\partial}{\partial x} + \sin\theta\,\dfrac{\partial}{\partial y} \\[2mm] \dfrac{\partial}{\partial\theta} = -r\sin\theta\,\dfrac{\partial}{\partial x} + r\cos\theta\,\dfrac{\partial}{\partial y} \end{cases}. \tag{9}$$

The appropriate interpretation for (9) is the following: Differentiation with respect to the polar coordinate r is the same as a certain combination of differentiation with respect to both Cartesian coordinates x and y (namely, the combination $\cos\theta\,\partial/\partial x + \sin\theta\,\partial/\partial y$). A similar comment applies to differentiation with respect to the polar coordinate θ. Note that, when $r \neq 0$, we can solve algebraically for $\partial/\partial x$ and $\partial/\partial y$ in (9), obtaining

$$\begin{cases} \dfrac{\partial}{\partial x} = \cos\theta\,\dfrac{\partial}{\partial r} - \dfrac{\sin\theta}{r}\,\dfrac{\partial}{\partial\theta} \\[2mm] \dfrac{\partial}{\partial y} = \sin\theta\,\dfrac{\partial}{\partial r} + \dfrac{\cos\theta}{r}\,\dfrac{\partial}{\partial\theta} \end{cases}. \tag{10}$$

We will have occasion to use the relations in (9) and (10), and the method of their derivation, later in this text. ◆

Addendum: Proof of Theorem 5.3

We begin by noting that the derivative matrices $D\mathbf{f}(\mathbf{x}_0)$ and $D\mathbf{x}(\mathbf{t}_0)$ both exist because $\mathbf{f}$ is assumed to be differentiable at $\mathbf{x}_0$ and $\mathbf{x}$ is assumed to be differentiable at $\mathbf{t}_0$. Thus, the product matrix $D\mathbf{f}(\mathbf{x}_0)D\mathbf{x}(\mathbf{t}_0)$ exists. We need to show that the limit in Definition 3.8 is satisfied by this product matrix, that is, that

$$\lim_{t\to t_0} \frac{\|(\mathbf{f}\circ\mathbf{x})(\mathbf{t}) - [(\mathbf{f}\circ\mathbf{x})(\mathbf{t}_0) + D\mathbf{f}(\mathbf{x}_0)D\mathbf{x}(\mathbf{t}_0)(\mathbf{t}-\mathbf{t}_0)]\|}{\|\mathbf{t}-\mathbf{t}_0\|} = 0. \tag{11}$$

In view of the uniqueness of the derivative matrix, it then automatically follows that $\mathbf{f}\circ\mathbf{x}$ is differentiable at $\mathbf{t}_0$ and that $D\mathbf{f}(\mathbf{x}_0)D\mathbf{x}(\mathbf{t}_0) = D(\mathbf{f}\circ\mathbf{x})(\mathbf{t}_0)$. Thus, we entirely concern ourselves with establishing the limit (11) above.

Consider the numerator of (11). First, we rewrite

$$(\mathbf{f}\circ\mathbf{x})(\mathbf{t}) - [(\mathbf{f}\circ\mathbf{x})(\mathbf{t}_0) + D\mathbf{f}(\mathbf{x}_0)D\mathbf{x}(\mathbf{t}_0)(\mathbf{t}-\mathbf{t}_0)]$$
$$= (\mathbf{f}\circ\mathbf{x})(\mathbf{t}) - (\mathbf{f}\circ\mathbf{x})(\mathbf{t}_0) - D\mathbf{f}(\mathbf{x}_0)(\mathbf{x}(\mathbf{t})-\mathbf{x}(t_0))$$
$$+ D\mathbf{f}(\mathbf{x}_0)(\mathbf{x}(\mathbf{t})-\mathbf{x}(\mathbf{t}_0)) - D\mathbf{f}(\mathbf{x}_0)D\mathbf{x}(\mathbf{t}_0)(\mathbf{t}-\mathbf{t}_0).$$

Then we use the triangle inequality:

$$\|(\mathbf{f}\circ\mathbf{x})(\mathbf{t}) - [(\mathbf{f}\circ\mathbf{x})(\mathbf{t}_0) + D\mathbf{f}(\mathbf{x}_0)D\mathbf{x}(\mathbf{t}_0)(\mathbf{t}-\mathbf{t}_0)]\|$$
$$\leq \|(\mathbf{f}\circ\mathbf{x})(\mathbf{t}) - (\mathbf{f}\circ\mathbf{x})(\mathbf{t}_0) - D\mathbf{f}(\mathbf{x}_0)(\mathbf{x}(\mathbf{t})-\mathbf{x}(t_0))\|$$
$$+ \|D\mathbf{f}(\mathbf{x}_0)(\mathbf{x}(\mathbf{t})-\mathbf{x}(\mathbf{t}_0)) - D\mathbf{f}(\mathbf{x}_0)D\mathbf{x}(\mathbf{t}_0)(\mathbf{t}-\mathbf{t}_0)\|$$
$$= \|(\mathbf{f}\circ\mathbf{x})(\mathbf{t}) - (\mathbf{f}\circ\mathbf{x})(\mathbf{t}_0) - D\mathbf{f}(\mathbf{x}_0)(\mathbf{x}(\mathbf{t})-\mathbf{x}(t_0))\|$$
$$+ \|D\mathbf{f}(\mathbf{x}_0)[(\mathbf{x}(\mathbf{t})-\mathbf{x}(\mathbf{t}_0)) - D\mathbf{x}(\mathbf{t}_0)(\mathbf{t}-\mathbf{t}_0)]\|.$$

By inequality (9) in the proof of Theorem 3.9, there is a constant K such that, for any vector $\mathbf{h} \in \mathbf{R}^n$, $\|D\mathbf{f}(\mathbf{x}_0)\mathbf{h}\| \leq K\|\mathbf{h}\|$. Thus,

$$\|(\mathbf{f} \circ \mathbf{x})(\mathbf{t}) - (\mathbf{f} \circ \mathbf{x})(\mathbf{t}_0) - D\mathbf{f}(\mathbf{x}_0)D\mathbf{x}(\mathbf{t}_0)(\mathbf{t} - \mathbf{t}_0)\|$$
$$\leq \|(\mathbf{f} \circ \mathbf{x})(\mathbf{t}) - (\mathbf{f} \circ \mathbf{x})(\mathbf{t}_0) - D\mathbf{f}(\mathbf{x}_0)(\mathbf{x}(\mathbf{t}) - \mathbf{x}(t_0))\| \quad (12)$$
$$+ K\|\mathbf{x}(\mathbf{t}) - \mathbf{x}(t_0) - D\mathbf{x}(\mathbf{t}_0)(\mathbf{t} - \mathbf{t}_0)\|.$$

To establish the limit (11) formally, we must show that given any $\epsilon > 0$, we may find a $\delta > 0$ such that if $0 < \|\mathbf{t} - \mathbf{t}_0\| < \delta$, then

$$\frac{\|(\mathbf{f} \circ \mathbf{x})(\mathbf{t}) - [(\mathbf{f} \circ \mathbf{x})(\mathbf{t}_0) + D\mathbf{f}(\mathbf{x}_0)D\mathbf{x}(\mathbf{t}_0)(\mathbf{t} - \mathbf{t}_0)]\|}{\|\mathbf{t} - \mathbf{t}_0\|} < \epsilon.$$

Consider the first term of the right side of (12). Using the differentiability of $\mathbf{x}$ at $\mathbf{t}_0$ and inequality (11) in the proof of Theorem 3.9, we can find some $\delta_0 > 0$ and a constant K_0 such that if $0 < \|\mathbf{t} - \mathbf{t}_0\| < \delta_0$, then

$$\|\mathbf{x}(\mathbf{t}) - \mathbf{x}(\mathbf{t}_0)\| < K_0\|\mathbf{t} - \mathbf{t}_0\|.$$

By the differentiability of $\mathbf{f}$ at $\mathbf{x}_0$, given any $\epsilon_1 > 0$, we may find some $\delta_1 > 0$ such that if $0 < \|\mathbf{x} - \mathbf{x}_0\| < \delta_1$, then

$$\frac{\|\mathbf{f}(\mathbf{x}) - [\mathbf{f}(\mathbf{x}_0) + D\mathbf{f}(\mathbf{x}_0)(\mathbf{x} - \mathbf{x}_0)]\|}{\|\mathbf{x} - \mathbf{x}_0\|} < \epsilon_1.$$

Set $\epsilon_1 = \epsilon/(2K_0)$. With $\mathbf{x} = \mathbf{x}(\mathbf{t})$, $\mathbf{x}_0 = \mathbf{x}(\mathbf{t}_0)$, we have that if both $0 < \|\mathbf{t} - \mathbf{t}_0\| < \delta_0$ and $0 < \|\mathbf{t} - \mathbf{t}_0\| < \delta_1/K_0$, then

$$\|\mathbf{x}(\mathbf{t}) - \mathbf{x}(\mathbf{t}_0)\| < K_0\|\mathbf{t} - \mathbf{t}_0\| < \delta_1.$$

Hence,

$$\|(\mathbf{f} \circ \mathbf{x})(\mathbf{t}) - (\mathbf{f} \circ \mathbf{x})(\mathbf{t}_0) - D\mathbf{f}(\mathbf{x}_0)(\mathbf{x}(\mathbf{t}) - \mathbf{x}(\mathbf{t}_0))\| < \epsilon_1\|\mathbf{x}(\mathbf{t}) - \mathbf{x}(\mathbf{t}_0)\|$$
$$< \epsilon_1 K_0\|\mathbf{t} - \mathbf{t}_0\| = \frac{\epsilon\|\mathbf{t} - \mathbf{t}_0\|}{2}. \quad (13)$$

Now look at the second term of the right side of (12). Since $\mathbf{x}$ is differentiable at $\mathbf{t}_0$, given any $\epsilon_2 > 0$, we may find some $\delta_2 > 0$ such that if $0 < \|\mathbf{t} - \mathbf{t}_0\| < \delta_2$, then

$$\frac{\|\mathbf{x}(\mathbf{t}) - [\mathbf{x}(\mathbf{t}_0) + D\mathbf{x}(\mathbf{t}_0)(\mathbf{t} - \mathbf{t}_0)]\|}{\|\mathbf{t} - \mathbf{t}_0\|} < \epsilon_2.$$

Set $\epsilon_2 = \epsilon/(2K)$. Then, for $0 < \|\mathbf{t} - \mathbf{t}_0\| < \delta_2$, we have

$$\|\mathbf{x}(\mathbf{t}) - [\mathbf{x}(\mathbf{t}_0) + D\mathbf{x}(\mathbf{t}_0)(\mathbf{t} - \mathbf{t}_0)]\| < \frac{\epsilon}{2K}\|\mathbf{t} - \mathbf{t}_0\|. \quad (14)$$

Finally, let δ be the smallest of δ_0, δ_1/K_0, and δ_2. Then, for $0 < \|\mathbf{t} - \mathbf{t}_0\| < \delta$, we have that both the inequalities (13) and (14) hold and thus (12) becomes

$$\|(\mathbf{f} \circ \mathbf{x})(\mathbf{t}) - (\mathbf{f} \circ \mathbf{x})(\mathbf{t}_0) - D\mathbf{f}(\mathbf{x}_0)D\mathbf{x}(\mathbf{t}_0)(\mathbf{t} - \mathbf{t}_0)\|$$
$$< \frac{\epsilon}{2}\|\mathbf{t} - \mathbf{t}_0\| + K\left(\frac{\epsilon}{2K}\|\mathbf{t} - \mathbf{t}_0\|\right)$$
$$= \epsilon\|\mathbf{t} - \mathbf{t}_0\|.$$

Hence,

$$\frac{\|(\mathbf{f} \circ \mathbf{x})(\mathbf{t}) - (\mathbf{f} \circ \mathbf{x})(\mathbf{t}_0) - D\mathbf{f}(\mathbf{x}_0)D\mathbf{x}(\mathbf{t}_0)(\mathbf{t} - \mathbf{t}_0)\|}{\|\mathbf{t} - \mathbf{t}_0\|} < \epsilon,$$

as desired.   ∎

2.5 Exercises

1. If $f(x, y, z) = x^2 - y^3 + xyz$, and $x = 6t + 7$, $y = \sin 2t$, $z = t^2$, verify the chain rule by finding df/dt in two different ways.

2. If $f(x, y) = \sin(xy)$ and $x = s + t$, $y = s^2 + t^2$, find $\partial f/\partial s$ and $\partial f/\partial t$ in two ways:

  (a) by substitution.

  (b) by means of the chain rule.

3. Suppose that a bird flies along the helical curve $x = 2 \cos t$, $y = 2 \sin t$, $z = 3t$. The bird suddenly encounters a weather front so that the barometric pressure is varying rather wildly from point to point as $P(x, y, z) = 6x^2 z/y$ atm.

  (a) Use the chain rule to determine how the pressure is changing at $t = \pi/4$ min.

  (b) Check your result in part (a) by direct substitution.

  (c) What is the approximate pressure at $t = \pi/4 + 0.01$ min?

4. Suppose that $z = x^2 + y^3$, where $x = st$ and y is a function of s and t. Suppose further that when $(s, t) = (2, 1)$, $\partial y/\partial t = 0$. Determine $\dfrac{\partial z}{\partial t}(2, 1)$.

5. You are the proud new owner of an Acme Deluxe Bread Kneading Machine, which you are using for the first time today. Suppose that at noon the dimensions of your (nearly rectangular) loaf of bread dough are $L = 7$ in (length), $W = 5$ in (width), and $H = 4$ in (height). At that time, you place the loaf in the machine for kneading and the machine begins by stretching the loaf's length at an initial rate of 0.75 in/min, punching down the loaf's height at a rate of 1 in/min, and increasing the loaf's width at a rate of 0.5 in/min. What is the rate of change of the volume of the loaf when the machine starts? Is the dough increasing or decreasing in size at that moment?

6. A rectangular stick of butter is placed in the microwave oven to melt. When the butter's length is 6 in and its square cross section measures 1.5 in on a side, its length is decreasing at a rate of 0.25 in/min and its cross-sectional edge is decreasing at a rate of 0.125 in/min. How fast is the butter melting (i.e., at what rate is the solid volume of butter turning to liquid) at that instant?

7. Suppose that the following function is used to model the monthly demand for bicycles:

$$P(x, y) = 200 + 20\sqrt{0.1x + 10} - 12\sqrt[3]{y}.$$

In this formula, x represents the price (in dollars per gallon) of automobile gasoline and y represents the selling price (in dollars) of each bicycle. Furthermore, suppose that the price of gasoline t months from now will be

$$x = 1 + 0.1t - \cos \frac{\pi t}{6}$$

and the price of each bicycle will be

$$y = 200 + 2t \sin \frac{\pi t}{6}.$$

At what rate will the monthly demand for bicycles be changing six months from now?

8. The Centers for Disease Control and Prevention provides information on the **body mass index** (BMI) to give a more meaningful assessment of a person's weight. The BMI is given by the formula

$$\text{BMI} = \frac{10{,}000w}{h^2},$$

where w is an individual's mass in kilograms and h the person's height in centimeters. While monitoring a child's growth, you estimate that at the time he turned 10 years old, his height showed a growth rate of 0.6 cm per month. At the same time, his mass showed a growth rate of 0.4 kg per month. Suppose that he was 140 cm tall and weighed 33 kg on his tenth birthday.

  (a) At what rate is his BMI changing on his tenth birthday?

  (b) The BMI of a typical 10-year-old male increases at an average rate of 0.04 BMI points per month. Should you be concerned about the child's weight gain?

9. A cement mixer is pouring concrete in a conical pile. At the time when the height and base radius of the concrete cone are, respectively, 30 cm and 12 cm, the rate at which the height is increasing is 1 cm/min and the rate at which the volume of cement in the pile is increasing is 320 cm³/min. At that moment, how fast is the radius of the cone changing?

10. A clarinetist is playing the glissando at the beginning of *Rhapsody in Blue*, while Hermione (who arrived late) is walking toward her seat. If the (changing) frequency of the note is f and Hermione is moving toward the clarinetist at speed v, then she actually hears the frequency ϕ given by

$$\phi = \frac{c + v}{c} f,$$

where c is the (constant) speed of sound in air, about 330 m/sec. At this particular moment, the frequency is $f = 440$ Hz and is increasing at a rate of 100 Hz per second. At that same moment, Hermione is moving toward the clarinetist at 4 m/sec and decelerating at

2 m/sec^2. What is the perceived frequency ϕ she hears at that moment? How fast is it changing? Does Hermione hear the clarinet's note becoming higher or lower?

11. Suppose $z = f(x, y)$ has continuous partial derivatives. Let $x = e^r \cos\theta$, $y = e^r \sin\theta$. Show that then

$$\left(\frac{\partial z}{\partial x}\right)^2 + \left(\frac{\partial z}{\partial y}\right)^2 = e^{-2r}\left[\left(\frac{\partial z}{\partial r}\right)^2 + \left(\frac{\partial z}{\partial \theta}\right)^2\right].$$

12. Suppose that $z = f(x, y)$ has continuous partial derivatives. Let $x = 2uv$ and $y = u^2 + v^2$. Show that then

$$\frac{\partial z}{\partial u}\frac{\partial z}{\partial v} = 2x\left[\left(\frac{\partial z}{\partial x}\right)^2 + \left(\frac{\partial z}{\partial y}\right)^2\right] + 4y\frac{\partial z}{\partial x}\frac{\partial z}{\partial y}.$$

13. If $w = g\left(u^2 - v^2, v^2 - u^2\right)$ has continuous partial derivatives with respect to $x = u^2 - v^2$ and $y = v^2 - u^2$, show that

$$v\frac{\partial w}{\partial u} + u\frac{\partial w}{\partial v} = 0.$$

14. Suppose that $z = f(x + y, x - y)$ has continuous partial derivatives with respect to $u = x + y$ and $v = x - y$. Show that

$$\frac{\partial z}{\partial x}\frac{\partial z}{\partial y} = \left(\frac{\partial z}{\partial u}\right)^2 - \left(\frac{\partial z}{\partial v}\right)^2.$$

15. If $w = f\left(\dfrac{xy}{x^2 + y^2}\right)$ is a differentiable function of $u = \dfrac{xy}{x^2 + y^2}$, show that

$$x\frac{\partial w}{\partial x} + y\frac{\partial w}{\partial y} = 0.$$

16. If $w = f\left(\dfrac{x^2 - y^2}{x^2 + y^2}\right)$ is a differentiable function of $u = \dfrac{x^2 - y^2}{x^2 + y^2}$, show that then

$$x\frac{\partial w}{\partial x} + y\frac{\partial w}{\partial y} = 0.$$

17. Suppose $w = f\left(\dfrac{y - x}{xy}, \dfrac{z - x}{xz}\right)$ is a differentiable function of $u = \dfrac{y - x}{xy}$ and $v = \dfrac{z - x}{xz}$. Show then that

$$x^2\frac{\partial w}{\partial x} + y^2\frac{\partial w}{\partial y} + z^2\frac{\partial w}{\partial z} = 0.$$

18. Suppose that $w = g\left(\dfrac{x}{y}, \dfrac{z}{y}\right)$ is a differentiable function of $u = x/y$ and $v = z/y$. Show then that

$$x\frac{\partial w}{\partial x} + y\frac{\partial w}{\partial y} + z\frac{\partial w}{\partial z} = 0.$$

In Exercises 19–27, calculate $D(\mathbf{f} \circ \mathbf{g})$ in two ways: (a) by first evaluating $\mathbf{f} \circ \mathbf{g}$ and (b) by using the chain rule and the derivative matrices $D\mathbf{f}$ and $D\mathbf{g}$.

19. $\mathbf{f}(x) = (3x^5, e^{2x})$, $g(s, t) = s - 7t$

20. $\mathbf{f}(x) = \left(x^2, \cos 3x, \ln x\right)$, $g(s, t, u) = s + t^2 + u^3$

21. $f(x, y) = ye^x$, $\mathbf{g}(s, t) = (s - t, s + t)$

22. $f(x, y) = x^2 - 3y^2$, $\mathbf{g}(s, t) = (st, s + t^2)$

23. $\mathbf{f}(x, y) = \left(xy - \dfrac{y}{x}, \dfrac{x}{y} + y^3\right)$, $\mathbf{g}(s, t) = \left(\dfrac{s}{t}, s^2 t\right)$

24. $\mathbf{f}(x, y, z) = (x^2 y + y^2 z, xyz, e^z)$, $\mathbf{g}(t) = (t - 2, 3t + 7, t^3)$

25. $\mathbf{f}(x, y) = \left(xy^2, x^2 y, x^3 + y^3\right)$, $\mathbf{g}(t) = (\sin t, e^t)$

26. $\mathbf{f}(x, y) = \left(x^2 - y, y/x, e^y\right)$, $\quad\mathbf{g}(s, t, u) = (s + 2t + 3u, stu)$

27. $\mathbf{f}(x, y, z) = (x + y + z, x^3 - e^{yz})$, $\mathbf{g}(s, t, u) = (st, tu, su)$

28. Let $\mathbf{g}: \mathbf{R}^3 \to \mathbf{R}^2$ be a differentiable function such that $\mathbf{g}(1, -1, 3) = (2, 5)$ and $D\mathbf{g}(1, -1, 3) = \begin{bmatrix} 1 & -1 & 0 \\ 4 & 0 & 7 \end{bmatrix}$. Suppose that $\mathbf{f}: \mathbf{R}^2 \to \mathbf{R}^2$ is defined by $\mathbf{f}(x, y) = (2xy, 3x - y + 5)$. What is $D(\mathbf{f} \circ \mathbf{g})(1, -1, 3)$?

29. Let $\mathbf{g}: \mathbf{R}^2 \to \mathbf{R}^2$ and $\mathbf{f}: \mathbf{R}^2 \to \mathbf{R}^2$ be differentiable functions such that $\mathbf{g}(0, 0) = (1, 2)$, $\mathbf{g}(1, 2) = (3, 5)$, $\mathbf{f}(0, 0) = (3, 5)$, $\mathbf{f}(4, 1) = (1, 2)$, $D\mathbf{g}(0, 0) = \begin{bmatrix} 1 & 0 \\ -1 & 4 \end{bmatrix}$, $D\mathbf{g}(1, 2) = \begin{bmatrix} 2 & 3 \\ 5 & 7 \end{bmatrix}$, $D\mathbf{f}(3, 5) = \begin{bmatrix} 1 & 1 \\ 3 & 5 \end{bmatrix}$, $D\mathbf{f}(4, 1) = \begin{bmatrix} -1 & 2 \\ 1 & 3 \end{bmatrix}$.

(a) Calculate $D(\mathbf{f} \circ \mathbf{g})(1, 2)$.

(b) Calculate $D(\mathbf{g} \circ \mathbf{f})(4, 1)$.

30. Let $z = f(x, y)$, where f has continuous partial derivatives. If we make the standard polar/rectangular substitution $x = r \cos\theta$, $y = r \sin\theta$, show that

$$\left(\frac{\partial z}{\partial x}\right)^2 + \left(\frac{\partial z}{\partial y}\right)^2 = \left(\frac{\partial z}{\partial r}\right)^2 + \frac{1}{r^2}\left(\frac{\partial z}{\partial \theta}\right)^2.$$

31. (a) Use the methods of Example 6 and formula (10) in this section to determine $\partial^2/\partial x^2$ and $\partial^2/\partial y^2$ in terms of the polar partial differential operators $\partial^2/\partial r^2$, $\partial^2/\partial \theta^2$, $\partial^2/\partial r\,\partial\theta$, $\partial/\partial r$, and $\partial/\partial\theta$. (Hint: You will need to use the product rule.)

(b) Use part (a) to show that the **Laplacian operator** $\partial^2/\partial x^2 + \partial^2/\partial y^2$ is given in polar coordinates by the formula

$$\frac{\partial^2}{\partial x^2} + \frac{\partial^2}{\partial y^2} = \frac{\partial^2}{\partial r^2} + \frac{1}{r}\frac{\partial}{\partial r} + \frac{1}{r^2}\frac{\partial^2}{\partial\theta^2}.$$

32. Show that the Laplacian operator $\partial^2/\partial x^2 + \partial^2/\partial y^2 + \partial^2/\partial z^2$ in three dimensions is given in cylindrical coordinates by the formula

$$\frac{\partial^2}{\partial x^2} + \frac{\partial^2}{\partial y^2} + \frac{\partial^2}{\partial z^2} = \frac{\partial^2}{\partial r^2} + \frac{1}{r}\frac{\partial}{\partial r} + \frac{1}{r^2}\frac{\partial^2}{\partial\theta^2} + \frac{\partial^2}{\partial z^2}.$$

33. In this problem, you will determine the formula for the Laplacian operator in spherical coordinates.

(a) First, note that the cylindrical/spherical conversions given by formula (6) of §1.7 express the cylindrical coordinates z and r in terms of the spherical coordinates ρ and φ by equations of precisely the same form as those that express x and y in terms of the polar coordinates r and θ. Use this fact to write $\partial/\partial r$ in terms of $\partial/\partial\rho$ and $\partial/\partial\varphi$. (Also see formula (10) of this section.)

(b) Use the ideas and result of part (a) to establish the following formula:

$$\frac{\partial^2}{\partial x^2} + \frac{\partial^2}{\partial y^2} + \frac{\partial^2}{\partial z^2}$$

$$= \frac{\partial^2}{\partial\rho^2} + \frac{1}{\rho^2}\frac{\partial^2}{\partial\varphi^2} + \frac{1}{\rho^2\sin^2\varphi}\frac{\partial^2}{\partial\theta^2}$$

$$+ \frac{2}{\rho}\frac{\partial}{\partial\rho} + \frac{\cot\varphi}{\rho^2}\frac{\partial}{\partial\varphi}.$$

34. Suppose that y is defined implicitly as a function $y(x)$ by an equation of the form

$$F(x, y) = 0.$$

(For example, the equation $x^3 - y^2 = 0$ defines y as two functions of x, namely, $y = x^{3/2}$ and $y = -x^{3/2}$. The equation $\sin(xy) - x^2 y^7 + e^y = 0$, on the other hand, cannot readily be solved for y in terms of x. See the end of §2.6 for more about implicit functions.)

(a) Show that if F and $y(x)$ are both assumed to be differentiable functions, then

$$\frac{dy}{dx} = -\frac{F_x(x, y)}{F_y(x, y)}$$

provided $F_y(x, y) \neq 0$.

(b) Use the result of part (a) to find dy/dx when y is defined implicitly in terms of x by the equation $x^3 - y^2 = 0$. Check your result by explicitly solving for y and differentiating.

35. Find dy/dx when y is defined implicitly by the equation $\sin(xy) - x^2 y^7 + e^y = 0$. (See Exercise 34.)

36. Suppose that you are given an equation of the form

$$F(x, y, z) = 0,$$

for example, something like $x^3 z + y\cos z + (\sin y)/z = 0$. Then we may consider z to be defined implicitly as a function $z(x, y)$.

(a) Use the chain rule to show that if F and $z(x, y)$ are both assumed to be differentiable, then

$$\frac{\partial z}{\partial x} = -\frac{F_x(x, y, z)}{F_z(x, y, z)}, \qquad \frac{\partial z}{\partial y} = -\frac{F_y(x, y, z)}{F_z(x, y, z)}.$$

(b) Use part (a) to find $\partial z/\partial x$ and $\partial z/\partial y$ where z is given by the equation $xyz = 2$. Check your result by explicitly solving for z and then calculating the partial derivatives.

37. Find $\partial z/\partial x$ and $\partial z/\partial y$, where z is given implicitly by the equation

$$x^3 z + y\cos z + \frac{\sin y}{z} = 0.$$

(See Exercise 36.)

38. Let

$$f(x, y) = \begin{cases} \dfrac{x^2 y}{x^2 + y^2} & \text{if } (x, y) \neq (0, 0) \\ 0 & \text{if } (x, y) = (0, 0) \end{cases}.$$

(a) Use the definition of the partial derivative to find $f_x(0, 0)$ and $f_y(0, 0)$.

(b) Let a be a nonzero constant and let $\mathbf{x}(t) = (t, at)$. Show that $f \circ \mathbf{x}$ is differentiable, and find $D(f \circ \mathbf{x})(0)$ directly.

(c) Calculate $Df(0, 0)D\mathbf{x}(0)$. How can you reconcile your answer with your answer in part (b) and the chain rule?

Let $w = f(x, y, z)$ be a differentiable function of x, y, and z. For example, suppose that $w = x + 2y + z$. Regarding the variables x, y, and z as independent, we have $\partial w/\partial x = 1$ and $\partial w/\partial y = 2$. But now suppose that $z = xy$. Then x, y, and z are not all independent and, by substitution, we have that $w = x + 2y + xy$ so that $\partial w/\partial x = 1 + y$ and $\partial w/\partial y = 2 + x$. To overcome the apparent ambiguity in the notation for partial derivatives, it is customary to indicate the complete set of independent variables by writing additional subscripts beside *the partial derivative. Thus,*

$$\left(\frac{\partial w}{\partial x}\right)_{y,z}$$

would signify the partial derivative of w with respect to x, while holding both y and z constant. Hence, x, y, and z are the complete set of independent variables in this case. On the other hand, we would use $(\partial w/\partial x)_y$ to indicate that x and y alone are the independent variables. In the case that $w = x + 2y + z$, this notation gives

$$\left(\frac{\partial w}{\partial x}\right)_{y,z} = 1, \quad \left(\frac{\partial w}{\partial y}\right)_{x,z} = 2, \quad and \quad \left(\frac{\partial w}{\partial z}\right)_{x,y} = 1.$$

If $z = xy$, then we also have

$$\left(\frac{\partial w}{\partial x}\right)_y = 1 + y, \quad and \quad \left(\frac{\partial w}{\partial y}\right)_x = 2 + x.$$

In this way, the ambiguity of notation can be avoided. Use this notation in Exercises 39–45.

39. Let $w = x + 7y - 10z$ and $z = x^2 + y^2$.

(a) Find $\left(\dfrac{\partial w}{\partial x}\right)_{y,z}$, $\left(\dfrac{\partial w}{\partial y}\right)_{x,z}$, $\left(\dfrac{\partial w}{\partial z}\right)_{x,y}$, $\left(\dfrac{\partial w}{\partial x}\right)_y$,

and $\left(\dfrac{\partial w}{\partial y}\right)_x$.

(b) Relate $(\partial w/\partial x)_{y,z}$ and $(\partial w/\partial x)_y$ by using the chain rule.

40. Repeat Exercise 39 where $w = x^3 + y^3 + z^3$ and $z = 2x - 3y$.

41. Suppose $s = x^2 y + xzw - z^2$ and $xyw - y^3 z + xz = 0$. Find

$$\left(\frac{\partial s}{\partial z}\right)_{x,y,w} \quad and \quad \left(\frac{\partial s}{\partial z}\right)_{x,w}.$$

42. Let $U = F(P, V, T)$ denote the internal energy of a gas. Suppose the gas obeys the ideal gas law $PV = kT$, where k is a constant.

(a) Find $\left(\dfrac{\partial U}{\partial T}\right)_P$.

(b) Find $\left(\dfrac{\partial U}{\partial T}\right)_V$.

(c) Find $\left(\dfrac{\partial U}{\partial P}\right)_V$.

43. Show that if x, y, z are related implicitly by an equation of the form $F(x, y, z) = 0$, then

$$\left(\frac{\partial x}{\partial y}\right)_z \left(\frac{\partial y}{\partial z}\right)_x \left(\frac{\partial z}{\partial x}\right)_y = -1.$$

This relation is used in thermodynamics. (Hint: Use Exercise 36.)

44. The ideal gas law $PV = kT$, where k is a constant, relates the pressure P, temperature T, and volume V of a gas. Verify the result of Exercise 43 for the ideal gas law equation.

45. Verify the result of Exercise 43 for the ellipsoid

$$ax^2 + by^2 + cz^2 = d$$

where a, b, c, and d are constants.

2.6 Directional Derivatives and the Gradient

In this section, we will consider some of the key geometric properties of the **gradient vector**

$$\nabla f = \left(\frac{\partial f}{\partial x_1}, \frac{\partial f}{\partial x_2}, \dots, \frac{\partial f}{\partial x_n}\right)$$

of a scalar-valued function of n variables. In what follows, n will usually be 2 or 3.

The Directional Derivative

Let $f(x, y)$ be a scalar-valued function of two variables. In §2.3, we understood the partial derivative $\frac{\partial f}{\partial x}(a, b)$ as the slope, at the point $(a, b, f(a, b))$, of the curve obtained as the intersection of the surface $z = f(x, y)$ with the plane $y = b$. The other partial derivative $\frac{\partial f}{\partial y}(a, b)$ has a similar geometric interpretation. However, the surface $z = f(x, y)$ contains infinitely many curves passing through $(a, b, f(a, b))$ whose slope we might choose to measure. The directional derivative enables us to do this.

An alternative way to view $\frac{\partial f}{\partial x}(a, b)$ is as the rate of change of f as we move "infinitesimally" from $\mathbf{a} = (a, b)$ in the $\mathbf{i}$-direction, as suggested by Figure 2.67. This is easy to see since, by the definition of the partial derivative,

$$\frac{\partial f}{\partial x}(a, b) = \lim_{h \to 0} \frac{f(a + h, b) - f(a, b)}{h}$$

$$= \lim_{h \to 0} \frac{f((a, b) + (h, 0)) - f(a, b)}{h}$$

$$= \lim_{h \to 0} \frac{f((a, b) + h(1, 0)) - f(a, b)}{h}$$

$$= \lim_{h \to 0} \frac{f(\mathbf{a} + h\mathbf{i}) - f(\mathbf{a})}{h}.$$

Note that we are identifying the point (a, b) with the vector $\mathbf{a} = (a, b) = a\mathbf{i} + b\mathbf{j}$. Similarly, we have

$$\frac{\partial f}{\partial y}(a, b) = \lim_{h \to 0} \frac{f(\mathbf{a} + h\mathbf{j}) - f(\mathbf{a})}{h}.$$

Writing partial derivatives as we just have enables us to see that they are special cases of a more general type of derivative. Suppose $\mathbf{v}$ is any unit vector in $\mathbf{R}^2$. (The reason for taking a unit vector will be made clear later.) The quantity

$$\lim_{h \to 0} \frac{f(\mathbf{a} + h\mathbf{v}) - f(\mathbf{a})}{h} \tag{1}$$

is nothing more than the rate of change of f as we move (infinitesimally) from $\mathbf{a} = (a, b)$ in the direction specified by $\mathbf{v} = (A, B) = A\mathbf{i} + B\mathbf{j}$. It's also the slope of the curve obtained as the intersection of the surface $z = f(x, y)$ with the vertical plane $B(x - a) - A(y - b) = 0$. (See Figure 2.68.) We can use the limit expression in (1) to define the derivative of any scalar-valued function in a particular direction.

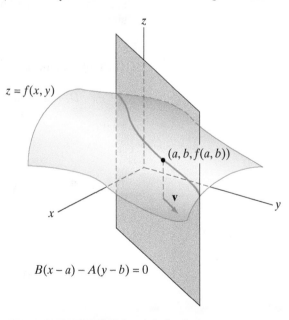

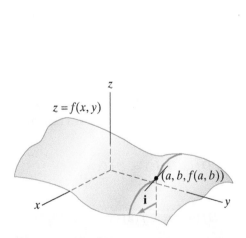

Figure 2.67 Another way to view the partial derivative $\partial f / \partial x$ at a point.

Figure 2.68 The directional derivative.

DEFINITION 6.1   Let X be open in $\mathbf{R}^n$, $f: X \subseteq \mathbf{R}^n \to \mathbf{R}$ a scalar-valued function, and $\mathbf{a} \in X$. If $\mathbf{v} \in \mathbf{R}^n$ is any unit vector, then the **directional derivative of f at a in the direction of v**, denoted $D_{\mathbf{v}} f(\mathbf{a})$, is

$$D_{\mathbf{v}} f(\mathbf{a}) = \lim_{h \to 0} \frac{f(\mathbf{a} + h\mathbf{v}) - f(\mathbf{a})}{h}$$

(provided that this limit exists).

EXAMPLE 1   Suppose $f(x, y) = x^2 - 3xy + 2x - 5y$. Then, if $\mathbf{v} = (v, w) \in \mathbf{R}^2$ is any unit vector, it follows that

$$D_{\mathbf{v}} f(0, 0) = \lim_{h \to 0} \frac{f((0, 0) + h(v, w)) - f(0, 0)}{h}$$

$$= \lim_{h \to 0} \frac{h^2 v^2 - 3h^2 vw + 2hv - 5hw}{h}$$

$$= \lim_{h \to 0} (hv^2 - 3hvw + 2v - 5w)$$

$$= 2v - 5w.$$

Thus, the rate of change of f is $2v - 5w$ if we move from the origin in the direction given by $\mathbf{v}$. The rate of change is zero if $\mathbf{v} = (5/\sqrt{29}, 2/\sqrt{29})$ or $(-5/\sqrt{29}, -2/\sqrt{29})$. ◆

Consequently, we see that the partial derivatives of a function are just the "tip of the iceberg." However, it turns out that when f is differentiable, the partial derivatives actually determine the directional derivatives for all directions $\mathbf{v}$. To see this rather remarkable result, we begin by defining a new function F of a single variable by

$$F(t) = f(\mathbf{a} + t\mathbf{v}).$$

Then, by Definition 6.1, we have

$$D_{\mathbf{v}} f(\mathbf{a}) = \lim_{t \to 0} \frac{f(\mathbf{a} + t\mathbf{v}) - f(\mathbf{a})}{t} = \lim_{t \to 0} \frac{F(t) - F(0)}{t - 0} = F'(0).$$

That is,

$$D_{\mathbf{v}} f(\mathbf{a}) = \frac{d}{dt} f(\mathbf{a} + t\mathbf{v})\Big|_{t=0}. \tag{2}$$

The significance of equation (2) is that, when f is differentiable at $\mathbf{a}$, we can apply the chain rule to the right-hand side. Indeed, let $\mathbf{x}(t) = \mathbf{a} + t\mathbf{v}$. Then, by the chain rule,

$$\frac{d}{dt} f(\mathbf{a} + t\mathbf{v}) = Df(\mathbf{x}) D\mathbf{x}(t) = Df(\mathbf{x})\mathbf{v}.$$

Evaluation at $t = 0$ gives

$$D_{\mathbf{v}} f(\mathbf{a}) = Df(\mathbf{a})\mathbf{v} = \nabla f(\mathbf{a}) \cdot \mathbf{v}. \tag{3}$$

The purpose of equation (3) is to emphasize the geometry of the situation. The result above says that the directional derivative is just the dot product of the gradient and the direction vector $\mathbf{v}$. Since the gradient is made up of the partial derivatives, we see that the more general notion of the directional derivative depends entirely on just the direction vector and the partial derivatives. To be more formal, we summarize this discussion with a theorem.

THEOREM 6.2   Let $X \subseteq \mathbf{R}^n$ be open and suppose $f : X \to \mathbf{R}$ is differentiable at $\mathbf{a} \in X$. Then the directional derivative $D_{\mathbf{v}} f(\mathbf{a})$ exists for all directions (unit vectors) $\mathbf{v} \in \mathbf{R}^n$ and, moreover, we have

$$D_{\mathbf{v}} f(\mathbf{a}) = \nabla f(\mathbf{a}) \cdot \mathbf{v}.$$

EXAMPLE 2   The function $f(x, y) = x^2 - 3xy + 2x - 5y$ we considered in Example 1 has continuous partials and hence, by Theorem 3.5, is differentiable. Thus, Theorem 6.2 applies to tell us that, for any unit vector $\mathbf{v} = v\mathbf{i} + w\mathbf{j} \in \mathbf{R}^2$,

$$D_{\mathbf{v}} f(0, 0) = \nabla f(0, 0) \cdot \mathbf{v} = (f_x(0, 0)\mathbf{i} + f_y(0, 0)\mathbf{j}) \cdot (v\mathbf{i} + w\mathbf{j})$$

$$= (2\mathbf{i} - 5\mathbf{j}) \cdot (v\mathbf{i} + w\mathbf{j})$$

$$= 2v - 5w,$$

as seen earlier.   ◆

EXAMPLE 3   The converse of Theorem 6.2 does not hold. That is, a function may have directional derivatives in all directions at a point yet fail to be differentiable. To see how this can happen, consider the function $f : \mathbf{R}^2 \to \mathbf{R}$ defined by

$$f(x, y) = \begin{cases} \dfrac{xy^2}{x^2 + y^4} & \text{if } (x, y) \neq (0, 0) \\[2mm] 0 & \text{if } (x, y) = (0, 0) \end{cases}.$$

This function is *not* continuous at the origin. (Why?) So, by Theorem 3.6, it fails to be differentiable there; however, we claim that all directional derivatives exist at the origin. To see this, let the direction vector $\mathbf{v}$ be $v\mathbf{i} + w\mathbf{j}$. Hence, by Definition 6.1, we observe that

$$D_{\mathbf{v}} f(0, 0) = \lim_{h \to 0} \frac{f((0, 0) + h(v\mathbf{i} + w\mathbf{j})) - f(0, 0)}{h}$$

$$= \lim_{h \to 0} \frac{1}{h} \left[\frac{hv(hw)^2}{(hv)^2 + (hw)^4} - 0 \right]$$

$$= \lim_{h \to 0} \frac{h^2 v w^2}{h^2(v^2 + h^2 w^4)}$$

$$= \lim_{h \to 0} \frac{v w^2}{v^2 + h^2 w^4} = \frac{v w^2}{v^2} = \frac{w^2}{v}.$$

Thus, the directional derivative exists whenever $v \neq 0$. When $v = 0$ (in which case $\mathbf{v} = \mathbf{j}$), we, again, must calculate

$$D_{\mathbf{j}} f(0, 0) = \lim_{h \to 0} \frac{f((0, 0) + h\mathbf{j}) - f(0, 0)}{h}$$

$$= \lim_{h \to 0} \frac{f(0, h) - f(0, 0)}{h}$$

$$= \lim_{h \to 0} \frac{0 - 0}{h} = 0.$$

Consequently, this directional derivative (which is, in fact, $\partial f / \partial y$) exists as well.

◆

The reason we have restricted the direction vector $\mathbf{v}$ to be of unit length in our discussion of directional derivatives has to do with the meaning of $D_{\mathbf{v}} f(\mathbf{a})$, not with any technicalities pertaining to Definition 6.1 or Theorem 6.2. Indeed, we can certainly define the limit in Definition 6.1 for any vector $\mathbf{v}$, not just one of unit length. So, suppose $\mathbf{w}$ is an arbitrary nonzero vector in $\mathbf{R}^n$ and f is differentiable. Then the proof of Theorem 6.2 goes through without change to give

$$\lim_{h \to 0} \frac{f(\mathbf{a} + h\mathbf{w}) - f(\mathbf{a})}{h} = \nabla f(\mathbf{a}) \cdot \mathbf{w}.$$

The problem is as follows: If $\mathbf{w} = k\mathbf{v}$ for some (nonzero) scalar k, then

$$\lim_{h \to 0} \frac{f(\mathbf{a} + h\mathbf{w}) - f(\mathbf{a})}{h} = \nabla f(\mathbf{a}) \cdot \mathbf{w}$$

$$= \nabla f(\mathbf{a}) \cdot (k\mathbf{v})$$

$$= k(\nabla f(\mathbf{a}) \cdot \mathbf{v})$$

$$= k \left(\lim_{h \to 0} \frac{f(\mathbf{a} + h\mathbf{v}) - f(\mathbf{a})}{h} \right).$$

That is, the "generalized directional derivative" in the direction of $k\mathbf{v}$ is k times the derivative in the direction of $\mathbf{v}$. But $\mathbf{v}$ and $k\mathbf{v}$ are parallel vectors, and it is undesirable to have this sort of ambiguity of terminology. So we avoid the trouble by insisting upon using unit vectors only (i.e., by allowing k to be ± 1 only) when working with directional derivatives.

Gradients and Steepest Ascent

Suppose you are traveling in space near the planet Nilrebo and that one of your spaceship's instruments measures the external atmospheric pressure on your ship as a function $f(x, y, z)$ of position. Assume, quite reasonably, that this function is differentiable. Then Theorem 6.2 applies and tells us that if you travel from point $\mathbf{a} = (a, b, c)$ in the direction of the (unit) vector $\mathbf{u} = u\mathbf{i} + v\mathbf{j} + w\mathbf{k}$, the rate of change of pressure is given by

$$D_{\mathbf{u}} f(\mathbf{a}) = \nabla f(\mathbf{a}) \cdot \mathbf{u}.$$

Now, we ask the following: In what direction is the pressure increasing the most? If θ is the angle between $\mathbf{u}$ and the gradient vector $\nabla f(\mathbf{a})$, then we have, by Theorem 3.3 of §1.3, that

$$D_{\mathbf{u}} f(\mathbf{a}) = \|\nabla f(\mathbf{a})\| \, \|\mathbf{u}\| \cos \theta = \|\nabla f(\mathbf{a})\| \cos \theta,$$

since **u** is a unit vector. Because $-1 \leq \cos\theta \leq 1$, we have

$$-\|\nabla f(\mathbf{a})\| \leq D_{\mathbf{u}} f(\mathbf{a}) \leq \|\nabla f(\mathbf{a})\|.$$

Moreover, $\cos\theta = 1$ when $\theta = 0$ and $\cos\theta = -1$ when $\theta = \pi$. Thus, we have established the following:

THEOREM 6.3   The directional derivative $D_{\mathbf{u}} f(\mathbf{a})$ is maximized, with respect to direction, when **u** points in the *same* direction as $\nabla f(\mathbf{a})$ and is minimized when **u** points in the *opposite* direction. Furthermore, the maximum and minimum values of $D_{\mathbf{u}} f(\mathbf{a})$ are $\|\nabla f(\mathbf{a})\|$ and $-\|\nabla f(\mathbf{a})\|$, respectively.

EXAMPLE 4   If the pressure function on Nilrebo is

$$f(x, y, z) = 5x^2 + 7y^4 + x^2 z^2 \text{ atm,}$$

where the origin is located at the center of Nilrebo and distance units are measured in thousands of kilometers, then the rate of change of pressure at $(1, -1, 2)$ in the direction of $\mathbf{i} + \mathbf{j} + \mathbf{k}$ may be calculated as $\nabla f(1, -1, 2) \cdot \mathbf{u}$, where $\mathbf{u} = (\mathbf{i} + \mathbf{j} + \mathbf{k})/\sqrt{3}$. (Note that we normalized the vector $\mathbf{i} + \mathbf{j} + \mathbf{k}$ to obtain a unit vector.) Using Theorem 6.2, we compute

$$D_{\mathbf{u}} f(1, -1, 2) = \nabla f(1, -1, 2) \cdot \mathbf{u}$$

$$= (18\mathbf{i} - 28\mathbf{j} + 4\mathbf{k}) \cdot \frac{\mathbf{i} + \mathbf{j} + \mathbf{k}}{\sqrt{3}}$$

$$= \frac{18 - 28 + 4}{\sqrt{3}} = -2\sqrt{3} \text{ atm/Mm.}$$

Additionally, in view of Theorem 6.3, the pressure will increase most rapidly in the direction of $\nabla f(1, -1, 2)$, that is, in the

$$\frac{18\mathbf{i} - 28\mathbf{j} + 4\mathbf{k}}{\|18\mathbf{i} - 28\mathbf{j} + 4\mathbf{k}\|} = \frac{9\mathbf{i} - 14\mathbf{j} + 2\mathbf{k}}{\sqrt{281}}$$

direction. Moreover, the *rate* of this increase is

$$\|\nabla f(1, -1, 2)\| = 2\sqrt{281} \text{ atm/Mm.} \qquad \blacklozenge$$

Theorem 6.3 is stated in a manner that is independent of dimension—that is, so that it applies to functions $f: X \subseteq \mathbf{R}^n \to \mathbf{R}$ for any $n \geq 2$. In the case $n = 2$, there is another geometric interpretation of Theorem 6.3: Suppose you are mountain climbing on the surface $z = f(x, y)$. Think of the value of f as the height of the mountain above (or below) sea level. If you are equipped with a map and compass (which supply information in the xy-plane only), then if you are at the point on the mountain with xy-coordinates (map coordinates) (a, b), Theorem 6.3 says that you should move in the direction parallel to the gradient $\nabla f(a, b)$ in order to climb the mountain most rapidly. (See Figure 2.69.) Similarly, you should move in the direction parallel to $-\nabla f(a, b)$ in order to descend most rapidly. Moreover, the slope of your ascent or descent in these cases is $\|\nabla f(a, b)\|$. Be sure that you understand that $\nabla f(a, b)$ *is a vector in* $\mathbf{R}^2$ that gives the optimal north–south, east–west direction of travel.

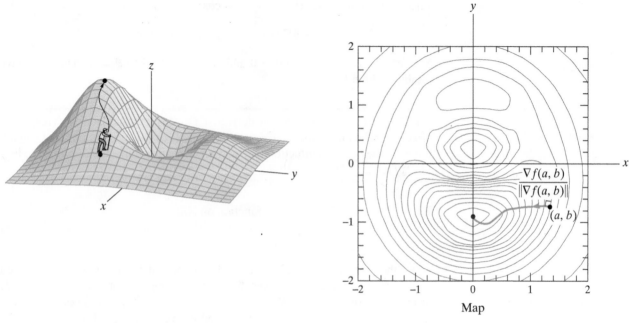

Figure 2.69 Select $\nabla f(a, b)/\|\nabla f(a, b)\|$ for direction of steepest ascent.

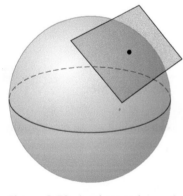

Figure 2.70 A sphere and one of its tangent planes.

Tangent Planes Revisited

In §2.1, we indicated that not all surfaces can be described by equations of the form $z = f(x, y)$. Indeed, a surface as simple and familiar as the sphere is not the graph of any single function of two variables. Yet the sphere is certainly smooth enough for us to see intuitively that it must have a tangent plane at every point. (See Figure 2.70.)

How can we find the equation of the tangent plane? In the case of the unit sphere $x^2 + y^2 + z^2 = 1$, we could proceed as follows: First decide whether the point of tangency is in the top or bottom hemisphere. Then apply equation (4) of §2.3 to the graph of $z = \sqrt{1 - x^2 - y^2}$ or $z = -\sqrt{1 - x^2 - y^2}$, as appropriate. The calculus is tedious but not conceptually difficult. However, the tangent planes to points on the equator are all vertical and so equation (4) of §2.3 does not apply. (It is possible to modify this approach to accommodate such points, but we will not do so.) In general, given a surface described by an equation of the form $F(x, y, z) = c$ (where c is a constant), it may be entirely impractical to solve for z even as several functions of x and y. Try solving for z in the equation $xyz + ye^{xz} - x^2 + yz^2 = 0$ and you'll see what we mean. We need some other way to get our hands on tangent planes to surfaces described as level sets of functions of three variables.

To get started on our quest, we present the following result, interesting in its own right:

THEOREM 6.4   Let $X \subseteq \mathbf{R}^n$ be open and $f: X \to \mathbf{R}$ be a function of class C^1. If $\mathbf{x}_0$ is a point on the level set $S = \{\mathbf{x} \in X \mid f(\mathbf{x}) = c\}$, then the vector $\nabla f(\mathbf{x}_0)$ is perpendicular to S.

PROOF We need to establish the following: If $\mathbf{v}$ is any vector tangent to S at $\mathbf{x}_0$, then $\nabla f(\mathbf{x}_0)$ is perpendicular to $\mathbf{v}$ (i.e., $\nabla f(\mathbf{x}_0) \cdot \mathbf{v} = 0$). By a tangent vector to S at $\mathbf{x}_0$, we mean that $\mathbf{v}$ is the velocity vector of a curve C that lies in S and passes through $\mathbf{x}_0$. The situation in $\mathbf{R}^3$ is pictured in Figure 2.71.

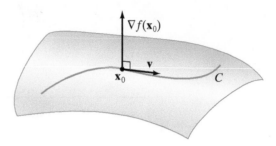

Figure 2.71 The level set surface
$S = \{\mathbf{x} \mid f(\mathbf{x}) = c\}.$

Thus, let C be given parametrically by $\mathbf{x}(t) = (x_1(t), x_2(t), \ldots, x_n(t))$, where $a < t < b$ and $\mathbf{x}(t_0) = \mathbf{x}_0$ for some number t_0 in (a, b). (Then, if $\mathbf{v}$ is the velocity vector at $\mathbf{x}_0$, we must have $\mathbf{x}'(t_0) = \mathbf{v}$. See §3.1 for more about velocity vectors.) Since C is contained in S, we have

$$f(\mathbf{x}(t)) = f(x_1(t), x_2(t), \ldots, x_n(t)) = c.$$

Hence,

$$\frac{d}{dt}[f(\mathbf{x}(t))] = \frac{d}{dt}[c] \equiv 0. \tag{4}$$

On the other hand, the chain rule applied to the composite function $f \circ \mathbf{x}: (a, b) \to \mathbf{R}$ tells us

$$\frac{d}{dt}[f(\mathbf{x}(t))] = \nabla f(\mathbf{x}(t)) \cdot \mathbf{x}'(t).$$

Evaluation at t_0 and equation (4) let us conclude that

$$\nabla f(\mathbf{x}(t_0)) \cdot \mathbf{x}'(t_0) = \nabla f(\mathbf{x}_0) \cdot \mathbf{v} = 0,$$

as desired. ∎

Here's how we can use the result of Theorem 6.4 to find the plane tangent to the sphere $x^2 + y^2 + z^2 = 1$ at the point $\left(-\frac{1}{\sqrt{2}}, 0, \frac{1}{\sqrt{2}}\right)$. From §1.5, we know that a plane is determined uniquely from two pieces of information: (i) a point in the plane and (ii) a vector perpendicular to the plane. We are given a point in the plane in the form of the point of tangency $\left(-\frac{1}{\sqrt{2}}, 0, \frac{1}{\sqrt{2}}\right)$. As for a vector normal to the plane, Theorem 6.4 tells us that the gradient of the function $f(x, y, z) = x^2 + y^2 + z^2$ that defines the sphere as a level set will do. We have

$$\nabla f(x, y, z) = 2x\mathbf{i} + 2y\mathbf{j} + 2z\mathbf{k},$$

so that

$$\nabla f\left(-\frac{1}{\sqrt{2}}, 0, \frac{1}{\sqrt{2}}\right) = -\sqrt{2}\mathbf{i} + \sqrt{2}\mathbf{k}.$$

Hence, the equation of the tangent plane is

$$\nabla f\left(-\frac{1}{\sqrt{2}}, 0, \frac{1}{\sqrt{2}}\right) \cdot \left(x + \frac{1}{\sqrt{2}}, y - 0, z - \frac{1}{\sqrt{2}}\right) = 0,$$

$$-\sqrt{2}\left(x + \frac{1}{\sqrt{2}}\right) + \sqrt{2}\left(z - \frac{1}{\sqrt{2}}\right) = 0,$$

or

$$z - x = \sqrt{2}.$$

In general, if S is a surface in $\mathbf{R}^3$ defined by an equation of the form

$$f(x, y, z) = c,$$

then if $\mathbf{x}_0 \in X$, the gradient vector $\nabla f(\mathbf{x}_0)$ is perpendicular to S and, consequently, if nonzero, is a vector normal to the plane tangent to S at $\mathbf{x}_0$. Thus, the equation

$$\nabla f(\mathbf{x}_0) \cdot (\mathbf{x} - \mathbf{x}_0) = 0 \tag{5}$$

or, equivalently,

$$f_x(x_0, y_0, z_0)(x - x_0) + f_y(x_0, y_0, z_0)(y - y_0)$$
$$+ f_z(x_0, y_0, z_0)(z - z_0) = 0 \tag{6}$$

is an equation for the tangent plane to S at $\mathbf{x}_0$.

Note that formula (5) can be used in $\mathbf{R}^n$ as well as in $\mathbf{R}^3$, in which case it defines the **tangent hyperplane** to the hypersurface $S \subset \mathbf{R}^n$ defined by $f(x_1, x_2, \ldots, x_n) = c$ at the point $\mathbf{x}_0 \in S$.

EXAMPLE 5   Consider the surface S defined by the equation $x^3 y - yz^2 + z^5 = 9$. We calculate the plane tangent to S at the point $(3, -1, 2)$.
To do this, we define $f(x, y, z) = x^3 y - yz^2 + z^5$. Then

$$\nabla f(3, -1, 2) = \left.(3x^2 y \mathbf{i} + (x^3 - z^2)\mathbf{j} + (5z^4 - 2yz)\mathbf{k})\right|_{(3,-1,2)}$$

$$= -27\mathbf{i} + 23\mathbf{j} + 84\mathbf{k}$$

is normal to S at $(3, -1, 2)$ by Theorem 6.4. Using formula (6), we see that the tangent plane has equation

$$-27(x - 3) + 23(y + 1) + 84(z - 2) = 0$$

or, equivalently,

$$-27x + 23y + 84z = 64. \qquad \blacklozenge$$

EXAMPLE 6   Consider the surface defined by $z^4 = x^2 + y^2$. This surface is the level set (at height 0) of the function

$$f(x, y, z) = x^2 + y^2 - z^4.$$

The gradient of f is

$$\nabla f(x, y, z) = 2x\mathbf{i} + 2y\mathbf{j} - 4z^3\mathbf{k}.$$

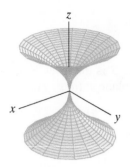

Figure 2.72 The surface of Example 6.

Note that the point $(0, 0, 0)$ lies on the surface. However, $\nabla f(0, 0, 0) = \mathbf{0}$, which makes the gradient vector unusable as a normal vector to a tangent plane. Thus, formula (6) doesn't apply. What we conclude from this example is that the surface fails to have a tangent plane at the origin, a fact that is easy to believe from the graph. (See Figure 2.72.) ◆

EXAMPLE 7   The equation $x^2 + y^2 + z^2 + w^2 = 4$ defines a **hypersphere** of radius 2 in $\mathbf{R}^4$. We use formula (5) to determine the hyperplane tangent to the hypersphere at $(-1, 1, 1, -1)$.

The hypersphere may be considered to be the level set at height 4 of the function $f(x, y, z, w) = x^2 + y^2 + z^2 + w^2$, so that the gradient vector is

$$\nabla f(x, y, z, w) = (2x, 2y, 2z, 2w),$$

so that

$$\nabla f(-1, 1, 1, -1) = (-2, 2, 2, -2).$$

Using formula (5), we obtain an equation for the tangent hyperplane as

$$(-2, 2, 2, -2) \cdot (x + 1, y - 1, z - 1, w + 1) = 0$$

or

$$-2(x + 1) + 2(y - 1) + 2(z - 1) - 2(w + 1) = 0.$$

Equivalently, we have the equation

$$x - y - z + w + 4 = 0. \qquad ◆$$

EXAMPLE 8   We determine the plane tangent to the paraboloid $z = x^2 + 3y^2$ at the point $(-2, 1, 7)$ in two ways: (i) by using formula (4) in §2.3, and (ii) by using our new formula (6).

First, the equation $z = x^2 + 3y^2$ explicitly describes the paraboloid as the graph of the function $f(x, y) = x^2 + 3y^2$, that is, by an equation of the form $z = f(x, y)$. Therefore, formula (4) of §2.3 applies to tell us that the tangent plane at $(-2, 1, 7)$ has equation

$$z = f(-2, 1) + f_x(-2, 1)(x + 2) + f_y(-2, 1)(y - 1)$$

or, equivalently,

$$z = 7 - 4(x + 2) + 6(y - 1). \qquad (7)$$

Second, if we write the equation of the paraboloid as $x^2 + 3y^2 - z = 0$, then we see that it describes the paraboloid as the level set of height 0 of the three-variable function $F(x, y, z) = x^2 + 3y^2 - z$. Hence, formula (6) applies and indicates that an equation for the tangent plane at $(-2, 1, 7)$ is

$$F_x(-2, 1, 7)(x + 2) + F_y(-2, 1, 7)(y - 1) + F_z(-2, 1, 7)(z - 7) = 0$$

or

$$-4(x + 2) + 6(y - 1) - 1(z - 7) = 0. \qquad (8)$$

As can be seen, equation (7) agrees with equation (8). ◆

Example 8 may be viewed in a more general context. If S is the surface in $\mathbf{R}^3$ given by the equation $z = f(x, y)$ (where f is differentiable), then formula (4) of §2.3 tells us that an equation for the plane tangent to S at the point $(a, b, f(a, b))$ is

$$z = f(a, b) + f_x(a, b)(x - a) + f_y(a, b)(y - b).$$

At the same time, the equation for S may be written as

$$f(x, y) - z = 0.$$

Then, if we let $F(x, y, z) = f(x, y) - z$, we see that S is the level set of F at height 0. Hence, formula (6) tells us that the tangent plane at $(a, b, f(a, b))$ is

$$F_x(a, b, f(a, b))(x - a) + F_y(a, b, f(a, b))(y - b)$$
$$+ F_z(a, b, f(a, b))(z - f(a, b)) = 0.$$

By construction of F,

$$\frac{\partial F}{\partial x} = \frac{\partial f}{\partial x}, \qquad \frac{\partial F}{\partial y} = \frac{\partial f}{\partial y}, \qquad \frac{\partial F}{\partial z} = -1.$$

Thus, the tangent plane formula becomes

$$f_x(a, b)(x - a) + f_y(a, b)(y - b) - (z - f(a, b)) = 0.$$

The last equation for the tangent plane is the same as the one given above by equation (4) of §2.3.

The result shows that equations (5) and (6) extend the formula (4) of §2.3 to the more general setting of level sets.

The Implicit Function and Inverse Function Theorems (optional)

We have previously noted that not all surfaces that are described by equations of the form $F(x, y, z) = c$ can be described by an equation of the form $z = f(x, y)$. We close this section with a brief—but theoretically important—digression about when and how the level set $\{(x, y, z) \mid F(x, y, z) = c\}$ can also be described as the graph of a function of two variables, that is, as the graph of $z = f(x, y)$. We also consider the more general question of when we can solve a system of equations for some of the variables in terms of the others.

We begin with an example.

EXAMPLE 9   Consider the hyperboloid $z^2/4 - x^2 - y^2 = 1$, which may be described as the level set (at height 1) of the function

$$F(x, y, z) = \frac{z^2}{4} - x^2 - y^2.$$

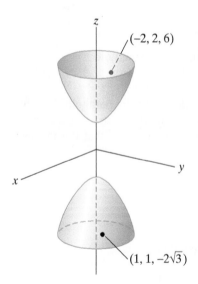

Figure 2.73 The two-sheeted hyperboloid $z^2/4 - x^2 - y^2 = 1$. The point $(-2, 2, 6)$ lies on the sheet given by $z = 2\sqrt{x^2 + y^2 + 1}$, and the point $(1, 1, -2\sqrt{3})$ lies on the sheet given by $z = -2\sqrt{x^2 + y^2 + 1}$.

(See Figure 2.73.) This surface *cannot* be described as the graph of an equation of the form $z = f(x, y)$, since particular values for x and y give rise to *two* values for z. Indeed, when we solve for z in terms of x and y, we find that there are two functional solutions:

$$z = 2\sqrt{x^2 + y^2 + 1} \quad \text{and} \quad z = -2\sqrt{x^2 + y^2 + 1}. \tag{9}$$

On the other hand, these two solutions show that, given any particular point (x_0, y_0, z_0) of the hyperboloid, we may solve *locally* for z in terms of x and y. That is, we may identify on which sheet of the hyperboloid the point (x_0, y_0, z_0) lies and then use the appropriate expression in (9) to describe that sheet.   ◆

Example 9 prompts us to pose the following question: Given a surface S, described as the level set $\{(x, y, z) \mid F(x, y, z) = c\}$, can we always determine at least a portion of S as the graph of a function $z = f(x, y)$? The result that follows, a special case of what is known as the **implicit function theorem**, provides relatively mild hypotheses under which we can.

THEOREM 6.5 (The implicit function theorem)   Let $F: X \subseteq \mathbf{R}^n \to \mathbf{R}$ be of class C^1 and let $\mathbf{a}$ be a point of the level set $S = \{\mathbf{x} \in \mathbf{R}^n \mid F(\mathbf{x}) = c\}$. If $F_{x_n}(\mathbf{a}) \neq 0$, then there is a neighborhood U of $(a_1, a_2, \ldots, a_{n-1})$ in $\mathbf{R}^{n-1}$, a neighborhood V of a_n in $\mathbf{R}$, and a function $f: U \subseteq \mathbf{R}^{n-1} \to V$ of class C^1 such that if $(x_1, x_2, \ldots, x_{n-1}) \in U$ and $x_n \in V$ satisfy $F(x_1, x_2, \ldots, x_n) = c$ (i.e., $(x_1, x_2, \ldots, x_n) \in S$), then $x_n = f(x_1, x_2, \ldots, x_{n-1})$.

The significance of Theorem 6.5 is that it tells us that *near* a point $\mathbf{a} \in S$ such that $\partial F / \partial x_n \neq 0$, the level set S given by the equation $F(x_1, \ldots, x_n) = c$ is *locally* also the graph of a function $x_n = f(x_1, \ldots, x_{n-1})$. In other words, we may solve locally for x_n in terms of $x_1, \ldots, x_{n-1}$, so that S is, at least locally, a differentiable hypersurface in $\mathbf{R}^n$.

EXAMPLE 10   Returning to Example 9, we recall that the hyperboloid is the level set (at height 1) of the function $F(x, y, z) = z^2/4 - x^2 - y^2$. We have

$$\frac{\partial F}{\partial z} = \frac{z}{2}.$$

Note that for any point (x_0, y_0, z_0) in the hyperboloid, we have $|z_0| \geq 2$. Hence, $\partial F_z(x_0, y_0, z_0) \neq 0$. Thus, Theorem 6.5 implies that we may describe a portion of the hyperboloid near any point as the graph of a function of two variables. This is consistent with what we observed in Example 9.   ◆

Of course, there is nothing special about solving for the particular variable x_n in terms of $x_1, \ldots, x_{n-1}$. Suppose $\mathbf{a}$ is a point on the level set S determined by the equation $F(\mathbf{x}) = c$ and suppose $\nabla F(\mathbf{a}) \neq \mathbf{0}$. Then $F_{x_i}(\mathbf{a}) \neq 0$ for some i. Hence, we can solve locally near $\mathbf{a}$ for x_i as a differentiable function of $x_1, \ldots, x_{i-1}, x_{i+1}, \ldots, x_n$. Therefore, S is locally a differentiable hypersurface in $\mathbf{R}^n$.

EXAMPLE 11   Let S denote the ellipsoid $x^2/4 + y^2/36 + z^2/9 = 1$. Then S is the level set (at height 1) of the function

$$F(x, y, z) = \frac{x^2}{4} + \frac{y^2}{36} + \frac{z^2}{9}.$$

At the point $(\sqrt{2}, \sqrt{6}, \sqrt{3})$, we have

$$\left. \frac{\partial F}{\partial z} \right|_{(\sqrt{2}, \sqrt{6}, \sqrt{3})} = \left. \frac{2z}{9} \right|_{(\sqrt{2}, \sqrt{6}, \sqrt{3})} = \frac{2\sqrt{3}}{9} \neq 0.$$

Thus, S may be realized near $(\sqrt{2}, \sqrt{6}, \sqrt{3})$ as the graph of an equation of the form $z = f(x, y)$, namely, $z = 3\sqrt{1 - x^2/4 - y^2/36}$. At the point $(0, -6, 0)$, however, we see that $\partial F / \partial z$ vanishes. On the other hand,

$$\left. \frac{\partial F}{\partial y} \right|_{(0, -6, 0)} = \left. \frac{2y}{36} \right|_{(0, -6, 0)} = -\frac{1}{3} \neq 0.$$

Consequently, near $(0, -6, 0)$, the ellipsoid may be described by solving for y as a function of x and z, namely, $y = -6\sqrt{1 - x^2/4 - z^2/9}$.   ◆

EXAMPLE 12 Consider the set of points S defined by the equation $x^2 z^2 - y = 0$. Then S is the level set at height 0 of the function $F(x, y, z) = x^2 z^2 - y$. Note that

$$\nabla F(x, y, z) = (2xz^2, -1, 2x^2 z).$$

Since $\partial F / \partial y$ never vanishes, we see that we can always solve for y as a function of x and z. (This is, of course, obvious from the equation.) On the other hand, near points where x and z are nonzero, both $\partial F / \partial x$ and $\partial F / \partial z$ are nonzero. Hence, we can solve for either x or z in this case. For example, near $(1, 1, -1)$, we have

$$x = \sqrt{\frac{y}{z^2}} \quad \text{and} \quad z = -\sqrt{\frac{y}{x^2}}. \qquad \blacklozenge$$

As just mentioned, Theorem 6.5 is actually a special case of a more general result. In Theorem 6.5 we are attempting to solve the equation

$$F(x_1, x_2, \ldots, x_n) = c$$

for x_n in terms of $x_1, \ldots, x_{n-1}$. In the general case, we have a *system* of m equations

$$\begin{cases} F_1(x_1, \ldots, x_n, y_1, \ldots, y_m) = c_1 \\ F_2(x_1, \ldots, x_n, y_1, \ldots, y_m) = c_2 \\ \quad \vdots \\ F_m(x_1, \ldots, x_n, y_1, \ldots, y_m) = c_m \end{cases}, \qquad (10)$$

and we desire to solve the system for $y_1, \ldots, y_m$ in terms of $x_1, \ldots, x_n$. Using vector notation, we can also write this system as $\mathbf{F}(\mathbf{x}, \mathbf{y}) = \mathbf{c}$, where $\mathbf{x} = (x_1, \ldots, x_n)$, $\mathbf{y} = (y_1, \ldots, y_m)$, $\mathbf{c} = (c_1, \ldots, c_m)$, and $F_1, \ldots, F_m$ make up the component functions of $\mathbf{F}$. With this notation, the general result is the following:

THEOREM 6.6 (THE IMPLICIT FUNCTION THEOREM, GENERAL CASE) Suppose $\mathbf{F}: A \to \mathbf{R}^m$ is of class C^1, where A is open in $\mathbf{R}^{n+m}$. Let $(\mathbf{a}, \mathbf{b}) = (a_1, \ldots, a_n, b_1, \ldots, b_m) \in A$ satisfy $\mathbf{F}(\mathbf{a}, \mathbf{b}) = \mathbf{c}$. If the determinant

$$\Delta(\mathbf{a}, \mathbf{b}) = \det \begin{bmatrix} \dfrac{\partial F_1}{\partial y_1}(\mathbf{a}, \mathbf{b}) & \cdots & \dfrac{\partial F_1}{\partial y_m}(\mathbf{a}, \mathbf{b}) \\ \vdots & \ddots & \vdots \\ \dfrac{\partial F_m}{\partial y_1}(\mathbf{a}, \mathbf{b}) & \cdots & \dfrac{\partial F_m}{\partial y_m}(\mathbf{a}, \mathbf{b}) \end{bmatrix} \neq 0,$$

then there is a neighborhood U of $\mathbf{a}$ in $\mathbf{R}^n$ and a unique function $\mathbf{f}: U \to \mathbf{R}^m$ of class C^1 such that $\mathbf{f}(\mathbf{a}) = \mathbf{b}$ and $\mathbf{F}(\mathbf{x}, \mathbf{f}(\mathbf{x})) = \mathbf{c}$ for all $\mathbf{x} \in U$. In other words, we can solve locally for $\mathbf{y}$ as a function $\mathbf{f}(\mathbf{x})$.

EXAMPLE 13 We show that, near the point $(x_1, x_2, x_3, y_1, y_2) = (-1, 1, 1, 2, 1)$, we can solve the system

$$\begin{cases} x_1 y_2 + x_2 y_1 = 1 \\ x_1^2 x_3 y_1 + x_2 y_2^3 = 3 \end{cases} \qquad (11)$$

for y_1 and y_2 in terms of x_1, x_2, x_3.

We apply the general implicit function theorem (Theorem 6.6) to the system

$$\begin{cases} F_1(x_1, x_2, x_3, y_1, y_2) = x_1 y_2 + x_2 y_1 = 1 \\ F_2(x_1, x_2, x_3, y_1, y_2) = x_1^2 x_3 y_1 + x_2 y_2^3 = 3 \end{cases}.$$

The relevant determinant is

$$\Delta(-1, 1, 1, 2, 1) = \det \left. \begin{bmatrix} \dfrac{\partial F_1}{\partial y_1} & \dfrac{\partial F_1}{\partial y_2} \\[2mm] \dfrac{\partial F_2}{\partial y_1} & \dfrac{\partial F_2}{\partial y_2} \end{bmatrix} \right|_{(x_1, x_2, x_3, y_1, y_2) = (-1, 1, 1, 2, 1)}$$

$$= \det \left. \begin{bmatrix} x_2 & x_1 \\[2mm] x_1^2 x_3 & 3x_2 y_2^2 \end{bmatrix} \right|_{(x_1, x_2, x_3, y_1, y_2) = (-1, 1, 1, 2, 1)}$$

$$= \det \begin{bmatrix} 1 & -1 \\ 1 & 3 \end{bmatrix} = 4 \neq 0.$$

Hence, we may solve locally, at least in principle.

We can also use the equations in (11) to determine, for example, $\dfrac{\partial y_2}{\partial x_1}(-1, 1, 1)$, where we treat x_1, x_2, x_3 as independent variables and y_1 and y_2 as functions of them.

Differentiating the equations in (11) implicitly with respect to x_1 and using the chain rule, we obtain

$$\begin{cases} y_2 + x_1 \dfrac{\partial y_2}{\partial x_1} + x_2 \dfrac{\partial y_1}{\partial x_1} = 0 \\[4mm] 2x_1 x_3 y_1 + x_1^2 x_3 \dfrac{\partial y_1}{\partial x_1} + 3x_2 y_2^2 \dfrac{\partial y_2}{\partial x_1} = 0 \end{cases}.$$

Now, let $(x_1, x_2, x_3, y_1, y_2) = (-1, 1, 1, 2, 1)$, so that the system becomes

$$\begin{cases} \dfrac{\partial y_1}{\partial x_1}(-1, 1, 1) - \dfrac{\partial y_2}{\partial x_1}(-1, 1, 1) = -1 \\[4mm] \dfrac{\partial y_1}{\partial x_1}(-1, 1, 1) + 3\dfrac{\partial y_2}{\partial x_1}(-1, 1, 1) = 4 \end{cases}.$$

We may easily solve this last system to find that $\dfrac{\partial y_2}{\partial x_1}(-1, 1, 1) = \dfrac{5}{4}$. ◆

Now, suppose we have a system of n equations that defines the variables $y_1, \ldots, y_n$ in terms of the variables $x_1, \ldots, x_n$, that is,

$$\begin{cases} y_1 = f_1(x_1, \ldots, x_n) \\ y_2 = f_2(x_1, \ldots, x_n) \\ \quad \vdots \\ y_n = f_n(x_1, \ldots, x_n) \end{cases}. \tag{12}$$

Note that the system given in (12) can be written in vector form as $\mathbf{y} = \mathbf{f(x)}$. The question we ask is, when can we *invert* this system? In other words, when can we solve for $x_1, \ldots, x_n$ in terms of $y_1, \ldots, y_n$, or, equivalently, when can we find a function $\mathbf{g}$ so that $\mathbf{x} = \mathbf{g}(\mathbf{y})$?

The solution is to apply Theorem 6.6 to the system

$$\begin{cases} F_1(x_1, \ldots, x_n, y_1, \ldots, y_n) = 0 \\ F_2(x_1, \ldots, x_n, y_1, \ldots, y_n) = 0 \\ \qquad\qquad\vdots \\ F_m(x_1, \ldots, x_n, y_1, \ldots, y_n) = 0 \end{cases},$$

where $F_i(x_1, \ldots, x_n, y_1, \ldots, y_n) = f_i(x_1, \ldots, x_n) - y_i$. (In vector form, we are setting $\mathbf{F}(\mathbf{x}, \mathbf{y}) = \mathbf{f}(\mathbf{x}) - \mathbf{y}$.) Then solvability for $\mathbf{x}$ in terms of $\mathbf{y}$ near $\mathbf{x} = \mathbf{a}, \mathbf{y} = \mathbf{b}$ is governed by the nonvanishing of the determinant

$$\det D\mathbf{f}(\mathbf{a}) = \det \begin{bmatrix} \dfrac{\partial f_1}{\partial x_1}(\mathbf{a}) & \cdots & \dfrac{\partial f_1}{\partial x_n}(\mathbf{a}) \\ \vdots & \ddots & \vdots \\ \dfrac{\partial f_n}{\partial x_1}(\mathbf{a}) & \cdots & \dfrac{\partial f_n}{\partial x_n}(\mathbf{a}) \end{bmatrix}.$$

This determinant is also denoted by

$$\left. \frac{\partial(f_1, \ldots, f_n)}{\partial(x_1, \ldots, x_n)} \right|_{\mathbf{x}=\mathbf{a}}$$

and is called the **Jacobian** of $\mathbf{f} = (f_1, \ldots, f_n)$. A more precise and complete statement of what we are observing is the following:

THEOREM 6.7 (THE INVERSE FUNCTION THEOREM)   Suppose $\mathbf{f} = (f_1, \ldots, f_n)$ is of class C^1 on an open set $A \subseteq \mathbf{R}^n$. If

$$\det D\mathbf{f}(\mathbf{a}) = \left. \frac{\partial(f_1, \ldots, f_n)}{\partial(x_1, \ldots, x_n)} \right|_{\mathbf{x}=\mathbf{a}} \neq 0,$$

then there is an open set $U \subseteq \mathbf{R}^n$ containing $\mathbf{a}$ such that $\mathbf{f}$ is one-one on U, the set $V = \mathbf{f}(U)$ is also open, and there is a uniquely determined inverse function $\mathbf{g}: V \to U$ to $\mathbf{f}$, which is also of class C^1. In other words, the system of equations $\mathbf{y} = \mathbf{f}(\mathbf{x})$ may be solved uniquely as $\mathbf{x} = \mathbf{g}(\mathbf{y})$ for $\mathbf{x}$ near $\mathbf{a}$ and $\mathbf{y}$ near $\mathbf{b}$.

EXAMPLE 14   Consider the equations that relate polar and Cartesian coordinates:

$$\begin{cases} x = r\cos\theta \\ y = r\sin\theta \end{cases}.$$

These equations define x and y as functions of r and θ. We use Theorem 6.7 to see near which points of the plane we can invert these equations, that is, solve for r and θ in terms of x and y.

To use Theorem 6.7, we compute the Jacobian

$$\frac{\partial(x, y)}{\partial(r, \theta)} = \begin{vmatrix} \cos\theta & -r\sin\theta \\ \sin\theta & r\cos\theta \end{vmatrix} = r.$$

Thus, we see that, away from the origin ($r = 0$), we can solve (locally) for r and θ uniquely in terms of x and y. At the origin, however, the inverse function theorem does not apply. Geometrically, this makes perfect sense, since at the origin the polar angle θ can have any value.   ◆

2.6 Exercises

1. Suppose $f(x, y, z)$ is a differentiable function of three variables.

  (a) Explain what the quantity $\nabla f(x, y, z) \cdot (-\mathbf{k})$ represents.

  (b) How does $\nabla f(x, y, z) \cdot (-\mathbf{k})$ relate to $\partial f / \partial z$?

In Exercises 2–8, calculate the directional derivative of the given function f at the point $\mathbf{a}$ in the direction parallel to the vector $\mathbf{u}$.

2. $f(x, y) = e^y \sin x$, $\mathbf{a} = \left(\dfrac{\pi}{3}, 0\right)$, $\mathbf{u} = \dfrac{3\mathbf{i} - \mathbf{j}}{\sqrt{10}}$

3. $f(x, y) = x^2 - 2x^3 y + 2y^3$, $\mathbf{a} = (2, -1)$, $\mathbf{u} = \dfrac{\mathbf{i} + 2\mathbf{j}}{\sqrt{5}}$

4. $f(x, y) = \dfrac{1}{(x^2 + y^2)}$, $\mathbf{a} = (3, -2)$, $\mathbf{u} = \mathbf{i} - \mathbf{j}$

5. $f(x, y) = e^x - x^2 y$, $\mathbf{a} = (1, 2)$, $\mathbf{u} = 2\mathbf{i} + \mathbf{j}$

6. $f(x, y, z) = xyz$, $\mathbf{a} = (-1, 0, 2)$, $\mathbf{u} = \dfrac{2\mathbf{k} - \mathbf{i}}{\sqrt{5}}$

7. $f(x, y, z) = e^{-(x^2 + y^2 + z^2)}$, $\mathbf{a} = (1, 2, 3)$, $\mathbf{u} = \mathbf{i} + \mathbf{j} + \mathbf{k}$

8. $f(x, y, z) = \dfrac{xe^y}{3z^2 + 1}$, $\mathbf{a} = (2, -1, 0)$, $\mathbf{u} = \mathbf{i} - 2\mathbf{j} + 3\mathbf{k}$

9. For the function

$$f(x, y) = \begin{cases} \dfrac{x|y|}{\sqrt{x^2 + y^2}} & \text{if } (x, y) \neq (0, 0) \\ 0 & \text{if } (x, y) = (0, 0) \end{cases},$$

  (a) calculate $f_x(0, 0)$ and $f_y(0, 0)$. (You will need to use the definition of the partial derivative.)

  (b) use Definition 6.1 to determine for which unit vectors $\mathbf{v} = v\mathbf{i} + w\mathbf{j}$ the directional derivative $D_{\mathbf{v}} f(0, 0)$ exists.

  (c) use a computer to graph the surface $z = f(x, y)$.

10. For the function

$$f(x, y) = \begin{cases} \dfrac{xy}{\sqrt{x^2 + y^2}} & \text{if } (x, y) \neq (0, 0) \\ 0 & \text{if } (x, y) = (0, 0) \end{cases},$$

  (a) calculate $f_x(0, 0)$ and $f_y(0, 0)$.

  (b) use Definition 6.1 to determine for which unit vectors $\mathbf{v} = v\mathbf{i} + w\mathbf{j}$ the directional derivative $D_{\mathbf{v}} f(0, 0)$ exists.

  (c) use a computer to graph the surface $z = f(x, y)$.

11. The surface of Lake Erehwon can be represented by a region D in the xy-plane such that the lake's depth (in meters) at the point (x, y) is given by the expression $400 - 3x^2 y^2$. If your calculus instructor is in the water at the point $(1, -2)$, in which direction should she swim

  (a) so that the depth increases most rapidly (i.e., so that she is most likely to drown)?

  (b) so that the depth remains constant?

12. A ladybug (who is very sensitive to temperature) is crawling on graph paper. She is at the point $(3, 7)$ and notices that if she moves in the $\mathbf{i}$-direction, the temperature *increases* at a rate of 3 deg/cm. If she moves in the $\mathbf{j}$-direction, she finds that her temperature *decreases* at a rate of 2 deg/cm. In what direction should the ladybug move if

  (a) she wants to warm up most rapidly?

  (b) she wants to cool off most rapidly?

  (c) she desires her temperature *not* to change?

13. You are atop Mt. Gradient, 5000 ft above sea level, equipped with the topographic map shown in Figure 2.74. A storm suddenly begins to blow, necessitating your immediate return home. If you begin heading due east from the top of the mountain, sketch the path that will take you down to sea level most rapidly.

14. It is raining and rainwater is running off an ellipsoidal dome with equation $4x^2 + y^2 + 4z^2 = 16$, where $z \geq 0$. Given that gravity will cause the raindrops to slide down the dome as rapidly as possible, describe the curves whose paths the raindrops must follow. (Hint: You will need to solve a simple differential equation.)

15. Igor, the inchworm, is crawling along graph paper in a magnetic field. The intensity of the field at the point (x, y) is given by $M(x, y) = 3x^2 + y^2 + 5000$. If Igor is at the point $(8, 6)$, describe the curve along which he should travel if he wishes to reduce the field intensity as rapidly as possible.

In Exercises 16–19, find an equation for the tangent plane to the surface given by the equation at the indicated point (x_0, y_0, z_0).

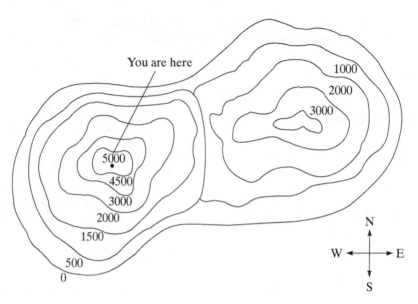

Figure 2.74 The topographic map of Mt. Gradient in Exercise 13.

16. $x^3 + y^3 + z^3 = 7$, $(x_0, y_0, z_0) = (0, -1, 2)$

17. $ze^y \cos x = 1$, $(x_0, y_0, z_0) = (\pi, 0, -1)$

18. $2xz + yz - x^2y + 10 = 0$, $(x_0, y_0, z_0) = (1, -5, 5)$

19. $2xy^2 = 2z^2 - xyz$, $(x_0, y_0, z_0) = (2, -3, 3)$

20. Calculate the plane tangent to the surface whose equation is $x^2 - 2y^2 + 5xz = 7$ at the point $(-1, 0, -\frac{6}{5})$ in two ways:

   (a) by solving for z in terms of x and y and using formula (4) in §2.3

   (b) by using formula (6) in this section.

21. Calculate the plane tangent to the surface $x \sin y + xz^2 = 2e^{yz}$ at the point $\left(2, \frac{\pi}{2}, 0\right)$ in two ways:

   (a) by solving for x in terms of y and z and using a variant of formula (4) in §2.3

   (b) by using formula (6) in this section.

22. Find the point on the surface $x^3 - 2y^2 + z^2 = 27$ where the tangent plane is perpendicular to the line given parametrically as $x = 3t - 5$, $y = 2t + 7$, $z = 1 - \sqrt{2}t$.

23. Find the points on the hyperboloid $9x^2 - 45y^2 + 5z^2 = 45$ where the tangent plane is parallel to the plane $x + 5y - 2z = 7$.

24. Show that the surfaces $z = 7x^2 - 12x - 5y^2$ and $xyz^2 = 2$ intersect orthogonally at the point $(2, 1, -1)$.

25. Suppose that two surfaces are given by the equations

$$F(x, y, z) = c \quad \text{and} \quad G(x, y, z) = k.$$

Moreover, suppose that these surfaces intersect at the point (x_0, y_0, z_0). Show that the surfaces are tangent at (x_0, y_0, z_0) if and only if

$$\nabla F(x_0, y_0, z_0) \times \nabla G(x_0, y_0, z_0) = \mathbf{0}.$$

26. Let S denote the cone $x^2 + 4y^2 = z^2$.

   (a) Find an equation for the plane tangent to S at the point $(3, -2, -5)$.

   (b) What happens if you try to find an equation for a tangent plane to S at the origin? Discuss how your findings relate to the appearance of S.

27. Consider the surface S defined by the equation $x^3 - x^2y^2 + z^2 = 0$.

   (a) Find an equation for the plane tangent to S at the point $(2, -3/2, 1)$.

   (b) Does S have a tangent plane at the origin? Why or why not?

If a curve is given by an equation of the form $f(x, y) = 0$, then the tangent line to the curve at a given point (x_0, y_0) on it may be found in two ways: (a) by using the technique of implicit differentiation from single-variable calculus and (b) by using a formula analogous to formula (6). In Exercises 28–30, use both of these methods to find the lines tangent to the given curves at the indicated points.

28. $x^2 + y^2 = 4$, $(x_0, y_0) = (-\sqrt{2}, \sqrt{2})$

29. $y^3 = x^2 + x^3$, $(x_0, y_0) = (1, \sqrt[3]{2})$

30. $x^5 + 2xy + y^3 = 16$, $(x_0, y_0) = (2, -2)$

*Let C be a curve in $\mathbf{R}^2$ given by an equation of the form $f(x, y) = 0$. The **normal line** to C at a point (x_0, y_0) on it is the line that passes through (x_0, y_0) and is perpendicular to C (meaning that it is perpendicular to the tangent line to C at (x_0, y_0)). In Exercises 31–33, find the normal lines to the given curves at the indicated points. Give both a set of parametric equations for the lines and an equation in the form $Ax + By = C$. (Hint: Use gradients.)*

31. $x^2 - y^2 = 9, (x_0, y_0) = (5, -4)$

32. $x^2 - x^3 = y^2, (x_0, y_0) = (-1, \sqrt{2})$

33. $x^3 - 2xy + y^5 = 11, (x_0, y_0) = (2, -1)$

34. This problem concerns the surface defined by the equation

$$x^3 z + x^2 y^2 + \sin(yz) = -3.$$

(a) Find an equation for the plane tangent to this surface at the point $(-1, 0, 3)$.

(b) The **normal line** to a surface S in $\mathbf{R}^3$ at a point (x_0, y_0, z_0) on it is the line that passes through (x_0, y_0, z_0) and is perpendicular to S. Find a set of parametric equations for the line normal to the surface given above at the point $(-1, 0, 3)$.

35. Give a set of parametric equations for the normal line to the surface defined by the equation $e^{xy} + e^{xz} - 2e^{yz} = 0$ at the point $(-1, -1, -1)$. (See Exercise 34.)

36. Give a general formula for parametric equations for the normal line to a surface given by the equation $F(x, y, z) = 0$ at the point (x_0, y_0, z_0) on the surface. (See Exercise 34.)

37. Generalizing upon the techniques of this section, find an equation for the hyperplane tangent to the hypersurface $\sin x_1 + \cos x_2 + \sin x_3 + \cos x_4 + \sin x_5 = -1$ at the point $(\pi, \pi, 3\pi/2, 2\pi, 2\pi) \in \mathbf{R}^5$.

38. Find an equation for the hyperplane tangent to the $(n-1)$-dimensional ellipsoid

$$x_1^2 + 2x_2^2 + 3x_3^2 + \cdots + nx_n^2 = \frac{n(n+1)}{2}$$

at the point $(-1, -1, \ldots, -1) \in \mathbf{R}^n$.

39. Find an equation for the tangent hyperplane to the $(n-1)$-dimensional sphere $x_1^2 + x_2^2 + \cdots + x_n^2 = 1$ in $\mathbf{R}^n$ at the point $(1/\sqrt{n}, 1/\sqrt{n}, \ldots, 1/\sqrt{n}, -1/\sqrt{n})$.

Exercises 40–49 concern the implicit function theorems and the inverse function theorem (Theorems 6.5, 6.6, and 6.7).

40. Let S be described by $z^2 y^3 + x^2 y = 2$.

(a) Use the implicit function theorem to determine near which points S can be described locally as the graph of a C^1 function $z = f(x, y)$.

(b) Near which points can S be described (locally) as the graph of a function $x = g(y, z)$?

(c) Near which points can S be described (locally) as the graph of a function $y = h(x, z)$?

41. Let S be the set of points described by the equation $\sin xy + e^{xz} + x^3 y = 1$.

(a) Near which points can we describe S as the graph of a C^1 function $z = f(x, y)$? What is $f(x, y)$ in this case?

(b) Describe the set of "bad" points of S, that is, the points $(x_0, y_0, z_0) \in S$ where we *cannot* describe S as the graph of a function $z = f(x, y)$.

(c) Use a computer to help give a *complete* picture of S.

42. Let $F(x, y) = c$ define a curve C in $\mathbf{R}^2$. Suppose (x_0, y_0) is a point of C such that $\nabla F(x_0, y_0) \neq \mathbf{0}$. Show that the curve can be represented near (x_0, y_0) as either the graph of a function $y = f(x)$ or the graph of a function $x = g(y)$.

43. Let $F(x, y) = x^2 - y^3$, and consider the curve C defined by the equation $F(x, y) = 0$.

(a) Show that $(0, 0)$ lies on C and that $F_y(0, 0) = 0$.

(b) Can we describe C as the graph of a function $y = f(x)$? Graph C.

(c) Comment on the results of parts (a) and (b) in light of the implicit function theorem (Theorem 6.5).

44. (a) Consider the family of level sets of the function $F(x, y) = xy + 1$. Use the implicit function theorem to identify which level sets of this family are actually unions of smooth curves in $\mathbf{R}^2$ (i.e., locally graphs of C^1 functions of a single variable).

(b) Now consider the family of level sets of $F(x, y, z) = xyz + 1$. Which level sets of this family are unions of smooth surfaces in $\mathbf{R}^3$?

45. Suppose that $F(u, v)$ is of class C^1 and is such that $F(-2, 1) = 0$ and $F_u(-2, 1) = 7$, $F_v(-2, 1) = 5$. Let $G(x, y, z) = F(x^3 - 2y^2 + z^5, xy - x^2 z + 3)$.

(a) Check that $G(-1, 1, 1) = 0$.

(b) Show that we can solve the equation $G(x, y, z) = 0$ for z in terms of x and y (i.e., as $z = g(x, y)$, for (x, y) near $(-1, 1)$ so that $g(-1, 1) = 1$).

46. Can you solve

$$\begin{cases} x_2 y_2 - x_1 \cos y_1 = 5 \\ x_2 \sin y_1 + x_1 y_2 = 2 \end{cases}$$

for y_1, y_2 as functions of x_1, x_2 near the point $(x_1, x_2, y_1, y_2) = (2, 3, \pi, 1)$? What about near the point $(x_1, x_2, y_1, y_2) = (0, 2, \pi/2, 5/2)$?

47. Consider the system

$$\begin{cases} x_1 y_2^2 - 2x_2 y_3 = 1 \\ x_1 y_1^5 + x_2 y_2 - 4 y_2 y_3 = -9 \ . \\ x_2 y_1 + 3 x_1 y_3^2 = 12 \end{cases}$$

(a) Show that, near the point $(x_1, x_2, y_1, y_2, y_3) = (1, 0, -1, 1, 2)$, it is possible to solve for y_1, y_2, y_3 in terms of x_1, x_2.

(b) From the result of part (a), we may consider y_1, y_2, y_3 to be functions of x_1 and x_2. Use implicit differentiation and the chain rule to evaluate $\dfrac{\partial y_1}{\partial x_1}(1, 0)$, $\dfrac{\partial y_2}{\partial x_1}(1, 0)$, and $\dfrac{\partial y_3}{\partial x_1}(1, 0)$.

48. Consider the equations that relate cylindrical and Cartesian coordinates in $\mathbf{R}^3$:

$$\begin{cases} x = r \cos \theta \\ y = r \sin \theta \ . \\ z = z \end{cases}$$

(a) Near which points of $\mathbf{R}^3$ can we solve for r, θ, and z in terms of the Cartesian coordinates?

(b) Explain the geometry behind your answer in part (a).

49. Recall that the equations relating spherical and Cartesian coordinates in $\mathbf{R}^3$ are

$$\begin{cases} x = \rho \sin \varphi \cos \theta \\ y = \rho \sin \varphi \sin \theta \ . \\ z = \rho \cos \varphi \end{cases}$$

(a) Near which points of $\mathbf{R}^3$ can we solve for ρ, φ, and θ in terms of x, y, and z?

(b) Describe the geometry behind your answer in part (a).

2.7 Newton's Method (optional)

When you studied single-variable calculus, you may have learned a method, known as **Newton's method** (or the **Newton–Raphson method**), for approximating the solution to an equation of the form $f(x) = 0$, where $f: X \subseteq \mathbf{R} \to \mathbf{R}$ is a differentiable function. Here's a reminder of how the method works.

We wish to find a number r such that $f(r) = 0$. To approximate r, we make an initial guess x_0 for r and, in general, we expect to find that $f(x_0) \neq 0$. So next we look at the tangent line to the graph of f at $(x_0, f(x_0))$. (See Figure 2.75.) Since the tangent line approximates the graph of f near $(x_0, f(x_0))$, we can find where the tangent line crosses the x-axis. The crossing point $(x_1, 0)$ will generally be closer to $(r, 0)$ than $(x_0, 0)$ is, so we take x_1 as a revised and improved approximation to the root r of $f(x) = 0$.

To find x_1, we begin with the equation of the tangent line

$$y = f(x_0) + f'(x_0)(x - x_0),$$

then set $y = 0$ to find where this line crosses the x-axis. Thus, we solve the equation

$$f(x_0) + f'(x_0)(x_1 - x_0) = 0$$

for x_1 to find that

$$x_1 = x_0 - \frac{f(x_0)}{f'(x_0)}.$$

Once we have x_1, we can start the process again using x_1 in place of x_0 and produce what we hope will be an even better approximation x_2 via the formula

$$x_2 = x_1 - \frac{f(x_1)}{f'(x_1)}.$$

Indeed, we may iterate this process and define x_k recursively by

$$x_k = x_{k-1} - \frac{f(x_{k-1})}{f'(x_{k-1})} \qquad k = 1, 2, \ldots \tag{1}$$

and thereby produce a sequence of numbers $x_0, x_1, \ldots, x_k, \ldots$.

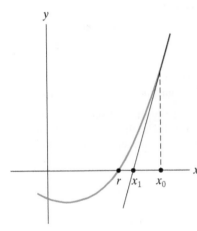

Figure 2.75 The tangent line to $y = f(x)$ at $(x_0, f(x_0))$ crosses the x-axis at $x = x_1$.

It is not always the case that the sequence $\{x_k\}$ converges. However, when it does, it must converge to a root of the equation $f(x) = 0$. To see this, let $L = \lim_{k \to \infty} x_k$. Then we also have $\lim_{k \to \infty} x_{k-1} = L$. Taking limits in formula (1), we find

$$L = L - \frac{f(L)}{f'(L)},$$

which immediately implies that $f(L) = 0$. Hence, L is a root of the equation.

Now that we have some understanding of derivatives in the multivariable case, we turn to the generalization of Newton's method for solving systems of n equations in n unknowns. We may write such a system as

$$\begin{cases} f_1(x_1, \ldots, x_n) = 0 \\ f_2(x_1, \ldots, x_n) = 0 \\ \qquad \vdots \\ f_n(x_1, \ldots, x_n) = 0 \end{cases} . \tag{2}$$

We consider the map $\mathbf{f}: X \subseteq \mathbf{R}^n \to \mathbf{R}^n$ defined as $\mathbf{f}(\mathbf{x}) = (f_1(\mathbf{x}), \ldots, f_n(\mathbf{x}))$ (i.e., $\mathbf{f}$ is the map whose component functions come from the equations in (2). The domain X of $\mathbf{f}$ may be taken to be the set where all the component functions are defined.) Then to solve system (2) means to find a vector $\mathbf{r} = (r_1, \ldots, r_n)$ such that $\mathbf{f}(\mathbf{r}) = \mathbf{0}$. To approximate such a vector $\mathbf{r}$, we may, as in the single-variable case, make an initial guess $\mathbf{x}_0$ for what $\mathbf{r}$ might be. If $\mathbf{f}$ is differentiable, then we know that $\mathbf{y} = \mathbf{f}(\mathbf{x})$ is approximated by the equation

$$\mathbf{y} = \mathbf{f}(\mathbf{x}_0) + D\mathbf{f}(\mathbf{x}_0)(\mathbf{x} - \mathbf{x}_0).$$

(Here we think of $\mathbf{f}(\mathbf{x}_0)$ and the vectors $\mathbf{x}$ and $\mathbf{x}_0$ as $n \times 1$ matrices.) Then we set $\mathbf{y}$ equal to $\mathbf{0}$ to find where this approximating function is zero. Thus, we solve the matrix equation

$$\mathbf{f}(\mathbf{x}_0) + D\mathbf{f}(\mathbf{x}_0)(\mathbf{x}_1 - \mathbf{x}_0) = \mathbf{0} \tag{3}$$

for $\mathbf{x}_1$ to give a revised approximation to the root $\mathbf{r}$. Evidently (3) is equivalent to

$$D\mathbf{f}(\mathbf{x}_0)(\mathbf{x}_1 - \mathbf{x}_0) = -\mathbf{f}(\mathbf{x}_0). \tag{4}$$

To continue our argument, suppose that $D\mathbf{f}(\mathbf{x}_0)$ is an invertible $n \times n$ matrix, meaning that there is a second $n \times n$ matrix $[D\mathbf{f}(\mathbf{x}_0)]^{-1}$ with the property that $[D\mathbf{f}(\mathbf{x}_0)]^{-1} D\mathbf{f}(\mathbf{x}_0) = D\mathbf{f}(\mathbf{x}_0)[D\mathbf{f}(\mathbf{x}_0)]^{-1} = I_n$, the $n \times n$ identity matrix. (See Exercises 20 and 30–38 in §1.6.) Then we may multiply equation (4) on the left by $[D\mathbf{f}(\mathbf{x}_0)]^{-1}$ to obtain

$$I_n(\mathbf{x}_1 - \mathbf{x}_0) = -[D\mathbf{f}(\mathbf{x}_0)]^{-1}\mathbf{f}(\mathbf{x}_0).$$

Since $I_n A = A$ for any $n \times k$ matrix A, this last equation implies that

$$\mathbf{x}_1 = \mathbf{x}_0 - [D\mathbf{f}(\mathbf{x}_0)]^{-1}\mathbf{f}(\mathbf{x}_0). \tag{5}$$

As we did in the one-variable case of Newton's method, we may iterate formula (5) to define recursively a sequence $\{\mathbf{x}_k\}$ of *vectors* by

$$\mathbf{x}_k = \mathbf{x}_{k-1} - [D\mathbf{f}(\mathbf{x}_{k-1})]^{-1}\mathbf{f}(\mathbf{x}_{k-1}) \tag{6}$$

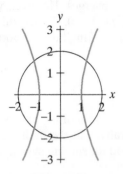

Figure 2.76 Finding the intersection points of the circle $x^2 + y^2 = 4$ and the hyperbola $4x^2 - y^2 = 4$ in Example 1.

Note the similarity between formulas (1) and (6). Moreover, just as in the case of formula (1), although the sequence $\{x_0, x_1, \ldots, x_k, \ldots\}$ may not converge, if it does, it must converge to a root of $f(x) = 0$. (See Exercise 4.)

EXAMPLE 1   Consider the problem of finding the intersection points of the circle $x^2 + y^2 = 4$ and the hyperbola $4x^2 - y^2 = 4$. (See Figure 2.76.) Analytically, we seek simultaneous solutions to the two equations

$$x^2 + y^2 = 4 \quad \text{and} \quad 4x^2 - y^2 = 4,$$

or, equivalently, solutions to the system

$$\begin{cases} x^2 + y^2 - 4 = 0 \\ 4x^2 - y^2 - 4 = 0 \end{cases}. \tag{7}$$

To use Newton's method, we define a function $f \colon \mathbf{R}^2 \to \mathbf{R}^2$ by $f(x, y) = (x^2 + y^2 - 4, 4x^2 - y^2 - 4)$ and try to approximate solutions to the vector equation $f(x, y) = (0, 0)$. We may begin with any initial guess, say,

$$\mathbf{x}_0 = \begin{bmatrix} x_0 \\ y_0 \end{bmatrix} = \begin{bmatrix} 1 \\ 1 \end{bmatrix},$$

and then produce successive approximations $x_1, x_2, \ldots$ to a solution using formula (6). In particular, we have

$$Df(x, y) = \begin{bmatrix} 2x & 2y \\ 8x & -2y \end{bmatrix}.$$

Note that $\det Df(x, y) = -20xy$. You may verify (see Exercise 36 in §1.6) that

$$[Df(x, y)]^{-1} = \frac{1}{-20xy} \begin{bmatrix} -2y & -2y \\ -8x & 2x \end{bmatrix} = \begin{bmatrix} \dfrac{1}{10x} & \dfrac{1}{10x} \\[2mm] \dfrac{2}{5y} & -\dfrac{1}{10y} \end{bmatrix}.$$

Thus,

$$\begin{bmatrix} x_k \\ y_k \end{bmatrix} = \begin{bmatrix} x_{k-1} \\ y_{k-1} \end{bmatrix} - [Df(x_{k-1}, y_{k-1})]^{-1} f(x_{k-1}, y_{k-1})$$

$$= \begin{bmatrix} x_{k-1} \\ y_{k-1} \end{bmatrix} - \begin{bmatrix} \dfrac{1}{10x_{k-1}} & \dfrac{1}{10x_{k-1}} \\[2mm] \dfrac{2}{5y_{k-1}} & -\dfrac{1}{10y_{k-1}} \end{bmatrix} \begin{bmatrix} x_{k-1}^2 + y_{k-1}^2 - 4 \\[2mm] 4x_{k-1}^2 - y_{k-1}^2 - 4 \end{bmatrix}$$

$$= \begin{bmatrix} x_{k-1} \\ y_{k-1} \end{bmatrix} - \begin{bmatrix} \dfrac{5x_{k-1}^2 - 8}{10x_{k-1}} \\[3mm] \dfrac{5y_{k-1}^2 - 12}{10y_{k-1}} \end{bmatrix} = \begin{bmatrix} x_{k-1} - \dfrac{5x_{k-1}^2 - 8}{10x_{k-1}} \\[3mm] y_{k-1} - \dfrac{5y_{k-1}^2 - 12}{10y_{k-1}} \end{bmatrix}.$$

Beginning with $x_0 = y_0 = 1$, we have

$$x_1 = 1 - \frac{5 \cdot 1^2 - 8}{10 \cdot 1} = 1.3 \qquad y_1 = 1 - \frac{5 \cdot 1^2 - 12}{10 \cdot 1} = 1.7$$

$$x_2 = 1.3 - \frac{5(1.3)^2 - 8}{10(1.3)} = 1.265385 \quad y_2 = 1.7 - \frac{5(1.7)^2 - 12}{10(1.7)}$$
$$= 1.555882, \quad \text{etc.}$$

It is also easy to hand off the details of the computation to a calculator or a computer. One finds the following results:

k	x_k	y_k
0	1	1
1	1.3	1.7
2	1.26538462	1.55588235
3	1.26491115	1.54920772
4	1.26491106	1.54919334
5	1.26491106	1.54919334

Thus, it appears that, to eight decimal places, an intersection point of the curves is $(1.26491106, 1.54919334)$.

In this particular example, it is not difficult to find the solutions to (7) exactly. We add the two equations in (7) to obtain

$$5x^2 - 8 = 0 \qquad \Longleftrightarrow \qquad x^2 = \tfrac{8}{5}.$$

Thus, $x = \pm\sqrt{8/5}$. If we substitute these values for x into the first equation of (7), we obtain

$$\tfrac{8}{5} + y^2 - 4 = 0 \qquad \Longleftrightarrow \qquad y^2 = \tfrac{12}{5}.$$

Hence, $y = \pm\sqrt{12/5}$. Therefore, the four intersection points are

$$\left(\sqrt{\tfrac{8}{5}}, \sqrt{\tfrac{12}{5}}\right), \quad \left(-\sqrt{\tfrac{8}{5}}, \sqrt{\tfrac{12}{5}}\right), \quad \left(-\sqrt{\tfrac{8}{5}}, -\sqrt{\tfrac{12}{5}}\right), \quad \left(\sqrt{\tfrac{8}{5}}, -\sqrt{\tfrac{12}{5}}\right).$$

Since $\sqrt{8/5} \approx 1.264911064$ and $\sqrt{12/5} \approx 1.54919334$, we see that Newton's method provided us with an accurate approximate solution very quickly. ◆

EXAMPLE 2   We use Newton's method to find solutions to the system

$$\begin{cases} x^3 - 5x^2 + 2x - y + 13 = 0 \\ x^3 + x^2 - 14x - y - 19 = 0 \end{cases}. \tag{8}$$

As in the previous example, we define $\mathbf{f}: \mathbf{R}^2 \to \mathbf{R}^2$ by $\mathbf{f}(x, y) = (x^3 - 5x^2 + 2x - y + 13, x^3 + x^2 - 14x - y - 19)$. Then

$$D\mathbf{f}(x, y) = \begin{bmatrix} 3x^2 - 10x + 2 & -1 \\ 3x^2 + 2x - 14 & -1 \end{bmatrix},$$

so that $\det D\mathbf{f}(x, y) = 12x - 16$ and

$$[D\mathbf{f}(x, y)]^{-1} = \begin{bmatrix} -\dfrac{1}{12x - 16} & \dfrac{1}{12x - 16} \\ \dfrac{-3x^2 - 2x + 14}{12x - 16} & \dfrac{-3x^2 - 10x + 2}{12x - 16} \end{bmatrix}.$$

Thus, formula (6) becomes

$$\begin{bmatrix} x_k \\ y_k \end{bmatrix} = \begin{bmatrix} x_{k-1} \\ y_{k-1} \end{bmatrix} - \begin{bmatrix} -\dfrac{1}{12x_{k-1} - 16} & \dfrac{1}{12x_{k-1} - 16} \\ \dfrac{-3x_{k-1}^2 - 2x_{k-1} + 14}{12x_{k-1} - 16} & \dfrac{-3x_{k-1}^2 - 10x_{k-1} + 2}{12x_{k-1} - 16} \end{bmatrix}$$

$$\times \begin{bmatrix} x_{k-1}^3 - 5x_{k-1}^2 + 2x_{k-1} - y_{k-1} + 13 \\ x_{k-1}^3 + x_{k-1}^2 - 14x_{k-1} - y_{k-1} - 19 \end{bmatrix}$$

$$= \begin{bmatrix} x_{k-1} - \dfrac{6x_{k-1}^2 - 16x_{k-1} - 32}{12x_{k-1} - 16} \\ y_{k-1} - \dfrac{3x_{k-1}^4 - 16x_{k-1}^3 - 14x_{k-1}^2 + 82x_{k-1} - 8y_{k-1} + 6x_{k-1}y_{k-1} + 72}{6x_{k-1} - 8} \end{bmatrix}.$$

This is the formula we iterate to obtain approximate solutions to (8).

If we begin with $\mathbf{x}_0 = (x_0, y_0) = (8, 10)$, then the successive approximations $\mathbf{x}_k$ quickly converge to $(4, 5)$, as demonstrated in the table below.

k	x_k	y_k
0	8	10
1	5.2	−98.2
2	4.1862069	−2.7412414
3	4.00607686	4.82161865
4	4.00000691	4.99981073
5	4.00000000	5.00000000
6	4.00000000	5.00000000

If we begin instead with $\mathbf{x}_0 = (50, 60)$, then convergence is, as you might predict, somewhat slower (although still quite rapid):

k	x_k	y_k
0	50	60
1	25.739726	−57257.438
2	13.682211	−7080.8238
3	7.79569757	−846.58548
4	5.11470969	−86.660453
5	4.1643023	−1.6486813
6	4.00476785	4.86119425
7	4.00000425	4.99988349
8	4.00000000	5.00000000
9	4.00000000	5.00000000

On the other hand, if we begin with $\mathbf{x}_0 = (-2, 12)$, then the sequence of points generated converges to a different solution, namely, $(-4/3, -25/27)$:

k	x_k	y_k
0	-2	12
1	-1.4	1.4
2	-1.3341463	-0.903122
3	-1.3333335	-0.9259225
4	-1.3333333	-0.9259259
5	-1.3333333	-0.9259259

In fact, when a system of equations has multiple solutions, it is not always easy to predict to which solution a given starting vector $\mathbf{x}_0$ will converge under Newton's method (if, indeed, there is convergence at all).   ◆

Finally, we make two remarks. First, if at any stage of the iteration process the matrix $D\mathbf{f}(\mathbf{x}_k)$ fails to be invertible (i.e., $[D\mathbf{f}(\mathbf{x}_k)]^{-1}$ does not exist), then formula (6) cannot be used. One way to salvage the situation is to make a different choice of initial vector $\mathbf{x}_0$ in the hope that the sequence $\{\mathbf{x}_k\}$ that it generates will not involve any noninvertible matrices. Second, we note that if, at any stage, $\mathbf{x}_k$ is *exactly* a root of $\mathbf{f}(\mathbf{x}) = \mathbf{0}$, then formula (6) will not change it. (See Exercise 7).

2.7 Exercises

1. Use Newton's method with initial vector $\mathbf{x}_0 = (1, -1)$ to approximate the real solution to the system

   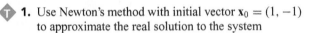

   $$\begin{cases} y^2 e^x = 3 \\ 2ye^x + 10y^4 = 0 \end{cases}.$$

2. In this problem, you will use Newton's method to estimate the locations of the points of intersection of the ellipses having equations $3x^2 + y^2 = 7$ and $x^2 + 4y^2 = 8$.

   (a) Graph the ellipses and use your graph to give a very rough estimate (x_0, y_0) of the point of intersection that lies in the first quadrant.

   (b) Denote the *exact* point of intersection in the first quadrant by (X, Y). Without solving, argue that the other points of intersection must be $(-X, Y)$, $(X, -Y)$, and $(-X, -Y)$.

   (c) Now use Newton's method with your estimate (x_0, y_0) in part (a) to approximate the first quadrant intersection point (X, Y).

   (d) Solve for the intersection points exactly, and compare your answer with your approximations.

3. This problem concerns the determination of the points of intersection of the two curves with equations $x^3 - 4y^3 = 1$ and $x^2 + 4y^2 = 2$.

   (a) Graph the curves and use your graph to give rough estimates for the points of intersection.

   (b) Now use Newton's method with different initial estimates to approximate the intersection points.

4. Consider the sequence of vectors $\mathbf{x}_0, \mathbf{x}_1, \ldots,$ where, for $k \geq 1$, the vector $\mathbf{x}_k$ is defined by the Newton's method recursion formula (6) given an initial "guess" $\mathbf{x}_0$ at a root of the equation $\mathbf{f}(\mathbf{x}) = \mathbf{0}$. (Here we assume that $\mathbf{f}: X \subseteq \mathbf{R}^n \to \mathbf{R}^n$ is a differentiable function.) By imitating the argument in the single-variable case, show that if the sequence $\{\mathbf{x}_k\}$ converges to a vector $\mathbf{L}$ and $D\mathbf{f}(\mathbf{L})$ is an invertible matrix, then $\mathbf{L}$ must satisfy $\mathbf{f}(\mathbf{L}) = \mathbf{0}$.

5. This problem concerns the Newton's method iteration in Example 1.

   (a) Use initial vector $\mathbf{x}_0 = (-1, 1)$ and calculate the successive approximations $\mathbf{x}_1, \mathbf{x}_2, \mathbf{x}_3$, etc. To what solution of the system of equations (7) do the approximations converge?

   (b) Repeat part (a) with $\mathbf{x}_0 = (1, -1)$. Repeat again with $\mathbf{x}_0 = (-1, -1)$.

   (c) Comment on the results of parts (a) and (b) and whether you might have predicted them. Describe the results in terms of Figure 2.76.

8. Suppose that $\mathbf{f}: X \subseteq \mathbf{R}^2 \to \mathbf{R}^2$ is differentiable and that we write $\mathbf{f}(x, y) = (f(x, y), g(x, y))$. Show that formula (6) implies that, for $k \geq 1$,

$$x_k = x_{k-1} - \frac{f(x_{k-1}, y_{k-1})g_y(x_{k-1}, y_{k-1}) - g(x_{k-1}, y_{k-1})f_y(x_{k-1}, y_{k-1})}{f_x(x_{k-1}, y_{k-1})g_y(x_{k-1}, y_{k-1}) - f_y(x_{k-1}, y_{k-1})g_x(x_{k-1}, y_{k-1})}$$

$$y_k = y_{k-1} - \frac{g(x_{k-1}, y_{k-1})f_x(x_{k-1}, y_{k-1}) - f(x_{k-1}, y_{k-1})g_x(x_{k-1}, y_{k-1})}{f_x(x_{k-1}, y_{k-1})g_y(x_{k-1}, y_{k-1}) - f_y(x_{k-1}, y_{k-1})g_x(x_{k-1}, y_{k-1})}.$$

6. Consider the Newton's method iteration in Example 2.

(a) Use initial vector $\mathbf{x}_0 = (1.4, 10)$ and calculate the successive approximations $\mathbf{x}_1, \mathbf{x}_2, \mathbf{x}_3$, etc. To what solution of the system of equations (8) do the approximations converge?

(b) Repeat part (a) with $\mathbf{x}_0 = (1.3, 10)$.

(c) In Example 2 we saw that $(4, 5)$ was a solution of the given system of equations. Is $(1.3, 10)$ closer to $(4, 5)$ or to the limiting point of the sequence you calculated in part (b)?

(d) Comment on your observations in part (c). What do these observations suggest about how easily you can use the initial vector $\mathbf{x}_0$ to predict the value of $\lim_{k \to \infty} \mathbf{x}_k$ (assuming that the limit exists)?

7. Suppose that at some stage in the Newton's method iteration using formula (6), we obtain a vector $\mathbf{x}_k$ that is an exact solution to the system of equations (2). Show that all the subsequent vectors $\mathbf{x}_{k+1}, \mathbf{x}_{k+2}, \ldots$ are equal to $\mathbf{x}_k$. Hence, if we happen to obtain an exact root via Newton's method, we will retain it.

9. As we will see in Chapter 4, when looking for maxima and minima of a differentiable function $F: X \subseteq \mathbf{R}^n \to \mathbf{R}$, we need to find the points where $DF(x_1, \ldots, x_n) = [0 \cdots 0]$, called **critical points** of F. Let $F(x, y) = 4\sin(xy) + x^3 + y^3$. Use Newton's method to approximate the critical point that lies near $(x, y) = (-1, -1)$.

10. Consider the problem of finding the intersection points of the sphere $x^2 + y^2 + z^2 = 4$, the circular cylinder $x^2 + y^2 = 1$, and the elliptical cylinder $4y^2 + z^2 = 4$.

(a) Use Newton's method to find one of the intersection points. By choosing a different initial vector $\mathbf{x}_0 = (x_0, y_0, z_0)$, approximate a second intersection point. (Note: You may wish to use a computer algebra system to determine appropriate inverse matrices.)

(b) Find all the intersection points exactly by means of algebra and compare with your results in part (a).

True/False Exercises for Chapter 2

1. The component functions of a vector-valued function are vectors.

2. The domain of $\mathbf{f}(x, y) = \left(x^2 + y^2 + 1, \dfrac{3}{x + y}, \dfrac{x}{y}\right)$ is $\{(x, y) \in \mathbf{R}^2 \mid y \neq 0, x \neq y\}$.

3. The range of $\mathbf{f}(x, y) = \left(x^2 + y^2 + 1, \dfrac{3}{x + y}, \dfrac{x}{y}\right)$ is $\{(u, v, w) \in \mathbf{R}^3 \mid u \geq 1\}$.

4. The function $\mathbf{f}: \mathbf{R}^3 - \{(0, 0, 0)\} \to \mathbf{R}^3$, $\mathbf{f}(\mathbf{x}) = 2\mathbf{x}/\|\mathbf{x}\|$ is one-one.

5. The graph of $x = 9y^2 + z^2/4$ is a paraboloid.

6. The graph of $z + x^2 = y^2$ is a hyperboloid.

7. The level set of a function $f(x, y, z)$ is either empty or a surface.

8. The graph of any function of two variables is a level set of a function of three variables.

9. The level set of any function of three variables is the graph of a function of two variables.

10. $\lim\limits_{(x,y) \to (0,0)} \dfrac{x^2 - 2y^2}{x^2 + y^2} = 1$.

11. If $f(x, y) = \begin{cases} \dfrac{y^4 - x^4}{x^2 + y^2} & \text{when } (x, y) \neq (0, 0) \\ 2 & \text{when } (x, y) = (0, 0) \end{cases}$, then f is continuous.

12. If $f(x, y)$ approaches a number L as $(x, y) \to (a, b)$ along all lines through (a, b), then $\lim_{(x,y) \to (a,b)} f(x, y) = L$.

13. If $\lim_{\mathbf{x} \to \mathbf{a}} \mathbf{f}(\mathbf{x})$ exists and is finite, then $\mathbf{f}$ is continuous at $\mathbf{a}$.

14. $f_x(a, b) = \lim\limits_{x \to a} \dfrac{f(x, b) - f(a, b)}{x - a}.$

15. If $f(x, y, z) = \sin y$, then $\nabla f(x, y, z) = \cos y$.

16. If $\mathbf{f} \colon \mathbf{R}^3 \to \mathbf{R}^4$ is differentiable, then $D\mathbf{f}(\mathbf{x})$ is a 3×4 matrix.

17. If $\mathbf{f}$ is differentiable at $\mathbf{a}$, then $\mathbf{f}$ is continuous at $\mathbf{a}$.

18. If $\mathbf{f}$ is continuous at $\mathbf{a}$, then $\mathbf{f}$ is differentiable at $\mathbf{a}$.

19. If all partial derivatives $\partial f / \partial x_1, \ldots, \partial f / \partial x_n$ of a function $f(x_1, \ldots, x_n)$ exist at $\mathbf{a} = (a_1, \ldots, a_n)$, then f is differentiable at $\mathbf{a}$.

20. If $\mathbf{f} \colon \mathbf{R}^4 \to \mathbf{R}^5$ and $\mathbf{g} \colon \mathbf{R}^4 \to \mathbf{R}^5$ are both differentiable at $\mathbf{a} \in \mathbf{R}^4$, then $D(\mathbf{f} - \mathbf{g})(\mathbf{a}) = D\mathbf{f}(\mathbf{a}) - D\mathbf{g}(\mathbf{a})$.

21. There's a function f of class C^2 such that $\dfrac{\partial f}{\partial x} = y^3 - 2x$ and $\dfrac{\partial f}{\partial y} = y - 3xy^2$.

22. If the second-order partial derivatives of f exist at (a, b), then $f_{xy}(a, b) = f_{yx}(a, b)$.

23. If $w = F(x, y, z)$ and $z = g(x, y)$ where F and g are differentiable, then

$$\frac{\partial w}{\partial x} = \frac{\partial F}{\partial x} + \frac{\partial F}{\partial z}\frac{\partial g}{\partial x}.$$

24. The tangent plane to $z = x^3/(y + 1)$ at the point $(-2, 0, -8)$ has equation $z = 12x + 8y + 16$.

25. The plane tangent to $xy/z^2 = 1$ at $(2, 8, -4)$ has equation $4x + y + 2z = 8$.

26. The plane tangent to the surface $x^2 + xye^z + y^3 = 1$ at the point $(2, -1, 0)$ is parallel to the vector $3\mathbf{i} + 5\mathbf{j} - 3\mathbf{k}$.

27. $D_{\mathbf{j}} f(x, y, z) = \dfrac{\partial f}{\partial y}.$

28. $D_{-\mathbf{k}} f(x, y, z) = \dfrac{\partial f}{\partial z}.$

29. If $f(x, y) = \sin x \cos y$ and $\mathbf{v}$ is a unit vector in $\mathbf{R}^2$, then $0 \le D_{\mathbf{v}} f\left(\dfrac{\pi}{4}, \dfrac{\pi}{3}\right) \le \dfrac{\sqrt{2}}{2}.$

30. If $\mathbf{v}$ is a unit vector in $\mathbf{R}^3$ and $f(x, y, z) = \sin x - \cos y + \sin z$, then

$$-\sqrt{3} \le D_{\mathbf{v}} f(x, y, z) \le \sqrt{3}.$$

Miscellaneous Exercises for Chapter 2

1. Let $\mathbf{f}(\mathbf{x}) = (\mathbf{i} + \mathbf{k}) \times \mathbf{x}$.

    (a) Write the component functions of $\mathbf{f}$.

    (b) Describe the domain and range of $\mathbf{f}$.

2. Let $\mathbf{f}(\mathbf{x}) = \mathrm{proj}_{3\mathbf{i} - 2\mathbf{j} + \mathbf{k}}\mathbf{x}$, where $\mathbf{x} = x\mathbf{i} + y\mathbf{j} + z\mathbf{k}$.

    (a) Describe the domain and range of $\mathbf{f}$.

    (b) Write the component functions of $\mathbf{f}$.

3. Let $f(x, y) = \sqrt{xy}$.

    (a) Find the domain and range of f.

    (b) Is the domain of f open or closed? Why?

4. Let $g(x, y) = \sqrt{\dfrac{x}{y}}$.

    (a) Determine the domain and range of g.

    (b) Is the domain of g open or closed? Why?

5. Figure 2.77 shows the graphs of six functions $f(x, y)$ and plots of the collections of their level curves in some order. Complete the following table by matching each function in the table with its graph and plot of its level curves.

Function $f(x, y)$	Graph (uppercase letter)	Level curves (lowercase letter)
$f(x, y) = \dfrac{1}{x^2 + y^2 + 1}$		
$f(x, y) = \sin\sqrt{x^2 + y^2}$		
$f(x, y) = (3y^2 - 2x^2)e^{-x^2 - 2y^2}$		
$f(x, y) = y^3 - 3x^2 y$		
$f(x, y) = x^2 y^2 e^{-x^2 - 2y^2}$		
$f(x, y) = ye^{-x^2 - y^2}$		

6. Consider the function $f(x, y) = 2 + \ln(x^2 + y^2)$.

    (a) Sketch some level curves of f. Give at least those at heights, 0, 1, and 2. (It will probably help if you give a few more.)

    (b) Using part (a) or otherwise, give a rough sketch of the graph of $z = f(x, y)$.

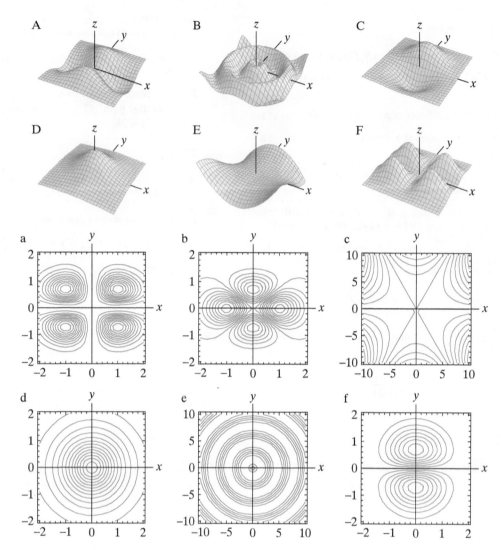

Figure 2.77 Figures for Exercise 5.

7. Use polar coordinates to evaluate

$$\lim_{(x,y)\to(0,0)} \frac{yx^2 - y^3}{x^2 + y^2}.$$

8. This problem concerns the function

$$f(x, y) = \begin{cases} \dfrac{2xy}{x^2 + y^2} & \text{if } (x, y) \neq (0, 0) \\ 0 & \text{if } (x, y) = (0, 0) \end{cases}.$$

(a) Use polar coordinates to describe this function.

(b) Using the polar coordinate description obtained in part (a), give some level curves for this function.

(c) Prepare a rough sketch of the graph of f.

(d) Determine $\lim_{(x,y)\to(0,0)} f(x, y)$, if it exists.

(e) Is f continuous? Why or why not?

9. Let

$$F(x, y) = \begin{cases} \dfrac{xy(xy + x^2)}{x^4 + y^4} & \text{if } (x, y) \neq (0, 0) \\ 0 & \text{if } (x, y) = (0, 0) \end{cases}.$$

Show that the function $g(x) = F(x, 0)$ is continuous at $x = 0$. Show that the function $h(y) = F(0, y)$ is continuous at $y = 0$. However, show that F fails to be continuous at $(0, 0)$. (Thus, continuity in each variable separately does not necessarily imply continuity of the function.)

10. Suppose $f: U \subseteq \mathbf{R}^n \to \mathbf{R}$ is not defined at a point $\mathbf{a} \in \mathbf{R}^n$ but is defined for all $\mathbf{x}$ near $\mathbf{a}$. In other words, the domain U of f includes, for some $r > 0$, the set $B_r = \{\mathbf{x} \in \mathbf{R}^n \mid 0 < \|\mathbf{x} - \mathbf{a}\| < r\}$. (The set B_r is just an open ball of radius r centered at $\mathbf{a}$ with the point

a deleted.) Then we say $\lim_{x \to a} f(\mathbf{x}) = +\infty$ if $f(\mathbf{x})$ grows without bound as $\mathbf{x} \to \mathbf{a}$. More precisely, this means that given any $N > 0$ (no matter how large), there is some $\delta > 0$ such that if $0 < \|\mathbf{x} - \mathbf{a}\| < \delta$ (i.e., if $\mathbf{x} \in B_r$), then $f(\mathbf{a}) > N$.

(a) Using intuitive arguments or the preceding technical definition, explain why $\lim_{x \to 0} 1/x^2 = \infty$.

(b) Explain why

$$\lim_{(x,y) \to (1,3)} \frac{2}{(x-1)^2 + (y-3)^2} = \infty.$$

(c) Formulate a definition of what it means to say that

$$\lim_{\mathbf{x} \to \mathbf{a}} f(\mathbf{x}) = -\infty.$$

(d) Explain why

$$\lim_{(x,y) \to (0,0)} \frac{1-x}{xy^4 - y^4 + x^3 - x^2} = -\infty.$$

Exercises 11–17 involve the notion of windchill temperature—see Example 7 in §2.1, and refer to the table of windchill values on page 85.

11. (a) Find the windchill temperature when the air temperature is $25\,°\mathrm{F}$ and the windspeed is 10 mph.

(b) If the windspeed is 20 mph, what air temperature causes a windchill temperature of $-15\,°\mathrm{F}$?

12. (a) If the air temperature is $10\,°\mathrm{F}$, estimate (to the nearest unit) what windspeed would give a windchill temperature of $-5\,°\mathrm{F}$.

(b) Do you think your estimate in part (a) is high or low? Why?

13. At a windspeed of 30 mph and air temperature of $35\,°\mathrm{F}$, estimate the rate of change of the windchill temperature with respect to air temperature if the windspeed is held constant.

14. At a windspeed of 15 mph and air temperature of $25\,°\mathrm{F}$, estimate the rate of change of the windchill temperature with respect to windspeed.

15. Windchill tables are constructed from empirically derived formulas for heat loss from an exposed surface. Early experimental work of P. A. Siple and C. F. Passel,[4] resulted in the following formula:

$$W = 91.4 + (t - 91.4)(0.474 + 0.304\sqrt{s} - 0.0203s).$$

Here W denotes windchill temperature (in degrees Fahrenheit), t the air temperature (for $t < 91.4\,°\mathrm{F}$), and s the windspeed in miles per hour (for $s \geq 4$ mph).[5]

(a) Compare your answers in Exercises 11 and 12 with those computed directly from the Siple formula just mentioned.

(b) Discuss any differences you observe between your answers to Exercises 11 and 12 and your answers to part (a).

(c) Why is it necessary to take $t < 91.4\,°\mathrm{F}$ and $s \geq 4$ mph in the Siple formula? (Don't look for a purely mathematical reason; think about the model.)

16. Recent research led the United States National Weather Service to employ a new formula for calculating windchill values beginning November 1, 2001. In particular, the table on page 85 was constructed from the formula

$$W = 35.74 + 0.621t - 35.75s^{0.16} + 0.4275ts^{0.16}.$$

Here, as in the Siple formula of Exercise 15, W denotes windchill temperature (in degrees Fahrenheit), t the air temperature (for $t \leq 50\,°\mathrm{F}$), and s the windspeed in miles per hour (for $s \geq 3$ mph).[6] Compare your answers in Exercises 13 and 14 with those computed directly from the National Weather Service formula above.

17. In this problem you will compare graphically the two windchill formulas given in Exercises 15 and 16.

(a) If $W_1(s,t)$ denotes the windchill function given by the Siple formula in Exercise 15 and $W_2(s,t)$ the windchill function given by the National Weather Service formula in Exercise 16, graph the curves $y = W_1(s, 40)$ and $y = W_2(s, 40)$ on the same set of axes. (Let s vary between 3 and 120 mph.) In addition, graph other pairs of curves $y = W_1(s, t_0)$, $y = W_2(s, t_0)$ for other values of t_0. Discuss what your results tell you about the two windchill formulas.

(b) Now graph pairs of curves $y = W_1(s_0, t)$, $y = W_2(s_0, t)$ for various constant values s_0 for windspeed. Discuss your results.

(c) Finally, graph the surfaces $z = W_1(s, t)$ and $z = W_2(s, t)$ and comment.

[4] "Measurements of dry atmospheric cooling in subfreezing temperatures," *Proc. Amer. Phil. Soc.*, **89** (1945), 177–199.

[5] From Bob Rilling, Atmospheric Technology Division, National Center for Atmospheric Research (NCAR), "Calculating Windchill Values," February 12, 1996. Found online at http://www.atd.ucar.edu/homes/rilling/wc_formula.html (July 31, 2010).

[6] NOAA, National Weather Service, Office of Climate, Water, and Weather Services, "NWS Wind Chill Temperature Index." February 26, 2004. <http://www.nws.noaa.gov/om/ windchill> (July 31, 2010).

18. Consider the sphere of radius 3 centered at the origin. The plane tangent to the sphere at $(1, 2, 2)$ intersects the x-axis at a point P. Find the coordinates of P.

19. Show that the plane tangent to a sphere at a point P on the sphere is always perpendicular to the vector $\overrightarrow{OP}$ from the center O of the sphere to P. (Hint: Locate the sphere so its center is at the origin in $\mathbf{R}^3$.)

20. The surface $z = 3x^2 + \frac{1}{6}x^3 - \frac{1}{8}x^4 - 4y^2$ is intersected by the plane $2x - y = 1$. The resulting intersection is a curve on the surface. Find a set of parametric equations for the line tangent to this curve at the point $(1, 1, -\frac{23}{24})$.

21. Consider the cone $z^2 = x^2 + y^2$.

(a) Find an equation of the plane tangent to the cone at the point $(3, -4, 5)$.

(b) Find an equation of the plane tangent to the cone at the point (a, b, c).

(c) Show that every tangent plane to the cone must pass through the origin.

22. Show that the two surfaces

$$S_1: \ z = xy \quad \text{and} \quad S_2: \ z = \tfrac{3}{4}x^2 - y^2$$

intersect perpendicularly at the point $(2, 1, 2)$.

23. Consider the surface $z = x^2 + 4y^2$.

(a) Find an equation for the plane that is tangent to the surface at the point $(1, -1, 5)$.

(b) Now suppose that the surface is intersected with the plane $x = 1$. The resulting intersection is a curve on the surface (and is a curve in the plane $x = 1$ as well). Give a set of parametric equations for the line in $\mathbf{R}^3$ that is tangent to this curve at the point $(1, -1, 5)$. A rough sketch may help your thinking.

24. A turtleneck sweater has been washed and is now tumbling in the dryer, along with the rest of the laundry. At a particular moment t_0, the neck of the sweater measures 18 inches in circumference and 3 inches in length. However, the sweater is 100% cotton, so that at t_0 the heat of the dryer is causing the neck circumference to shrink at a rate of 0.2 in/min, while the twisting and tumbling action is causing the length of the neck to stretch at the rate of 0.1 in/min. How is the volume V of the space inside the neck changing at $t = t_0$? Is V increasing or decreasing at that moment?

25. A factory generates air pollution each day according to the formula

$$P(S, T) = 330S^{2/3}T^{4/5},$$

where S denotes the number of machine stations in operation and T denotes the average daily temperature. At the moment, 75 stations are in regular use and the average daily temperature is $15\,^\circ$C. If the average temperature is rising at the rate of $0.2\,^\circ$C/day and the number of stations being used is falling at a rate of 2 per month, at what rate is the amount of pollution changing? (Note: Assume that there are 24 workdays per month.)

26. Economists attempt to quantify how useful or satisfying people find goods or services by means of **utility functions.** Suppose that the utility a particular individual derives from consuming x ounces of soda per week and watching y minutes of television per week is

$$u(x, y) = 1 - e^{-0.001x^2 - 0.00005y^2}.$$

Further suppose that she currently drinks 80 oz of soda per week and watches 240 min of TV each week. If she were to increase her soda consumption by 5 oz/week and cut back on her TV viewing by 15 min/week, is the utility she derives from these changes increasing or decreasing? At what rate?

27. Suppose that $w = x^2 + y^2 + z^2$ and $x = \rho \cos\theta \sin\varphi$, $y = \rho \sin\theta \sin\varphi, z = \rho \cos\varphi$. (Note that the equations for x, y, and z in terms of ρ, φ, and θ are just the conversion relations from spherical to rectangular coordinates.)

(a) Use the chain rule to compute $\partial w / \partial \rho$, $\partial w / \partial \varphi$, and $\partial w / \partial \theta$. Simplify your answers as much as possible.

(b) Substitute ρ, φ, and θ for x, y, and z in the original expression for w. Can you explain your answer in part (a)?

28. If $w = f\left(\dfrac{x + y}{xy}\right)$, show that

$$x^2 \frac{\partial w}{\partial x} - y^2 \frac{\partial w}{\partial y} = 0.$$

(You should assume that f is a differentiable function of one variable.)

29. Let $z = g(x, y)$ be a function of class C^2, and let $x = e^r \cos\theta$, $y = e^r \sin\theta$.

(a) Use the chain rule to find $\partial z / \partial r$ and $\partial z / \partial \theta$ in terms of $\partial z / \partial x$ and $\partial z / \partial y$. Use your results to solve for $\partial z / \partial x$ and $\partial z / \partial y$ in terms of $\partial z / \partial r$ and $\partial z / \partial \theta$.

(b) Use part (a) and the product rule to show that

$$\frac{\partial^2 z}{\partial x^2} + \frac{\partial^2 z}{\partial y^2} = e^{-2r}\left(\frac{\partial^2 z}{\partial r^2} + \frac{\partial^2 z}{\partial \theta^2}\right).$$

30. (a) Use the function $f(x, y) = x^y \ (= e^{y \ln x})$ and the multivariable chain rule to calculate $\dfrac{d}{du}(u^u)$.

(b) Use the multivariable chain rule to calculate $\dfrac{d}{dt}((\sin t)^{\cos t})$.

31. Use the function $f(x, y, z) = x^{y^z}$ and the multivariable chain rule to calculate $\dfrac{d}{du}\left(u^{u^u}\right)$.

32. Suppose that $f: \mathbf{R}^n \to \mathbf{R}$ is a function of class C^2. The **Laplacian** of f, denoted $\nabla^2 f$, is defined to be

$$\nabla^2 f = \frac{\partial^2 f}{\partial x_1^2} + \frac{\partial^2 f}{\partial x_2^2} + \cdots + \frac{\partial^2 f}{\partial x_n^2}.$$

When $n = 2$ or 3, this construction is important when studying certain differential equations that model physical phenomena, such as the heat or wave equations. (See Exercises 28 and 29 of §2.4.) Now suppose that f depends only on the distance $\mathbf{x} = (x_1, \ldots, x_n)$ is from the origin in $\mathbf{R}^n$; that is, suppose that $f(\mathbf{x}) = g(r)$ for some function g, where $r = \|\mathbf{x}\|$. Show that for all $\mathbf{x} \neq \mathbf{0}$, the Laplacian is given by

$$\nabla^2 f = \frac{n-1}{r} g'(r) + g''(r).$$

33. (a) Consider a function $f(x, y)$ of class C^4. Show that if we apply the Laplacian operator $\nabla^2 = \partial^2/\partial x^2 + \partial^2/\partial y^2$ twice to f, we obtain

$$\nabla^2(\nabla^2 f) = \frac{\partial^4 f}{\partial x^4} + 2\frac{\partial^4 f}{\partial x^2 \partial y^2} + \frac{\partial^4 f}{\partial y^4}.$$

(b) Now suppose that f is a function of n variables of class C^4. Show that

$$\nabla^2(\nabla^2 f) = \sum_{i,j=1}^{n} \frac{\partial^4 f}{\partial x_i^2 \partial x_j^2}.$$

Functions that satisfy the partial differential equation $\nabla^2(\nabla^2 f) = 0$ are called **biharmonic functions** and arise in the theoretical study of elasticity.

34. Livinia, the housefly, finds herself caught in the oven at the point $(0, 0, 1)$. The temperature at points in the oven is given by the function

$$T(x, y, z) = 10(xe^{-y^2} + ze^{-x^2}),$$

where the units are in degrees Celsius.

(a) If Livinia begins to move toward the point $(2, 3, 1)$, at what rate (in deg/cm) does she find the temperature changing?

(b) In what direction should she move in order to cool off as rapidly as possible?

(c) Suppose that Livinia can fly at a speed of 3 cm/sec. If she moves in the direction of part (b), at what (instantaneous) rate (in deg/sec) will she find the temperature to be changing?

35. Consider the surface given in cylindrical coordinates by the equation $z = r \cos 3\theta$.

(a) Describe this surface in Cartesian coordinates, that is, as $z = f(x, y)$.

(b) Is f continuous at the origin? (Hint: Think cylindrical.)

(c) Find expressions for $\partial f/\partial x$ and $\partial f/\partial y$ at points other than $(0, 0)$. Give values for $\partial f/\partial x$ and $\partial f/\partial y$ at $(0, 0)$ by looking at the partial functions of f through $(x, 0)$ and $(0, y)$ and taking one-variable limits.

(d) Show that the directional derivative $D_{\mathbf{u}} f(0, 0)$ exists for every direction (unit vector) $\mathbf{u}$. (Hint: Think in cylindrical coordinates again and note that you can specify a direction through the origin in the xy-plane by choosing a particular constant value for θ.)

(e) Show directly (by examining the expression for $\partial f/\partial y$ when $(x, y) \neq (0, 0)$ and also using part (c)) that $\partial f/\partial y$ is *not* continuous at $(0, 0)$.

(f) Sketch the graph of the surface, perhaps using a computer to do so.

36. The partial differential equation

$$\frac{\partial^2 u}{\partial x^2} + \frac{\partial^2 u}{\partial y^2} + \frac{\partial^2 u}{\partial z^2} = c\frac{\partial^2 u}{\partial t^2}$$

is known as the **wave equation**. It models the motion of a wave $u(x, y, z, t)$ in $\mathbf{R}^3$ and was originally derived by Johann Bernoulli in 1727. In this equation, c is a positive constant, the variables x, y, and z represent spatial coordinates, and the variable t represents time.

(a) Let $u = \cos(x - t) + \sin(x + t) - 2e^{z+t} - (y - t)^3$. Show that u satisfies the wave equation with $c = 1$.

(b) More generally, show that if f_1, f_2, g_1, g_2, h_1, and h_2 are any twice differentiable functions of a single variable, then

$$u(x, y, z, t) = f_1(x - t) + f_2(x + t)$$
$$+ g_1(y - t) + g_2(y + t)$$
$$+ h_1(z - t) + h_2(z + t)$$

satisfies the wave equation with $c = 1$.

*Let X be an open set in $\mathbf{R}^n$. A function $F: X \to \mathbf{R}$ is said to be **homogeneous of degree** d if, for all $\mathbf{x} = (x_1, x_2, \ldots, x_n) \in X$ and all $t \in \mathbf{R}$ such that $t\mathbf{x} \in X$, we have*

$$F(tx_1, tx_2, \ldots, tx_n) = t^d F(x_1, x_2, \ldots, x_n).$$

Exercises 37–44 concern homogeneous functions.

In Exercises 37–41, which of the given functions are homogeneous? For those that are, indicate the degree d of homogeneity.

37. $F(x, y) = x^3 + xy^2 - 6y^3$

38. $F(x, y, z) = x^3 y - x^2 z^2 + z^8$

39. $F(x, y, z) = zy^2 - x^3 + x^2 z$

40. $F(x, y) = e^{y/x}$.

41. $F(x, y, z) = \dfrac{x^3 + x^2 y - yz^2}{xyz + 7xz^2}$

42. If $F(x, y, z)$ is a polynomial, characterize what it means to say that F is homogeneous of degree d (i.e., explain what must be true about the polynomial if it is to be homogeneous of degree d).

43. Suppose $F(x_1, x_2, \ldots, x_n)$ is differentiable and homogeneous of degree d. Prove **Euler's formula**:

$$x_1 \frac{\partial F}{\partial x_1} + x_2 \frac{\partial F}{\partial x_2} + \cdots + x_n \frac{\partial F}{\partial x_n} = dF.$$

(Hint: Take the equation $F(tx_1, tx_2, \ldots, tx_n) = t^d F(x_1, x_2, \ldots, x_n)$ that defines homogeneity and differentiate with respect to t.)

44. Generalize Euler's formula as follows: If F is of class C^2 and homogeneous of degree d, then

$$\sum_{i,j=1}^{n} x_i x_j \frac{\partial^2 F}{\partial x_i \partial x_j} = d(d-1)F.$$

Can you conjecture what an analogous formula involving the kth-order partial derivatives should look like?

4 | Maxima and Minima in Several Variables

4.1 Differentials and Taylor's Theorem

Among all classes of functions of one or several variables, polynomials are without a doubt the nicest in that they are continuous and differentiable everywhere and display intricate and interesting behavior. Our goal in this section is to provide a means of approximating any scalar-valued function by a polynomial of given degree, known as the **Taylor polynomial**. Because of the relative ease with which one can calculate with them, Taylor polynomials are useful for work in computer graphics and computer-aided design, to name just two areas.

Taylor's Theorem in One Variable: A Review

Suppose you have a function $f: X \subseteq \mathbf{R} \to \mathbf{R}$ that is differentiable at a point a in X. Then the equation for the tangent line gives the best linear approximation for f near a. That is, when we define p_1 by

$$p_1(x) = f(a) + f'(a)(x - a), \quad \text{we have} \quad p_1(x) \approx f(x) \text{ if } x \approx a.$$

(See Figure 4.1.) As explained in §2.3, the phrase "best linear approximation" means that if we take $R_1(x, a)$ to be $f(x) - p_1(x)$, then

$$\lim_{x \to a} \frac{R_1(x, a)}{x - a} = 0.$$

Note that, in particular, we have $p_1(a) = f(a)$ and $p_1'(a) = f'(a)$.

Generally, tangent lines approximate graphs of functions only over very small neighborhoods containing the point of tangency. For a better approximation, we might try to fit a parabola that hugs the function's graph more closely as in Figure 4.2. In this case, we want p_2 to be the quadratic function such that

$$p_2(a) = f(a), \quad p_2'(a) = f'(a), \quad \text{and} \quad p_2''(a) = f''(a).$$

The only quadratic polynomial that satisfies these three conditions is

$$p_2(x) = f(a) + f'(a)(x - a) + \frac{f''(a)}{2}(x - a)^2.$$

It can be proved that, if f is of class C^2, then

$$f(x) = p_2(x) + R_2(x, a),$$

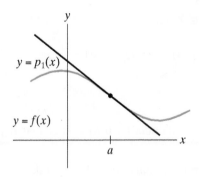

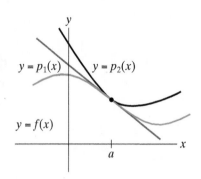

Figure 4.1 The graph of $y = f(x)$ and its tangent line $y = p_1(x)$ at $x = a$.

Figure 4.2 The tangent graphs of f, p_1, and p_2.

where

$$\lim_{x \to a} \frac{R_2(x, a)}{(x - a)^2} = 0.$$

EXAMPLE 1   If $f(x) = \ln x$, then, for $a = 1$, we have

$$f(1) = \ln 1 = 0,$$

$$f'(1) = \frac{1}{1} = 1,$$

$$f''(1) = -\frac{1}{1^2} = -1.$$

Hence,

$$p_1(x) = 0 + 1(x - 1) = x - 1,$$

$$p_2(x) = 0 + 1(x - 1) - \tfrac{1}{2}(x - 1)^2 = -\tfrac{1}{2}x^2 + 2x - \tfrac{3}{2}.$$

The approximating polynomials p_1 and p_2 are shown in Figure 4.3.   ◆

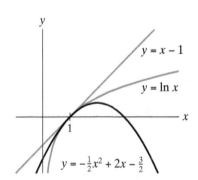

Figure 4.3 Approximations to $f(x) = \ln x$.

There is no reason to stop with quadratic polynomials. Suppose we want to approximate f by a polynomial p_k of degree k, where k is a positive integer. Analogous to the work above, we require that p_k and its first k derivatives agree with f and its first k derivatives at the point a. Thus, we demand that

$$p_k(a) = f(a),$$

$$p_k'(a) = f'(a),$$

$$p_k''(a) = f''(a),$$

$$\vdots$$

$$p_k^{(k)}(a) = f^{(k)}(a).$$

Given these requirements, we have only one choice for p_k, stated in the following theorem:

THEOREM 1.1 (**TAYLOR'S THEOREM IN ONE VARIABLE**)   Let X be open in $\mathbf{R}$ and suppose $f: X \subseteq \mathbf{R} \to \mathbf{R}$ is differentiable up to (at least) order k.

Given $a \in X$, let

$$p_k(x) = f(a) + f'(a)(x - a) + \frac{f''(a)}{2}(x - a)^2 + \cdots + \frac{f^{(k)}(a)}{k!}(x - a)^k. \quad (1)$$

Then

$$f(x) = p_k(x) + R_k(x, a),$$

where the remainder term R_k is such that $R_k(x, a)/(x - a)^k \to 0$ as $x \to a$.

The polynomial defined by formula (1) is called the k**th-order Taylor polynomial of** f **at** a. The essence of Taylor's theorem is this: For x near a, the Taylor polynomial p_k approximates f in the sense that the error R_k involved in making this approximation tends to zero even faster than $(x - a)^k$ does. When k is large, this is very fast indeed, as we see graphically in Figure 4.4.

EXAMPLE 2   Consider $\ln x$ with $a = 1$ again. We calculate

$$f(1) = \ln 1 = 0,$$

$$f'(1) = \frac{1}{1} = 1,$$

$$f''(1) = -\frac{1}{1^2} = -1,$$

$$\vdots$$

$$f^{(k)}(1) = \frac{(-1)^{k-1}(k - 1)!}{1^k} = (-1)^{k+1}(k - 1)!.$$

Therefore,

$$p_k(x) = (x - 1) - \frac{1}{2}(x - 1)^2 + \frac{1}{3}(x - 1)^3 - \cdots + \frac{(-1)^{k-1}}{k}(x - 1)^k. \quad \blacklozenge$$

Taylor's theorem as stated in Theorem 1.1 says nothing explicit about the remainder term R_k. However, it is possible to establish the following derivative form for the remainder:

PROPOSITION 1.2   If f is of class C^{k+1}, then there exists some number z between a and x such that

$$R_k(x, a) = \frac{f^{(k+1)}(z)}{(k + 1)!}(x - a)^{k+1}. \quad (2)$$

In practice, formula (2) is quite useful for estimating the error involved with a Taylor polynomial approximation. Both Theorem 1.1 (under the slightly stronger hypothesis that f is of class C^{k+1}) and Proposition 1.2 are proved in the addendum to this section.

EXAMPLE 3   The fifth-order Taylor polynomial of $f(x) = \cos x$ about $x = \pi/2$ is

$$p_5(x) = -\left(x - \frac{\pi}{2}\right) + \frac{1}{6}\left(x - \frac{\pi}{2}\right)^3 - \frac{1}{120}\left(x - \frac{\pi}{2}\right)^5.$$

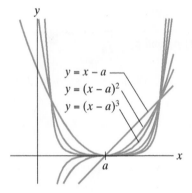

Figure 4.4 The graphs of
(1) $y = x - a$,
(2) $y = (x - a)^2$, and
(3) $y = (x - a)^3$.
Note how much more closely the graph of (3) hugs the x-axis than that of (1) or (2).

(You should verify this calculation.) According to formula (2), the difference between p_5 and $\cos x$ is

$$R_5\left(x, \frac{\pi}{2}\right) = \frac{f^{(6)}(z)}{6!}\left(x - \frac{\pi}{2}\right)^6 = -\frac{\cos z}{6!}\left(x - \frac{\pi}{2}\right)^6,$$

where z is some number between $\pi/2$ and x. Since $|\cos x|$ is never larger than 1, we have

$$\left|R_5\left(x, \frac{\pi}{2}\right)\right| = \left|\frac{\cos z}{6!}\left(x - \frac{\pi}{2}\right)^6\right| \le \frac{(x - \pi/2)^6}{720}.$$

Thus, for x in the interval $[0, \pi]$, we have

$$\left|R_5\left(x, \frac{\pi}{2}\right)\right| \le \frac{(\pi - \pi/2)^6}{720} = \frac{\pi^6}{46{,}080} \approx 0.0209.$$

In other words, the use of the polynomial p_5 above in place of $\cos x$ will be accurate to at least 0.0209 throughout the interval $[0, \pi]$.   ◆

Taylor's Theorem in Several Variables: The First-order Formula

For the moment, suppose that $f : X \subseteq \mathbf{R}^2 \to \mathbf{R}$ is a function of two variables, where X is open in $\mathbf{R}^2$ and of class C^1. Then near the point $(a, b) \in X$, the best linear approximation to f is provided by the equation giving the tangent plane at $(a, b, f(a, b))$. That is,

$$f(x, y) \approx p_1(x, y),$$

where

$$p_1(x, y) = f(a, b) + f_x(a, b)(x - a) + f_y(a, b)(y - b).$$

Note that the linear polynomial p_1 has the property that

$$p_1(a, b) = f(a, b);$$
$$\frac{\partial p_1}{\partial x}(a, b) = \frac{\partial f}{\partial x}(a, b),$$
$$\frac{\partial p_1}{\partial y}(a, b) = \frac{\partial f}{\partial y}(a, b).$$

Such an approximation is shown in Figure 4.5.

To generalize this situation to the case of a function $f : X \subseteq \mathbf{R}^n \to \mathbf{R}$ of class C^1, we naturally use the equation for the *tangent hyperplane*. That is, if

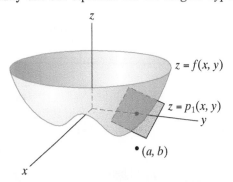

Figure 4.5 The graph of $z = f(x, y)$ and $z = p_1(x, y)$.

$\mathbf{a} = (a_1, a_2, \ldots, a_n) \in X$, then

$$f(x_1, x_2, \ldots, x_n) \approx p_1(x_1, x_2, \ldots, x_n),$$

where

$$p_1(x_1, \ldots, x_n) = f(\mathbf{a}) + f_{x_1}(\mathbf{a})(x_1 - a_1) + f_{x_2}(\mathbf{a})(x_2 - a_2)$$
$$+ \cdots + f_{x_n}(\mathbf{a})(x_n - a_n).$$

Of course, the formula for p_1 can be written more compactly using either Σ-notation or, better still, matrices:

$$p_1(x_1, \ldots, x_n) = f(\mathbf{a}) + \sum_{i=1}^{n} f_{x_i}(\mathbf{a})(x_i - a_i) = f(\mathbf{a}) + Df(\mathbf{a})(\mathbf{x} - \mathbf{a}). \quad (3)$$

EXAMPLE 4   Let $f(x_1, x_2, x_3, x_4) = x_1 + 2x_2 + 3x_3 + 4x_4 + x_1 x_2 x_3 x_4$. Then

$$\frac{\partial f}{\partial x_1} = 1 + x_2 x_3 x_4, \qquad \frac{\partial f}{\partial x_2} = 2 + x_1 x_3 x_4,$$

$$\frac{\partial f}{\partial x_3} = 3 + x_1 x_2 x_4, \qquad \frac{\partial f}{\partial x_4} = 4 + x_1 x_2 x_3.$$

At $\mathbf{a} = \mathbf{0} = (0, 0, 0, 0)$, we have

$$\frac{\partial f}{\partial x_1}(\mathbf{0}) = 1, \qquad \frac{\partial f}{\partial x_2}(\mathbf{0}) = 2, \qquad \frac{\partial f}{\partial x_3}(\mathbf{0}) = 3, \qquad \frac{\partial f}{\partial x_4}(\mathbf{0}) = 4.$$

Thus,

$$p_1(x_1, x_2, x_3, x_4) = 0 + 1(x_1 - 0) + 2(x_2 - 0) + 3(x_3 - 0) + 4(x_4 - 0)$$
$$= x_1 + 2x_2 + 3x_3 + 4x_4.$$

Note that p_1 contains precisely the linear terms of the original function f. On the other hand, if $\mathbf{a} = (1, 2, 3, 4)$, then

$$\frac{\partial f}{\partial x_1}(1, 2, 3, 4) = 25, \qquad \frac{\partial f}{\partial x_2}(1, 2, 3, 4) = 14,$$

$$\frac{\partial f}{\partial x_3}(1, 2, 3, 4) = 11, \qquad \frac{\partial f}{\partial x_4}(1, 2, 3, 4) = 10,$$

so that, in this case,

$$p_1(x_1, x_2, x_3, x_4) = 54 + 25(x_1 - 1) + 14(x_2 - 2) + 11(x_3 - 3) + 10(x_4 - 4).$$

◆

The relevant theorem regarding the first-order Taylor polynomial is just a re-statement of the definition of differentiability. However, since we plan to consider higher-order Taylor polynomials, we state the theorem explicitly.

THEOREM 1.3 (**FIRST-ORDER TAYLOR'S FORMULA IN SEVERAL VARIABLES**)   Let X be open in $\mathbf{R}^n$ and suppose that $f: X \subseteq \mathbf{R}^n \to \mathbf{R}$ is differentiable at the point $\mathbf{a}$ in X. Let

$$p_1(\mathbf{x}) = f(\mathbf{a}) + Df(\mathbf{a})(\mathbf{x} - \mathbf{a}). \quad (4)$$

Then

$$f(\mathbf{x}) = p_1(\mathbf{x}) + R_1(\mathbf{x}, \mathbf{a}),$$

where $R_1(\mathbf{x}, \mathbf{a})/\|\mathbf{x} - \mathbf{a}\| \to 0$ as $\mathbf{x} \to \mathbf{a}$.

Note that we may also express the first-order Taylor polynomial using the gradient. In place of (4), we would have

$$p_1(\mathbf{x}) = f(\mathbf{a}) + \nabla f(\mathbf{a}) \cdot (\mathbf{x} - \mathbf{a}).$$

Differentials

Before we explore higher-order versions of Taylor's theorem in several variables, we consider the linear (or first-order) approximation in further detail.

Let $\mathbf{h} = \mathbf{x} - \mathbf{a}$. Then formula (3) becomes

$$p_1(\mathbf{x}) = f(\mathbf{a}) + Df(\mathbf{a})\mathbf{h} = f(\mathbf{a}) + \sum_{i=1}^{n} \frac{\partial f}{\partial x_i}(\mathbf{a})h_i. \tag{5}$$

We focus on the sum appearing in formula (5) and summarize its salient features as follows:

DEFINITION 1.4 Let $f : X \subseteq \mathbf{R}^n \to \mathbf{R}$ and let $\mathbf{a} \in X$. The **incremental change of** f, denoted Δf, is

$$\Delta f = f(\mathbf{a} + \mathbf{h}) - f(\mathbf{a}).$$

The **total differential of** f, denoted $df(\mathbf{a}, \mathbf{h})$, is

$$df(\mathbf{a}, \mathbf{h}) = \frac{\partial f}{\partial x_1}(\mathbf{a})h_1 + \frac{\partial f}{\partial x_2}(\mathbf{a})h_2 + \cdots + \frac{\partial f}{\partial x_n}(\mathbf{a})h_n.$$

The significance of the differential is that for $\mathbf{h} \approx \mathbf{0}$,

$$\Delta f \approx df.$$

(We have abbreviated $df(\mathbf{a}, \mathbf{h})$ by df.)

Sometimes h_i is replaced by the expression Δx_i or dx_i to emphasize that it represents a change in the ith independent variable, in which case we write

$$df = \frac{\partial f}{\partial x_1}\,dx_1 + \frac{\partial f}{\partial x_2}\,dx_2 + \cdots + \frac{\partial f}{\partial x_n}\,dx_n.$$

(We've suppressed the evaluation of the partial derivatives at $\mathbf{a}$, as is customary.)

EXAMPLE 5 Suppose $f(x, y, z) = \sin(xyz) + \cos(xyz)$. Then

$$\begin{aligned}
df &= \frac{\partial f}{\partial x}\,dx + \frac{\partial f}{\partial y}\,dy + \frac{\partial f}{\partial z}\,dz \\
&= yz[\cos(xyz) - \sin(xyz)]dx + xz[\cos(xyz) - \sin(xyz)]dy \\
&\quad + xy[\cos(xyz) - \sin(xyz)]dz \\
&= (\cos(xyz) - \sin(xyz))(yz\,dx + xz\,dy + xy\,dz).
\end{aligned}$$
◆

The geometry of the differential arises, naturally enough, from tangent lines and planes. (See Figures 4.6 and 4.7.) In particular, the incremental change Δf measures the change in the height of the graph of f when moving from $\mathbf{a}$ to $\mathbf{a} + \mathbf{h}$; the differential change df measures the corresponding change in the height of

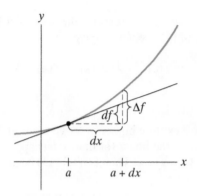

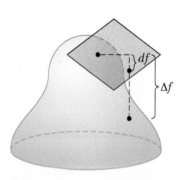

Figure 4.6 The incremental change Δf equals the change in y-coordinate of the graph of $y = f(x)$ as the x-coordinate of a point changes from a to $a + dx$. The differential df equals the change in y-coordinate of the graph of the tangent line at a (i.e., the graph of $y = p_1(x)$).

Figure 4.7 The incremental change Δf equals the change in z-coordinate of the graph of $z = f(x, y)$ as a point in $\mathbf{R}^2$ changes from $\mathbf{a} = (a, b)$ to $\mathbf{a} + \mathbf{h} = (a + h, b + k)$. The differential df equals the change in z-coordinate of the graph of the tangent plane at (a, b).

the graph of the (hyper)plane tangent to the graph at $\mathbf{a}$. When $\|\mathbf{h}\|$ is small (i.e., when $\mathbf{a} + \mathbf{h}$ is close to $\mathbf{a}$), the differential df approximates the increment Δf and it is often easier from a technical standpoint to work with the differential.

EXAMPLE 6   Let $f(x, y) = x - y + 2x^2 + xy^2$. Then for $(a, b) = (2, -1)$, we have that the increment is

$$\begin{aligned}
\Delta f &= f(2 + \Delta x, -1 + \Delta y) - f(2, -1) \\
&= 2 + \Delta x - (-1 + \Delta y) + 2(2 + \Delta x)^2 + (2 + \Delta x)(-1 + \Delta y)^2 - 13 \\
&= 10\Delta x - 5\Delta y + 2(\Delta x)^2 - 2\Delta x \Delta y + 2(\Delta y)^2 + \Delta x(\Delta y)^2.
\end{aligned}$$

On the other hand,

$$\begin{aligned}
df((2, -1), (\Delta x, \Delta y)) &= f_x(2, -1)\Delta x + f_y(2, -1)\Delta y \\
&= (1 + 4x + y^2)|_{(2,-1)}\Delta x + (-1 + 2xy)|_{(2,-1)}\Delta y \\
&= 10\Delta x - 5\Delta y.
\end{aligned}$$

We see that df consists of exactly the terms of Δf that are linear in Δx and Δy (i.e., appear to first power only). This will always be the case, of course, since that is the nature of the first-order Taylor approximation. Use of the differential approximation is often sufficient in practice, for when Δx and Δy are small, higher powers of them will be small enough to make virtually negligible contributions to Δf. For example, if Δx and Δy are both 0.01, then

$$df = (0.1 - 0.05) = 0.05$$

and

$$\begin{aligned}
\Delta f &= (0.1 - 0.05) + 0.0002 - 0.0002 + 0.0002 + 0.000001 \\
&= 0.05 + 0.000201 = 0.050201.
\end{aligned}$$

Thus, the values of df and Δf are the same to three decimal places.   ◆

EXAMPLE 7 A wooden rectangular block is to be manufactured with dimensions 3 in × 4 in × 6 in. Suppose that the possible errors in measuring each dimension of the block are the same. We use differentials to estimate how accurately we must measure the dimensions so that the resulting calculated error in volume is no more than 0.1 in^3.

Let the dimensions of the block be denoted by x ($\approx$ 3 in), y ($\approx$ 4 in), and z ($\approx$ 6 in). Then the volume of the block is

$$V = xyz \quad \text{and} \quad V \approx 3 \cdot 4 \cdot 6 = 72 \text{ in}^3.$$

The error in calculated volume is ΔV, which is approximated by the total differential dV. Thus,

$$\Delta V \approx dV = V_x(3, 4, 6)\Delta x + V_y(3, 4, 6)\Delta y + V_z(3, 4, 6)\Delta z$$
$$= 24\Delta x + 18\Delta y + 12\Delta z.$$

If the error in measuring each dimension is ϵ, then we have $\Delta x = \Delta y = \Delta z = \epsilon$. Therefore,

$$dV = 24\Delta x + 18\Delta y + 12\Delta z = 24\epsilon + 18\epsilon + 12\epsilon = 54\epsilon.$$

To ensure (approximately) that $|\Delta V| \leq 0.1$, we demand

$$|dV| = |54\epsilon| \leq 0.1.$$

Hence,

$$|\epsilon| \leq \frac{0.1}{54} = 0.0019 \text{ in}.$$

So the measurements in each dimension must be accurate to within 0.0019 in. ◆

EXAMPLE 8 The formula for the volume of a cylinder of radius r and height h is $V(r, h) = \pi r^2 h$. If the dimensions are changed by small amounts Δr and Δh, then the resulting change ΔV in volume is approximated by the differential change dV. That is,

$$\Delta V \approx dV = \frac{\partial V}{\partial r}\Delta r + \frac{\partial V}{\partial h}\Delta h = 2\pi rh\Delta r + \pi r^2\Delta h.$$

Suppose the cylinder is actually a beer can, so that it has approximate dimensions of $r = 1$ in and $h = 5$ in. Then

$$dV = \pi(10\Delta r + \Delta h).$$

This statement shows that, for these particular values of r and h, the volume is approximately 10 times **more sensitive** to changes in radius than changes in height. That is, if the radius is changed by an amount ϵ, then the height must be changed by roughly 10ϵ to keep the volume constant (i.e., to make ΔV zero). We use the word "approximate" because our analysis arises from considering the differential change dV rather than the actual incremental change ΔV.

This beer can example has real application to product marketing strategies. Because the volume is so much more sensitive to changes in radius than height, it is possible to make a can appear to be larger than standard by decreasing its radius slightly (little enough so as to be hardly noticeable) and increasing the height so no change in volume results. (See Figure 4.8.) This sensitivity analysis shows that even a tiny decrease in radius can force an appreciable compensating increase in height. The result can be quite striking, and these ideas apparently

Figure 4.8 Which would you buy?

have been adopted by at least one brewery. Indeed, this is how the author came to fully appreciate differentials and sensitivity analysis.[1]   ◆

Taylor's Theorem in Several Variables: The Second-order Formula

Suppose $f: X \subseteq \mathbf{R}^2 \to \mathbf{R}$ is a C^2 function of two variables. Then we know that the tangent plane gives rise to a linear approximation p_1 of f near a given point (a, b) of X. We can improve on this result by looking for the *quadric surface* that best approximates the graph of $z = f(x, y)$ near $(a, b, f(a, b))$. See Figure 4.9 for an illustration. That is, we search for a degree 2 polynomial $p_2(x, y) = Ax^2 + Bxy + Cy^2 + Dx + Ey + F$ such that, for $(x, y) \approx (a, b)$,

$$f(x, y) \approx p_2(x, y).$$

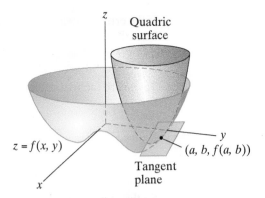

Figure 4.9 The tangent plane and quadric surface.

Analogous to the linear approximation p_1, it is reasonable to require that p_2 and all of its first- and second-order partial derivatives agree with those of f at the point (a, b). That is, we demand

$$p_2(a, b) = f(a, b),$$

$$\frac{\partial p_2}{\partial x}(a, b) = \frac{\partial f}{\partial x}(a, b), \qquad \frac{\partial p_2}{\partial y}(a, b) = \frac{\partial f}{\partial y}(a, b),$$

$$\frac{\partial^2 p_2}{\partial x^2}(a, b) = \frac{\partial^2 f}{\partial x^2}(a, b), \qquad \frac{\partial^2 p_2}{\partial x \partial y}(a, b) = \frac{\partial^2 f}{\partial x \partial y}(a, b), \tag{6}$$

$$\frac{\partial^2 p_2}{\partial y^2}(a, b) = \frac{\partial^2 f}{\partial y^2}(a, b).$$

After some algebra, we see that the only second-degree polynomial meeting these requirements is

$$p_2(x, y) = f(a, b) + f_x(a, b)(x - a) + f_y(a, b)(y - b)$$
$$+ \tfrac{1}{2} f_{xx}(a, b)(x - a)^2 + f_{xy}(a, b)(x - a)(y - b)$$
$$+ \tfrac{1}{2} f_{yy}(a, b)(y - b)^2. \tag{7}$$

---

[1] See S. J. Colley, *The College Mathematics Journal*, **25** (1994), no. 3, 226–227. Art reproduced with permission from the Mathematical Association of America.

How does formula (7) generalize to functions of n variables? We need to begin by demanding conditions analogous to those in (6) for a function $f: X \subseteq \mathbf{R}^n \to \mathbf{R}$. For $\mathbf{a} = (a_1, a_2, \ldots, a_n) \in X$, these conditions are

$$p_2(\mathbf{a}) = f(\mathbf{a}),$$

$$\frac{\partial p_2}{\partial x_i}(\mathbf{a}) = \frac{\partial f}{\partial x_i}(\mathbf{a}), \qquad i = 1, 2, \ldots, n, \tag{8}$$

$$\frac{\partial^2 p_2}{\partial x_i \partial x_j}(\mathbf{a}) = \frac{\partial^2 f}{\partial x_i \partial x_j}(\mathbf{a}), \quad i, j = 1, 2, \ldots, n.$$

If you do some algebra (which we omit), you will find that the only polynomial of degree 2 that satisfies the conditions in (8) is

$$p_2(\mathbf{x}) = f(\mathbf{a}) + \sum_{i=1}^{n} f_{x_i}(\mathbf{a})(x_i - a_i) + \frac{1}{2} \sum_{i,j=1}^{n} f_{x_i x_j}(\mathbf{a})(x_i - a_i)(x_j - a_j). \tag{9}$$

(Note that the second sum appearing in (9) is a double sum consisting of n^2 terms.) To check that everything is consistent when $n = 2$, we have

$$\begin{aligned} p_2(x_1, x_2) = {} & f(a_1, a_2) + f_{x_1}(a_1, a_2)(x_1 - a_1) + f_{x_2}(a_1, a_2)(x_2 - a_2) \\ & + \tfrac{1}{2} \big[f_{x_1 x_1}(a_1, a_2)(x_1 - a_1)^2 + f_{x_1 x_2}(a_1, a_2)(x_1 - a_1)(x_2 - a_2) \\ & + f_{x_2 x_1}(a_1, a_2)(x_2 - a_2)(x_1 - a_1) + f_{x_2 x_2}(a_1, a_2)(x_2 - a_2)^2 \big]. \end{aligned}$$

When f is a C^2 function, the two mixed partials are the same, so this formula agrees with formula (7).

EXAMPLE 9   Let $f(x, y, z) = e^{x+y+z}$ and let $\mathbf{a} = (a, b, c) = (0, 0, 0)$. Then

$$f(0, 0, 0) = e^0 = 1,$$

$$f_x(0, 0, 0) = f_y(0, 0, 0) = f_z(0, 0, 0) = e^0 = 1,$$

$$f_{xx}(0, 0, 0) = f_{xy}(0, 0, 0) = f_{xz}(0, 0, 0) = f_{yy}(0, 0, 0)$$

$$= f_{yz}(0, 0, 0) = f_{zz}(0, 0, 0) = e^0 = 1.$$

Thus,

$$\begin{aligned} p_2(x, y, z) = {} & 1 + 1(x - 0) + 1(y - 0) + 1(z - 0) \\ & + \tfrac{1}{2}\big[1(x - 0)^2 + 2 \cdot 1(x - 0)(y - 0) + 2 \cdot 1(x - 0)(z - 0) \\ & + 1(y - 0)^2 + 2 \cdot 1(y - 0)(z - 0) + 1(z - 0)^2 \big] \\ = {} & 1 + x + y + z + \tfrac{1}{2}x^2 + xy + xz + \tfrac{1}{2}y^2 + yz + \tfrac{1}{2}z^2 \\ = {} & 1 + (x + y + z) + \tfrac{1}{2}(x + y + z)^2. \end{aligned}$$

We have made use of the fact that, since f is of class C^2, a term like

$$f_{xy}(0, 0, 0)(x - 0)(y - 0) \quad \text{is equal to} \quad f_{yx}(0, 0, 0)(y - 0)(x - 0). \quad \blacklozenge$$

Now we state the second-order version of Taylor's theorem precisely.

THEOREM 1.5 (SECOND-ORDER TAYLOR'S FORMULA)   Let X be open in $\mathbf{R}^n$, and suppose that $f: X \subseteq \mathbf{R}^n \to \mathbf{R}$ is of class C^2. Let

$$p_2(\mathbf{x}) = f(\mathbf{a}) + \sum_{i=1}^{n} f_{x_i}(\mathbf{a})(x_i - a_i) + \frac{1}{2} \sum_{i,j=1}^{n} f_{x_i x_j}(\mathbf{a})(x_i - a_i)(x_j - a_j).$$

Then

$$f(\mathbf{x}) = p_2(\mathbf{x}) + R_2(\mathbf{x}, \mathbf{a}),$$

where $|R_2|/\|\mathbf{x} - \mathbf{a}\|^2 \to 0$ as $\mathbf{x} \to \mathbf{a}$.

A version of Theorem 1.5, under the stronger assumption that f is of class C^3, is established in the addendum to this section.

EXAMPLE 10   Let $f(x, y) = \cos x \cos y$ and $(a, b) = (0, 0)$. Then

$$f(0, 0) = 1;$$

$$f_x(0, 0) = -\sin x \cos y|_{(0,0)} = 0, \qquad f_y(0, 0) = -\cos x \sin y|_{(0,0)} = 0;$$

$$f_{xx}(0, 0) = -\cos x \cos y|_{(0,0)} = -1,$$

$$f_{xy}(0, 0) = \sin x \sin y|_{(0,0)} = 0,$$

$$f_{yy}(0, 0) = -\cos x \cos y|_{(0,0)} = -1.$$

Hence,

$$f(x, y) \approx p_2(x, y) = 1 + \tfrac{1}{2}(-1 \cdot x^2 - 1 \cdot y^2) = 1 - \tfrac{1}{2}x^2 - \tfrac{1}{2}y^2.$$

We can also solve this problem another way since f is a product of two functions. We can multiply the two Taylor polynomials:

$$p_2(x, y) = (\text{Taylor polynomial for } \cos x) \cdot (\text{Taylor polynomial for } \cos y)$$

$$= \left(1 - \tfrac{1}{2}x^2\right)\left(1 - \tfrac{1}{2}y^2\right)$$

$$= 1 - \tfrac{1}{2}x^2 - \tfrac{1}{2}y^2 + \tfrac{1}{4}x^2 y^2$$

$$= 1 - \tfrac{1}{2}x^2 - \tfrac{1}{2}y^2 \qquad \text{up to terms of degree 2.}$$

This method is justified by noting that if q_2 is the Taylor polynomial for cosine and R_2 is the corresponding remainder term, then

$$\cos x \, \cos y = [q_2(x) + R_2(x, 0)][q_2(y) + R_2(y, 0)]$$

$$= q_2(x)q_2(y) + q_2(y)R_2(x, 0) + q_2(x)R_2(y, 0) + R_2(x, 0)R_2(y, 0)$$

$$= q_2(x)q_2(y) + \text{other stuff},$$

where $(\text{other stuff})/\|(x, y)\|^2 \to 0$ as $(x, y) \to (0, 0)$, since both $R_2(x, 0)$ and $R_2(y, 0)$ do. ◆

The Hessian

Recall that the formula for the first-order Taylor polynomial p_1 was written quite concisely in formula (5) by using vector and matrix notation. It turns out that it is possible to do something similar for the second-order polynomial p_2.

DEFINITION 1.6   The **Hessian** of a function $f: X \subseteq \mathbf{R}^n \to \mathbf{R}$ is the matrix whose ijth entry is $\partial^2 f / \partial x_j \partial x_i$. That is,

$$Hf = \begin{bmatrix} f_{x_1 x_1} & f_{x_1 x_2} & \cdots & f_{x_1 x_n} \\ f_{x_2 x_1} & f_{x_2 x_2} & \cdots & f_{x_2 x_n} \\ \vdots & \vdots & \ddots & \vdots \\ f_{x_n x_1} & f_{x_n x_2} & \cdots & f_{x_n x_n} \end{bmatrix}.$$

The term "Hessian" comes from Ludwig Otto Hesse, the mathematician who first introduced it, not from the German mercenaries who fought in the American revolution.

Now let's look again at the formula for p_2 in Theorem 1.5:

$$p_2(\mathbf{x}) = f(\mathbf{a}) + \sum_{i=1}^{n} f_{x_i}(\mathbf{a}) h_i + \frac{1}{2} \sum_{i,j=1}^{n} f_{x_i x_j}(\mathbf{a}) h_i h_j.$$

(We have let $\mathbf{h} = (h_1, \ldots, h_n) = \mathbf{x} - \mathbf{a}$.) This can be written as

$$p_2(\mathbf{x}) = f(\mathbf{a}) + \begin{bmatrix} f_{x_1}(\mathbf{a}) & f_{x_2}(\mathbf{a}) & \cdots & f_{x_n}(\mathbf{a}) \end{bmatrix} \begin{bmatrix} h_1 \\ h_2 \\ \vdots \\ h_n \end{bmatrix}$$

$$+ \frac{1}{2} \begin{bmatrix} h_1 & h_2 & \cdots & h_n \end{bmatrix} \begin{bmatrix} f_{x_1 x_1}(\mathbf{a}) & f_{x_1 x_2}(\mathbf{a}) & \cdots & f_{x_1 x_n}(\mathbf{a}) \\ f_{x_2 x_1}(\mathbf{a}) & f_{x_2 x_2}(\mathbf{a}) & \cdots & f_{x_2 x_n}(\mathbf{a}) \\ \vdots & \vdots & \ddots & \vdots \\ f_{x_n x_1}(\mathbf{a}) & f_{x_n x_2}(\mathbf{a}) & \cdots & f_{x_n x_n}(\mathbf{a}) \end{bmatrix} \begin{bmatrix} h_1 \\ h_2 \\ \vdots \\ h_n \end{bmatrix}.$$

Thus, we see that

$$p_2(\mathbf{x}) = f(\mathbf{a}) + Df(\mathbf{a})\mathbf{h} + \tfrac{1}{2}\mathbf{h}^T Hf(\mathbf{a})\mathbf{h}. \tag{10}$$

(Remember that $\mathbf{h}^T$ is the *transpose* of the $n \times 1$ matrix $\mathbf{h}$.)

EXAMPLE 11   (Example 10 revisited)   For $f(x, y) = \cos x \cos y$, $\mathbf{a} = (0, 0)$, we have

$$Df(x, y) = \begin{bmatrix} -\sin x \cos y & -\cos x \sin y \end{bmatrix}$$

and

$$Hf(x, y) = \begin{bmatrix} -\cos x \cos y & \sin x \sin y \\ \sin x \sin y & -\cos x \cos y \end{bmatrix}.$$

Hence,

$$p_2(x, y) = f(0, 0) + Df(0, 0)\mathbf{h} + \tfrac{1}{2}\mathbf{h}^T Hf(0, 0)\mathbf{h}$$

$$= 1 + \begin{bmatrix} 0 & 0 \end{bmatrix} \begin{bmatrix} h_1 \\ h_2 \end{bmatrix} + \tfrac{1}{2}\begin{bmatrix} h_1 & h_2 \end{bmatrix} \begin{bmatrix} -1 & 0 \\ 0 & -1 \end{bmatrix} \begin{bmatrix} h_1 \\ h_2 \end{bmatrix}$$

$$= 1 - \tfrac{1}{2}h_1^2 - \tfrac{1}{2}h_2^2.$$

Once we recall that $\mathbf{h} = (h_1, h_2) = (x - 0, y - 0) = (x, y)$, we see that this result checks with our work in Example 10, just as it should.   ◆

Higher-order Taylor Polynomials

So far we have said nothing about Taylor polynomials of degree greater than 2 in the case of functions of several variables. The main reasons for this are (i) the general formula is quite complicated and has no compact matrix reformulation analogous to (10) and (ii) we will have little need for such formulas in this text. Nonetheless, if your curiosity cannot be denied, here is the third-order Taylor polynomial for a function $f: X \subseteq \mathbf{R}^n \to \mathbf{R}$ of class C^3 near $\mathbf{a} \in X$:

$$p_3(\mathbf{x}) = f(\mathbf{a}) + \sum_{i=1}^{n} f_{x_i}(\mathbf{a})(x_i - a_i) + \frac{1}{2} \sum_{i,j=1}^{n} f_{x_i x_j}(\mathbf{a})(x_i - a_i)(x_j - a_j)$$

$$+ \frac{1}{3!} \sum_{i,j,k=1}^{n} f_{x_i x_j x_k}(\mathbf{a})(x_i - a_i)(x_j - a_j)(x_k - a_k).$$

(The relevant theorem regarding p_3 is that $f(\mathbf{x}) = p_3(\mathbf{x}) + R_3(\mathbf{x}, \mathbf{a})$, where $|R_3(\mathbf{x}, \mathbf{a})|/\|\mathbf{x} - \mathbf{a}\|^3 \to 0$ as $\mathbf{x} \to \mathbf{a}$.) If you must know even more, the kth-order Taylor polynomial is

$$p_k(\mathbf{x}) = f(\mathbf{a}) + \sum_{i=1}^{n} f_{x_i}(\mathbf{a})(x_i - a_i) + \frac{1}{2} \sum_{i,j=1}^{n} f_{x_i x_j}(\mathbf{a})(x_i - a_i)(x_j - a_j)$$

$$+ \cdots + \frac{1}{k!} \sum_{i_1,\ldots,i_k=1}^{n} f_{x_{i_1} \cdots x_{i_k}}(\mathbf{a})(x_{i_1} - a_{i_1}) \cdots (x_{i_k} - a_{i_k}).$$

Formulas for Remainder Terms (optional)

Under slightly stricter hypotheses than those appearing in Theorems 1.3 and 1.5, integral formulas for the remainder terms may be derived as follows. Set $\mathbf{h} = \mathbf{x} - \mathbf{a}$. If f is of class C^2, then

$$R_1(\mathbf{x}, \mathbf{a}) = \sum_{i,j=1}^{n} \int_0^1 (1 - t) f_{x_i x_j}(\mathbf{a} + t\mathbf{h}) h_i h_j \, dt$$

$$= \int_0^1 \left[\mathbf{h}^T Hf(\mathbf{a} + t\mathbf{h})\mathbf{h} \right] (1 - t) \, dt.$$

If f is of class C^3, then

$$R_2(\mathbf{x}, \mathbf{a}) = \sum_{i,j,k=1}^{n} \int_0^1 \frac{(1-t)^2}{2} f_{x_i x_j x_k}(\mathbf{a} + t\mathbf{h}) h_i h_j h_k \, dt,$$

and if f is of class C^{k+1}, then

$$R_k(\mathbf{x}, \mathbf{a}) = \sum_{i_i,\ldots,i_{k+1}=1}^{n} \int_0^1 \frac{(1-t)^k}{k!} f_{x_{i_1} x_{i_2} \cdots x_{i_{k+1}}}(\mathbf{a} + t\mathbf{h}) h_{i_1} h_{i_2} \cdots h_{i_{k+1}} \, dt.$$

Although explicit, these formulas are not very useful in practice. By artful application of Taylor's formula for a single variable, we can arrive at derivative versions of these remainder terms (known as **Lagrange's form of the remainder**) that are similar to those in the one-variable case.

Lagrange's form of the remainder. If f is of class C^2, then in Theorem 1.3 the remainder R_1 is

$$R_1(\mathbf{x}, \mathbf{a}) = \frac{1}{2} \sum_{i,j=1}^{n} f_{x_i x_j}(\mathbf{z}) h_i h_j$$

for a suitable point $\mathbf{z}$ in the domain of f on the line segment joining $\mathbf{a}$ and $\mathbf{x} = \mathbf{a} + \mathbf{h}$. Similarly, if f is of class C^3, then the remainder R_2 in Theorem 1.5 is

$$R_2(\mathbf{x}, \mathbf{a}) = \frac{1}{3!} \sum_{i,j,k=1}^{n} f_{x_i x_j x_k}(\mathbf{z}) h_i h_j h_k$$

for a suitable point $\mathbf{z}$ on the line segment joining $\mathbf{a}$ and $\mathbf{x} = \mathbf{a} + \mathbf{h}$. More generally, if f is of class C^{k+1}, then the remainder R_k is

$$R_k(\mathbf{x}, \mathbf{a}) = \frac{1}{(k+1)!} \sum_{i_1,\ldots,i_{k+1}=1}^{n} f_{x_{i_1} x_{i_2} \cdots x_{i_{k+1}}}(\mathbf{z}) h_{i_1} h_{i_2} \cdots h_{i_{k+1}}$$

for a suitable point $\mathbf{z}$ on the line segment joining $\mathbf{a}$ and $\mathbf{x} = \mathbf{a} + \mathbf{h}$.

The remainder formulas above are established in the addendum to this section.

EXAMPLE 12   For $f(x, y) = \cos x \cos y$, we have

$$|R_2(x, y, 0, 0)| = \frac{1}{3!} \left| \sum_{i,j,k=1}^{2} f_{x_i x_j x_k}(\mathbf{z}) h_i h_j h_k \right|$$

$$\leq \frac{1}{3!} \sum_{i,j,k=1}^{2} 1 \cdot |h_i h_j h_k|,$$

since all partial derivatives of f will be a product of sines and cosines and, hence, no larger than 1 in magnitude. Expanding the sum, we get

$$|R_2(x, y, 0, 0)| \leq \tfrac{1}{6} \left(|h_1|^3 + 3h_1^2 |h_2| + 3|h_1| h_2^2 + |h_2|^3 \right).$$

If both $|h_1|$ and $|h_2|$ are no more than, say, 0.1, then

$$|R_2(x, y, 0, 0)| \leq \tfrac{1}{6} \left(8 \cdot (0.1)^3 \right) = 0.001\bar{3}.$$

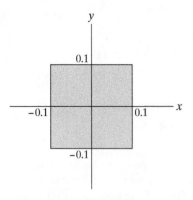

Figure 4.10 The polynomial p_2 approximates f to within $0.001\bar{3}$ on the square shown. (See Example 12.)

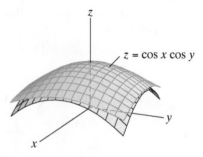

Figure 4.11 The graph of $f(x, y) = \cos x \cos y$ and its Taylor polynomial $p_2(x, y) = 1 - \frac{1}{2}x^2 - \frac{1}{2}y^2$ over the square $\{(x, y) \mid -1 \le x \le 1, -1 \le y \le 1\}$.

So throughout the square of side 0.2 centered at the origin and shown in Figure 4.10, the second-order Taylor polynomial is accurate to at least $0.001\bar{3}$ (i.e., to two decimal places) as an approximation of $f(x, y) = \cos x \ \cos y$. In Figure 4.11, we show the graph of $f(x, y) = \cos x \cos y$ over the square domain $\{(x, y) \mid -1 \le x \le 1, \ -1 \le y \le 1\}$ together with the graph of its second-order Taylor polynomial $p_2(x, y) = 1 - \frac{1}{2}x^2 - \frac{1}{2}y^2$ (calculated in Example 10). Note how closely the surfaces coincide near the point $(0, 0, 1)$, just as the analysis above indicates. ◆

Addendum: Proofs of Theorem 1.1, Proposition 1.2, and Theorem 1.5

Below we establish some of the fundamental results used in this section. We begin by proving Theorem 1.1, Taylor's theorem for function of a single variable, and Proposition 1.2 regarding the remainder term in Theorem 1.1. We then use these results to "bootstrap" a proof of the multivariable result of Theorem 1.5 and to derive Lagrange's formula for the remainder term appearing in it.

Proof of Theorem 1.1 We prove the result under the stronger assumption that f is of class C^{k+1} rather than assuming that f is only differentiable up to order k. (This distinction matters little in practice.)

By the fundamental theorem of calculus,

$$f(x) - f(a) = \int_a^x f'(t) \, dt. \tag{11}$$

We evaluate the integral on the right side of (11) by means of integration by parts. Recall that the relevant formula is

$$\int u \, dv = uv - \int v \, du.$$

We use this formula with $u = f'(t)$ and $v = x - t$ so that $dv = -dt$. (Note that in the right side of (11), x plays the role of a constant.) We obtain

$$\int_a^x f'(t) \, dt = -f'(t)(x - t) \Big|_a^x + \int_a^x (x - t) f''(t) \, dt$$

$$= f'(a)(x - a) + \int_a^x (x - t) f''(t) \, dt. \tag{12}$$

Combining (11) and (12), we have

$$f(x) = f(a) + f'(a)(x-a) + \int_a^x (x-t)f''(t)\,dt. \qquad (13)$$

Thus, we have shown, when f is differentiable up to (at least) second order, that

$$R_1(x, a) = \int_a^x (x-t)f''(t)\,dt.$$

This provides an integral formula for the remainder in formula (1) of Theorem 1.1 when $k = 1$, although we have not yet established that $R_1(x, a)/(x-a) \to 0$ as $x \to a$.

To obtain the second-order formula, the case $k = 2$ of (1), we focus on $R_1(x, a) = \int_a^x (x-t)f''(t)\,dt$ and integrate by parts again, this time with $u = f''(t)$ and $v = (x-t)^2/2$, so that $dv = -(x-t)\,dt$. We obtain

$$\int_a^x (x-t)f''(t)\,dt = -\frac{f''(t)(x-t)^2}{2}\Big|_a^x + \int_a^x \frac{(x-t)^2}{2}f'''(t)\,dt$$

$$= \frac{f''(a)(x-a)^2}{2} + \int_a^x \frac{(x-t)^2}{2}f'''(t)\,dt.$$

Hence (13) becomes

$$f(x) = f(a) + f'(a)(x-a) + \frac{f''(a)}{2}(x-a)^2 + \int_a^x \frac{(x-t)^2}{2}f'''(t)\,dt.$$

Therefore, we have shown, when f is differentiable up to (at least) third order, that

$$R_2(x, a) = \int_a^x \frac{(x-t)^2}{2}f'''(t)\,dt.$$

We can continue to argue in this manner or use mathematical induction to show that formula (1) holds in general with

$$R_k(x, a) = \int_a^x \frac{(x-t)^k}{k!}f^{(k+1)}(t)\,dt, \qquad (14)$$

assuming that f is differentiable up to order (at least) $k + 1$.

It remains to see that $R_k(x, a)/(x-a)^k \to 0$ as $x \to a$. In formula (14) we are only considering t between a and x, so that $|x-t| \le |x-a|$. Moreover, since we are assuming that f is of class C^{k+1}, we have that $f^{(k+1)}(t)$ is continuous and, therefore, bounded for t between a and x (i.e., that $|f^{(k+1)}(t)| \le M$ for some constant M). Thus,

$$|R_k(x, a)| \le \left| \int_a^x \frac{(x-t)^k}{k!}f^{(k+1)}(t)\,dt \right| \le \pm \int_a^x \left| \frac{(x-t)^k}{k!}f^{(k+1)}(t) \right|\,dt,$$

where the plus sign applies if $x \ge a$ and the negative sign if $x < a$,

$$\le \pm \int_a^x \frac{M}{k!}|x-a|^k\,dt = \frac{M}{k!}|x-a|^{k+1}.$$

Thus,

$$\left| \frac{R_k(x, a)}{(x-a)^k} \right| \le \frac{M}{k!}|x-a| \to 0$$

as $x \to a$, as desired.   ∎

Proof of Proposition 1.2 We establish Proposition 1.2 by means of a general version of the mean value theorem for integrals. This theorem states that for continuous functions g and h such that h does not change sign on $[a, b]$ (i.e., either $h(t) \geq 0$ on $[a, b]$ or $h(t) \leq 0$ on $[a, b]$), there is some number z between a and b such that

$$\int_a^b g(t)h(t)\,dt = g(z)\int_a^b h(t)\,dt.$$

(We omit the proof but remark that this theorem is a consequence of the intermediate value theorem.) Applying this result to formula (14) with $g(t) = f^{(k+1)}(t)$ and $h(t) = (x-t)^k/k!$, we find that there must exist some z between a and x such that

$$R_k(x, a) = f^{(k+1)}(z)\int_a^x \frac{(x-t)^k}{k!}\,dt = f^{(k+1)}(z)\left(-\frac{(x-t)^{k+1}}{(k+1)!}\right)\Big|_{t=a}^{t=x}$$

$$= \frac{f^{(k+1)}(z)}{(k+1)!}(x-a)^{k+1}. \qquad \blacksquare$$

Proof of Theorem 1.5 As in the proof of Theorem 1.1, we establish Theorem 1.5 under the stronger assumption that f is of class C^3. Begin by setting $\mathbf{h} = \mathbf{x} - \mathbf{a}$, so that $\mathbf{x} = \mathbf{a} + \mathbf{h}$, and consider $\mathbf{a}$ and $\mathbf{h}$ to be fixed. We define the one-variable function F by $F(t) = f(\mathbf{a} + t\mathbf{h})$. Since f is assumed to be of class C^3 on an open set X, if we take $\mathbf{x}$ sufficiently close to $\mathbf{a}$, then F is of class C^3 on an open interval containing $[0, 1]$. Thus, Theorem 1.1 with $k = 2$, $a = 0$, and $x = 1$ may be applied to give

$$F(1) = F(0) + F'(0)(1-0) + \frac{F''(0)}{2!}(1-0)^2 + R_2(1, 0)$$

$$= F(0) + F'(0) + \frac{F''(0)}{2} + R_2(1, 0), \qquad (15)$$

where $R_2(1, 0) = \int_0^1 \frac{(1-t)^2}{2} F'''(t)\,dt$. Now we use the chain rule to calculate derivatives of F in terms of partial derivatives of f:

$$F'(t) = Df(\mathbf{a} + t\mathbf{h})\mathbf{h} = \sum_{i=1}^n f_{x_i}(\mathbf{a} + t\mathbf{h})h_i;$$

$$F''(t) = \sum_{i=1}^n\left[\sum_{j=1}^n f_{x_ix_j}(\mathbf{a} + t\mathbf{h})h_j\right]h_i = \sum_{i,j=1}^n f_{x_ix_j}(\mathbf{a} + t\mathbf{h})h_ih_j;$$

$$F'''(t) = \sum_{k=1}^n\left[\sum_{i,j=1}^n f_{x_ix_jx_k}(\mathbf{a} + t\mathbf{h})h_ih_j\right]h_k = \sum_{i,j,k=1}^n f_{x_ix_jx_k}(\mathbf{a} + t\mathbf{h})h_ih_jh_k.$$

Thus, (15) becomes

$$f(\mathbf{a} + \mathbf{h}) = f(\mathbf{a}) + \sum_{i=1}^n f_{x_i}(\mathbf{a})h_i + \frac{1}{2}\sum_{i,j=1}^n f_{x_ix_j}(\mathbf{a})h_ih_j$$

$$+ \sum_{i,j,k=1}^n \int_0^1 \frac{(1-t)^2}{2} f_{x_ix_jx_k}(\mathbf{a} + t\mathbf{h})h_ih_jh_k\,dt,$$

or, equivalently,

$$f(\mathbf{x}) = f(\mathbf{a}) + \sum_{i=1}^{n} f_{x_i}(\mathbf{a})(x_i - a_i) + \frac{1}{2} \sum_{i,j=1}^{n} f_{x_i x_j}(\mathbf{a})(x_i - a_i)(x_j - a_j)$$
$$+ R_2(\mathbf{x}, \mathbf{a}),$$

where the multivariable remainder is

$$R_2(\mathbf{x}, \mathbf{a}) = \sum_{i,j,k=1}^{n} \int_0^1 \frac{(1-t)^2}{2} f_{x_i x_j x_k}(\mathbf{a} + t\mathbf{h}) h_i h_j h_k \, dt. \qquad (16)$$

We must still show that $|R_2(\mathbf{x}, \mathbf{a})| / \|\mathbf{x} - \mathbf{a}\|^2 \to 0$ as $\mathbf{x} \to \mathbf{a}$, or, equivalently, that $|R_2(\mathbf{x}, \mathbf{a})| / \|\mathbf{h}\|^2 \to 0$ as $\mathbf{h} \to \mathbf{0}$. To demonstrate this, note that, for $\mathbf{a}$ and $\mathbf{h}$ fixed, the expression $(1-t)^2 f_{x_i x_j x_k}(\mathbf{a} + t\mathbf{h})$ is continuous for t in $[0, 1]$ (since f is assumed to be of class C^3), hence bounded. In addition, for $i = 1, \ldots, n$, we have that $|h_i| \leq \|\mathbf{h}\|$. Hence,

$$|R_2(\mathbf{x}, \mathbf{a})| = \left| \sum_{i,j,k=1}^{n} \int_0^1 \frac{(1-t)^2}{2} f_{x_i x_j x_k}(\mathbf{a} + t\mathbf{h}) h_i h_j h_k \, dt \right|$$

$$\leq \sum_{i,j,k=1}^{n} \int_0^1 \left| \frac{(1-t)^2}{2} f_{x_i x_j x_k}(\mathbf{a} + t\mathbf{h}) h_i h_j h_k \right| dt$$

$$\leq \sum_{i,j,k=1}^{n} \int_0^1 M\|h\|^3 \, dt = n^3 M \|\mathbf{h}\|^3 = n^3 M \|\mathbf{x} - \mathbf{a}\|^3.$$

Thus,

$$\frac{|R_2(\mathbf{x}, \mathbf{a})|}{\|\mathbf{x} - \mathbf{a}\|^2} \leq n^3 M \|\mathbf{x} - \mathbf{a}\| \to 0$$

as $\mathbf{x} \to \mathbf{a}$.

Finally, we remark that entirely similar arguments may be given to establish results for Taylor polynomials of orders higher than two. ■

Lagrange's formula for the remainder (see page 257) Using the function $F(t) = f(\mathbf{a} + t\mathbf{h})$ defined in the proof of Theorem 1.5, Proposition 1.2 implies that there must be some number c between 0 and 1 such that the one-variable remainder is

$$R_2(1, 0) = \frac{F'''(c)}{3!}(1 - 0)^3.$$

Now, the remainder term $R_2(1, 0)$ from Proposition 1.2 is precisely $R_2(\mathbf{x}, \mathbf{a})$ in Theorem 1.5 and

$$F'''(c) = \sum_{i,j,k=1}^{n} f_{x_i x_j x_k}(\mathbf{a} + c\mathbf{h}) h_i h_j h_k = \sum_{i,j,k=1}^{n} f_{x_i x_j x_k}(\mathbf{z}) h_i h_j h_k,$$

where $\mathbf{z} = \mathbf{a} + c\mathbf{h}$. Since c is between 0 and 1, the point $\mathbf{z}$ lies on the line segment joining $\mathbf{a}$ and $\mathbf{x} = \mathbf{a} + \mathbf{h}$, and so

$$R_2(\mathbf{x}, \mathbf{a}) = \frac{1}{3!} \sum_{i,j,k=1}^{n} f_{x_i x_j x_k}(\mathbf{z}) h_i h_j h_k,$$

which is the result we desire. The derivation of the formula for $R_k(\mathbf{x}, \mathbf{a})$ for $k > 2$ is analogous. ■

4.1 Exercises

In Exercises 1–7, find the Taylor polynomials p_k of given order k at the indicated point a.

1. $f(x) = e^{2x}, a = 0, k = 4$

2. $f(x) = \ln(1+x), a = 0, k = 3$

3. $f(x) = 1/x^2, a = 1, k = 4$

4. $f(x) = \sqrt{x}, a = 1, k = 3$

5. $f(x) = \sqrt{x}, a = 9, k = 3$

6. $f(x) = \sin x, a = 0, k = 5$

7. $f(x) = \sin x, a = \pi/2, k = 5$

*In Exercises 8–15, find the first- and second-order Taylor polynomials for the given function f at the given point **a**.*

8. $f(x, y) = 1/(x^2 + y^2 + 1), \mathbf{a} = (0, 0)$

9. $f(x, y) = 1/(x^2 + y^2 + 1), \mathbf{a} = (1, -1)$

10. $f(x, y) = e^{2x+y}, \mathbf{a} = (0, 0)$

11. $f(x, y) = e^{2x} \cos 3y, \mathbf{a} = (0, \pi)$

12. $f(x, y, z) = ye^{3x} + ze^{2y}, \mathbf{a} = (0, 0, 2)$

13. $f(x, y, z) = xy - 3y^2 + 2xz, \mathbf{a} = (2, -1, 1)$

14. $f(x, y, z) = 1/(x^2 + y^2 + z^2 + 1), \mathbf{a} = (0, 0, 0)$

15. $f(x, y, z) = \sin xyz, \mathbf{a} = (0, 0, 0)$

*In Exercises 16–20, calculate the Hessian matrix $Hf(\mathbf{a})$ for the indicated function f at the indicated point **a**.*

16. $f(x, y) = 1/(x^2 + y^2 + 1), \mathbf{a} = (0, 0)$

17. $f(x, y) = \cos x \sin y, \mathbf{a} = (\pi/4, \pi/3)$

18. $f(x, y, z) = \dfrac{z}{\sqrt{xy}}, \mathbf{a} = (1, 2, -4)$

19. $f(x, y, z) = x^3 + x^2y - yz^2 + 2z^3, \mathbf{a} = (1, 0, 1)$

20. $f(x, y, z) = e^{2x-3y} \sin 5z, \mathbf{a} = (0, 0, 0)$

21. For f and **a** as given in Exercise 8, express the second-order Taylor polynomial $p_2(x, y)$, using the derivative matrix and the Hessian matrix as in formula (10) of this section.

22. For f and **a** as given in Exercise 11, express the second-order Taylor polynomial $p_2(x, y)$, using the derivative matrix and the Hessian matrix as in formula (10) of this section.

23. For f and **a** as given in Exercise 12, express the second-order Taylor polynomial $p_2(x, y, z)$, using the derivative matrix and the Hessian matrix as in formula (10) of this section.

24. For f and **a** as given in Exercise 19, express the second-order Taylor polynomial $p_2(x, y, z)$, using the derivative matrix and the Hessian matrix as in formula (10) of this section.

25. Consider the function

$$f(x_1, x_2, \ldots, x_n) = e^{x_1 + 2x_2 + \cdots + nx_n}.$$

(a) Calculate $Df(0, 0, \ldots, 0)$ and $Hf(0, 0, \ldots, 0)$.

(b) Determine the first- and second-order Taylor polynomials of f at **0**.

(c) Use formulas (3) and (10) to write the Taylor polynomials in terms of the derivative and Hessian matrices.

26. Find the third-order Taylor polynomial $p_3(x, y, z)$ of

$$f(x, y, z) = e^{x+2y+3z}$$

at $(0, 0, 0)$.

27. Find the third-order Taylor polynomial of

$$f(x, y, z) = x^4 + x^3y + 2y^3 - xz^2 + x^2y + 3xy - z + 2$$

(a) at $(0, 0, 0)$.

(b) at $(1, -1, 0)$.

Determine the total differential of the functions given in Exercises 28–32.

28. $f(x, y) = x^2y^3$

29. $f(x, y, z) = x^2 + 3y^2 - 2z^3$

30. $f(x, y, z) = \cos(xyz)$

31. $f(x, y, z) = e^x \cos y + e^y \sin z$

32. $f(x, y, z) = 1/\sqrt{xyz}$

33. Use the fact that the total differential df approximates the incremental change Δf to provide estimates of the following quantities:

(a) $(7.07)^2(1.98)^3$

(b) $1/\sqrt{(4.1)(1.96)(2.05)}$

(c) $(1.1)\cos((\pi - 0.03)(0.12))$

34. Near the point $(1, -2, 1)$, is the function $g(x, y, z) = x^3 - 2xy + x^2z + 7z$ most sensitive to changes in x, y, or z?

35. To which entry in the matrix is the value of the determinant

$$\begin{vmatrix} 2 & 3 \\ -1 & 5 \end{vmatrix}$$

most sensitive?

36. If you measure the radius of a cylinder to be 2 in, with a possible error of ± 0.1 in, and the height to be 3 in, with a possible error of ± 0.05 in, use differentials to determine the approximate error in

(a) the calculated volume of the cylinder.

(b) the calculated surface area.

37. A can of mushrooms is currently manufactured to have a diameter of 5 cm and a height of 12 cm. The manufacturer plans to reduce the diameter by 0.5 cm. Use differentials to estimate how much the height of the can would need to be increased in order to keep the volume of the can the same.

38. Consider a triangle with sides of lengths a and b that make an interior angle θ.

(a) If $a = 3$, $b = 4$, and $\theta = \pi/3$, to changes in which of these measurements is the area of the triangle most sensitive?

(b) If the length measurements in part (a) are in error by as much as 5% and the angle measurement is in error by as much as 2%, estimate the resulting maximum percentage error in calculated area.

39. To estimate the volume of a cone of radius approximately 2 m and height approximately 6 m, how accurately should the radius and height be measured so that the error in the calculated volume estimate does

not exceed 0.2 m^3? Assume that the possible errors in measuring the radius and height are the same.

40. Suppose that you measure the dimensions of a block of tofu to be (approximately) 3 in by 4 in by 2 in. Assuming that the possible errors in each of your measurements are the same, about how accurate must your measurements be so that the error in the calculated volume of the tofu is not more than 0.2 in^3? What percentage error in volume does this represent?

41. (a) Calculate the second-order Taylor polynomial for $f(x, y) = \cos x \, \sin y$ at the point $(0, \pi/2)$.

(b) If $\mathbf{h} = (h_1, h_2) = (x, y) - (0, \pi/2)$ is such that $|h_1|$ and $|h_2|$ are no more than 0.3, estimate how accurate your Taylor approximation is.

42. (a) Determine the second-order Taylor polynomial of $f(x, y) = e^{x+2y}$ at the origin.

(b) Estimate the accuracy of the approximation if $|x|$ and $|y|$ are no more than 0.1.

43. (a) Determine the second-order Taylor polynomial of $f(x, y) = e^{2x} \cos y$ at the point $(0, \pi/2)$.

(b) If $\mathbf{h} = (h_1, h_2) = (x, y) - (0, \pi/2)$ is such that $|h_1| \leq 0.2$ and $|h_2| \leq 0.1$, estimate the accuracy of the approximation to f given by your Taylor polynomial in part (a).

4.2 Extrema of Functions

The power of calculus resides at least in part in its role in helping to solve a wide variety of optimization problems. With any quantity that changes, it is natural to ask when, if ever, does that quantity reach its largest, its smallest, its fastest or slowest? You have already learned how to find maxima and minima of a function of a single variable, and no doubt you have applied your techniques to a number of situations. However, many phenomena are not appropriately modeled by functions of only one variable. Thus, there is a genuine need to adapt and extend optimization methods to the case of functions of more than one variable. We develop the necessary theory in this section and the next and explore a few applications in §4.4.

Critical Points of Functions

Let X be open in $\mathbf{R}^n$ and $f: X \subseteq \mathbf{R}^n \to \mathbf{R}$ a scalar-valued function.

Figure 4.12 The graph of $z = f(x, y)$.

DEFINITION 2.1 We say that f has a **local minimum** at the point $\mathbf{a}$ in X if there is some neighborhood U of $\mathbf{a}$ such that $f(\mathbf{x}) \geq f(\mathbf{a})$ for all $\mathbf{x}$ in U. Similarly, we say that f has a **local maximum** at $\mathbf{a}$ if there is some neighborhood U of $\mathbf{a}$ such that $f(\mathbf{x}) \leq f(\mathbf{a})$ for all $\mathbf{x}$ in U.

When $n = 2$, local extrema of $f(x, y)$ are precisely the pits and peaks of the surface given by the graph of $z = f(x, y)$, as suggested by Figure 4.12.

We emphasize our use of the adjective "local." When a local maximum of a function f occurs at a point **a**, this means that the values of f at points *near* **a** can be no larger, *not* that *all* values of f are no larger. Indeed, f may have local maxima and no **global** (or **absolute**) maximum. Consider the graphs in Figure 4.13. (Of course, analogous comments apply to local and global minima.)

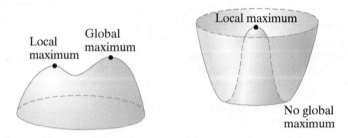

Figure 4.13 Examples of local and global maxima.

Recall that, if a differentiable function of one variable has a local extremum at a point, then the derivative vanishes there (i.e., the tangent line to the graph of the function is horizontal). Figures 4.12 and 4.13 suggest strongly that, if a function of two variables has a local maximum or minimum at a point in the domain, then the tangent plane at the corresponding point of the graph must be horizontal. Such is indeed the case, as the following general result (plus formula (4) of §2.3) implies.

THEOREM 2.2   Let X be open in $\mathbf{R}^n$ and let $f\colon X \subseteq \mathbf{R}^n \to \mathbf{R}$ be differentiable. If f has a local extremum at $\mathbf{a} \in X$, then $Df(\mathbf{a}) = \mathbf{0}$.

PROOF   Suppose, for argument's sake, that f has a local maximum at **a**. Then the one-variable function F defined by $F(t) = f(\mathbf{a} + t\mathbf{h})$ must have a local maximum at $t = 0$ for *any* **h**. (Geometrically, the function F is just the restriction of f to the line through **a** parallel to **h** as shown in Figure 4.14.) From one-variable calculus, we must therefore have $F'(0) = 0$. By the chain rule

$$F'(t) = \frac{d}{dt}[f(\mathbf{a} + t\mathbf{h})] = Df(\mathbf{a} + t\mathbf{h})\mathbf{h} = \nabla f(\mathbf{a} + t\mathbf{h}) \cdot \mathbf{h}.$$

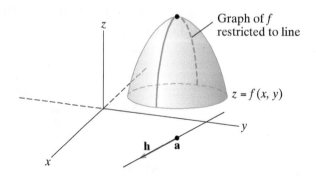

Figure 4.14 The graph of f restricted to a line.

Hence,

$$0 = F'(0) = Df(\mathbf{a})\mathbf{h} = f_{x_1}(\mathbf{a})h_1 + f_{x_2}(\mathbf{a})h_2 + \cdots + f_{x_n}(\mathbf{a})h_n.$$

Since this last result must hold for all $\mathbf{h} \in \mathbf{R}^n$, we find that by setting $\mathbf{h}$ in turn equal to $(1, 0, \ldots, 0), (0, 1, 0, \ldots, 0), \ldots, (0, \ldots, 0, 1)$, we have

$$f_{x_1}(\mathbf{a}) = f_{x_2}(\mathbf{a}) = \cdots = f_{x_n}(\mathbf{a}) = 0.$$

Therefore, $Df(\mathbf{a}) = \mathbf{0}$, as desired. ∎

A point $\mathbf{a}$ in the domain of f where $Df(\mathbf{a})$ is either zero or undefined is called a **critical point** of f. Theorem 2.2 says that any extremum of f must occur at a critical point. However, it is by no means the case that every critical point must be the site of an extremum.

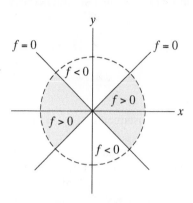

Figure 4.15 The function f is strictly positive on the shaded region, strictly negative on the unshaded region, and zero along the lines $y = \pm x$.

EXAMPLE 1 If $f(x, y) = x^2 - y^2$, then $Df(x, y) = \begin{bmatrix} 2x & -2y \end{bmatrix}$ so that, clearly, $(0, 0)$ is the only critical point. However, neither a maximum nor a minimum occurs at $(0, 0)$. Indeed, inside every open disk centered at $(0, 0)$, no matter how small, there are points for which $f(x, y) > f(0, 0) = 0$ and also points where $f(x, y) < f(0, 0)$. (See Figure 4.15.) ◆

This type of critical point is called a **saddle point**. Its name derives from the fact that the graph of $z = f(x, y)$ looks somewhat like a saddle. (See Figure 4.16.)

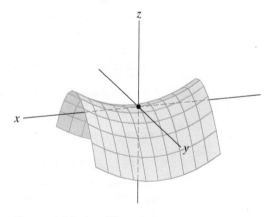

Figure 4.16 A saddle point.

EXAMPLE 2 Let $f(x, y) = \sqrt[3]{x^2 + y^2}$. The domain of f is all of $\mathbf{R}^2$. We compute that $Df(x, y) = \begin{bmatrix} \dfrac{2x}{3(x^2 + y^2)^{2/3}} & \dfrac{2y}{3(x^2 + y^2)^{2/3}} \end{bmatrix}$; note that Df is undefined at $(0, 0)$ and nonzero at all other $(x, y) \in \mathbf{R}^2$. Hence, $(0, 0)$ is the only critical point. Since $f(x, y) \geq 0$ for all (x, y) and has value 0 only at $(0, 0)$, we see that f has a unique (global) minimum at $(0, 0)$. ◆

The Nature of a Critical Point: The Hessian Criterion

We illustrate our current understanding regarding extrema with the following example:

EXAMPLE 3 We find the extrema of

$$f(x, y) = x^2 + xy + y^2 + 2x - 2y + 5.$$

Since f is a polynomial, it is differentiable everywhere, and Theorem 2.2 implies that any extremum must occur where $\partial f/\partial x$ and $\partial f/\partial y$ vanish simultaneously. Thus, we solve

$$\begin{cases} \dfrac{\partial f}{\partial x} = 2x + y + 2 = 0 \\[2mm] \dfrac{\partial f}{\partial y} = x + 2y - 2 = 0 \end{cases},$$

and find that the only solution is $x = -2$, $y = 2$. Consequently, $(-2, 2)$ is the only critical point of this function.

To determine whether $(-2, 2)$ is a maximum or minimum (or neither), we could try graphing the function and drawing what we hope would be an obvious conclusion. Of course, such a technique does not extend to functions of more than two variables, so a graphical method is of limited value at best. Instead, we'll see how f changes as we move away from the critical point:

$$\begin{aligned} \Delta f &= f(-2+h, 2+k) - f(-2, 2) \\ &= [(-2+h)^2 + (-2+h)(2+k) + (2+k)^2 \\ &\quad + 2(-2+h) - 2(2+k) + 5] - 1 \\ &= h^2 + hk + k^2. \end{aligned}$$

If the quantity $\Delta f = h^2 + hk + k^2$ is nonnegative for all small values of h and k, then $(-2, 2)$ yields a local minimum. Similarly, if Δf is always nonpositive, then $(-2, 2)$ must yield a local maximum. Finally, if Δf is positive for some values of h and k and negative for others, then $(-2, 2)$ is a saddle point. To determine which possibility holds, we complete the square:

$$\Delta f = h^2 + hk + k^2 = h^2 + hk + \tfrac{1}{4}k^2 + \tfrac{3}{4}k^2 = \left(h + \tfrac{1}{2}k\right)^2 + \tfrac{3}{4}k^2.$$

Thus, $\Delta f \geq 0$ for all values of h and k, so $(-2, 2)$ necessarily yields a local minimum.   ◆

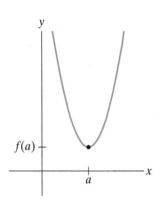

Figure 4.17 An upward-opening parabola.

Example 3 with its attendant algebra clearly demonstrates the need for a better way of determining when a critical point yields a local maximum or minimum (or neither). In the case of a twice differentiable function $f\colon X \subseteq \mathbf{R} \to \mathbf{R}$, you already know a quick method, namely, consideration of the sign of the second derivative. This method derives from looking at the second-order Taylor polynomial of f near the critical point a, namely,

$$\begin{aligned} f(x) \approx p_2(x) &= f(a) + f'(a)(x - a) + \frac{f''(a)}{2}(x - a)^2 \\ &= f(a) + \frac{f''(a)}{2}(x - a)^2, \end{aligned}$$

since f' is zero at the critical point a of f. If $f''(a) > 0$, the graph of $y = p_2(x)$ is an upward-opening parabola, as in Figure 4.17, whereas if $f''(a) < 0$, then the graph of $y = p_2(x)$ looks like the one shown in Figure 4.18. If $f''(a) = 0$, then the graph of $y = p_2(x)$ is just a horizontal line, and we would need to use a higher-order Taylor polynomial to determine if f has an extremum at a. (You may recall that when $f''(a) = 0$, the second derivative test from single-variable calculus gives no information about the nature of the critical point a.)

The concept is similar in the context of n variables. Suppose that

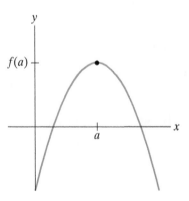

Figure 4.18 A downward-opening parabola.

$$f(\mathbf{x}) = f(x_1, x_2, \ldots, x_n)$$

is of class C^2 and that $\mathbf{a} = (a_1, a_2, \ldots, a_n)$ is a critical point of f. Then the second-order Taylor approximation to f gives

$$\Delta f = f(\mathbf{x}) - f(\mathbf{a}) \approx p_2(\mathbf{x}) - f(\mathbf{a})$$
$$= Df(\mathbf{a})(\mathbf{x} - \mathbf{a}) + \tfrac{1}{2}(\mathbf{x} - \mathbf{a})^T Hf(\mathbf{a})(\mathbf{x} - \mathbf{a})$$

when $\mathbf{x} \approx \mathbf{a}$. (See Theorem 1.5 and formula (10) in §4.1.) Since f is of class C^2 and $\mathbf{a}$ is a critical point, all the partial derivatives vanish at $\mathbf{a}$, so that we have $Df(\mathbf{a}) = \mathbf{0}$ and, hence,

$$\Delta f \approx \tfrac{1}{2}(\mathbf{x} - \mathbf{a})^T Hf(\mathbf{a})(\mathbf{x} - \mathbf{a}). \tag{1}$$

The approximation in (1) suggests that we may be able to see whether the increment Δf remains positive (respectively, remains negative) for $\mathbf{x}$ near $\mathbf{a}$ and, hence, whether f has a local minimum (respectively, a local maximum) at $\mathbf{a}$ by seeing what happens to the right side.

Note that the right side of (1), when expanded, is quadratic in the terms $(x_i - a_i)$. More generally, a **quadratic form** in $h_1, h_2, \ldots, h_n$ is a function Q that can be written as

$$Q(h_1, h_2, \ldots, h_n) = \sum_{i,j=1}^{n} b_{ij} h_i h_j,$$

where the b_{ij}'s are constants. The quadratic form Q can also be written in terms of matrices as

$$Q(\mathbf{h}) = \begin{bmatrix} h_1 & h_2 & \cdots & h_n \end{bmatrix} \begin{bmatrix} b_{11} & b_{12} & \cdots & b_{1n} \\ b_{21} & b_{22} & \cdots & b_{2n} \\ \vdots & \vdots & \ddots & \vdots \\ b_{n1} & b_{n2} & \cdots & b_{nn} \end{bmatrix} \begin{bmatrix} h_1 \\ h_2 \\ \vdots \\ h_n \end{bmatrix} = \mathbf{h}^T B \mathbf{h}, \tag{2}$$

where $B = (b_{ij})$. Note that the function Q is unchanged if we replace all b_{ij} with $\tfrac{1}{2}(b_{ij} + b_{ji})$. Hence, we may always assume that the matrix B associated to Q is **symmetric**, that is, that $b_{ij} = b_{ji}$ (or, equivalently, that $B^T = B$). Ignoring the factor of $1/2$, we see that the right side of (1) is the quadratic form in $\mathbf{h} = \mathbf{x} - \mathbf{a}$, corresponding to the matrix $B = Hf(\mathbf{a})$.

A quadratic form Q (respectively, its associated symmetric matrix B) is said to be **positive definite** if $Q(\mathbf{h}) > 0$ for all $\mathbf{h} \neq \mathbf{0}$ and **negative definite** if $Q(\mathbf{h}) < 0$ for all $\mathbf{h} \neq \mathbf{0}$. Note that if Q is positive definite, then Q has a global minimum (of 0) at $\mathbf{h} = \mathbf{0}$. Similarly, if Q is negative definite, then Q has a global maximum at $\mathbf{h} = \mathbf{0}$.

The importance of quadratic forms to us is that we can judge whether f has a local extremum at a critical point $\mathbf{a}$ by seeing if the quadratic form in the right side of (1) has a maximum or minimum at $\mathbf{x} = \mathbf{a}$. The precise result, whose proof is given in the addendum to this section, is the following:

THEOREM 2.3 Let $U \subseteq \mathbf{R}^n$ be open and $f: U \to \mathbf{R}$ a function of class C^2. Suppose that $\mathbf{a} \in U$ is a critical point of f.

1. If the Hessian $Hf(\mathbf{a})$ is positive definite, then f has a local minimum at $\mathbf{a}$.

2. If the Hessian $Hf(\mathbf{a})$ is negative definite, then f has a local maximum at $\mathbf{a}$.

3. If $\det Hf(\mathbf{a}) \neq 0$ but $Hf(\mathbf{a})$ is neither positive nor negative definite, then f has a saddle point at $\mathbf{a}$.

In view of Theorem 2.3, the issue thus becomes to determine when the Hessian $Hf(\mathbf{a})$ is positive or negative definite. Fortunately, linear algebra provides an effective means for making such a determination, which we state without proof. Given a symmetric matrix B (which, as we have seen, corresponds to a quadratic form Q), let B_k, for $k = 1, \ldots, n$, denote the upper leftmost $k \times k$ submatrix of B. Calculate the following sequence of determinants:

$$\det B_1 = b_{11}, \quad \det B_2 = \begin{vmatrix} b_{11} & b_{12} \\ b_{21} & b_{22} \end{vmatrix},$$

$$\det B_3 = \begin{vmatrix} b_{11} & b_{12} & b_{13} \\ b_{21} & b_{22} & b_{23} \\ b_{31} & b_{32} & b_{33} \end{vmatrix}, \ldots, \det B_n = \det B.$$

If this sequence consists entirely of positive numbers, then B and Q are positive definite. If this sequence is such that $\det B_k < 0$ for k odd and $\det B_k > 0$ for k even, then B and Q are negative definite. Finally, if $\det B \neq 0$, but the sequence of determinants $\det B_1, \det B_2, \ldots, \det B_n$ is neither of the first two types, then B and Q are neither positive nor negative definite. Combining these remarks with Theorem 2.3, we can establish the following test for local extrema:

Second derivative test for local extrema. Given a critical point $\mathbf{a}$ of a function f of class C^2, look at the Hessian matrix evaluated at $\mathbf{a}$:

$$Hf(\mathbf{a}) = \begin{bmatrix} f_{x_1x_1}(\mathbf{a}) & f_{x_1x_2}(\mathbf{a}) & \cdots & f_{x_1x_n}(\mathbf{a}) \\ f_{x_2x_1}(\mathbf{a}) & f_{x_2x_2}(\mathbf{a}) & \cdots & f_{x_2x_n}(\mathbf{a}) \\ \vdots & \vdots & \ddots & \vdots \\ f_{x_nx_1}(\mathbf{a}) & f_{x_nx_2}(\mathbf{a}) & \cdots & f_{x_nx_n}(\mathbf{a}) \end{bmatrix}.$$

From the Hessian, calculate the **sequence of principal minors** of $Hf(\mathbf{a})$. This is the sequence of the determinants of the upper leftmost square submatrices of $Hf(\mathbf{a})$. More explicitly, this is the sequence $d_1, d_2, \ldots, d_n$, where $d_k = \det H_k$, and H_k is the upper leftmost $k \times k$ submatrix of $Hf(\mathbf{a})$. That is,

$$d_1 = f_{x_1x_1}(\mathbf{a}),$$

$$d_2 = \begin{vmatrix} f_{x_1x_1}(\mathbf{a}) & f_{x_1x_2}(\mathbf{a}) \\ f_{x_2x_1}(\mathbf{a}) & f_{x_2x_2}(\mathbf{a}) \end{vmatrix},$$

$$d_3 = \begin{vmatrix} f_{x_1x_1}(\mathbf{a}) & f_{x_1x_2}(\mathbf{a}) & f_{x_1x_3}(\mathbf{a}) \\ f_{x_2x_1}(\mathbf{a}) & f_{x_2x_2}(\mathbf{a}) & f_{x_2x_3}(\mathbf{a}) \\ f_{x_3x_1}(\mathbf{a}) & f_{x_3x_2}(\mathbf{a}) & f_{x_3x_3}(\mathbf{a}) \end{vmatrix}, \ldots, d_n = |Hf(\mathbf{a})|.$$

The numerical test is as follows:
Assume that $d_n = \det Hf(\mathbf{a}) \neq 0$.

1. If $d_k > 0$ for $k = 1, 2, \ldots, n$, then f has a local minimum at $\mathbf{a}$.

2. If $d_k < 0$ for k odd and $d_k > 0$ for k even, then f has a local maximum at $\mathbf{a}$.

3. If neither case 1 nor case 2 holds, then f has a saddle point at $\mathbf{a}$.

In the event that $\det Hf(\mathbf{a}) = 0$, we say that the critical point $\mathbf{a}$ is **degenerate** and must use another method to determine whether or not it is the site of an extremum of f.

EXAMPLE 4   Consider the function

$$f(x, y) = x^2 + xy + y^2 + 2x - 2y + 5$$

in Example 3. We have already seen that $(-2, 2)$ is the only critical point. The Hessian is

$$Hf(x, y) = \begin{bmatrix} f_{xx} & f_{xy} \\ f_{yx} & f_{yy} \end{bmatrix} = \begin{bmatrix} 2 & 1 \\ 1 & 2 \end{bmatrix}.$$

The sequence of principal minors is $d_1 = f_{xx}(-2, 2) = 2$ (> 0), $d_2 = |Hf(-2, 2)| = 3$ (> 0). Hence, f has a minimum at $(-2, 2)$, as we saw before, but this method uses less algebra.   ◆

EXAMPLE 5   **(Second derivative test for functions of two variables)** Let us generalize Example 4. Suppose that $f(x, y)$ is a function of two variables of class C^2 and further suppose that f has a critical point at $\mathbf{a} = (a, b)$. The Hessian matrix of f evaluated at (a, b) is

$$Hf(a, b) = \begin{bmatrix} f_{xx}(a, b) & f_{xy}(a, b) \\ f_{xy}(a, b) & f_{yy}(a, b) \end{bmatrix}.$$

Note that we have used the fact that $f_{xy} = f_{yx}$ (since f is of class C^2) in constructing the Hessian. The sequence of principal minors thus consists of two numbers:

$$d_1 = f_{xx}(a, b) \quad \text{and} \quad d_2 = f_{xx}(a, b)f_{yy}(a, b) - f_{xy}(a, b)^2.$$

Hence, in this case, the second derivative test tells us that

1. f has a local minimum at (a, b) if

$$f_{xx}(a, b) > 0 \quad \text{and} \quad f_{xx}(a, b)f_{yy}(a, b) - f_{xy}(a, b)^2 > 0.$$

2. f has a local maximum at (a, b) if

$$f_{xx}(a, b) < 0 \quad \text{and} \quad f_{xx}(a, b)f_{yy}(a, b) - f_{xy}(a, b)^2 > 0.$$

3. f has a saddle point at (a, b) if

$$f_{xx}(a, b)f_{yy}(a, b) - f_{xy}(a, b)^2 < 0.$$

Note that if $f_{xx}(a, b)f_{yy}(a, b) - f_{xy}(a, b)^2 = 0$, then f has a *degenerate* critical point at (a, b) and we cannot immediately determine if (a, b) is the site of a local extremum of f.   ◆

EXAMPLE 6   Let $f(x, y, z) = x^3 + xy^2 + x^2 + y^2 + 3z^2$. To find any local extrema of f, we must first identify the critical points. Thus, we solve

$$Df(x, y, z) = \begin{bmatrix} 3x^2 + y^2 + 2x & 2xy + 2y & 6z \end{bmatrix} = \begin{bmatrix} 0 & 0 & 0 \end{bmatrix}.$$

From this, it is not hard to see that there are two critical points: $(0, 0, 0)$ and $\left(-\frac{2}{3}, 0, 0\right)$. The Hessian of f is

$$Hf(x, y, z) = \begin{bmatrix} 6x + 2 & 2y & 0 \\ 2y & 2x + 2 & 0 \\ 0 & 0 & 6 \end{bmatrix}.$$

At the critical point $(0, 0, 0)$, we have

$$Hf(0, 0, 0) = \begin{bmatrix} 2 & 0 & 0 \\ 0 & 2 & 0 \\ 0 & 0 & 6 \end{bmatrix},$$

and its sequence of principal minors is $d_1 = 2$, $d_2 = 4$, $d_3 = 24$. Since these determinants are all positive, we conclude that f has a local minimum at $(0,0,0)$. At $\left(-\frac{2}{3}, 0, 0\right)$, we calculate that

$$Hf\left(-\frac{2}{3}, 0, 0\right) = \begin{bmatrix} -2 & 0 & 0 \\ 0 & \frac{2}{3} & 0 \\ 0 & 0 & 6 \end{bmatrix}.$$

The sequence of minors is $-2, -\frac{4}{3}, -8$. Hence, f has a saddle point at $\left(-\frac{2}{3}, 0, 0\right)$. ◆

EXAMPLE 7 To get a feeling for what happens in the case of a degenerate critical point (i.e., a critical point **a** such that $\det Hf(\mathbf{a}) = 0$), consider the three functions

$$f(x, y) = x^4 + x^2 + y^4,$$

$$g(x, y) = -x^4 - x^2 - y^4,$$

and

$$h(x, y) = x^4 - x^2 + y^4.$$

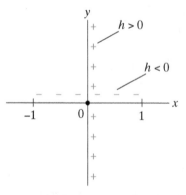

We leave it to you to check that the origin $(0, 0)$ is a degenerate critical point of each of these functions. (In fact, the Hessians themselves look very similar.) Since f is 0 at $(0, 0)$ and strictly positive at all $(x, y) \neq (0, 0)$, we see that f has a strict minimum at the origin. Similar reasoning shows that g has a strict maximum at the origin. For h, the situation is slightly more complicated. Along the y-axis, we have $h(0, y) = y^4$, which is zero at $y = 0$ (the origin) and strictly positive everywhere else. Along the x-axis,

$$h(x, 0) = x^4 - x^2 = x^2(x - 1)(x + 1).$$

For $-1 < x < 1$ and $x \neq 0$, $h(x, 0) < 0$. We have the situation depicted in Figure 4.19. Thus, every neighborhood of $(0, 0)$ contains some points (x, y) where h is positive and also some points where h is negative. Therefore, h has a saddle point at the origin. The "moral of the story" is that a degenerate critical point can exhibit any type of behavior, and more detailed consideration of the function itself, rather than its Hessian, is necessary to understand its nature as a site of an extremum. ◆

Figure 4.19 Away from the origin, the function h of Example 7 is negative along the x-axis and positive along the y-axis.

Global Extrema on Compact Regions

Thus far our discussion has been limited to consideration of only local extrema. We have said nothing about how to identify global extrema, because there really is no general, effective method for looking at an arbitrary function and determining whether and where it reaches an absolute maximum or minimum value. For the purpose of applications, where finding an absolute maximum or minimum is essential, such a state of affairs is indeed unfortunate. Nonetheless, we can say something about global extrema for functions defined on a certain type of domain.

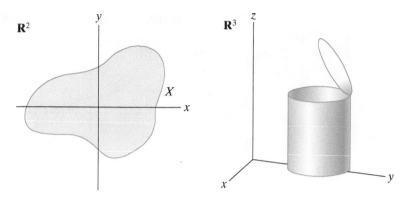

Figure 4.20 Compact regions.

DEFINITION 2.4   A subset $X \subseteq \mathbf{R}^n$ is said to be **compact** if it is both closed and bounded.

Recall that X is closed if it contains all the points that make up its boundary. (See Definition 2.3 of §2.2.) To say that X is bounded means that there is some (open or closed) ball B that contains it. (That is, X is bounded if there is some positive number M such that $\|\mathbf{x}\| < M$ for all $\mathbf{x} \in X$.) Thus, compact sets contain their boundaries (a consequence of being closed) and have only finite extent (a consequence of being bounded). Some typical compact sets in $\mathbf{R}^2$ and $\mathbf{R}^3$ are shown in Figure 4.20.

For our purposes the notion of compactness is of value because of the next result, which we state without proof.

THEOREM 2.5 (EXTREME VALUE THEOREM)   If $X \subseteq \mathbf{R}^n$ is compact and f: $X \to \mathbf{R}$ is continuous, then f must have both a global maximum and a global minimum somewhere on X. That is, there must exist points $\mathbf{a}_{\max}$ and $\mathbf{a}_{\min}$ in X such that, for all $\mathbf{x} \in X$,

$$f(\mathbf{a}_{\min}) \leq f(\mathbf{x}) \leq f(\mathbf{a}_{\max}).$$

We need the compactness hypothesis since a function defined over a noncompact domain may increase or decrease without bound and, hence, fail to have any global extremum, as suggested by Figure 4.21. This is analogous to the situation in one variable where a continuous function defined on an open interval may fail to have any extrema, but one defined on a closed interval (which is a compact subset of $\mathbf{R}$) must attain both maximum and minimum values. (See Figure 4.22.) In the one-variable case, extrema can occur either in the interior of the interval or else at the endpoints. Therefore, you must compare the values of f at any interior critical points with those at the endpoints to determine which is largest and smallest. In the case of functions of n variables, we do something similar, namely, compare the values of f at any critical points with values at any restricted critical points that may occur along the boundary of the domain.

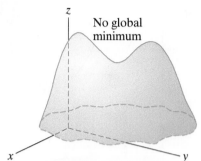

Figure 4.21 A graph that lacks a global minimum.

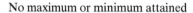

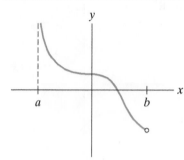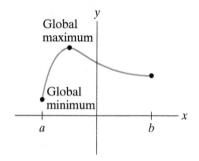

Figure 4.22 The function depicted by the graph on the left has no global extrema—the function is defined on the open interval (a, b). By contrast, the function defined on the closed interval $[a, b]$, and with the graph on the right, has both a global maximum and minimum.

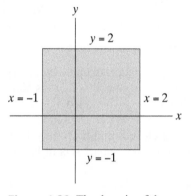

Figure 4.23 The domain of the function T of Example 8.

EXAMPLE 8 Let $T: X \subseteq \mathbf{R}^2 \to \mathbf{R}$ be given by

$$T(x, y) = x^2 - xy + y^2 + 1,$$

where X is the closed square in Figure 4.23. (Note that X is compact.) Think of the square as representing a flat metal plate and the function T as the temperature of the plate at each point. Finding the global extrema amounts to finding the warmest and coldest points on the plate. According to Theorem 2.5, such points must exist.

We need to find all possible critical points of T. Momentarily considering T as a function on all of $\mathbf{R}^2$, we find the usual critical points by setting $DT(x, y)$ equal to $\mathbf{0}$. The result is the system of two equations

$$\begin{cases} 2x - y = 0 \\ -x + 2y = 0 \end{cases},$$

which has $(0, 0)$ as its only solution. Whether it is a local maximum or minimum is not important for now, because we seek global extrema. Because there is only one critical point, at least one global extremum must occur along the boundary of X (which consists of the four edges of the square). We now find all critical points of the *restriction* of T to this boundary:

1. The bottom edge of X is the set

$$E_1 = \{(x, y) \mid y = -1, -1 \leq x \leq 2\}.$$

The restriction of T to E_1 defines a new function $f_1: [-1, 2] \to \mathbf{R}$ given by

$$f_1(x) = T(x, -1) = x^2 + x + 2.$$

As $f_1'(x) = 2x + 1$, the function f_1 has a critical point at $x = -\frac{1}{2}$. Thus, we must examine the following points of X for possible extrema: $\left(-\frac{1}{2}, -1\right)$, $(-1, -1)$, and $(2, -1)$. (The first point is the critical point of f_1, and the second two are the vertices of X that lie on E_1.)

2. The top edge of X is given by

$$E_2 = \{(x, y) \mid y = 2, -1 \leq x \leq 2\}.$$

Consequently, we define $f_2 \colon [-1, 2] \to \mathbf{R}$ by

$$f_2(x) = T(x, 2) = x^2 - 2x + 5.$$

(f_2 is the restriction of T to E_2.) We calculate $f_2'(x) = 2x - 2$, which implies that $x = 1$ is a critical point of f_2. Hence, we must consider $(1, 2)$, $(-1, 2)$, and $(2, 2)$ as possible sites for global extrema of T. (The points $(-1, 2)$ and $(2, 2)$ are the remaining two vertices of X.)

3. The left edge of X is

$$E_3 = \{(x, y) \mid x = -1, -1 \le y \le 2\}.$$

Therefore, we define $f_3 \colon [-1, 2] \to \mathbf{R}$ by

$$f_3(y) = T(-1, y) = y^2 + y + 2.$$

We have $f_3'(y) = 2y + 1$, and so $y = -\frac{1}{2}$ is the only critical point of f_3. Thus $\left(-1, -\frac{1}{2}\right)$ is a potential site of a global extremum. (We need not worry again about the vertices $(-1, -1)$ and $(-1, 2)$.)

4. The right edge of X is

$$E_4 = \{(x, y) \mid x = 2, -1 \le y \le 2\}.$$

We define $f_4 \colon [-1, 2] \to \mathbf{R}$ by

$$f_4(y) = T(2, y) = y^2 - 2y + 5.$$

We have $f_4'(y) = 2y - 2$, and so $y = 1$ is the only critical point of f_4. Hence, we must include $(2, 1)$ in our consideration.

Consequently, we have nine possible locations for global extrema, shown in Figure 4.24. Now we need only to compare the actual values of T at these points to see that $(0, 0)$ is the coldest point on the plate and both $(2, -1)$ and $(-1, 2)$ are the hottest points. $\blacklozenge$

If a function is defined over a noncompact region, there is no general result like the extreme value theorem (Theorem 2.5) to guarantee existence of any global extrema. However, ad hoc arguments frequently can be used to identify global extrema.

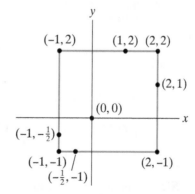

(x,y)	$T(x,y)$
$(0, 0)$	1
$\left(-\frac{1}{2}, -1\right)$	$\frac{7}{4}$
$(-1, -1)$	2
$(2, -1)$	8
$(1, 2)$	4
$(-1, 2)$	8
$(2, 2)$	5
$\left(-1, -\frac{1}{2}\right)$	$\frac{7}{4}$
$(2, 1)$	4

Figure 4.24 Possible global extrema for T.

EXAMPLE 9   Consider the function $f(x, y) = e^{1-3x^2-y^2}$ defined on all of $\mathbf{R}^2$ (so the domain is certainly not compact). Verifying that f has a unique critical point at $(0, 0)$ is straightforward. We leave it to you to check that the Hessian criterion implies that f has a local maximum there. In any case, for all $(x, y) \in \mathbf{R}^2$, we have

$$1 - 3x^2 - y^2 \leq 1.$$

Therefore, because the exponential function is always increasing (i.e., if $u_1 \leq u_2$, then $e^{u_1} \leq e^{u_2}$),

$$e^{1-3x^2-y^2} \leq e^1 = e.$$

As $f(0, 0) = e$, we see that f has a global maximum at $(0, 0)$. ◆

WARNING   It is tempting to assume that if a function has a unique critical point that is a local extremum, then it must be a global extremum as well. Although true for the case of a function of a single variable, it is not true for functions of two or more variables. (See Exercise 52 for an example.)

Addendum: Proof of Theorem 2.3

Step 1. We show the following key property of a quadratic form Q, namely, that if $\lambda \in \mathbf{R}$, then

$$Q(\lambda \mathbf{h}) = \lambda^2 Q(\mathbf{h}). \tag{3}$$

This is straightforward to establish if we write Q in terms of its associated symmetric matrix B and use some of the properties of matrix arithmetic given in §1.6:

$$Q(\lambda \mathbf{h}) = (\lambda \mathbf{h})^T B(\lambda \mathbf{h}) = \lambda \mathbf{h}^T B(\lambda \mathbf{h}) = \lambda^2 \mathbf{h}^T B \mathbf{h} = \lambda^2 Q(\mathbf{h}).$$

Step 2. We show that if B is the symmetric matrix associated to a positive definite quadratic form Q, then there is a positive constant M such that

$$Q(\mathbf{h}) \geq M \|\mathbf{h}\|^2$$

for all $\mathbf{h} \in \mathbf{R}^n$.

First, note that when $\mathbf{h} = \mathbf{0}$, then $Q(\mathbf{h}) = Q(\mathbf{0}) = 0$ so the conclusion holds trivially in this case.

Next, suppose that $\mathbf{h}$ is a unit vector (i.e., $\|\mathbf{h}\| = 1$). The (endpoints of the) set of all unit vectors in $\mathbf{R}^n$ is an $(n-1)$-dimensional sphere S, which is a compact set. Hence, by the extreme value theorem (Theorem 2.5), the restriction of Q to S must achieve a global minimum value M somewhere on S. Thus, $Q(\mathbf{h}) \geq M$ for all $\mathbf{h} \in S$.

Finally, let $\mathbf{h}$ be any nonzero vector in $\mathbf{R}^n$. Then its normalization $\mathbf{h}/\|\mathbf{h}\|$ is a unit vector and so lies in S. Therefore, by the result of Step 1, we have

$$Q(\mathbf{h}) = Q\left(\|\mathbf{h}\|\frac{\mathbf{h}}{\|\mathbf{h}\|}\right) = \|\mathbf{h}\|^2 Q\left(\frac{\mathbf{h}}{\|\mathbf{h}\|}\right) \geq \|\mathbf{h}\|^2 M,$$

since $\mathbf{h}/\|\mathbf{h}\|$ is in S.

Step 3. Now we prove the theorem. By the second-order Taylor formula Theorem 1.5 and formula (10) of §4.1, we have that, for the critical point $\mathbf{a}$ of f,

$$\Delta f = f(\mathbf{x}) - f(\mathbf{a}) = \tfrac{1}{2}(\mathbf{x} - \mathbf{a})^T H f(\mathbf{a})(\mathbf{x} - \mathbf{a}) + R_2(\mathbf{x}, \mathbf{a}), \tag{4}$$

where $|R_2(\mathbf{x}, \mathbf{a})|/\|\mathbf{x} - \mathbf{a}\|^2 \to 0$ as $\mathbf{x} \to \mathbf{a}$.

Suppose first that $Hf(\mathbf{a})$ is positive definite. Then by Step 2 with $\mathbf{h} = \mathbf{x} - \mathbf{a}$, there must exist a constant $M > 0$ such that

$$\tfrac{1}{2}(\mathbf{x} - \mathbf{a})^T Hf(\mathbf{a})(\mathbf{x} - \mathbf{a}) \geq M \|\mathbf{x} - \mathbf{a}\|^2. \tag{5}$$

Because $|R_2(\mathbf{x}, \mathbf{a})|/\|\mathbf{x} - \mathbf{a}\|^2 \to 0$ as $\mathbf{x} \to \mathbf{a}$, there must be some $\delta > 0$ so that if $0 < \|\mathbf{x} - \mathbf{a}\| < \delta$, then $|R_2(\mathbf{x}, \mathbf{a})|/\|\mathbf{x} - \mathbf{a}\|^2 < M$, or, equivalently,

$$|R_2(\mathbf{x}, \mathbf{a})| < M \|\mathbf{x} - \mathbf{a}\|^2. \tag{6}$$

Therefore, (4), (5), and (6) imply that, for $0 < \|\mathbf{x} - \mathbf{a}\| < \delta$,

$$\Delta f > 0$$

so that f has a (strict) local minimum at $\mathbf{a}$.

If $Hf(\mathbf{a})$ is negative definite, then consider $g = -f$. We see that $\mathbf{a}$ is also a critical point of g and that $Hg(\mathbf{a}) = -Hf(\mathbf{a})$, so $Hg(\mathbf{a})$ is positive definite. Hence, the argument in the preceding paragraph shows that g has a local minimum at $\mathbf{a}$, so f has a local maximum at $\mathbf{a}$.

Now suppose $\det Hf(\mathbf{a}) \neq 0$, but that $Hf(\mathbf{a})$ is neither positive nor negative definite. Let $\mathbf{x}_1$ be such that

$$\tfrac{1}{2}(\mathbf{x}_1 - \mathbf{a})^T Hf(\mathbf{a})(\mathbf{x}_1 - \mathbf{a}) > 0$$

and $\mathbf{x}_2$ such that

$$\tfrac{1}{2}(\mathbf{x}_2 - \mathbf{a})^T Hf(\mathbf{a})(\mathbf{x}_2 - \mathbf{a}) < 0.$$

(Since $\det Hf(\mathbf{a}) \neq 0$, such points must exist.) For $i = 1, 2$ let

$$\mathbf{y}_i(t) = t(\mathbf{x}_i - \mathbf{a}) + \mathbf{a},$$

the vector parametric equation for the line through $\mathbf{a}$ and $\mathbf{x}_i$. Applying formula (4) with $\mathbf{x} = \mathbf{y}_i(t)$, we see

$$\Delta f = f(\mathbf{y}_i(t)) - f(\mathbf{a}) = \tfrac{1}{2}(\mathbf{y}_i(t) - \mathbf{a})^T Hf(\mathbf{a})(\mathbf{y}_i(t) - \mathbf{a}) + R_2(\mathbf{y}_i(t), \mathbf{a})$$

$$= \tfrac{1}{2}(\mathbf{y}_i(t) - \mathbf{a})^T Hf(\mathbf{a})(\mathbf{y}_i(t) - \mathbf{a}) + \|\mathbf{y}_i(t) - \mathbf{a}\|^2 \frac{R_2(\mathbf{y}_i(t), \mathbf{a})}{\|\mathbf{y}_i(t) - \mathbf{a}\|^2}.$$

Note that $\mathbf{y}_i(t) - \mathbf{a} = t(\mathbf{x}_i - \mathbf{a})$. Therefore, using the property of quadratic forms given in Step 1 and the fact that $\|\mathbf{y}_i(t) - \mathbf{a}\|^2 = \|t(\mathbf{x}_i - \mathbf{a})\|^2 = t^2\|\mathbf{x}_i - \mathbf{a}\|^2$, we have

$$f(\mathbf{y}_i(t)) - f(\mathbf{a})$$
$$= t^2\left[\tfrac{1}{2}(\mathbf{x}_i - \mathbf{a})^T Hf(\mathbf{a})(\mathbf{x}_i - \mathbf{a}) + \|\mathbf{x}_i - \mathbf{a}\|^2 \frac{R_2(\mathbf{y}_i(t), \mathbf{a})}{\|\mathbf{y}_i(t) - \mathbf{a}\|^2} \right]. \tag{7}$$

Now note that, for $i = 1$, the first term in the brackets in the right side of (7) is a positive number P and, for $i = 2$, it is a negative number N. Set

$$M = \min\left(\frac{P}{\|\mathbf{x}_1 - \mathbf{a}\|^2}, -\frac{N}{\|\mathbf{x}_2 - \mathbf{a}\|^2} \right).$$

Because we know that $|R_2(\mathbf{y}_i(t), \mathbf{a})|/\|\mathbf{y}_i(t) - \mathbf{a}\|^2 \to 0$ as $t \to 0$, we can find some $\delta > 0$ so that if $0 < t < \delta$, then

$$\frac{|R_2(\mathbf{y}_i(t), \mathbf{a})|}{\|\mathbf{y}_i(t) - \mathbf{a}\|^2} < M.$$

But this implies that, for $0 < t < \delta$,

$$\Delta f = f(\mathbf{y}_1(t)) - f(\mathbf{a}) > 0,$$

while

$$\Delta f = f(\mathbf{y}_2(t)) - f(\mathbf{a}) < 0.$$

Thus, f has a saddle point at $\mathbf{x} = \mathbf{a}$. ∎

4.2 Exercises

1. Concerning the function $f(x, y) = 4x + 6y - 12 - x^2 - y^2$:
   (a) There is a unique critical point. Find it.
   (b) By considering the increment Δf, determine whether this critical point is a maximum, a minimum, or a saddle point.
   (c) Now use the Hessian criterion to determine the nature of the critical point.

2. This problem concerns the function $g(x, y) = x^2 - 2y^2 + 2x + 3$.
   (a) Find any critical points of g.
   (b) Use the increment Δg to determine the nature of the critical points of g.
   (c) Use the Hessian criterion to determine the nature of the critical points.

In Exercises 3–20, identify and determine the nature of the critical points of the given functions.

3. $f(x, y) = 2xy - 2x^2 - 5y^2 + 4y - 3$
4. $f(x, y) = \ln(x^2 + y^2 + 1)$
5. $f(x, y) = x^2 + y^3 - 6xy + 3x + 6y$
6. $f(x, y) = y^4 - 2xy^2 + x^3 - x$
7. $f(x, y) = xy + \dfrac{8}{x} + \dfrac{1}{y}$
8. $f(x, y) = e^x \sin y$
9. $f(x, y) = e^{-y}(x^2 - y^2)$
10. $f(x, y) = (x + y)(1 - xy)$
11. $f(x, y) = x^2 - y^3 - x^2y + y$
12. $f(x, y) = e^{-x}(x^2 + 3y^2)$
13. $f(x, y) = 2x - 3y + \ln xy$
14. $f(x, y) = \cos x \sin y$
15. $f(x, y, z) = x^2 - xy + z^2 - 2xz + 6z$
16. $f(x, y, z) = (x^2 + 2y^2 + 1)\cos z$
17. $f(x, y, z) = x^2 + y^2 + 2z^2 + xz$

18. $f(x, y, z) = x^3 + xz^2 - 3x^2 + y^2 + 2z^2$
19. $f(x, y, z) = xy + xz + 2yz + \dfrac{1}{x}$
20. $f(x, y, z) = e^x(x^2 - y^2 - 2z^2)$
21. (a) Find all critical points of $f(x, y) = \dfrac{2y^3 - 3y^2 - 36y + 2}{1 + 3x^2}$.
    (b) Identify any and all extrema of f.
22. (a) Under what conditions on the constant k will the function
    $$f(x, y) = kx^2 - 2xy + ky^2$$
    have a nondegenerate local minimum at $(0, 0)$? What about a local maximum?
    (b) Under what conditions on the constant k will the function
    $$g(x, y, z) = kx^2 + kxz - 2yz - y^2 + \dfrac{k}{2}z^2$$
    have a nondegenerate local maximum at $(0, 0, 0)$? What about a nondegenerate local minimum?
23. (a) Consider the function $f(x, y) = ax^2 + by^2$, where a and b are nonzero constants. Show that the origin is the only critical point of f, and determine the nature of that critical point in terms of a and b.
    (b) Now consider the function $f(x, y, z) = ax^2 + by^2 + cz^2$, where a, b, and c are all nonzero. Show that the origin in $\mathbf{R}^3$ is the only critical point of f, and determine the nature of that critical point in terms of a, b, and c.
    (c) Finally, let $f(x_1, x_2, \ldots, x_n) = a_1x_1^2 + a_2x_2^2 + \cdots + a_nx_n^2$, where a_i is a nonzero constant for $i = 1, 2, \ldots, n$. Show that the origin in $\mathbf{R}^n$ is the only critical point of f, and determine its nature.

Sometimes it can be difficult to determine the critical point of a function f because the system of equations that arises from setting ∇f equal to zero may be very complicated to solve by hand. For the functions given in Exercises 24–27, (a) use a computer to assist you in identifying all the critical points of the given function f, and (b) use a computer to construct the

Hessian matrix and determine the nature of the critical points found in part (a).

24. $f(x, y) = y^4 + x^3 - 2xy^2 - x$

25. $f(x, y) = 2x^3 y - y^2 - 3xy$

26. $f(x, y, z) = yz - xyz - x^2 - y^2 - 2z^2$

27. $f(x, y, z, w) = yw - xyz - x^2 - 2z^2 + w^2$

28. Show that the largest rectangular box having a fixed surface area must be a cube.

29. What point on the plane $3x - 4y - z = 24$ is closest to the origin?

30. Find the points on the surface $xy + z^2 = 4$ that are closest to the origin. Be sure to give a convincing argument that your answer is correct.

31. Suppose that you are in charge of manufacturing two types of television sets. The revenue function, in dollars, is given by

$$R(x, y) = 8x + 6y - x^2 - 2y^2 + 2xy,$$

where x denotes the quantity of model X sets sold, and y the quantity of model Y sets sold, both in units of 100. Determine the quantity of each type of set that you should produce in order to maximize the resulting revenue.

32. Find the absolute extrema of $f(x, y) = x^2 + xy + y^2 - 6y$ on the rectangle $\{(x, y) \mid -3 \le x \le 3,\ 0 \le y \le 5\}$.

33. Find the absolute maximum and minimum of

$$f(x, y, z) = x^2 + xz - y^2 + 2z^2 + xy + 5x$$

on the block $\{(x, y, z) \mid -5 \le x \le 0,\ 0 \le y \le 3,\ 0 \le z \le 2\}$.

34. A metal plate has the shape of the region $x^2 + y^2 \le 1$. The plate is heated so that the temperature at any point (x, y) on it is indicated by

$$T(x, y) = 2x^2 + y^2 - y + 3.$$

Find the hottest and coldest points on the plate and the temperature at each of these points. (Hint: Parametrize the boundary of the plate in order to find any critical points there.)

35. Find the (absolute) maximum and minimum values of $f(x, y) = \sin x \cos y$ on the square $R = \{(x, y) \mid 0 \le x \le 2\pi,\ 0 \le y \le 2\pi\}$.

36. Find the absolute extrema of $f(x, y) = 2 \cos x + 3 \sin y$ on the rectangle $\{(x, y) \mid 0 \le x \le 4,\ 0 \le y \le 3\}$.

37. Determine the absolute minimum and maximum values of the function $f(x, y) = 2x^2 - 2xy + y^2$

$- y + 3$ on the closed triangular region with vertices $(0, 0)$, $(2, 0)$, and $(0, 2)$.

38. Determine the absolute minimum and maximum values of the function $f(x, y) = x^2 y$ on the elliptical region $D = \{(x, y) \mid 3x^2 + 4y^2 \le 12\}$.

39. Find the absolute extrema of $f(x, y, z) = e^{1-x^2-y^2+2y-z^2-4z}$ on the ball $\{(x, y, z) \mid x^2 + y^2 - 2y + z^2 + 4z \le 0\}$.

Each of the functions in Exercises 40–45 has a critical point at the origin. For each function, (a) check that the Hessian fails to provide any information about the nature of the critical point at the origin, and (b) find another way to determine if the function has a maximum, minimum, or neither at the origin.

40. $f(x, y) = x^2 y^2$

41. $f(x, y) = 4 - 3x^2 y^2$

42. $f(x, y) = x^3 y^3$

43. $f(x, y, z) = x^2 y^3 z^4$

44. $f(x, y, z) = x^2 y^2 z^4$

45. $f(x, y, z) = 2 - x^4 y^4 - z^4$

In Exercises 46–48, (a) find all critical points of the given function f and identify their nature as local extrema and (b) determine, with explanation, any global extrema of f.

46. $f(x, y) = e^{x^2 + 5y^2}$

47. $f(x, y, z) = e^{2 - x^2 - 2y^2 - 3z^4}$

48. $f(x, y) = x^3 + y^3 - 3xy + 7$

49. Determine the global extrema, if any, of

$$f(x, y) = xy + 2y - \ln x - 2 \ln y,$$

where $x, y > 0$.

50. Find all local and global extrema of the function $f(x, y, z) = x^3 + 3x^2 + e^{y^2+1} + z^2 - 3xz$.

51. Let $f(x, y) = 3 - [(x-1)(y-2)]^{2/3}$.
  (a) Determine all critical points of f.
  (b) Identify all extrema of f.

52. (a) Suppose $f: \mathbf{R} \to \mathbf{R}$ is a differentiable function of a single variable. Show that if f has a unique critical point at x_0 that is the site of a strict local extremum of f, then f must attain a global extremum at x_0.

  (b) Let $f(x, y) = 3ye^x - e^{3x} - y^3$. Verify that f has a unique critical point and that f attains a local maximum there. However, show that f does not have a global maximum by considering how f behaves along the y-axis. Hence, the result of part (a) does not carry over to functions of more than one variable.

53. (a) Let f be a continuous function of one variable. Show that if f has two local maxima, then f must also have a local minimum.

(b) The analogue of part (a) does not necessarily hold for continuous functions of more than one variable,

as we now see. Consider the function

$$f(x, y) = 2 - (xy^2 - y - 1)^2 - (y^2 - 1)^2.$$

Show that f has just two critical points—and that both of them are local maxima.

 (c) Use a computer to graph the function f in part (b).

4.3 Lagrange Multipliers

Constrained Extrema

Frequently, when working with applications of calculus, you will find that you do not need simply to maximize or minimize a function but that you must do so subject to one or more additional constraints that depend on the specifics of the situation. The following example is a typical situation:

EXAMPLE 1   An open rectangular box is to be manufactured having a (fixed) volume of 4 ft^3. What dimensions should the box have so as to minimize the amount of material used to make it?

We'll let the three dimensions of the box be independent variables x, y, and z, shown in Figure 4.25. To determine how to use as little material as possible, we need to minimize the surface area function A given by

$$A(x, y, z) = \underset{\text{front and back}}{2xy} + \underset{\text{sides}}{2yz} + \underset{\text{bottom only}}{xz}.$$

For $x, y, z > 0$, this function has neither minimum nor maximum. However, we have not yet made use of the fact that the volume is to be maintained at a constant 4 ft^3. This fact provides a **constraint equation**,

$$V(x, y, z) = xyz = 4.$$

The constraint is absolutely essential if we are to solve the problem. In particular, the constraint enables us to solve for z in terms of x and y:

$$z = \frac{4}{xy}.$$

We can thus create a new area function of only two variables:

$$a(x, y) = A\left(x, y, \frac{4}{xy}\right)$$

$$= 2xy + 2y\left(\frac{4}{xy}\right) + x\left(\frac{4}{xy}\right)$$

$$= 2xy + \frac{8}{x} + \frac{4}{y}.$$

Now we can find the critical points of a by setting Da equal to **0**:

$$\begin{cases} \dfrac{\partial a}{\partial x} = 2y - \dfrac{8}{x^2} = 0 \\[2mm] \dfrac{\partial a}{\partial y} = 2x - \dfrac{4}{y^2} = 0 \end{cases}$$

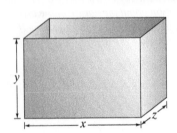

Figure 4.25 The open box of Example 1.

The first equation implies

$$y = \frac{4}{x^2},$$

so that the second equation becomes

$$2x - 4\left(\frac{x^4}{16}\right) = 0$$

or, equivalently,

$$x\left(1 - \frac{1}{8}x^3\right) = 0.$$

The solutions to this equation are $x = 0$ (which we reject) and $x = 2$. Thus, the critical point of a of interest is $(2, 1)$, and the **constrained critical point** of the original function A is $(2, 1, 2)$.

We can use the Hessian criterion to check that $x = 2$, $y = 1$ yields a local minimum of a:

$$Ha(x, y) = \begin{bmatrix} 16/x^3 & 2 \\ 2 & 8/y^3 \end{bmatrix} \quad \text{so} \quad Ha(2, 1) = \begin{bmatrix} 2 & 2 \\ 2 & 8 \end{bmatrix}.$$

The sequence of minors is 2, 12 so we conclude that $(2, 1)$ does yield a local minimum of a. Because $a(x, y) \to \infty$ as either $x \to 0^+$, $y \to 0^+$, $x \to \infty$, or $y \to \infty$, we conclude that the critical point must yield a global minimum as well. Thus, the solution to the original question is to make the box with a square base of side 2 ft and a height of 1 ft. ◆

The abstract setting for the situation discussed in Example 1 is to find maxima or minima of a function $f(x_1, x_2, \ldots, x_n)$ subject to the **constraint** that $g(x_1, x_2, \ldots, x_n) = c$ for some function g and constant c. (In Example 1, the function f is $A(x, y, z)$, and the constraint is $xyz = 4$.) One method for finding constrained critical points is used implicitly in Example 1: Use the constraint equation $g(\mathbf{x}) = c$ to solve for one of the variables in terms of the others. Then substitute for this variable in the expression for $f(\mathbf{x})$, thereby creating a new function of one fewer variables. This new function can then be maximized or minimized using the techniques of §4.2. In theory, this is an entirely appropriate way to approach such problems, but in practice there is one major drawback: It may be impossible to solve explicitly for any one of the variables in terms of the others. For example, you might wish to maximize

$$f(x, y, z) = x^2 + 3y^2 + y^2 z^4$$

subject to

$$g(x, y, z) = e^{xy} - x^5 y^2 z + \cos\left(\frac{x}{yz}\right) = 2.$$

There is no means of isolating any of x, y, or z on one side of the constraint equation, and so it is impossible for us to proceed any further along the lines of Example 1.

The Lagrange Multiplier

The previous discussion points to the desirability of having another method for solving constrained optimization problems. The key to such an alternative method is the following theorem:

THEOREM 3.1   Let X be open in $\mathbf{R}^n$ and $f, g\colon X \to \mathbf{R}$ be functions of class C^1. Let $S = \{\mathbf{x} \in X \mid g(\mathbf{x}) = c\}$ denote the level set of g at height c. Then if $f\mid_S$ (the restriction of f to S) has an extremum at a point $\mathbf{x}_0 \in S$ such that $\nabla g(\mathbf{x}_0) \neq \mathbf{0}$, there must be some scalar λ such that

$$\nabla f(\mathbf{x}_0) = \lambda \nabla g(\mathbf{x}_0).$$

The conclusion of Theorem 3.1 implies that to find possible sites for extrema of f subject to the constraint that $g(\mathbf{x}) = c$, we can proceed in the following manner:

1. Form the vector equation $\nabla f(\mathbf{x}) = \lambda \nabla g(\mathbf{x})$.

2. Solve the system

$$\begin{cases} \nabla f(\mathbf{x}) = \lambda \nabla g(\mathbf{x}) \\ g(\mathbf{x}) = c \end{cases}$$

for $\mathbf{x}$ and λ. When expanded, this is actually a system of $n + 1$ equations in $n + 1$ unknowns $x_1, x_2, \ldots, x_n, \lambda$, namely,

$$\begin{cases} f_{x_1}(x_1, x_2, \ldots, x_n) = \lambda g_{x_1}(x_1, x_2, \ldots, x_n) \\ f_{x_2}(x_1, x_2, \ldots, x_n) = \lambda g_{x_2}(x_1, x_2, \ldots, x_n) \\ \quad\quad\quad\quad\quad\vdots \\ f_{x_n}(x_1, x_2, \ldots, x_n) = \lambda g_{x_n}(x_1, x_2, \ldots, x_n) \\ \quad g(x_1, x_2, \ldots, x_n) = c \end{cases}$$

The solutions for $\mathbf{x} = (x_1, x_2, \ldots, x_n)$ in the system above, along with any other points $\mathbf{x}$ satisfying the constraint $g(\mathbf{x}) = c$ and such that ∇f is undefined, or ∇g vanishes or is undefined, are the candidates for extrema for the problem.

3. Determine the nature of f (as maximum, minimum, or neither) at the critical points found in Step 2.

The scalar λ appearing in Theorem 3.1 is called a **Lagrange multiplier**, after the Italian-born French mathematician Joseph-Louis Lagrange (1736–1813) who first developed this method for solving constrained optimization problems. In practice, Step 2 can involve some algebra, so it is important to keep your work organized. (Alternatively, you can use a computer to solve the system.) In fact, since the Lagrange multiplier λ is usually not of primary interest, you can avoid solving for it explicitly, thereby reducing the algebra and arithmetic somewhat. Determining the nature of a constrained critical point (Step 3) can be a tricky business. We'll have more to say about that issue in the examples and discussions that follow.

EXAMPLE 2   Let us use the method of Lagrange multipliers to identify the critical point found in Example 1. Thus, we wish to find the minimum of

$$A(x, y, z) = 2xy + 2yz + xz$$

subject to the constraint

$$V(x, y, z) = xyz = 4.$$

Theorem 3.1 suggests that we form the equation

$$\nabla A(x, y, z) = \lambda \nabla V(x, y, z).$$

This relation of gradients coupled with the constraint equation gives rise to the system

$$\begin{cases} 2y + \quad z = \lambda yz \\ 2x + \quad 2z = \lambda xz \\ 2y + \quad x = \lambda xy \\ \qquad xyz = 4 \end{cases}.$$

Since λ is not essential for our final solution, we can eliminate it by means of any of the first three equations. Hence,

$$\lambda = \frac{2y + z}{yz} = \frac{2x + 2z}{xz} = \frac{2y + x}{xy}.$$

Simplifying, this implies that

$$\frac{2}{z} + \frac{1}{y} = \frac{2}{z} + \frac{2}{x} = \frac{2}{x} + \frac{1}{y}.$$

The first equality yields

$$\frac{1}{y} = \frac{2}{x} \quad \text{or} \quad x = 2y,$$

while the second equality implies that

$$\frac{2}{z} = \frac{1}{y} \quad \text{or} \quad z = 2y.$$

Substituting these relations into the constraint equation $xyz = 4$ yields

$$(2y)(y)(2y) = 4,$$

so that we find that the only solution is $y = 1$, $x = z = 2$, which agrees with our work in Example 1. (Note that $\nabla V = \mathbf{0}$ only along the coordinate axes, and such points do not satisfy the constraint $V(x, y, z) = 4$.)   ◆

An interesting consequence of Theorem 3.1 is this: By Theorem 6.4 of Chapter 2, we know that the gradient ∇g, when nonzero, is perpendicular to the level sets of g. Thus, the equation $\nabla f = \lambda \nabla g$ gives the condition for the normal vector to a level set of f to be parallel to that of a level set of g. Hence, for a point $\mathbf{x}_0$ to be the site of an extremum of f on the level set $S = \{\mathbf{x} \mid g(\mathbf{x}) = c\}$, where $\nabla g(\mathbf{x}_0) \neq \mathbf{0}$, we must have that the level set R of f that contains $\mathbf{x}_0$ is tangent to S at $\mathbf{x}_0$.

EXAMPLE 3   Consider the problem of finding the extrema of $f(x, y) = x^2/4 + y^2$ subject to the condition that $x^2 + y^2 = 1$. We let $g(x, y) = x^2 + y^2$, and so the Lagrange multiplier equation $\nabla f(x, y) = \lambda \nabla g(x, y)$, along with the constraint equation, yields the system

$$\begin{cases} \dfrac{x}{2} = 2\lambda x \\[2mm] 2y = 2\lambda y \\[2mm] x^2 + y^2 = 1 \end{cases}$$

(There are no points simultaneously satisfying $g(x, y) = 1$ and $\nabla g(x, y) = (0, 0)$.) The first equation of this system implies that either $x = 0$ or $\lambda = \frac{1}{4}$. If $x = 0$, then the second two equations, taken together, imply that $y = \pm 1$ and $\lambda = 1$. If $\lambda = \frac{1}{4}$, then the second two equations imply $y = 0$ and $x = \pm 1$. Therefore, there are four constrained critical points: $(0, \pm 1)$, corresponding to $\lambda = 1$, and $(\pm 1, 0)$, corresponding to $\lambda = \frac{1}{4}$.

We can understand the nature of these critical points by using geometry and the preceding remarks. The collection of level sets of the function f is the family of ellipses $x^2/4 + y^2 = k$ whose major and minor axes lie along the x- and y-axes, respectively. In fact, the value $f(x, y) = x^2/4 + y^2 = k$ is the square of the length of the semiminor axis of the ellipse $x^2/4 + y^2 = k$. The optimization problem then is to find those points on the unit circle $x^2 + y^2 = 1$ that, when considered as points in the family of ellipses, minimize and maximize the length of the minor axis. When we view the problem in this way, we see that such points must occur where the circle is tangent to one of the ellipses in the family. A sketch shows that constrained minima of f occur at $(\pm 1, 0)$ and constrained maxima at $(0, \pm 1)$. In this case, the Lagrange multiplier λ represents the square of the length of the semiminor axis. (See Figure 4.26.)   ◆

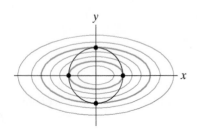

Figure 4.26 The level sets of the function $f(x, y) = x^2/4 + y^2$ define a family of ellipses. The extrema of f subject to the constraint that $x^2 + y^2 = 1$ (i.e., that lie on the unit circle) occur at points where an ellipse of the family is tangent to the unit circle.

EXAMPLE 4   Consider the problem of determining the extrema of $f(x, y) = 2x + y$ subject to the constraint that $\sqrt{x} + \sqrt{y} = 3$. We let $g(x, y) = \sqrt{x} + \sqrt{y}$, so that the Lagrange multiplier equation $\nabla f(x, y) = \lambda \nabla g(x, y)$, along with the constraint equation, yields the system

$$\begin{cases} 2 = \dfrac{\lambda}{2\sqrt{x}} \\[3mm] 1 = \dfrac{\lambda}{2\sqrt{y}} \\[3mm] \sqrt{x} + \sqrt{y} = 3 \end{cases}$$

The first two equations of this system imply that $\lambda = 4\sqrt{x} = 2\sqrt{y}$ so that $\sqrt{y} = 2\sqrt{x}$. Using this in the last equation, we find that $3\sqrt{x} = 3$ and, hence, $x = 1$. Thus, the system of equations above yields the unique solution $(1, 4)$.

Since the constraint defines a closed, bounded curve segment, the extreme value theorem (Theorem 2.5) applies to guarantee that f must attain *both* a global maximum *and* a global minimum on this segment. However, the Lagrange multiplier method has provided us with just a single critical point. But note that the points $(9, 0)$ and $(0, 9)$ satisfy the constraint $\sqrt{x} + \sqrt{y} = 3$; they are both points where ∇g is undefined. Moreover, we have $f(1, 4) = 2$, while $f(9, 0) = 18$ and $f(0, 9) = 9$. Evidently then, the minimum of f occurs at $(1, 4)$ and the maximum at $(9, 0)$.

We can understand the geometry of the situation in the following manner. The collection of level sets of the function f is the family of parallel lines $2x + y = k$. Note that the height k of each level set is just the y-intercept of the corresponding line in the family. Thus, the problem we are considering is to find the largest and

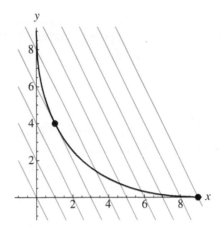

Figure 4.27 The level sets of the function $f(x, y) = 2x + y$ define a family of lines. The minimum of f subject to the constraint that $\sqrt{x} + \sqrt{y} = 3$ occurs at a point where one of the lines is tangent to the constraint curve and the maximum at one of the endpoints of the curve.

smallest y-intercepts of any line in the family that meets the curve $\sqrt{x} + \sqrt{y} = 3$. These extreme values of k occur either when one of the lines is tangent to the constraint curve or at an endpoint of the curve. (See Figure 4.27.)

This example illustrates the importance of locating all the points where extrema may occur by considering places where ∇f or ∇g is undefined (or where $\nabla g = \mathbf{0}$) as well as the solutions to the system of equations determined using Lagrange multipliers. ◆

Sketch of a proof of Theorem 3.1 We present the key ideas of the proof, which are geometric in nature. Try to visualize the situation for the case $n = 3$, where the constraint equation $g(x, y, z) = c$ defines a surface S in $\mathbf{R}^3$. (See Figure 4.28.) In general, if S is defined as $\{\mathbf{x} \mid g(\mathbf{x}) = c\}$ with $\nabla g(\mathbf{x}_0) \neq \mathbf{0}$, then (at least locally near $\mathbf{x}_0$) S is a hypersurface in $\mathbf{R}^n$. The proof that this is the case involves the implicit function theorem (Theorem 6.5 in §2.6), and this is why our proof here is just a sketch.

Thus, suppose that $\mathbf{x}_0$ is an extremum of f restricted to S. We consider a further restriction of f—to a curve lying in S and passing through $\mathbf{x}_0$. This will enable us to use results from one-variable calculus. The notation and analytic particulars are as follows: Let $\mathbf{x} \colon I \subseteq \mathbf{R} \to S \subset \mathbf{R}^3$ be a C^1 path lying in S with $\mathbf{x}(t_0) = \mathbf{x}_0$ for some $t_0 \in I$. Then the restriction of f to $\mathbf{x}$ is given by the function F, where

$$F(t) = f(\mathbf{x}(t)).$$

Because $\mathbf{x}_0$ is an extremum of f on S, it must also be an extremum on $\mathbf{x}$. Consequently, we must have $F'(t_0) = 0$, and the chain rule implies that

$$0 = F'(t_0) = \frac{d}{dt} f(\mathbf{x}(t))\Big|_{t=t_0} = \nabla f(\mathbf{x}(t_0)) \cdot \mathbf{x}'(t_0) = \nabla f(\mathbf{x}_0) \cdot \mathbf{x}'(t_0).$$

Thus, $\nabla f(\mathbf{x}_0)$ is perpendicular to any curve in S passing through $\mathbf{x}_0$; that is, $\nabla f(\mathbf{x}_0)$ is normal to S at $\mathbf{x}_0$. We've seen previously in §2.6 that the gradient $\nabla g(\mathbf{x}_0)$ is also normal to S at $\mathbf{x}_0$. Since the normal direction to the level set S is

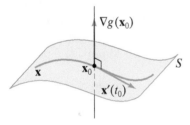

Figure 4.28 The gradient $\nabla g(\mathbf{x}_0)$ is perpendicular to $S = \{\mathbf{x} \mid g(\mathbf{x}) = c\}$, hence, to the tangent vector at $\mathbf{x}_0$ to any curve $\mathbf{x}(t)$ lying in S and passing through $\mathbf{x}_0$. If f has an extremum at $\mathbf{x}_0$, then the restriction of f to the curve also has an extremum at $\mathbf{x}_0$.

uniquely determined and $\nabla g(\mathbf{x}_0) \neq \mathbf{0}$, we must conclude that $\nabla f(\mathbf{x}_0)$ and $\nabla g(\mathbf{x}_0)$ are parallel vectors. Therefore,

$$\nabla f(\mathbf{x}_0) = \lambda \nabla g(\mathbf{x}_0)$$

for some scalar $\lambda \in \mathbf{R}$, as desired.   ∎

The Case of More than One Constraint

It is natural to generalize the situation of finding extrema of a function f subject to a single constraint equation to that of finding extrema subject to several constraints. In other words, we may wish to maximize or minimize f subject to k simultaneous conditions of the form

$$\begin{cases} g_1(\mathbf{x}) = c_1 \\ g_2(\mathbf{x}) = c_2 \\ \quad \vdots \\ g_k(\mathbf{x}) = c_k \end{cases}.$$

The result that generalizes Theorem 3.1 is as follows:

THEOREM 3.2   Let X be open in $\mathbf{R}^n$ and let $f, g_1, \ldots, g_k \colon X \subseteq \mathbf{R}^n \to \mathbf{R}$ be C^1 functions, where $k < n$. Let $S = \{\mathbf{x} \in X \mid g_1(\mathbf{x}) = c_1, \ldots, g_k(\mathbf{x}) = c_k\}$. If $f|_S$ has an extremum at a point $\mathbf{x}_0$, where $\nabla g_1(\mathbf{x}_0), \ldots, \nabla g_k(\mathbf{x}_0)$ are linearly independent vectors, then there must exist scalars $\lambda_1, \ldots, \lambda_k$ such that

$$\nabla f(\mathbf{x}_0) = \lambda_1 \nabla g_1(\mathbf{x}_0) + \lambda_2 \nabla g_2(\mathbf{x}_0) + \cdots + \lambda_k \nabla g_k(\mathbf{x}_0).$$

(Note: k vectors $\mathbf{v}_1, \ldots, \mathbf{v}_k$ in $\mathbf{R}^n$ are said to be **linearly independent** if the only way to satisfy $a_1 \mathbf{v}_1 + \cdots + a_k \mathbf{v}_k = \mathbf{0}$ for scalars $a_1, \ldots, a_k$ is if $a_1 = a_2 = \cdots = a_k = 0$.)

Idea of proof   First, note that S is the intersection of the k hypersurfaces $S_1, \ldots, S_k$, where $S_j = \{\mathbf{x} \in \mathbf{R}^n \mid g_j(\mathbf{x}) = c_j\}$. Therefore, any vector tangent to S must also be tangent to each of these hypersurfaces, and so, by Theorem 6.4 of Chapter 2, perpendicular to each of the ∇g_j's. Given these remarks, the main ideas of the proof of Theorem 3.1 can be readily adapted to provide a proof of Theorem 3.2.

Therefore, we let $\mathbf{x}_0 \in S$ be an extremum of f restricted to S and consider the one-variable function obtained by further restricting f to a curve in S through $\mathbf{x}_0$. Thus, let $\mathbf{x} \colon I \to S \subset \mathbf{R}^n$ be a C^1 curve in S with $\mathbf{x}(t_0) = \mathbf{x}_0$ for some $t_0 \in I$. Then, as in the proof of Theorem 3.1, we define F by

$$F(t) = f(\mathbf{x}(t)).$$

It follows, since $\mathbf{x}_0$ is assumed to be a constrained extremum, that

$$F'(t_0) = 0.$$

The chain rule then tells us that

$$0 = F'(t_0) = \nabla f(\mathbf{x}(t_0)) \cdot \mathbf{x}'(t_0) = \nabla f(\mathbf{x}_0) \cdot \mathbf{x}'(t_0).$$

That is, $\nabla f(\mathbf{x}_0)$ is perpendicular to all vectors tangent to S at $\mathbf{x}_0$. Therefore, it can be shown that $\nabla f(\mathbf{x}_0)$ is in the k-dimensional plane spanned by the normal vectors

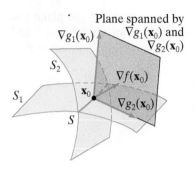

Plane spanned by
$\nabla g_1(\mathbf{x}_0)$ and
$\nabla g_2(\mathbf{x}_0)$

Figure 4.29 Illustration of the proof of Theorem 3.2. The constraints $g_1(\mathbf{x}) = c_1$ and $g_2(\mathbf{x}) = c_2$ are the surfaces S_1 and S_2. Any extremum of f must occur at points where ∇f is in the plane spanned by ∇g_1 and ∇g_2.

to the individual hypersurfaces $S_1, \ldots, S_k$ whose intersection is S. It follows (via a little more linear algebra) that there must be scalars $\lambda_1, \ldots, \lambda_k$ such that

$$\nabla f(\mathbf{x}_0) = \lambda_1 \nabla g_1(\mathbf{x}_0) + \lambda_2 \nabla g_2(\mathbf{x}_0) + \cdots + \lambda_k \nabla g_k(\mathbf{x}_0).$$

A suggestion of the geometry of this proof is provided by Figure 4.29 (where $k = 2$ and $n = 3$). ∎

EXAMPLE 5   Suppose the cone $z^2 = x^2 + y^2$ is sliced by the plane $z = x + y + 2$ so that a conic section C is created. We use Lagrange multipliers to find the points on C that are nearest to and farthest from the origin in $\mathbf{R}^3$.

The problem is to find the minimum and maximum distances from $(0, 0, 0)$ of points (x, y, z) on C. For algebraic simplicity, we look at the square of the distance rather than the actual distance. Thus, we desire to find the extrema of

$$f(x, y, z) = x^2 + y^2 + z^2$$

(the square of the distance from the origin to (x, y, z)) subject to the constraints

$$\begin{cases} g_1(x, y, z) = x^2 + y^2 - z^2 = 0 \\ g_2(x, y, z) = x + y - z = -2 \end{cases}.$$

Note that

$$\nabla g_1(x, y, z) = (2x, 2y, -2z) \quad \text{and} \quad \nabla g_2(x, y, z) = (1, 1, -1).$$

These vectors are linearly dependent only when $x = y = z$. However, no point of the form (x, x, x) simultaneously satisfies $g_1 = 0$ and $g_2 = -2$. Hence, ∇g_1 and ∇g_2 are linearly independent at all points that satisfy the two constraints. Therefore, by Theorem 3.2, we know that any constrained critical points (x_0, y_0, z_0) must satisfy

$$\nabla f(x_0, y_0, z_0) = \lambda_1 \nabla g_1(x_0, y_0, z_0) + \lambda_2 \nabla g_2(x_0, y_0, z_0),$$

as well as the two constraint equations. Thus, we must solve the system

$$\begin{cases} 2x = 2\lambda_1 x + \lambda_2 \\ 2y = 2\lambda_1 y + \lambda_2 \\ 2z = -2\lambda_1 z - \lambda_2 \\ x^2 + y^2 - z^2 = 0 \\ x + y - z = -2 \end{cases}.$$

Eliminating λ_2 from the first two equations yields

$$\lambda_2 = 2x - 2\lambda_1 x = 2y - 2\lambda_1 y,$$

which implies that

$$2(x - y)(1 - \lambda_1) = 0.$$

Therefore, either

$$x = y \quad \text{or} \quad \lambda_1 = 1.$$

The condition $\lambda_1 = 1$ implies immediately $\lambda_2 = 0$, and the third equation of the system becomes $2z = -2z$, so z must equal 0. If $z = 0$, then x and y must be zero by the fourth equation. However, $(0, 0, 0)$ is not a point on the plane $z = x + y + 2$. Thus, the condition $\lambda_1 = 1$ leads to no critical point. On the other hand, if $x = y$, then the constraint equations (the last two in the original system of five) become

$$\begin{cases} 2x^2 - z^2 = 0 \\ 2x - z = -2 \end{cases}.$$

Substituting $z = 2x + 2$ yields

$$2x^2 - (2x + 2)^2 = 0,$$

equivalent to

$$2x^2 + 8x + 4 = 0,$$

whose solutions are $x = -2 \pm \sqrt{2}$. Therefore, there are two constrained critical points

$$\mathbf{a}_1 = \left(-2 + \sqrt{2}, -2 + \sqrt{2}, -2 + 2\sqrt{2}\right)$$

and

$$\mathbf{a}_2 = \left(-2 - \sqrt{2}, -2 - \sqrt{2}, -2 - 2\sqrt{2}\right).$$

We can check that

$$f(\mathbf{a}_1) = 24 - 16\sqrt{2}, \qquad f(\mathbf{a}_2) = 24 + 16\sqrt{2},$$

so it seems that $\mathbf{a}_1$ must be the point on C lying nearest the origin, and $\mathbf{a}_2$ must be the point that lies farthest. However, we don't know a priori if there is a farthest point. If the conic section C is a hyperbola or a parabola, then there is no point that is farthest from the origin. To understand what kind of curve C is, note that $\mathbf{a}_1$ has positive z-coordinate and $\mathbf{a}_2$ has negative z-coordinate. Therefore, the plane $z = x + y + 2$ intersects both nappes of the cone $z^2 = x^2 + y^2$. The only conic section that intersects both nappes of a cone is a hyperbola. Hence, C is a hyperbola, and we see that the point $\mathbf{a}_1$ is indeed the point nearest the origin, but the point $\mathbf{a}_2$ is not the farthest point. Instead, $\mathbf{a}_2$ is the point nearest the origin on the branch of the hyperbola not containing $\mathbf{a}_1$. That is, local constrained minima occur at both $\mathbf{a}_1$ and $\mathbf{a}_2$, but only $\mathbf{a}_1$ is the site of the global minimum. (See Figure 4.30.)   ◆

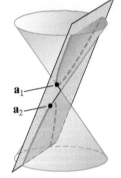

Figure 4.30 The point $\mathbf{a}_1$ is the point on the hyperbola closest to the origin. The point $\mathbf{a}_2$ is the point on the lower branch of the hyperbola closest to the origin.

A Hessian Criterion for Constrained Extrema (optional) —

As Example 5 indicates, it is often possible to determine the nature of a critical point (constrained or unconstrained) from considerations particular to the problem at hand. Sometimes this is not difficult to do in practice and can provide useful insight into the problem. Nonetheless, occasionally it is advantageous to have a more automatic means of discerning the nature of a constrained critical point. We therefore present a Hessian criterion for constrained critical points. Like the one in the unconstrained case, this criterion only determines the *local* nature of a critical point. It does not provide information about global constrained extrema.[2]

---

[2] We invite the reader to consult D. Spring, *Amer. Math. Monthly*, **92** (1985), no. 9, 631–643 for a more complete discussion.

In general, the context for the Hessian criterion is this: We seek extrema of a function $f: X \subseteq \mathbf{R}^n \to \mathbf{R}$ subject to the k constraints

$$
\begin{cases}
g_1(x_1, x_2, \ldots, x_n) = c_1 \\
g_2(x_1, x_2, \ldots, x_n) = c_2 \\
\qquad\qquad \vdots \\
g_k(x_1, x_2, \ldots, x_n) = c_k
\end{cases}.
$$

We assume that $f, g_1, \ldots, g_k$ are all of class C^2, and assume, for simplicity, that f and the g_j's all have the same domain X. Finally, we assume that $\nabla g_1, \ldots, \nabla g_k$ are linearly independent at the constrained critical point $\mathbf{a}$. Then, by Theorem 3.2, any constrained extremum $\mathbf{a}$ must satisfy

$$
\nabla f(\mathbf{a}) = \lambda_1 \nabla g_1(\mathbf{a}) + \lambda_2 \nabla g_2(\mathbf{a}) + \cdots + \lambda_k \nabla g_k(\mathbf{a})
$$

for some scalars $\lambda_1, \ldots, \lambda_k$. We can consider a constrained critical point to be a pair of vectors

$$
(\lambda; \mathbf{a}) = (\lambda_1, \ldots, \lambda_k; a_1, \ldots, a_n)
$$

satisfying the aforementioned equation. In fact, we can check that $(\lambda; \mathbf{a})$ is an **unconstrained** critical point of the so-called Lagrangian function L defined by

$$
L(l_1, \ldots, l_k; x_1, \ldots, x_n) = f(x_1, \ldots, x_n) - \sum_{i=1}^{k} l_i(g_i(x_1, \ldots, x_n) - c_i).
$$

The Hessian criterion comes from considering the Hessian of L at the critical point $(\lambda; \mathbf{a})$. Before we give the criterion, we note the following fact from linear algebra: Since $\nabla g_1(\mathbf{a}), \ldots, \nabla g_k(\mathbf{a})$ are assumed to be linearly independent, the derivative matrix of $\mathbf{g} = (g_1, \ldots, g_k)$ at $\mathbf{a}$,

$$
D\mathbf{g}(\mathbf{a}) = \begin{bmatrix}
\dfrac{\partial g_1}{\partial x_1}(\mathbf{a}) & \cdots & \dfrac{\partial g_1}{\partial x_n}(\mathbf{a}) \\
\vdots & \ddots & \vdots \\
\dfrac{\partial g_k}{\partial x_1}(\mathbf{a}) & \cdots & \dfrac{\partial g_k}{\partial x_n}(\mathbf{a})
\end{bmatrix},
$$

has a $k \times k$ submatrix (obtained by deleting $n - k$ columns of $D\mathbf{g}(\mathbf{a})$) with nonzero determinant. By relabeling the variables if necessary, we will assume that

$$
\det \begin{bmatrix}
\dfrac{\partial g_1}{\partial x_1}(\mathbf{a}) & \cdots & \dfrac{\partial g_1}{\partial x_k}(\mathbf{a}) \\
\vdots & \ddots & \vdots \\
\dfrac{\partial g_k}{\partial x_1}(\mathbf{a}) & \cdots & \dfrac{\partial g_k}{\partial x_k}(\mathbf{a})
\end{bmatrix} \neq 0
$$

(i.e., that we may delete the *last $n - k$* columns).

Second derivative test for constrained local extrema. Given a constrained critical point $\mathbf{a}$ of f subject to the conditions $g_1(\mathbf{x}) = c_1$, $g_2(\mathbf{x}) = c_2, \ldots,$ $g_k(\mathbf{x}) = c_k$, consider the matrix

$$
HL(\lambda; \mathbf{a}) =
\begin{bmatrix}
0 & \cdots & 0 & -\dfrac{\partial g_1}{\partial x_1}(\mathbf{a}) & \cdots & -\dfrac{\partial g_1}{\partial x_n}(\mathbf{a}) \\[2mm]
\vdots & \ddots & \vdots & \vdots & \ddots & \vdots \\[2mm]
0 & \cdots & 0 & -\dfrac{\partial g_k}{\partial x_1}(\mathbf{a}) & \cdots & -\dfrac{\partial g_k}{\partial x_n}(\mathbf{a}) \\[2mm]
-\dfrac{\partial g_1}{\partial x_1}(\mathbf{a}) & \cdots & -\dfrac{\partial g_k}{\partial x_1}(\mathbf{a}) & h_{11} & \cdots & h_{1n} \\[2mm]
\vdots & \ddots & \vdots & \vdots & \ddots & \vdots \\[2mm]
-\dfrac{\partial g_1}{\partial x_n}(\mathbf{a}) & \cdots & -\dfrac{\partial g_k}{\partial x_n}(\mathbf{a}) & h_{n1} & \cdots & h_{nn}
\end{bmatrix},
$$

where

$$
h_{ij} = \frac{\partial^2 f}{\partial x_j \partial x_i}(\mathbf{a}) - \lambda_1 \frac{\partial^2 g_1}{\partial x_j \partial x_i}(\mathbf{a}) - \lambda_2 \frac{\partial^2 g_2}{\partial x_j \partial x_i}(\mathbf{a}) - \cdots - \lambda_k \frac{\partial^2 g_k}{\partial x_j \partial x_i}(\mathbf{a}).
$$

(Note that $HL(\lambda; \mathbf{a})$ is an $(n + k) \times (n + k)$ matrix.) By relabeling the variables as necessary, assume that

$$
\det
\begin{bmatrix}
\dfrac{\partial g_1}{\partial x_1}(\mathbf{a}) & \cdots & \dfrac{\partial g_1}{\partial x_k}(\mathbf{a}) \\[2mm]
\vdots & \ddots & \vdots \\[2mm]
\dfrac{\partial g_k}{\partial x_1}(\mathbf{a}) & \cdots & \dfrac{\partial g_k}{\partial x_k}(\mathbf{a})
\end{bmatrix}
\neq 0.
$$

As in the unconstrained case, let H_j be the upper leftmost $j \times j$ submatrix of $HL(\lambda, \mathbf{a})$. For $j = 1, 2, \ldots, k + n$, let $d_j = \det H_j$, and calculate the following sequence of $n - k$ numbers:

$$
(-1)^k d_{2k+1}, \quad (-1)^k d_{2k+2}, \ldots, \quad (-1)^k d_{k+n}. \tag{1}
$$

Note that, if $k \geq 1$, the sequence in (1) is *not* the complete sequence of principal minors of $HL(\lambda, \mathbf{a})$. Assume $d_{k+n} = \det HL(\lambda, \mathbf{a}) \neq 0$. The numerical test is as follows:

1. If the sequence in (1) consists entirely of positive numbers, then f has a local minimum at $\mathbf{a}$ subject to the constraints

$$
g_1(\mathbf{x}) = c_1, \quad g_2(\mathbf{x}) = c_2, \ldots, \quad g_k(\mathbf{x}) = c_k.
$$

2. If the sequence in (1) begins with a negative number and thereafter alternates in sign, then f has a local maximum at $\mathbf{a}$ subject to the constraints

$$
g_1(\mathbf{x}) = c_1, \quad g_2(\mathbf{x}) = c_2, \ldots, \quad g_k(\mathbf{x}) = c_k.
$$

3. If neither case 1 nor case 2 holds, then f has a constrained saddle point at $\mathbf{a}$.

In the event that $\det HL(\lambda, \mathbf{a}) = 0$, the constrained critical point $\mathbf{a}$ is **degenerate**, and we must use another method to determine whether or not it is the site of an extremum.

Finally, in the case of no constraint equations $g_i(\mathbf{x}) = c_i$ (i.e., $k = 0$), the preceding criterion becomes the usual Hessian test for a function f of n variables.

EXAMPLE 6 In Example 1, we found the minimum of the area function

$$A(x, y, z) = 2xy + 2yz + xz$$

of an open rectangular box subject to the condition

$$V(x, y, z) = xyz = 4.$$

Using Lagrange multipliers, we found that the only constrained critical point was $(2, 1, 2)$. The value of the multiplier λ corresponding to this point is 2. To use the Hessian criterion to check that $(2, 1, 2)$ really does yield a local minimum, we construct the Lagrangian function

$$L(l; x, y, z) = A(x, y, z) - l(V(x, y, z) - 4)$$

$$= 2xy + 2yz + xz - l(xyz - 4).$$

Then

$$HL(l; x, y, z) = \begin{bmatrix} 0 & -yz & -xz & -xy \\ -yz & 0 & 2 - lz & 1 - ly \\ -xz & 2 - lx & 0 & 2 - lx \\ -xy & 1 - ly & 2 - lx & 0 \end{bmatrix}.$$

At the constrained critical point $(2; 2, 1, 2)$, we have

$$HL(2; 2, 1, 2) = \begin{bmatrix} 0 & -2 & -4 & -2 \\ -2 & 0 & -2 & -1 \\ -4 & -2 & 0 & -2 \\ -2 & -1 & -2 & 0 \end{bmatrix}.$$

The sequence of determinants to consider is

$$(-1)^1 \det H_{2(1)+1} = -\det \begin{bmatrix} 0 & -2 & -4 \\ -2 & 0 & -2 \\ -4 & -2 & 0 \end{bmatrix} = 32,$$

$$(-1)^1 \det H_4 = -\det \begin{bmatrix} 0 & -2 & -4 & -2 \\ -2 & 0 & -2 & -1 \\ -4 & -2 & 0 & -2 \\ -2 & -1 & -2 & 0 \end{bmatrix} = 48.$$

Since these numbers are both positive, we see that $(2, 1, 2)$ indeed minimizes the area of the box subject to the constant volume constraint. ◆

EXAMPLE 7 In Example 5, we found points on the conic section C defined by equations

$$\begin{cases} g_1(x, y, z) = x^2 + y^2 - z^2 = 0 \\ g_2(x, y, z) = x + y - z = -2 \end{cases}$$

that are (constrained) critical points of the "distance" function

$$f(x, y, z) = x^2 + y^2 + z^2.$$

To apply the Hessian criterion in this case, we construct the Lagrangian function

$$L(l, m; x, y, z) = x^2 + y^2 + z^2 - l(x^2 + y^2 - z^2) - m(x + y - z + 2).$$

The critical points of L, found by setting $DL(l, m; x, y, z)$ equal to $\mathbf{0}$, are

$$(\lambda_1; \mathbf{a}_1) = (-3 + 2\sqrt{2}, -24 + 16\sqrt{2}; -2 + \sqrt{2}, -2 + \sqrt{2}, -2 + 2\sqrt{2})$$

and

$$(\lambda_2; \mathbf{a}_2) = (-3 - 2\sqrt{2}, -24 - 16\sqrt{2}; -2 - \sqrt{2}, -2 - \sqrt{2}, -2 - 2\sqrt{2}).$$

The Hessian of L is

$$HL(l, m; x, y, z) = \begin{bmatrix} 0 & 0 & -2x & -2y & 2z \\ 0 & 0 & -1 & -1 & 1 \\ -2x & -1 & 2 - 2l & 0 & 0 \\ -2y & -1 & 0 & 2 - 2l & 0 \\ 2z & 1 & 0 & 0 & 2 + 2l \end{bmatrix}.$$

After we evaluate this matrix at each of the critical points, we need to compute

$$(-1)^2 \det H_{2(2)+1} = \det H_5.$$

We leave it to you to check that for $(\lambda_1; \mathbf{a}_1)$ this determinant is $128 - 64\sqrt{2} \approx 37.49$, and for $(\lambda_2; \mathbf{a}_2)$ it is $128 + 64\sqrt{2} \approx 218.51$. Since both numbers are positive, the points $(-2 \pm \sqrt{2}, -2 \pm \sqrt{2}, -2 \pm 2\sqrt{2})$ are both sites of local minima. By comparing the values of f at these two points, we see that $(-2 + \sqrt{2}, -2 + \sqrt{2}, -2 + 2\sqrt{2})$ must be the global minimum. ◆

4.3 Exercises

1. In this problem, find the point on the plane $2x - 3y - z = 4$ that is closest to the origin in two ways:
   (a) by using the methods in §4.2 (i.e., by finding the minimum value of an appropriate function of two variables);
   (b) by using a Lagrange multiplier.

In Exercises 2–12, use Lagrange multipliers to identify the critical points of f subject to the given constraints.

2. $f(x, y) = y, \quad 2x^2 + y^2 = 4$

3. $f(x, y) = 5x + 2y, \quad 5x^2 + 2y^2 = 14$

4. $f(x, y) = xy, \quad 2x - 3y = 6$

5. $f(x, y, z) = xyz, \quad 2x + 3y + z = 6$

6. $f(x, y, z) = x^2 + y^2 + z^2, \quad x + y - z = 1$

7. $f(x, y, z) = 3 - x^2 - 2y^2 - z^2, \quad 2x + y + z = 2$

8. $f(x, y, z) = x^6 + y^6 + z^6, \quad x^2 + y^2 + z^2 = 6$

9. $f(x, y, z) = 2x + y^2 - z^2, \quad x - 2y = 0, \ x + z = 0$

10. $f(x, y, z) = 2x + y^2 + 2z, \quad x^2 - y^2 = 1, \ x + y + z = 2$

11. $f(x, y, z) = xy + yz, \quad x^2 + y^2 = 1, \ yz = 1$

12. $f(x, y, z) = x + y + z, \quad y^2 - x^2 = 1, \quad x + 2z = 1$

13. (a) Find the critical points of $f(x, y) = x^2 + y$ subject to $x^2 + 2y^2 = 1$.
    (b) Use the Hessian criterion to determine the nature of the critical point.

14. (a) Find any critical points of $f(x, y, z, w) = x^2 + y^2 + z^2 + w^2$ subject to $2x + y + z = 1, x - 2z - w = -2, 3x + y + 2w = -1$.
    (b) Use the Hessian criterion to determine the nature of the critical point. (Note: You may wish to use a computer algebra system for the calculations.)

Just as sometimes is the case when finding ordinary (i.e., unconstrained) critical points of functions, it can be difficult to solve a Lagrange multiplier problem because the system of equations that results may be prohibitively difficult to solve by hand. In Exercises 15–19, use a computer algebra system to find the critical points of the given function f subject to the constraints indicated. (Note: You may find it helpful to provide numerical approximations in some cases.)

15. $f(x, y, z) = 3xy - 4z, 3x + y - 2xz = 1$

16. $f(x, y, z) = 3xy - 4yz + 5xz, \quad 3x + y + 2z = 12, 2x - 3y + 5z = 0$

17. $f(x, y, z) = y^3 + 2xyz - x^2, x^2 + y^2 + z^2 = 1$

18. $f(x, y, z) = x^2 + y^2 - xz^2, xy + z^2 = 1$

19. $f(x, y, z, w) = x^2 + y^2 + z^2 + w^2, \quad x^2 + y^2 = 1, \\ x + y + z + w = 1, x - y + z - w = 0$

20. Consider the problem of determining the extreme values of the function $f(x, y) = x^3 + 3y^2$ subject to the constraint that $xy = -4$.

    (a) Use a Lagrange multiplier to find the critical points of f that satisfy the constraint.

    (b) Give an analytic argument to determine if the critical points you found in part (a) yield (constrained) maxima or minima of f.

    (c) Use a computer to plot, on a single set of axes, several level curves of f together with the constraint curve $xy = -4$. Use your plot to give a geometric justification for your answers in parts (a) and (b).

21. Find three positive numbers whose sum is 18 and whose product is as large as possible.

22. Find the maximum and minimum values of $f(x, y, z) = x + y - z$ on the sphere $x^2 + y^2 + z^2 = 81$. Explain how you know that there must be both a maximum and a minimum attained.

23. Find the maximum and minimum values of $f(x, y) = x^2 + xy + y^2$ on the closed disk $D = \{(x, y) \mid x^2 + y^2 \le 4\}$.

24. You are sending a birthday present to your calculus instructor. Fly-By-Night Delivery Service insists that any package it ships be such that the sum of the length plus the girth be at most 108 in. (The girth is the perimeter of the cross section perpendicular to the length axis—see Figure 4.31.) What are the dimensions of the largest present you can send?

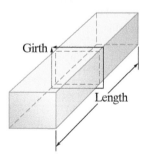

Figure 4.31 Diagram for Exercise 24.

25. A cylindrical metal can is to be manufactured from a fixed amount of sheet metal. Use the method of Lagrange multipliers to determine the ratio between the dimensions of the can with the largest capacity.

26. An industrious farmer is designing a silo to hold her 900π ft^3 supply of grain. The silo is to be cylindrical in shape with a hemispherical roof. (See Figure 4.32.) Suppose that it costs five times as much (per square foot of sheet metal used) to fashion the roof of the silo as it does to make the circular floor and twice as much to make the cylindrical walls as the floor. If you were to act as consultant for this project, what dimensions would you recommend so that the *total* cost would be a minimum? On what do you base your recommendation? (Assume that the entire silo can be filled with grain.)

Figure 4.32 The grain silo of Exercise 26.

27. You are in charge of erecting a space probe on the newly discovered planet Nilrebo. To minimize interference to the probe's sensors, you must place the probe where the magnetic field of the planet is weakest. Nilrebo is perfectly spherical with a radius of 3 (where the units are thousands of miles). Based on a coordinate system whose origin is at the center of Nilrebo, the strength of the magnetic field in space is given by the function $M(x, y, z) = xz - y^2 + 3x + 3$. Where should you locate the probe?

28. Heron's formula for the area of a triangle whose sides have lengths x, y, and z is

$$\text{Area} = \sqrt{s(s - x)(s - y)(s - z)},$$

where $s = \frac{1}{2}(x + y + z)$ is the so-called semiperimeter of the triangle. Use Heron's formula to show that, for a fixed perimeter P, the triangle with the largest area is equilateral.

29. Use a Lagrange multiplier to find the largest sphere centered at the origin that can be inscribed in the ellipsoid $3x^2 + 2y^2 + z^2 = 6$. (Be careful with this problem; drawing a picture may help.)

30. Find the point closest to the origin and on the line of intersection of the planes $2x + y + 3z = 9$ and $3x + 2y + z = 6$.

31. Find the point closest to the point $(2, 5, -1)$ and on the line of intersection of the planes $x - 2y + 3z = 8$ and $2z - y = 3$.

32. The plane $x + y + z = 4$ intersects the paraboloid $z = x^2 + y^2$ in an ellipse. Find the points on the ellipse nearest to and farthest from the origin.

33. Find the highest and lowest points on the ellipse obtained by intersecting the paraboloid $z = x^2 + y^2$ with the plane $x + y + 2z = 2$.

34. Find the minimum distance between a point on the ellipse $x^2 + 2y^2 = 1$ and a point on the line $x + y = 4$. (Hint: Consider a point (x, y) on the ellipse and a point (u, v) on the line. Minimize the square of the distance between them as a function of four variables. This problem is difficult to solve without a computer.)

35. (a) Use the method of Lagrange multipliers to find critical points of the function $f(x, y) = x + y$ subject to the constraint $xy = 6$.

(b) Explain geometrically why f has no extrema on the set $\{(x, y) \mid xy = 6\}$.

36. Let $\alpha, \beta,$ and γ denote the (interior) angles of a triangle. Determine the maximum value of $\sin \alpha \sin \beta \sin \gamma$.

37. Let S be a surface in $\mathbf{R}^3$ given by the equation $g(x, y, z) = c$, where g is a function of class C^1 with nonvanishing gradient and c is a constant. Suppose that there is a point P on S whose distance from the origin is a maximum. Show that the displacement vector from the origin to P must be perpendicular to S.

38. The cylinder $x^2 + y^2 = 4$ and the plane $2x + 2y + z = 2$ intersect in an ellipse. Find the points on the ellipse that are nearest to and farthest from the origin.

39. Find the points on the ellipse $3x^2 - 4xy + 3y^2 = 50$ that are nearest to and farthest from the origin.

40. This problem concerns the determination of the extrema of $f(x, y) = \sqrt{x} + 8\sqrt{y}$ subject to the constraint $x^2 + y^2 = 17$, where $x \geq 0$ and $y \geq 0$.

(a) Explain why f must attain both a global minimum and a global maximum on the given constraint curve.

(b) Use a Lagrange multiplier to solve the system of equations

$$\begin{cases} \nabla f(x, y) = \lambda \nabla g(x, y) \\ g(x, y) = 0 \end{cases},$$

where $g(x, y) = x^2 + y^2$. You should identify a single critical point of f.

(c) Identify the global minimum and the global maximum of f subject to the constraint.

41. Consider the problem of finding extrema of $f(x, y) = x$ subject to the constraint $y^2 - 4x^3 + 4x^4 = 0$.

(a) Use a Lagrange multiplier and solve the system of equations

$$\begin{cases} \nabla f(x, y) = \lambda \nabla g(x, y) \\ g(x, y) = 0 \end{cases},$$

where $g(x, y) = y^2 - 4x^3 + 4x^4$. By doing so, you will identify critical points of f subject to the given constraint.

(b) Graph the curve $y^2 - 4x^3 + 4x^4 = 0$ and use the graph to determine where the extrema of $f(x, y) = x$ occur.

(c) Compare your result in part (a) with what you found in part (b). What accounts for any differences that you observed?

42. Consider the problem of finding extrema of $f(x, y, z) = x^2 + y^2$ subject to the constraint $z = c$, where c is any constant.

(a) Use the method of Lagrange multipliers to identify the critical points of f subject to the constraint given above.

(b) Using the usual alphabetical ordering of variables (i.e., $x_1 = x, x_2 = y, x_3 = z$), construct the Hessian matrix $HL(\lambda; a_1, a_2, a_3)$ (where $L(l; x, y, z) = f(x, y, z) - l(z - c)$) for each critical point you found in part (a). Try to use the second derivative test for constrained extrema to determine the nature of the critical points you found in part (a). What happens?

(c) Repeat part (b), this time using the variable ordering $x_1 = z, x_2 = y, x_3 = x$. What does the second derivative test tell you now?

(d) Without making any detailed calculations, discuss why f must attain its minimum value at the point $(0, 0, c)$. Then try to reconcile your results in parts (b) and (c). This exercise demonstrates that the assumption that

$$\det \begin{bmatrix} \dfrac{\partial g_1}{\partial x_1}(\mathbf{a}) & \cdots & \dfrac{\partial g_1}{\partial x_k}(\mathbf{a}) \\ \vdots & \ddots & \vdots \\ \dfrac{\partial g_k}{\partial x_1}(\mathbf{a}) & \cdots & \dfrac{\partial g_k}{\partial x_k}(\mathbf{a}) \end{bmatrix} \neq 0$$

is important.

43. Consider the problem of finding critical points of the function $f(x_1, \ldots, x_n)$ subject to the set of k constraints

$$g_1(x_1, \ldots, x_n) = c_1, \quad g_2(x_1, \ldots, x_n) = c_2, \ldots,$$

$$g_k(x_1, \ldots, x_n) = c_k.$$

Assume that $f, g_1, g_2, \ldots, g_k$ are all of class C^2.

(a) Show that we can relate the method of Lagrange multipliers for determining constrained critical points to the techniques in §4.2 for finding unconstrained critical points as follows: If

$$(\lambda, \mathbf{a}) = (\lambda_1, \ldots, \lambda_k; a_1, \ldots, a_n)$$

is a pair consisting of k values for Lagrange multipliers $\lambda_1, \ldots, \lambda_k$ and n values $a_1, \ldots, a_n$ for the variables $x_1, \ldots, x_n$ such that $\mathbf{a}$ is a constrained critical point, then $(\lambda, \mathbf{a})$ is an ordinary (i.e., unconstrained) critical point of the function

$$L(l_1, \ldots, l_k; x_1, \ldots, x_n)$$

$$= f(x_1, \ldots, x_n) - \sum_{i=1}^{k} l_i(g_i(x_1, \ldots, x_n) - c_i).$$

(b) Calculate the Hessian $HL(\lambda, \mathbf{a})$, and verify that it is the matrix used in §4.3 to provide the criterion for determining the nature of constrained critical points.

44. The unit hypersphere in $\mathbf{R}^n$ (centered at the origin $\mathbf{0} = (0, \ldots, 0)$) is defined by the equation $x_1^2 + x_2^2 + \cdots + x_n^2 = 1$. Find the pair of points $\mathbf{x} = (x_1, \ldots, x_n)$ and $\mathbf{y} = (y_1, \ldots, y_n)$, each of which lies on the unit hypersphere, that maximizes and minimizes the function

$$f(x_1, \ldots, x_n, y_1, \ldots, y_n) = \sum_{i=1}^{n} x_i y_i.$$

What are the maximum and minimum values of f?

45. Let $\mathbf{x} = (x_1, \ldots, x_n)$ and $\mathbf{y} = (y_1, \ldots, y_n)$ be any vectors in $\mathbf{R}^n$ and, for $i = 1, \ldots, n$, set

$$u_i = \frac{x_i}{\sqrt{\sum_{i=1}^{n} x_i^2}} \quad \text{and} \quad v_i = \frac{y_i}{\sqrt{\sum_{i=1}^{n} y_i^2}}.$$

(a) Show that $\mathbf{u} = (u_1, \ldots, u_n)$ and $\mathbf{v} = (v_1, \ldots, v_n)$ lie on the unit hypersphere in $\mathbf{R}^n$.

(b) Use the result of Exercise 44 to establish the Cauchy–Schwarz inequality

$$|\mathbf{x} \cdot \mathbf{y}| \leq \|\mathbf{x}\| \, \|\mathbf{y}\|.$$

4.4 Some Applications of Extrema

In this section, we present several applications of the methods for finding both constrained and unconstrained extrema discussed previously.

Least Squares Approximation

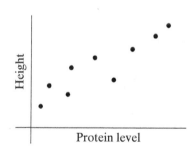

Figure 4.33 Height versus protein level.

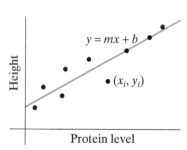

Figure 4.34 Fitting a line to the data.

The simplest relation between two quantities x and y is, without doubt, a linear one: $y = mx + b$ (where m and b are constants). When a biologist, chemist, psychologist, or economist postulates the most direct connection between two types of observed data, that connection is assumed to be linear. Suppose that Bob Biologist and Carol Chemist have measured certain blood protein levels in an adult population and have graphed these levels versus the heights of the subjects as in Figure 4.33. If Prof. Biologist and Dr. Chemist assume a linear relationship between the protein and height, then they desire to pass a line through the data as closely as possible, as suggested by Figure 4.34.

To make this standard empirical method of **linear regression** precise (instead of merely graphical and intuitive), we first need some notation. Suppose we have collected n pairs of data $(x_1, y_1), (x_2, y_2), \ldots, (x_n, y_n)$. (In the example just described, x_i is the protein level of the ith subject and y_i his or her height.) We assume that there is some underlying relationship of the form $y = mx + b$, and we want to find the constants m and b so that the line fits the data as accurately as possible. Normally, we use the **method of least squares**. The idea is to find the values of m and b that minimize the sum of the squares of the differences between the observed y-values and those predicted by the linear formula. That is, we minimize the quantity

$$D(m, b) = [y_1 - (mx_1 + b)]^2 + [y_2 - (mx_2 + b)]^2 \\ + \cdots + [y_n - (mx_n + b)]^2, \tag{1}$$

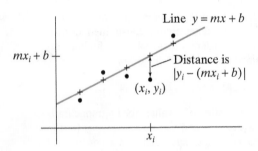

Figure 4.35 The method of least squares.

where, for $i = 1, \ldots, n$, y_i represents the observed y-value of the data, and $mx_i + b$ represents the y-value predicted by the linear relationship. Hence, each expression in D of the form $y_i - (mx_i + b)$ represents the error between the observed and predicted y-values. (See Figure 4.35.) They are squared in the expression for D in order to avoid the possibility of having large negative and positive terms cancel one another, thereby leaving little or no "net error," which would be misleading. Moreover, $D(m, b)$ is the square of the distance in $\mathbf{R}^n$ between the point $(y_1, y_2, \ldots, y_n)$ and the point $(mx_1 + b, mx_2 + b, \ldots, mx_n + b)$.

Thus, we have an ordinary minimization problem at hand. To solve it, we need to find the critical points of D. First, we can rewrite D as

$$D(m, b) = \sum_{i=1}^{n} [y_i - (mx_i + b)]^2$$

$$= \sum_{i=1}^{n} y_i^2 - 2m \sum_{i=1}^{n} x_i y_i - 2b \sum_{i=1}^{n} y_i + \sum_{i=1}^{n} (mx_i + b)^2.$$

Then

$$\frac{\partial D}{\partial m} = -2 \sum_{i=1}^{n} x_i y_i + \sum_{i=1}^{n} 2(mx_i + b)x_i$$

$$= -2 \sum_{i=1}^{n} x_i y_i + 2m \sum_{i=1}^{n} x_i^2 + 2b \sum_{i=1}^{n} x_i$$

and

$$\frac{\partial D}{\partial b} = -2 \sum_{i=1}^{n} y_i + \sum_{i=1}^{n} 2(mx_i + b)$$

$$= -2 \sum_{i=1}^{n} y_i + 2m \sum_{i=1}^{n} x_i + 2nb.$$

When we set both partial derivatives equal to zero, we obtain the following pair of equations, which have been simplified slightly:

$$\begin{cases} \left(\sum x_i^2 \right) m + \left(\sum x_i \right) b = \sum x_i y_i \\ \left(\sum x_i \right) m + nb = \sum y_i \end{cases} \qquad (2)$$

(All sums are taken from $i = 1$ to n.) Although (2) may look complicated, it is nothing more than a linear system of two equations in the two unknowns m and b.

It is not difficult to see that system (2) has a single solution. Therefore, we have shown the following:

PROPOSITION 4.1 Given n data points $(x_1, y_1), (x_2, y_2), \ldots, (x_n, y_n)$ with not all of $x_1, x_2, \ldots, x_n$ equal, the function

$$D(m, b) = \sum_{i=1}^{n} [y_i - (mx_i + b)]^2$$

has a single critical point (m_0, b_0) given by

$$m_0 = \frac{n \sum x_i y_i - \left(\sum x_i \right)\left(\sum y_i \right)}{n \sum x_i^2 - \left(\sum x_i \right)^2},$$

and

$$b_0 = \frac{\left(\sum x_i^2 \right)\left(\sum y_i \right) - \left(\sum x_i \right)\left(\sum x_i y_i \right)}{n \sum x_i^2 - \left(\sum x_i \right)^2}.$$

Since $D(m, b)$ is a quadratic polynomial in m and b, the graph of $z = D(m, b)$ is a quadric surface. (See §2.1.) The only such surfaces that are graphs of functions are paraboloids and hyperbolic paraboloids. We show that, in the present case, the graph is that of a paraboloid by demonstrating that D has a local minimum at the critical point (m_0, b_0) given in Proposition 4.1.

We can use the Hessian criterion to check that D has a local minimum at (m_0, b_0). We have

$$HD(m, b) = \begin{bmatrix} 2 \sum x_i^2 & 2 \sum x_i \\ 2 \sum x_i & 2n \end{bmatrix}.$$

The principal minors are $2 \sum x_i^2$ and $4n \sum x_i^2 - 4 \left(\sum x_i \right)^2$. The first minor is obviously positive, but determining the sign of the second requires a bit more algebra. (If you wish, you can omit reading the details of this next calculation and rest assured that the story has a happy ending.) Ignoring the factor of 4, we examine the expression $n \sum x_i^2 - \left(\sum x_i \right)^2$. Expanding the second term yields

$$n \sum_{i=1}^{n} x_i^2 - \left(\sum_{i=1}^{n} x_i \right)^2 = n \sum_{i=1}^{n} x_i^2 - \left(\sum_{i=1}^{n} x_i^2 + \sum_{i<j} 2x_i x_j \right)$$

$$= (n - 1) \sum_{i=1}^{n} x_i^2 - \sum_{i<j} 2x_i x_j. \qquad (3)$$

On the other hand, we have

$$\sum_{i<j} (x_i - x_j)^2 = \sum_{i<j} \left(x_i^2 - 2x_i x_j + x_j^2 \right) = (n - 1) \sum_{i=1}^{n} x_i^2 - \sum_{i<j} 2x_i x_j. \qquad (4)$$

(To see that equation (4) holds, you need to convince yourself that

$$\sum_{i<j} \left(x_i^2 + x_j^2 \right) = (n - 1) \sum_{i=1}^{n} x_i^2$$

by counting the number of times a particular term of the form x_k^2 appears in the left-hand sum.) Thus, we have

$$\det HD(m, b) = 4\left(n\sum_{i=1}^{n} x_i^2 - \left(\sum_{i=1}^{n} x_i\right)^2\right)$$

$$= 4\left((n-1)\sum_{i=1}^{n} x_i^2 - \sum_{i<j} 2x_i x_j\right) \quad \text{by equation (3),}$$

$$= 4\sum_{i<j}(x_i - x_j)^2 \quad \text{by equation (4).}$$

Because this last expression is a sum of squares, it is nonnegative. Therefore, the Hessian criterion shows that D does indeed have a local minimum at the critical point. Hence, the graph of $z = D(m, b)$ is that of a paraboloid. Since the (unique) local minimum of a paraboloid is in fact a global minimum (consider a typical graph), we see that D is indeed minimized at (m_0, b_0).

EXAMPLE 1 To see how the preceding discussion applies to a specific set of data, consider the situation depicted in Figure 4.36.

We have $n = 5$, and the function D to be minimized is

$$D(m, b) = [2 - (m + b)]^2 + [1 - (2m + b)]^2 + [5 - (3m + b)]^2$$
$$+ [3 - (4m + b)]^2 + [4 - (5m + b)]^2.$$

We compute

$$\sum x_i = 15, \qquad \sum x_i^2 = 55, \qquad \sum y_i = 15, \qquad \sum x_i y_i = 51.$$

Thus, using Proposition 4.1,

$$m = \frac{5 \cdot 51 - 15 \cdot 15}{5 \cdot 55 - 15 \cdot 15} = \frac{3}{5}, \qquad b = \frac{55 \cdot 15 - 15 \cdot 51}{5 \cdot 55 - 15 \cdot 15} = \frac{6}{5}.$$

The best fit line in terms of least squares approximation is

$$y = \frac{3}{5}x + \frac{6}{5}.$$

◆

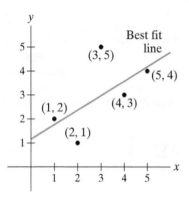

Figure 4.36 Data for the linear regression of Example 1.

Of course, linear regression is not always an appropriate technique. It may not be reasonable to assume that the data points fall nearly on a straight line. Some formula other than $y = mx + b$ may have to be assumed to describe the data with any accuracy. Such a postulated relation might be quadratic,

$$y = ax^2 + bx + c,$$

or x and y might be inversely related,

$$y = \frac{a}{x} + b.$$

You can still apply the method of least squares to construct a function analogous to D in equation (1) to find the relation of a given form that best fits the data.

Another way that least squares arise is if y depends not on one variable but on several: $x_1, x_2, \ldots, x_n$. For example, perhaps adult height is measured against blood levels of 10 different proteins instead of just one. **Multiple regression** is the statistical method of finding the linear function

$$y = a_1 x_1 + a_2 x_2 + \cdots + a_n x_n + b$$

that best fits a data set of $(n + 1)$-tuples

$$\left\{ (x_1^{(1)}, x_2^{(1)}, \ldots, x_n^{(1)}, y_1), (x_1^{(2)}, x_2^{(2)}, \ldots, x_n^{(2)}, y_2), \ldots, (x_1^{(k)}, x_2^{(k)}, \ldots, x_n^{(k)}, y_k) \right\}.$$

We can find such a "best fit hyperplane" by minimizing the sum of the squares of the differences between the y-values furnished by the data set and those predicted by the linear formula. We leave the details to you.[3]

Physical Equilibria

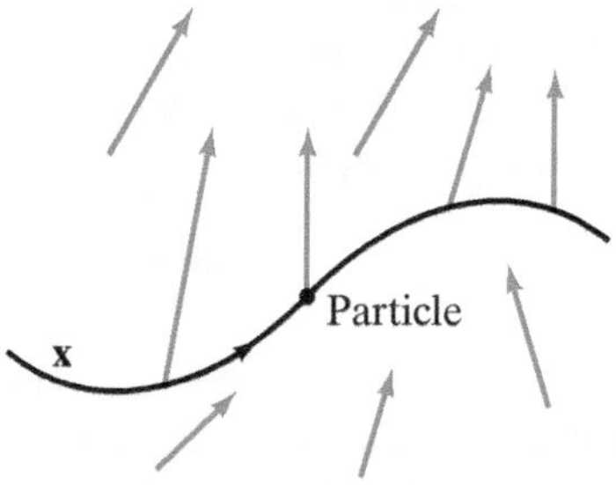

Let $\mathbf{F} \colon X \subseteq \mathbf{R}^3 \to \mathbf{R}^3$ be a continuous force field acting on a particle that moves along a path $\mathbf{x} \colon I \subseteq \mathbf{R} \to \mathbf{R}^3$ as in Figure 4.37. Newton's second law of motion states that

$$\mathbf{F}(\mathbf{x}(t)) = m\mathbf{x}''(t), \tag{5}$$

where m is the mass of the particle. For the remainder of this discussion, we will assume that $\mathbf{F}$ is a gradient field, that is, that $\mathbf{F} = -\nabla V$ for some C^1 potential function $V \colon X \subseteq \mathbf{R}^3 \to \mathbf{R}$. (See §3.3 for a brief comment about the negative sign.) We first establish the law of conservation of energy.

Figure 4.37 A particle traveling in a force field $\mathbf{F}$.

THEOREM 4.2 (CONSERVATION OF ENERGY)   Given the set-up above, the quantity

$$\tfrac{1}{2} m \| \mathbf{x}'(t) \|^2 + V(\mathbf{x}(t))$$

is constant.

The term $\tfrac{1}{2} m \| \mathbf{x}'(t) \|^2$ is usually referred to as the **kinetic energy** of the particle and the term $V(\mathbf{x}(t))$ as the **potential energy**. The significance of Theorem 4.2 is that it states that the sum of the kinetic and potential energies of a particle is always fixed (conserved) when the particle travels along a path in a gradient vector field. For this reason, gradient vector fields are also called **conservative** vector fields.

Proof of Theorem 4.2 As usual, we show that the total energy is constant by showing that its derivative is zero. Thus, using the product rule and the chain rule, we calculate

$$\frac{d}{dt} \left[\tfrac{1}{2} m\mathbf{x}'(t) \cdot \mathbf{x}'(t) + V(\mathbf{x}(t)) \right] = m\mathbf{x}''(t) \cdot \mathbf{x}'(t) + \nabla V(\mathbf{x}(t)) \cdot \mathbf{x}'(t)$$

$$= m\mathbf{x}''(t) \cdot \mathbf{x}'(t) - \mathbf{F}(\mathbf{x}(t)) \cdot \mathbf{x}'(t)$$

$$= m\mathbf{x}''(t) \cdot \mathbf{x}'(t) - m\mathbf{x}''(t) \cdot \mathbf{x}'(t)$$

$$= 0,$$

from the definitions of $\mathbf{F}$ and V and by formula (5).   ∎

---

[3] Or you might consult S. Weisberg, *Applied Linear Regression*, 2nd ed., Wiley-Interscience, 1985, Chapter 2. Be forewarned, however, that to treat multiple regression with any elegance requires somewhat more linear algebra than we have presented.

In physical applications it is important to identify those points in space that are "rest positions" for particles moving under the influence of a force field. These positions, known as **equilibrium points**, are such that the force field does not act on the particle so as to move it from that position. Equilibrium points are of two kinds: **stable** equilibria, namely, equilibrium points such that a particle perturbed slightly from these positions tends to remain nearby (for example, a pendulum hanging down at rest) and **unstable** equilibria, such as the act of balancing a ball on your nose. The precise definition is somewhat technical.

DEFINITION 4.3   Let $\mathbf{F}: X \subseteq \mathbf{R}^n \to \mathbf{R}^n$ be any force field. Then $\mathbf{x}_0 \in X$ is called an **equilibrium point** of $\mathbf{F}$ if $\mathbf{F}(\mathbf{x}_0) = \mathbf{0}$. An equilibrium point $\mathbf{x}_0$ is said to be **stable** if, for every $r, \epsilon > 0$, we can find other numbers $r_0, \epsilon_0 > 0$ such that if we place a particle at position $\mathbf{x}$ with $\|\mathbf{x} - \mathbf{x}_0\| < r_0$ and provide it with a kinetic energy less than ϵ_0, then the particle will always remain within distance r of $\mathbf{x}_0$ with kinetic energy less than ϵ.

In other words, a stable equilibrium point $\mathbf{x}_0$ has the following property: You can keep a particle inside a specific ball centered at $\mathbf{x}_0$ with a small kinetic energy by starting the particle inside some other (possibly smaller) ball about $\mathbf{x}_0$ and imparting to it some (possibly smaller) initial kinetic energy. (See Figure 4.38.)

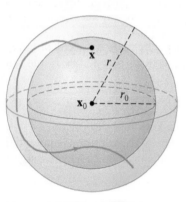

Figure 4.38 For a stable equilibrium point, the path of a nearby particle with a sufficiently small kinetic energy will remain nearby with a bounded kinetic energy.

THEOREM 4.4   For a C^1 potential function V of a vector field $\mathbf{F} = -\nabla V$,

1. The critical points of the potential function are precisely the equilibrium points of $\mathbf{F}$.
2. If $\mathbf{x}_0$ gives a strict local minimum of V, then $\mathbf{x}_0$ is a stable equilibrium point of $\mathbf{F}$.

EXAMPLE 2   The vector field $\mathbf{F} = (-6x - 2y - 2)\mathbf{i} + (-2x - 4y + 2)\mathbf{j}$ is conservative and has

$$V(x, y) = 3x^2 + 2xy + 2x + 2y^2 - 2y + 4$$

as a potential function (meaning that $\mathbf{F} = -\nabla V$, according to our current sign convention). There is only one equilibrium point, namely, $\left(-\frac{3}{5}, \frac{4}{5}\right)$. To see if it is stable, we look at the Hessian of V:

$$HV\left(-\tfrac{3}{5}, \tfrac{4}{5}\right) = \begin{bmatrix} 6 & 2 \\ 2 & 4 \end{bmatrix}.$$

The sequence of principal minors is 6, 20. By the Hessian criterion, $\left(-\frac{3}{5}, \frac{4}{5}\right)$ is a strict local minimum of V and, by Theorem 4.4, it must be a stable equilibrium point of $\mathbf{F}$.   ◆

Proof of Theorem 4.4   The proof of part 1 is straightforward. Since $\mathbf{F} = -\nabla V$, we see that $\mathbf{F}(\mathbf{x}) = \mathbf{0}$ if and only if $\nabla V(\mathbf{x}) = \mathbf{0}$. Thus, equilibrium points of $\mathbf{F}$ are the critical points of V.

To prove part 2, let $\mathbf{x}_0$ be a strict local minimum of V and $\mathbf{x}: I \to \mathbf{R}^n$ a C^1 path such that $\mathbf{x}(t_0) = \mathbf{x}_0$ for some $t_0 \in I$. By conservation of energy, we must have, for all $t \in I$, that

$$\tfrac{1}{2}m\|\mathbf{x}'(t)\|^2 + V(\mathbf{x}(t)) = \tfrac{1}{2}m\|\mathbf{x}'(t_0)\|^2 + V(\mathbf{x}(t_0)).$$

To show that $\mathbf{x}_0$ is a stable equilibrium point, we desire to show that we can bound the distance between $\mathbf{x}(t)$ and $\mathbf{x}_0 = \mathbf{x}(t_0)$ by any amount r and the kinetic energy by any amount ϵ. That is, we want to show we can achieve

$$\|\mathbf{x}(t) - \mathbf{x}_0\| < r$$

(i.e., $\mathbf{x}(t) \in B_r(\mathbf{x}_0)$ in the notation of §2.2) and

$$\tfrac{1}{2}m\|\mathbf{x}'(t)\|^2 < \epsilon.$$

As the particle moves along $\mathbf{x}$ away from $\mathbf{x}_0$, the potential energy must increase (since $\mathbf{x}_0$ is assumed to be a strict local minimum of potential energy), so the kinetic energy must decrease by the same amount. For the particle to escape from $B_r(\mathbf{x}_0)$, the potential energy must increase by a certain amount. If ϵ_0 is chosen to be smaller than that amount, then the kinetic energy cannot decrease sufficiently (so that the conservation equation holds) without becoming negative. This being clearly impossible, the particle cannot escape from $B_r(\mathbf{x}_0)$. ∎

Often a particle is not only acted on by a force field but also constrained to lie in a surface in space. The set-up is as follows: $\mathbf{F}$ is a continuous vector field on $\mathbf{R}^3$ acting on a particle that lies in the surface $S = \{\mathbf{x} \in \mathbf{R}^3 \mid g(\mathbf{x}) = c\}$, where g is a C^1 function such that $\nabla g(\mathbf{x}) \neq \mathbf{0}$ for all $\mathbf{x}$ in S. Most of the comments made in the unconstrained case still hold true, provided $\mathbf{F}$ is replaced by the vector component of $\mathbf{F}$ tangent to S. Since, at $\mathbf{x} \in S$, $\nabla g(\mathbf{x})$ is normal to S, this tangential component of $\mathbf{F}$ at $\mathbf{x}$ is

$$\mathbf{\Phi}(\mathbf{x}) = \mathbf{F}(\mathbf{x}) - \text{proj}_{\nabla g(\mathbf{x})}\mathbf{F}(\mathbf{x}). \tag{6}$$

(See Figure 4.39.) Then in place of formula (5), we have, for a path $\mathbf{x}: I \subseteq \mathbf{R} \to S$,

$$\mathbf{\Phi}(\mathbf{x}(t)) = m\mathbf{x}''(t). \tag{7}$$

We can now state a "constrained version" of Theorem 4.4.

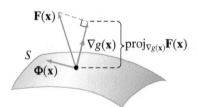

Figure 4.39 On the surface $S = \{\mathbf{x} \mid g(\mathbf{x}) = c\}$, the component of $\mathbf{F}$ that is tangent to S at $\mathbf{x}$ is denoted by $\mathbf{\Phi}(\mathbf{x})$.

THEOREM 4.5   For a C^1 potential function V of a vector field $\mathbf{F} = -\nabla V$,

1. If $V|_S$ has an extremum at $\mathbf{x}_0 \in S$, then $\mathbf{x}_0$ is an equilibrium point in S.
2. If $V|_S$ has a strict local minimum at $\mathbf{x}_0 \in S$, then $\mathbf{x}_0$ is a stable equilibrium point.

Sketch of proof   For part 1, if $V|_S$ has an extremum at $\mathbf{x}_0$, then, by Theorem 3.1, we have, for some scalar λ, that

$$\nabla V(\mathbf{x}_0) = \lambda \nabla g(\mathbf{x}_0).$$

Hence, because $\mathbf{F} = -\nabla V$,

$$\mathbf{F}(\mathbf{x}_0) = -\lambda \nabla g(\mathbf{x}_0),$$

implying that $\mathbf{F}$ is normal to S at $\mathbf{x}_0$. Thus, there can be no component of $\mathbf{F}$ tangent to S at $\mathbf{x}_0$ (i.e., $\mathbf{\Phi}(\mathbf{x}_0) = \mathbf{0}$). Since the particle is constrained to lie in S, we see that the particle is in equilibrium in S.

The proof of part 2 is essentially the same as the proof of part 2 of Theorem 4.4. The main modification is that the conservation of energy formula in Theorem 4.2 must be established anew, as its derivation rests on formula (5), which has been replaced by formula (7). Consequently, using the product and chain rules, we check, for $\mathbf{x}: I \to S$,

$$\frac{d}{dt}\left[\tfrac{1}{2}m\|\mathbf{x}'(t)\|^2 + V(\mathbf{x}(t))\right] = \frac{d}{dt}\left[\tfrac{1}{2}m\mathbf{x}'(t)\cdot\mathbf{x}'(t) + V(\mathbf{x}(t))\right]$$

$$= m\mathbf{x}''(t)\cdot\mathbf{x}'(t) + \nabla V(\mathbf{x}(t))\cdot\mathbf{x}'(t).$$

Then, using formula (6), we have

$$\frac{d}{dt}\left[\tfrac{1}{2}m\|\mathbf{x}'(t)\|^2 + V(\mathbf{x}(t))\right] = \mathbf{x}'(t)\cdot m\mathbf{x}''(t) - \mathbf{F}(\mathbf{x}(t))\cdot\mathbf{x}'(t)$$

$$= \mathbf{x}'(t)\cdot\boldsymbol{\Phi}(\mathbf{x}(t)) - \mathbf{F}(\mathbf{x}(t))\cdot\mathbf{x}'(t)$$

$$= \mathbf{x}'(t)\cdot\left[\mathbf{F}(\mathbf{x}(t)) - \text{proj}_{\nabla g(\mathbf{x}(t))}\mathbf{F}(\mathbf{x}(t))\right]$$

$$\quad - \mathbf{F}(\mathbf{x}(t))\cdot\mathbf{x}'(t)$$

$$= -\mathbf{x}'(t)\cdot\text{proj}_{\nabla g(\mathbf{x}(t))}\mathbf{F}(\mathbf{x}(t))$$

after cancellation. Thus, we conclude that

$$\frac{d}{dt}\left[\tfrac{1}{2}m\|\mathbf{x}'(t)\|^2 + V(\mathbf{x}(t))\right] = 0,$$

since $\mathbf{x}'(t)$ is tangent to the path in S and, hence, tangent to S itself at $\mathbf{x}(t)$, while $\text{proj}_{\nabla g(\mathbf{x}(t))}\mathbf{F}(\mathbf{x}(t))$ is parallel to $\nabla g(\mathbf{x}(t))$ and, hence, perpendicular to S at $\mathbf{x}(t)$. ∎

EXAMPLE 3 Near the surface of the earth, the gravitational field is approximately

$$\mathbf{F} = -mg\mathbf{k}.$$

(We're assuming that, locally, the surface of the earth is represented by the plane $z = 0$.) Note that $\mathbf{F} = -\nabla V$, where

$$V(x, y, z) = mgz.$$

Now suppose a particle of mass m lies on a small sphere with equation

$$h(x, y, z) = x^2 + y^2 + (z - 2r)^2 = r^2.$$

We can find constrained equilibria for this situation, using a Lagrange multiplier. The gradient equation $\nabla V = \lambda \nabla h$, along with the constraint, yields the system

$$\begin{cases} 0 = 2\lambda x \\ 0 = 2\lambda y \\ mg = 2\lambda(z - 2r) \\ x^2 + y^2 + (z - 2r)^2 = r^2 \end{cases}.$$

Because m and g are nonzero, λ cannot be zero. The first two equations imply $x = y = 0$. Therefore, the last equation becomes

$$(z - 2r)^2 = r^2,$$

which implies

$$z = r, 3r$$

are the solutions. Consequently, the positions of equilibrium are $(0, 0, r)$ and $(0, 0, 3r)$ (corresponding to $\lambda = -mg/2r$ and $+mg/2r$, respectively). From geometric considerations, we see V is strictly minimized at S at $(0, 0, r)$ and maximized at $(0, 0, 3r)$ as shown in Figure 4.40. From physical considerations, $(0, 0, r)$

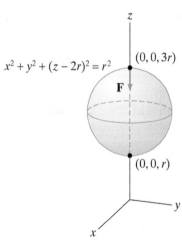

$x^2 + y^2 + (z - 2r)^2 = r^2$

$(0, 0, 3r)$

$\mathbf{F}$

$(0, 0, r)$

Figure 4.40 On the sphere $x^2 + y^2 + (z - 2r)^2 = r^2$, the points $(0, 0, r)$ and $(0, 0, 3r)$ are equilibrium points for the gravitational force field $\mathbf{F} = -mg\mathbf{k}$.

is a stable equilibrium and $(0, 0, 3r)$ is an unstable one. (Try balancing a marble on top of a ball.)   ◆

Applications to Economics

We present two illustrations of how Lagrange multipliers occur in problems involving economic models.

EXAMPLE 4   The usefulness of amounts $x_1, x_2, \ldots, x_n$ of (respectively) different capital goods $G_1, G_2, \ldots, G_n$ can sometimes be measured by a function $U(x_1, x_2, \ldots, x_n)$, called the **utility** of these goods. Perhaps the goods are individual electronic components needed in the manufacture of a stereo or computer, or perhaps U measures an individual consumer's utility for different commodities available at different prices. If item G_i costs a_i per unit and if M is the total amount of money allocated for the purchase of these n goods, then the consumer or the company needs to maximize $U(x_1, x_2, \ldots, x_n)$ subject to

$$a_1 x_1 + a_2 x_2 + \cdots + a_n x_n = M.$$

This is a standard constrained optimization problem that can readily be approached by using the method of Lagrange multipliers.

For instance, suppose you have a job ordering stationery supplies for an office. The office needs three different types of products a, b, and c, which you will order in amounts x, y, and z, respectively. The usefulness of these products to the smooth operation of the office turns out to be modeled fairly well by the utility function $U(x, y, z) = xy + xyz$. If product a costs \$3 per unit, product b \$2 a unit, and product c \$1 a unit and the budget allows a total expenditure of not more than \$899, what should you do? The answer should be clear: You need to maximize

$$U(x, y, z) = xy + xyz \quad \text{subject to} \quad B(x, y, z) = 3x + 2y + z = 899.$$

The Lagrange multiplier equation, $\nabla U(x, y, z) = \lambda \nabla B(x, y, z)$, and the budget constraint yield the system

$$\begin{cases} y + yz = 3\lambda \\ x + xz = 2\lambda \\ xy = \lambda \\ 3x + 2y + z = 899 \end{cases}.$$

Solving for λ in the first three equations yields

$$\lambda = y\left(\frac{z+1}{3}\right) = x\left(\frac{z+1}{2}\right) = xy.$$

The last equality implies that either $x = 0$ or $y = (z + 1)/2$. We can reject the first possibility, since $U(0, y, z) = 0$ and the utility $U(x, y, z) > 0$ whenever x, y, and z are all positive. Thus, we are left with $y = (z + 1)/2$. This in turn implies that $\lambda = (z + 1)^2/6$. Substituting for y in the constraint equation shows that $x = (898 - 2z)/3$, so that equation $xy = \lambda$ becomes

$$\left(\frac{898 - 2z}{3}\right)\left(\frac{z+1}{2}\right) = \frac{(z+1)^2}{6},$$

which is satisfied by either $z = -1$ (which we reject) or by $z = 299$. The only realistic critical point for this problem is $(100, 150, 299)$. We leave it to you to check that this point is indeed the site of a maximum value for the utility.   ◆

EXAMPLE 5 In 1928, C. W. Cobb and P. M. Douglas developed a simple model for the gross output Q of a company or a nation, indicated by the function

$$Q(K, L) = AK^a L^{1-a},$$

where K represents the capital investment (in the form of machinery or other equipment), L the amount of labor used, and A and a positive constants with $0 < a < 1$. (The function Q is known now as the **Cobb–Douglas production function**.) If you are president of a company or nation, you naturally wish to maximize output, but equipment and labor cost money and you have a total amount of M dollars to invest. If the price of capital is p dollars per unit and the cost of labor (in the form of wages) is w dollars per unit, so that you are constrained by

$$B(K, L) = pK + wL \leq M,$$

what do you do?

Again, we have a situation ripe for the use of Lagrange multipliers. Before we consider the technical formalities, however, we consider a graphical solution. Draw the level curves of Q, called **isoquants**, as in Figure 4.41. Note that Q increases as we move away from the origin in the first quadrant. The budget constraint means that you can only consider values of K and L that lie inside or on the shaded triangle. It is clear that the optimum solution occurs at the point (K, L) where the level curve is tangent to the constraint line $pK + wL = M$.

Here is the analytical solution: From the equation $\nabla Q(K, L) = \lambda \nabla B(K, L)$ plus the constraint, we obtain the system

$$\begin{cases} AaK^{a-1}L^{1-a} = \lambda p \\ A(1-a)K^a L^{-a} = \lambda w \, . \\ pK + wL = M \end{cases}$$

Solving for p and w in the first two equations yields

$$p = \frac{Aa}{\lambda} K^{a-1} L^{1-a} \quad \text{and} \quad w = \frac{A(1-a)}{\lambda} K^a L^{-a}.$$

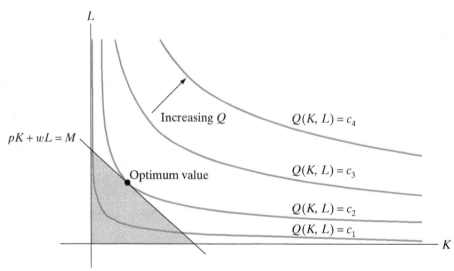

Figure 4.41 A family of isoquants. The optimum value of $Q(K, L)$ subject to the constraint $pK + wL = M$ occurs where a curve of the form $Q = c$ is tangent to the constraint line.

Substitution of these values into the third equation gives

$$\frac{Aa}{\lambda} K^a L^{1-a} + \frac{A(1-a)}{\lambda} K^a L^{1-a} = M.$$

Thus,

$$\lambda = \frac{A}{M} K^a L^{1-a},$$

and the only critical point is

$$(K, L) = \left(\frac{Ma}{p}, \frac{M(1-a)}{w} \right).$$

From this geometric discussion, we know that the critical point must yield the maximum output Q.

From the Lagrange multiplier equation, at the optimum values for L and K, we have

$$\lambda = \frac{1}{p} \frac{\partial Q}{\partial K} = \frac{1}{w} \frac{\partial Q}{\partial L}.$$

This relation says that, at the optimum values, the marginal change in output per dollar's worth of extra capital equals the marginal change per dollar's worth of extra labor. In other words, at the optimum values, exchanging labor for capital (or vice versa) won't change the output. This is by no means the case away from the optimum values.

There is not much that is special about the function Q chosen. Most of our observations remain true for any C^2 function Q that satisfies the conditions

$$\frac{\partial Q}{\partial K}, \frac{\partial Q}{\partial L} \geq 0, \qquad \frac{\partial^2 Q}{\partial K^2}, \frac{\partial^2 Q}{\partial L^2} < 0.$$

If you consider what these relations mean qualitatively about the behavior of the output function with respect to increases in capital and labor, you will see that they are entirely reasonable assumptions.[4]   ◆

4.4 Exercises

1. Find the line that best fits the following data: $(0, 2)$, $(1, 3)$, $(2, 5)$, $(3, 3)$, $(4, 2)$, $(5, 7)$, $(6, 7)$.

2. Show that if you have only two data points (x_1, y_1) and (x_2, y_2), then the best fit line given by the method of least squares is, in fact, the line through (x_1, y_1) and (x_2, y_2).

3. Suppose that you are given n pairs of data (x_1, y_1), $(x_2, y_2), \ldots, (x_n, y_n)$ and you seek to fit a function of the form $y = a/x + b$ to these data.

(a) Use the method of least squares as outlined in this section to construct a function $D(a, b)$ that gives the sum of the squares of the distances between observed and predicted y-values of the data.

(b) Show that the "best fit" curve of the form $y = a/x + b$ should have

$$a = \frac{n \sum y_i / x_i - \left(\sum 1/x_i \right) \left(\sum y_i \right)}{n \sum 1/x_i^2 - \left(\sum 1/x_i \right)^2}$$

and

$$b = \frac{\left(\sum 1/x_i^2 \right) \left(\sum y_i \right) - \left(\sum 1/x_i \right) \left(\sum y_i / x_i \right)}{n \sum 1/x_i^2 - \left(\sum 1/x_i \right)^2}.$$

(All sums are from $i = 1$ to n.)

---

[4] For more about the history and derivation of the Cobb–Douglas function, consult R. Geitz, "The Cobb–Douglas production function," *UMAP Module No. 509*, Birkhäuser, 1981.

4. Find the curve of the form $y = a/x + b$ that best fits the following data: $(1, 0), (2, -1), (\frac{1}{2}, 1)$, and $(3, -\frac{1}{2})$. (See Exercise 3.)

5. Suppose that you have n pairs of data (x_1, y_1), $(x_2, y_2), \ldots, (x_n, y_n)$ and you desire to fit a quadratic function of the form $y = ax^2 + bx + c$ to the data. Show that the "best fit" parabola must have coefficients a, b, and c satisfying

$$\begin{cases} \left(\sum x_i^4\right)a + \left(\sum x_i^3\right)b + \left(\sum x_i^2\right)c = \sum x_i^2 y_i \\ \left(\sum x_i^3\right)a + \left(\sum x_i^2\right)b + \left(\sum x_i\right)c = \sum x_i y_i \\ \left(\sum x_i^2\right)a + \left(\sum x_i\right)b + nc = \sum y_i \end{cases}.$$

(All sums are from $i = 1$ to n.)

6. (Note: This exercise will be facilitated by the use of a spreadsheet or computer algebra system.) Egbert recorded the number of hours he slept the night before a major exam versus the score he earned, as shown in the table below.

(a) Find the line that best fits these data.

(b) Find the parabola $y = ax^2 + bx + c$ that best fits these data. (See Exercise 5.)

(c) Last night Egbert slept 6.8 hr. What do your answers in parts (a) and (b) predict for his score on the calculus final he takes today?

Hours of sleep	Test score
8	85
8.5	72
9	95
7	68
4	52
8.5	75
7.5	90
6	65

7. Let $\mathbf{F} = (-2x - 2y - 1)\mathbf{i} + (-2x - 6y - 2)\mathbf{j}$.

(a) Show that $\mathbf{F}$ is conservative and has potential function

$$V(x, y) = x^2 + 2xy + 3y^2 + x + 2y$$

(i.e., $\mathbf{F} = -\nabla V$).

(b) What are the equilibrium points of $\mathbf{F}$? The stable equilibria?

8. Suppose a particle moves in a vector field $\mathbf{F}$ in $\mathbf{R}^2$ with physical potential

$$V(x, y) = 2x^2 - 8xy - y^2 + 12x - 8y + 12.$$

Find all equilibrium points of $\mathbf{F}$ and indicate which, if any, are stable equilibria.

9. Let a particle move in the vector field $\mathbf{F}$ in $\mathbf{R}^3$ whose physical potential is given by

$$V(x, y, z) = 3x^2 + 2xy + z^2 - 2yz + 3x + 5y - 10.$$

Determine the equilibria of $\mathbf{F}$ and identify those that are stable.

10. Suppose that a particle of mass m is constrained to move on the ellipsoid $2x^2 + 3y^2 + z^2 = 1$ subject to both a gravitational force $\mathbf{F} = -mg\mathbf{k}$, as well as to an additional potential $V(x, y, z) = 2x$.

(a) Find any equilibrium points for this situation.

(b) Are there any stable equilibria?

11. The Sukolux Vacuum Cleaner Company manufactures and sells three types of vacuum cleaners: the standard, executive, and deluxe models. The annual revenue in dollars as a function of the numbers x, y, and z (respectively) of standard, executive, and deluxe models sold is

$$R(x, y, z) = xyz^2 - 25,000x - 25,000y - 25,000z.$$

The manufacturing plant can produce 200,000 total units annually. Assuming that everything that is manufactured is sold, how should production be distributed among the models so as to maximize the annual revenue?

12. Some simple electronic devices are to be designed to include three digital component modules, types 1, 2, and 3, which are to be kept in inventory in respective amounts x_1, x_2, and x_3. Suppose that the relative importance of these components to the various devices is modeled by the utility function

$$U(x_1, x_2, x_3) = x_1 x_2 + 2x_1 x_3 + x_1 x_2 x_3.$$

You are authorized to purchase $90 worth of these parts to make prototype devices. If type 1 costs $1 per component, type 2 $4 per component, and type 3 $2 per component, how should you place your order?

13. A farmer has determined that her cornfield will yield corn (in bushels) according to the formula

$$B(x, y) = 4x^2 + y^2 + 600,$$

where x denotes the amount of water (measured in hundreds of gallons) used to irrigate the field and y the number of pounds of fertilizer applied to the field. The fertilizer costs $10 per pound and water costs $15 per hundred gallons. If she can allot $500 to prepare her field through irrigation and fertilization, use a Lagrange multiplier to determine how much water and fertilizer she should purchase in order to maximize her yield.

14. A textile manufacturer plans to produce a cashmere/cotton fabric blend for use in making sweaters. The amount of fabric that can be produced is given by

$$f(x, y) = 4xy - 2x - 8y + 3,$$

where x denotes the number of pounds of raw cashmere used is and y is the number of pounds of raw cotton. Cotton costs \$2 per pound and cashmere costs \$8 per pound.

(a) If the manufacturer can spend \$1000 on raw materials, use a Lagrange multiplier to advise him how he should adjust the ratio of materials in order to produce the most cloth.

(b) Now suppose that the manufacturer has a budget of B dollars. What should the ratio of cotton to cashmere be (in terms of B)? What is the limiting value of this ratio as B increases?

15. The CEO of the Wild Widget Company has decided to invest \$360,000 in his Michigan factory. His economic analysts have noted that the output of this factory is modeled by the function $Q(K, L) = 60K^{1/3}L^{2/3}$, where K represents the amount (in thousands of dollars) spent on capital equipment and L represents the amount (also in thousands of dollars) spent on labor.

(a) How should the CEO allocate the \$360,000 between labor and equipment?

(b) Check that $\partial Q/\partial K = \partial Q/\partial L$ at the optimal values for K and L.

16. Let $Q(K, L)$ be a production function for a company where K and L represent the respective amounts spent on capital equipment and labor. Let p denote the price of capital equipment per unit and w the cost of labor per unit. Show that, subject to a fixed production $Q(K, L) = c$, the total cost M of production is minimized when K and L are such that

$$\frac{1}{p}\frac{\partial Q}{\partial K} = \frac{1}{w}\frac{\partial Q}{\partial L}.$$

True/False Exercises for Chapter 4

1. If f is a function of class C^2 and p_2 denotes the second-order Taylor polynomial of f at $\mathbf{a}$, then $f(\mathbf{x}) \approx p_2(\mathbf{x})$ when $\mathbf{x} \approx \mathbf{a}$.

2. The increment Δf of a function $f(x, y)$ measures the change in the z-coordinate of the tangent plane to the graph of f.

3. The differential df of a function $f(x, y)$ measures the change in the z-coordinate of the tangent plane to the graph of f.

4. The second-order Taylor polynomial of $f(x, y, z) = x^2 + 3xz + y^2$ at $(1, -1, 2)$ is $p_2(x, y, z) = x^2 + 3xz + y^2$.

5. The second-order Taylor polynomial of $f(x, y) = x^3 + 2xy + y$ at $(0, 0)$ is $p_2(x, y) = 2xy + y$.

6. The second-order Taylor polynomial of $f(x, y) = x^3 + 2xy + y$ at $(1, -1)$ is $p_2(x, y) = 2xy + y$.

7. Near the point $(1, 3, 5)$, the function $f(x, y, z) = 3x^4 + 2y^3 + z^2$ is most sensitive to changes in z.

8. The Hessian matrix $Hf(x_1, \ldots, x_n)$ of f has the property that $Hf(x_1, \ldots, x_n)^T = Hf(x_1, \ldots, x_n)$.

9. If $\nabla f(a_1, \ldots, a_n) = \mathbf{0}$, then f has a local extremum at $\mathbf{a} = (a_1, \ldots, a_n)$.

10. If f is differentiable and has a local extremum at $\mathbf{a} = (a_1, \ldots, a_n)$, then $\nabla f(\mathbf{a}) = \mathbf{0}$.

11. The set $\{(x, y, z) \mid 4 \leq x^2 + y^2 + z^2 \leq 9\}$ is compact.

12. The set $\{(x, y) \mid 2x - 3y = 1\}$ is compact.

13. Any continuous function $f(x, y)$ must attain a global maximum on the disk $\{(x, y) \mid x^2 + y^2 < 1\}$.

14. Any continuous function $f(x, y, z)$ must attain a global maximum on the ball $\{(x, y, z) \mid (x - 1)^2 + (y + 1)^2 + z^2 \leq 4\}$.

15. If $f(x, y)$ is of class C^2, has a critical point at (a, b), and $f_{xx}(a, b)f_{yy}(a, b) - f_{xy}(a, b)^2 < 0$, then f has a saddle point at (a, b).

16. If $\det Hf(\mathbf{a}) = 0$, then f has a saddle point at $\mathbf{a}$.

17. The function $f(x, y, z) = x^3y^2z - x^2(y + z)$ has a saddle point at $(1, -1, 2)$.

18. The function $f(x, y, z) = x^2 + y^2 + z^2 - yz$ has a local maximum at $(0, 0, 0)$.

19. The function $f(x, y, z) = xy^3 - x^2z + z$ has a degenerate critical point at $(-1, 0, 0)$.

20. The function $F(x_1, \ldots, x_n) = 2(x_1 - 1)^2 - 3(x_2 - 2)^2 + \cdots + (-1)^{n+1}(n + 1)(x_n - n)^2$ has a critical point at $(1, 2, \ldots, n)$.

21. The function $F(x_1, \ldots, x_n) = 2(x_1 - 1)^2 - 3(x_2 - 2)^2 + \cdots + (-1)^{n+1}(n + 1)(x_n - n)^2$ has a minimum at $(1, 2, \ldots, n)$.

22. All local extrema of a function of more than one variable occur where all partial derivatives simultaneously vanish.

23. All points $\mathbf{a} = (a_1, \ldots, a_2)$ where the function $f(x_1, \ldots, x_n)$ has an extremum subject to the constraint that $g(x_1, \ldots, x_n) = c$, are solutions to the system of equations

$$\begin{cases} \dfrac{\partial f}{\partial x_1} = \lambda \dfrac{\partial g}{\partial x_1} \\ \quad \vdots \\ \dfrac{\partial f}{\partial x_n} = \lambda \dfrac{\partial g}{\partial x_n} \\ g(x_1, \ldots, x_n) = c \end{cases}$$

24. Any solution $(\lambda_1, \ldots, \lambda_k, x_1, \ldots, x_n)$ to the system of equations

$$\begin{cases} \dfrac{\partial f}{\partial x_1} = \lambda_1 \dfrac{\partial g_1}{\partial x_1} + \cdots + \lambda_k \dfrac{\partial g_k}{\partial x_1} \\ \quad \vdots \\ \dfrac{\partial f}{\partial x_n} = \lambda_1 \dfrac{\partial g_1}{\partial x_n} + \cdots + \lambda_k \dfrac{\partial g_k}{\partial x_n} \\ g_1(x_1, \ldots, x_n) = c_1 \\ \quad \vdots \\ g_1(x_1, \ldots, x_n) = c_k \end{cases}$$

yields a point $(x_1, \ldots, x_n)$ that is an extreme value of f subject to the simultaneous constraints $g_1 = c_1, \ldots, g_k = c_k$.

25. To find the critical points of the function $f(x, y, z, w)$ subject to the simultaneous constraints $g(x, y, z, w) = c, h(x, y, z, w) = d, k(x, y, z, w) = e$ using the technique of Lagrange multipliers, one will have to solve a system of four equations in four unknowns.

26. Suppose that $f(x, y, z)$ and $g(x, y, z)$ are of class C^1 and that (x_0, y_0, z_0) is a point where f achieves a maximum value subject to the constraint that $g(x, y, z) = c$ and that $\nabla g(x_0, y_0, z_0)$ is nonzero. Then the level set of f that contains (x_0, y_0, z_0) must be tangent to the level set $S = \{(x, y, z) \mid g(x, y, z) = c\}$.

27. The critical points of $f(x, y, z) = xy + 2xz + 2yz$ subject to the constraint that $xyz = 4$ are the same as the critical points of the function $F(x, y) = xy + \dfrac{8}{x} + \dfrac{8}{y}$.

28. Given data points $(3, 1), (4, 10), (5, 8), (6, 12)$, to find the best fit line by regression, we find the minimum value of the function $D(m, b) = (3m + b - 1)^2 + (4m + b - 10)^2 + (5m + b - 8)^2 + (6m + b - 12)^2$.

29. All equilibrium points of a gradient vector field are minimum points of the vector field's potential function.

30. Given an output function for a company, the marginal change in output per dollar investment in capital is the same as the marginal change in the output per dollar investment in labor.

Miscellaneous Exercises for Chapter 4

1. Let $V = \pi r^2 h$, where $r \approx r_0$ and $h \approx h_0$. What relationship must hold between r_0 and h_0 for V to be equally sensitive to small changes in r and h?

2. (a) Find the unique critical point of the function

$$f(x_1, x_2, \ldots, x_n) = e^{-x_1^2 - x_2^2 - \cdots - x_n^2}.$$

   (b) Use the Hessian criterion to determine the nature of this critical point.

3. The Java Joint Gourmet Coffee House sells top-of-the-line Arabian Mocha and Hawaiian Kona beans. If Mocha beans are priced at x dollars per pound and Kona beans at y dollars per pound, then market research has shown that each week approximately $80 - 100x + 40y$ pounds of Mocha beans will be sold and $20 + 60x - 35y$ pounds of Kona beans will be sold. The wholesale cost to the Java Joint owners is \$2 per pound for Mocha beans and \$4 per pound for Kona beans. How should the owners price the coffee beans in order to maximize their profits?

4. The Crispy Crunchy Cereal Company produces three brands, X, Y, and Z, of breakfast cereal. Each month, x, y, and z (respectively) 1000-box cases of brands X, Y, and Z are sold at a selling price (per box) of each cereal given as follows:

Brand	No. cases sold	Selling price per box
X	x	$4.00 - 0.02x$
Y	y	$4.50 - 0.05y$
Z	z	$5.00 - 0.10z$

   (a) What is the total revenue R if x cases of brand X, y cases of brand Y, and z cases of brand Z are sold?

   (b) Suppose that during the month of November, brand X sells for \$3.88 per box, brand Y for \$4.25, and brand Z for \$4.60. If the price of each brand is increased by \$0.10, what effect will this have on the total revenue?

   (c) What selling prices maximize the total revenue?

5. Find the maximum and minimum values of the function

$$f(x, y, z) = x - \sqrt{3}\, y$$

on the sphere $x^2 + y^2 + z^2 = 4$ in two ways:

   (a) by using a Lagrange multiplier;

(b) by substituting spherical coordinates (thereby describing the point (x, y, z) on the sphere as $x = 2\sin\varphi\cos\theta$, $y = 2\sin\varphi\sin\theta$, $z = 2\cos\varphi$) and then finding the ordinary (i.e., unconstrained) extrema of $f(x(\varphi, \theta), y(\varphi, \theta), z(\varphi, \theta))$.

6. Suppose that the temperature in a space is given by the function

$$T(x, y, z) = 200xyz^2.$$

Find the hottest point(s) on the unit sphere in two ways:

(a) by using Lagrange multipliers;

(b) by letting $x = \sin\varphi\cos\theta$, $y = \sin\varphi\sin\theta$, $z = \cos\varphi$ and maximizing T as a function of the two independent variables φ and θ. (Note: It will help if you use appropriate trigonometric identities where possible.)

7. Consider the function $f(x, y) = (y - 2x^2)(y - x^2)$.

(a) Show that f has a single critical point at the origin.

(b) Show that this critical point is *degenerate*. Hence, it will require means other than the Hessian criterion to determine the nature of the critical point as a local extremum.

(c) Show that, when restricted to any line that passes through the origin, f has a minimum at $(0, 0)$. (That is, consider the function $F(x) = f(x, mx)$, where m is a constant and the function $G(y) = f(0, y)$.)

(d) However, show that, when restricted to the parabola $y = \frac{3}{2}x^2$, the function f has a global maximum at $(0, 0)$. Thus, the origin must be a saddle point.

(e) Use a computer to graph the surface $z = f(x, y)$.

8. (a) Find all critical points of $f(x, y) = xy$ that satisfy $x^2 + y^2 = 1$.

(b) Draw a collection of level curves of f and, on the same set of axes, the constraint curve $x^2 + y^2 = 1$, and the critical points you found in part (a).

(c) Use the plot you obtained in part (b) and a geometric argument to determine the nature of the critical points found in part (a).

9. (a) Find all critical points of $f(x, y, z) = xy$ that satisfy $x^2 + y^2 + z^2 = 1$.

(b) Give a rough sketch of a collection of level surfaces of f and, on the same set of axes, the constraint surface $x^2 + y^2 + z^2 = 1$, and the critical points you found in part (a).

(c) Use part (b) and a geometric argument to determine the nature of the critical points found in part (a).

10. Find the area A of the largest rectangle so that two squares of total area 1 can be placed snugly inside the rectangle without overlapping, except along their edges. (See Figure 4.42.)

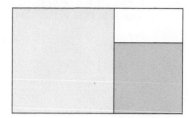

Figure 4.42 Figure for Exercise 10.

11. Find the minimum value of

$$f(x_1, x_2, \ldots, x_n) = x_1^2 + x_2^2 + \cdots + x_n^2$$

subject to the constraint that $a_1x_1 + a_2x_2 + \cdots + a_nx_n = 1$, assuming that $a_1^2 + a_2^2 + \cdots + a_n^2 > 0$.

12. Find the maximum value of

$$f(x_1, x_2, \ldots, x_n) = (a_1x_1 + a_2x_2 + \cdots + a_nx_n)^2,$$

subject to $x_1^2 + x_2^2 + \cdots + x_n^2 = 1$. Assume that not all of the a_i's are zero.

13. Find the dimensions of the largest rectangular box that can be inscribed in the ellipsoid $x^2 + 2y^2 + 4z^2 = 12$. Assume that the faces of the box are parallel to the coordinate planes.

14. Your company must design a storage tank for Super Suds liquid laundry detergent. The customer's specifications call for a cylindrical tank with hemispherical ends (see Figure 4.43), and the tank is to hold 8000 gal of detergent. Suppose that it costs twice as much (per square foot of sheet metal used) to machine the hemispherical ends of the tank as it does to make the cylindrical part. What radius and height do you recommend for the cylindrical portion so as to minimize the *total* cost of manufacturing the tank?

Figure 4.43 The storage tank of Exercise 14.

15. Find the minimum distance from the origin to the surface $x^2 - (y - z)^2 = 1$.

16. Determine the dimensions of the largest cone that can be inscribed in a sphere of radius a.

17. Find the dimensions of the largest rectangular box (whose faces are parallel to the coordinate planes) that can be inscribed in the tetrahedron having three faces in the coordinate planes and fourth face in the plane with equation $bcx + acy + abz = abc$, where a, b, and c are positive constants. (See Figure 4.44.)

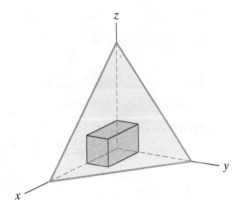

Figure 4.44 Figure for Exercise 17.

18. You seek to mail a poster to your friend as a gift. You roll up the poster and put it in a cylindrical tube of diameter x and length y. The postal regulations demand that the sum of the length of the tube plus its girth (i.e., the circumference of the tube) be at most 108 in.

(a) Use the method of Lagrange multipliers to find the dimensions of the largest-volume tube that you can mail.

(b) Use techniques from single-variable calculus to solve this problem in another way.

19. Find the distance between the line $y = 2x + 2$ and the parabola $x = y^2$ by minimizing the distance between a point (x_1, y_1) on the line and a point (x_2, y_2) on the parabola. Draw a sketch indicating that you have found the minimum value.

20. A ray of light travels at a constant speed in a uniform medium, but in different media (such as air and water) light travels at different speeds. For example, if a ray of light passes from air to water, it is bent (or **refracted**) as shown in Figure 4.45. Suppose the speed of light

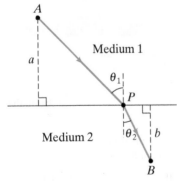

Figure 4.45 Snell's law of refraction.

in medium 1 is v_1 and in medium 2 is v_2. Then, by Fermat's principle of least time, the light will strike the boundary between medium 1 and medium 2 at a point P so that the total time the light travels is minimized.

(a) Determine the total time the light travels in going from point A to point B via point P as shown in Figure 4.45.

(b) Use the method of Lagrange multipliers to establish **Snell's law of refraction**: that the total travel time is minimized when

$$\frac{\sin \theta_1}{\sin \theta_2} = \frac{v_1}{v_2}.$$

(Hint: The horizontal and vertical separations of A and B are constant.)

21. Use Lagrange multipliers to establish the formula

$$D = \frac{|ax_0 + by_0 - d|}{\sqrt{a^2 + b^2}}$$

for the distance D from the point (x_0, y_0) to the line $ax + by = d$.

22. Use Lagrange multipliers to establish the formula

$$D = \frac{|ax_0 + by_0 + cz_0 - d|}{\sqrt{a^2 + b^2 + c^2}}$$

for the distance D from the point (x_0, y_0, z_0) to the plane $ax + by + cz = d$.

23. (a) Show that the maximum value of $f(x, y, z) = x^2 y^2 z^2$ subject to the constraint that $x^2 + y^2 + z^2 = a^2$ is

$$\frac{a^6}{27} = \left(\frac{a^2}{3}\right)^3.$$

(b) Use part (a) to show that, for all x, y, and z,

$$(x^2 y^2 z^2)^{1/3} \leq \frac{x^2 + y^2 + z^2}{3}.$$

(c) Show that, for any positive numbers $x_1, x_2, \ldots, x_n$,

$$(x_1 x_2 \cdots x_n)^{1/n} \leq \frac{x_1 + x_2 + \cdots + x_n}{n}.$$

The quantity on the right of the inequality is the **arithmetic mean** of the numbers $x_1, x_2, \ldots, x_n$, and the quantity on the left is called the **geometric mean**. The inequality itself is, appropriately, called the **arithmetic–geometric inequality**.

(d) Under what conditions will equality hold in the arithmetic–geometric inequality?

In Exercises 24–27 you will explore how some ideas from matrix algebra and the technique of Lagrange multipliers come together to treat the problem of finding the points on the unit hypersphere

$$g(x_1, \ldots, x_n) = x_1^2 + x_2^2 + \cdots + x_n^2 = 1$$

that give extreme values of the quadratic form

$$f(x_1, \ldots, x_n) = \sum_{i,j=1}^{n} a_{ij} x_i x_j,$$

where the a_{ij}'s are constants.

24. (a) Use a Lagrange multiplier λ to set up a system of $n+1$ equations in $n+1$ unknowns $x_1, \ldots, x_n, \lambda$ whose solutions provide the appropriate constrained critical points.

(b) Recall that formula (2) in §4.2 shows that the quadratic form f may be written in terms of matrices as

$$f(x_1, \ldots, x_n) = \mathbf{x}^T A \mathbf{x}, \qquad (1)$$

where the vector $\mathbf{x}$ is written as the $n \times 1$ matrix $\begin{bmatrix} x_1 \\ \vdots \\ x_n \end{bmatrix}$ and A is the $n \times n$ matrix whose ijth entry is a_{ij}. Moreover, as noted in the discussion in §4.2, the matrix A may be taken to be symmetric (i.e., so that $A^T = A$), and we will therefore assume that A is symmetric. Show that the gradient equation $\nabla f = \lambda \nabla g$ is equivalent to the matrix equation

$$A\mathbf{x} = \lambda \mathbf{x}. \qquad (2)$$

Since the point $(x_1, \ldots, x_n)$ satisfies the constraint $x_1^2 + \cdots + x_n^2 = 1$, the vector $\mathbf{x}$ is nonzero. If you have studied some linear algebra, you will recognize that you have shown that a constrained critical point $(x_1, \ldots, x_n)$ for this problem corresponds precisely to an **eigenvector** of the matrix A associated with the **eigenvalue** λ.

(c) Now suppose that $\mathbf{x} = \begin{bmatrix} x_1 \\ \vdots \\ x_n \end{bmatrix}$ is one of the eigenvectors of the symmetric matrix A, with associated eigenvalue λ. Use equations (1) and (2) to show, if $\mathbf{x}$ is a unit vector, that

$$f(x_1, \ldots, x_n) = \lambda.$$

Hence, the (absolute) minimum value that f attains on the unit hypersphere must be the smallest eigenvalue of A and the (absolute) maximum value must be the largest eigenvalue.

25. Let $n = 2$ in the situation of Exercise 24, so that we are considering the problem of finding points on the circle

$x^2 + y^2 = 1$ that give extreme values of the function

$$f(x, y) = ax^2 + 2bxy + cy^2$$

$$= \begin{bmatrix} x & y \end{bmatrix} \begin{bmatrix} a & b \\ b & c \end{bmatrix} \begin{bmatrix} x \\ y \end{bmatrix}.$$

(a) Find the eigenvalues of $A = \begin{bmatrix} a & b \\ b & c \end{bmatrix}$ by identifying the constrained critical points of the optimization problem described above.

(b) Now use some algebra to show that the eigenvalues you found in part (a) must be real. It is a fact (that you need not demonstrate here) that any $n \times n$ symmetric matrix always has real eigenvalues.

26. In Exercise 25 you noted that the eigenvalues λ_1, λ_2 that you obtained are both real.

(a) Under what conditions does $\lambda_1 = \lambda_2$?

(b) Suppose that λ_1 and λ_2 are both positive. Explain why f must be positive on all points of the unit circle.

(c) Suppose that λ_1 and λ_2 are both negative. Explain why f must be negative on all points of the unit circle.

27. Let f be a general quadratic form in n variables determined by an $n \times n$ symmetric matrix A, that is, $f(x_1, \ldots, x_n) = \sum_{i,j=1}^{n} a_{ij} x_i x_j = \mathbf{x}^T A \mathbf{x}$.

(a) Show, for any real number k, that $f(kx_1, \ldots, kx_n) = k^2 f(x_1, \ldots, x_n)$. (This means that a quadratic form is a homogeneous polynomial of degree 2—see Exercises 37–44 of the Miscellaneous Exercises for Chapter 2 for more about homogeneous functions.)

(b) Use part (a) to show that if f has a positive minimum on the unit hypersphere, then f must be positive for *all* nonzero $\mathbf{x} \in \mathbf{R}^n$ and that if f has a negative maximum on the unit hypersphere, then f must be negative for all nonzero $\mathbf{x} \in \mathbf{R}^n$. (Hint: For $\mathbf{x} \neq \mathbf{0}$, let $\mathbf{u} = \mathbf{x}/\|\mathbf{x}\|$, so that $\mathbf{x} = k\mathbf{u}$, where $k = \|\mathbf{x}\|$.)

(c) Recall from §4.2 that a quadratic form f is said to be **positive definite** if $f(\mathbf{x}) > 0$ for all nonzero $\mathbf{x} \in \mathbf{R}^n$ and **negative definite** if $f(\mathbf{x}) < 0$ for all nonzero $\mathbf{x} \in \mathbf{R}^n$. Use part (b) and Exercise 24 to show that the quadratic form f is positive definite if and only if all eigenvalues of A are positive, and negative definite if and only if all eigenvalues of A are negative. (Note: As remarked in part (b) of Exercise 25, all the eigenvalues of A will be real.)

Suggestions for Further Reading

General

Francis J. Flanigan and Jerry L. Kazdan, *Calculus Two: Linear and Nonlinear Functions*, 2nd ed., Springer, 1990. The essentials of vector calculus are presented from a linear-algebraic perspective.

John H. Hubbard and Barbara Burke Hubbard, *Vector Calculus, Linear Algebra, and Differential Forms: A Unified Approach*, 2nd ed., Prentice Hall, 2002. Treats the main topics of multivariable calculus, plus a significant amount of linear algebra. More sophisticated in approach than the current book, using differential forms to treat integration.

Jerrold E. Marsden and Anthony J. Tromba, *Vector Calculus*, 5th ed., W. H. Freeman, 2003. This text is probably the one most similar to the current book in both coverage and approach, using matrices and vectors to treat multivariable calculus in $\mathbf{R}^n$.

Jerrold E. Marsden, Anthony J. Tromba, and Alan Weinstein, *Basic Multivariable Calculus*, Springer/W. H. Freeman, 1993. Somewhat similar to Marsden and Tromba's *Vector Calculus*, but with less emphasis on a rigorous development of the subject. A good guide to the main ideas.

George B. Thomas and Ross L. Finney, *Calculus and Analytic Geometry*, 9th ed., Addison-Wesley, 1996. A complete treatment of the techniques of both single-variable and multivariable calculus. No linear algebra needed. A good reference for the main methods of vector calculus of functions of two and three variables.

Richard E. Williamson, Richard H. Crowell, and Hale F. Trotter, *Calculus of Vector Functions*, 3rd ed., Prentice Hall, 1972. A smooth and careful treatment of multivariable calculus and vector analysis, using linear algebra.

More Advanced Treatments

The following texts all offer relatively rigorous and theoretical developments of the main results of multivariable calculus. As such, they are especially useful for studying the foundations of the subject.

Tom M. Apostol, *Mathematical Analysis: A Modern Approach to Advanced Calculus*, 1st ed., Addison-Wesley, 1957. Look at the first edition, since the second edition contains much less regarding multivariable topics.

R. Creighton Buck, *Advanced Calculus*, 3rd ed., McGraw-Hill, 1978. Treats foundational issues in both single-variable and multivariable calculus. Uses the notation of differential forms for considering Green's, Stokes's, and Gauss's theorems.

Richard Courant and Fritz John, *Introduction to Calculus and Analysis*, Vol. Two, Wiley-Interscience, 1974. A famous and encyclopedic work on the analysis of functions of more than one variable (Volume One treats functions of a single variable), with fascinating examples.

Wilfred Kaplan, *Advanced Calculus*, 3rd ed., Addison-Wesley, 1984. A full treatment of advanced calculus of functions of two and three variables, plus material on calculus of functions of n variables (including some discussion of tensors). In addition, there are chapters on infinite series, differential equations, and functions of a complex variable.

O. D. Kellogg, *Foundations of Potential Theory*, originally published by Springer, 1929. Reprinted by Dover Publications, 1954. A classic work that ventures well beyond the subject of the current book. The writing style may seem somewhat old-fashioned, but Kellogg includes details of certain arguments that are difficult to find anywhere else.

James R. Munkres, *Analysis on Manifolds*, Addison-Wesley, 1991. A superbly well written and sophisticated treatment of calculus in $\mathbf{R}^n$. Requires a knowledge of linear algebra. Includes a full development of differential forms and exterior algebra to treat integration. For advanced mathematics students.

David V. Widder, *Advanced Calculus*, 2nd ed., originally published by Prentice-Hall, 1961. Reprinted by Dover Publications, 1989. Careful treatment of differentiation and integration of functions of one and several variables. Chapters on differential geometry, too.

Physics Oriented Texts

Mary L. Boas, *Mathematical Methods in the Physical Sciences*, 2nd ed., Wiley, 1983. A wide variety of topics that extend well beyond vector calculus. For the student interested in physics as well as mathematics.

Harry F. Davis and Arthur D. Snider, *Introduction to Vector Analysis*, 6th ed., William C. Brown, 1991. A detailed and relatively sophisticated treatment of multivariable topics. Includes appendices on classical mechanics and electromagnetism.

Edward M. Purcell, *Electricity and Magnetism*, 2nd ed., McGraw-Hill, 1985. This is a physics, not a mathematics, text. Provides excellent intuition regarding the meaning of line and surface integrals, differential operations on vector and scalar fields, and the significance of vector analysis.

Other

Alfred Gray, *Modern Differential Geometry of Curves and Surfaces with Mathematica*®, 2nd ed., CRC Press, 1998. Not a vector calculus text by any means, but rather a delightful library of geometric objects and how to understand them via *Mathematica*. Some of the differential geometric topics are somewhat remote from the subject of the current book, but the many illustrations are worth viewing. An outstanding aid for developing one's visualization skills.

H. M. Schey, *Div, Grad, Curl, and All That*: *An Informal Text on Vector Calculus*, 3rd ed., W. W. Norton, 1997. The classic "alternative" book on vector analysis, aimed at students of electricity and magnetism. Brief, but well done, intuitive account of vector analysis.

Answers to Selected Exercises

Chapter 2

Section 2.1

1. (a) Domain = $\mathbf{R}$; range = $\{y \mid y \geq 1\}$
   (b) No
   (c) No

3. Domain = $\{(x, y) \mid y \neq 0\}$; range = $\mathbf{R}$

5. Domain = $\mathbf{R}^3$; range = $[0, \infty)$

7. Domain = $\{(x, y) \mid y \neq 1\}$;
   range = $\{(x, y, z) \mid y \neq 0, y^2 z = (xy - y - 1)^2 + (y + 1)^2\}$

9. $v_1(x, y, z, t) = xyzt$,
   $v_2(x, y, z, t) = x^2 - y^2$,
   $v_3(x, y, z, t) = 3z + t$

11. (a) $\mathbf{f}(\mathbf{x}) = -2\mathbf{x}/\|\mathbf{x}\|$
    (b) $f_1(x, y, z) = -2x/\sqrt{x^2 + y^2 + z^2}$,
        $f_2(x, y, z) = -2y/\sqrt{x^2 + y^2 + z^2}$,
        $f_3(x, y, z) = -2z/\sqrt{x^2 + y^2 + z^2}$

13. (a) $f_1(\mathbf{x}) = 2x_1 - x_3 - x_4$,
        $f_2(\mathbf{x}) = 3x_2$,
        $f_3(\mathbf{x}) = 2x_1 - x_3 - x_4$
    (b) Range = $\{(y_1, y_2, y_3) \mid y_1 = y_3\}$

15.

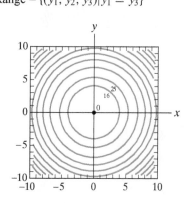

17.

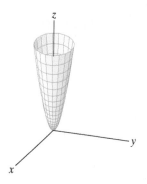

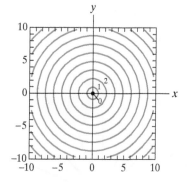

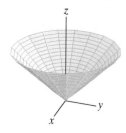

19.

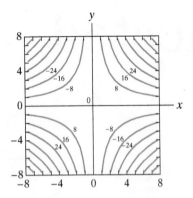

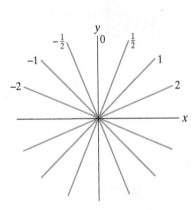

21.

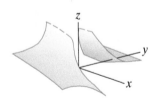

23.

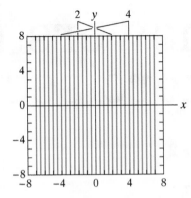

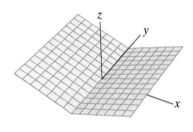

25.

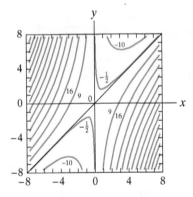

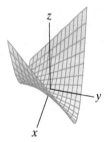

27.

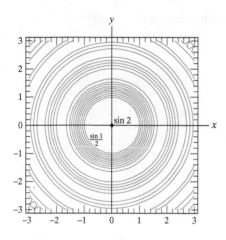

(c)

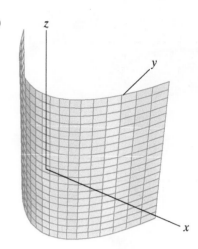

31. No

33.

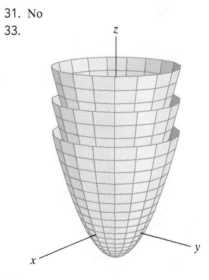

35.

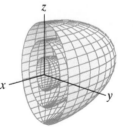

29. (a)

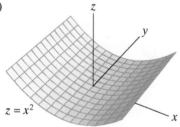

$z = x^2$

$z = y^2$

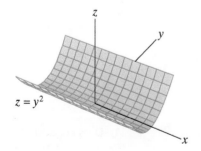

37. (a)

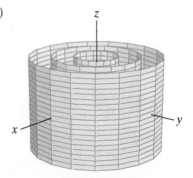

39.

41.

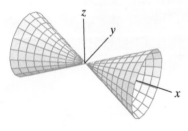

43.

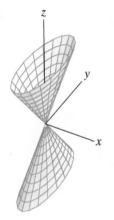

45.

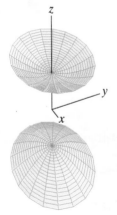

47. Cone with vertex at $(1, -1, -3)$

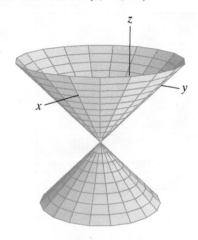

49. Ellipsoid centered at $(-1, 0, 0)$

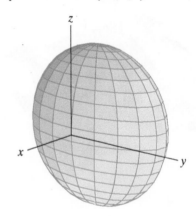

51. Paraboloid with vertex at $(3, 0, 1)$

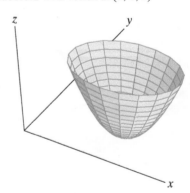

Section 2.2

1. Open   3. Neither

5. Neither   7. 2

9. Does not exist   11. Does not exist

13. 0   15. 0   17. 0   19. −1

21. Limit does not exist.

23. Limit does not exist.

25. Limit does not exist.

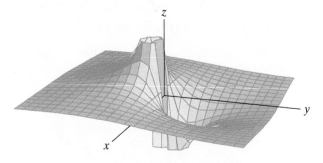

27. Limit is 0.

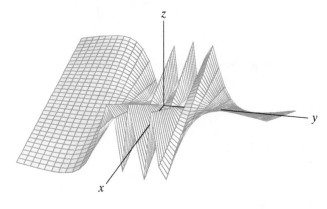

29. Limit does not exist.

31. 2

33. Limit does not exist.

35. 0

37. Limit does not exist.

39. Continuous

41. Continuous

43. Not continuous at $(0, 0)$

45. Continuous

47. Hint: Write $f(\mathbf{x})$ in terms of the components of $\mathbf{x}$.

Section 2.3

1. $f_x(x, y) = y^2 + 2xy, \ f_y(x, y) = 2xy + x^2$

3. $f_x(x, y) = y \cos xy - y \sin xy,$
   $f_y(x, y) = x \cos xy - x \sin xy$

5. $f_x(x, y) = 4xy^2/(x^2 + y^2)^2,$
   $f_y(x, y) = -4x^2y/(x^2 + y^2)^2$

7. $f_x(x, y) = -3x^2y \sin x^3 y,$
   $f_y(x, y) = -x^3 \sin x^3 y$

9. $f_x(x, y) = e^y + 2xy \cos(x^2 + y),$
   $f_y(x, y) = xe^y + \sin(x^2 + y) + y \cos(x^2 + y)$

11. $F_x = 1/(y + z),$
    $F_y = -(x + z)/(y + z)^2,$
    $F_z = (y - x)/(y + z)^2$

13. $F_x = x/\sqrt{x^2 + y^2 + z^2},$
    $F_y = y/\sqrt{x^2 + y^2 + z^2},$
    $F_z = z/\sqrt{x^2 + y^2 + z^2}$

15. $F_x = \dfrac{1 - 2x^2 - 3xy + y^2 - 3xz + z^2}{(1 + x^2 + y^2 + z^2)^{5/2}},$

    $F_y = \dfrac{1 + x^2 - 3xy - 2y^2 - 3yz + z^2}{(1 + x^2 + y^2 + z^2)^{5/2}},$

    $F_z = \dfrac{1 + x^2 + y^2 - 3xz - 3yz - 2z^2}{(1 + x^2 + y^2 + z^2)^{5/2}}$

17. $F_x = \dfrac{x^4 - 2xyz + 3x^2z^2 + 3x^2}{(x^2 + z^2 + 1)^2},$

    $F_y = \dfrac{z}{x^2 + z^2 + 1},$

    $F_z = \dfrac{x^2y - 2x^3z - yz^2 + y}{(x^2 + z^2 + 1)^2}$

19. $-\frac{1}{6}\mathbf{i}$

21. $-\mathbf{i} + (2\pi + 1)\mathbf{j} - 2\mathbf{k}$

23. $\mathbf{i} + \mathbf{j} - 2\mathbf{k}$

25. $\mathbf{i} - \frac{1}{9}\mathbf{j} + \frac{1}{9}\mathbf{k}$

27. $[-4 \quad -3/e \quad -3/e]$

29. $\begin{bmatrix} 0 & -2 & 0 \\ 1/\sqrt{5} & 0 & -2/\sqrt{5} \end{bmatrix}$

31. $\begin{bmatrix} 3 & -7 & 1 & 0 \\ 5 & 0 & 2 & -8 \\ 0 & 1 & -17 & 3 \end{bmatrix}$

33. $\begin{bmatrix} -2 & 0 \\ 1 & -1 \\ 0 & 2 \end{bmatrix}$

37. (a) The function has continuous partial derivatives.
    (b) $z = 3x + 8y + 3$

39. $z = e(x + y)$

41. $x_5 = -4x_1 + 6x_2 - 4x_3 - 6x_4 + 28$

43. (a) $h(0.1, -0.1) = 1$
    (b) $f(0.1, -0.1) = 1$

45. (a) $h(1.01, 1.95, 2.2) = 21.76$
    (b) $f(1.01, 1.95, 2.2) = 21.6657$

47. (a) $f_x(x, y) = (3x^4 + 8x^2y^2 + y^4)/(x^2 + y^2)^2,$
    $f_y(x, y) = -(x^4 + 4x^3y + 2x^2y^2 + y^4)/(x^2 + y^2)^2$
    (b) $f_x(0, 0) = 3, \ f_y(0, 0) = -1$

49. (a) $(8 + 4\sqrt{2})x - 8y = \sqrt{2}(\pi - 4)$

(b)

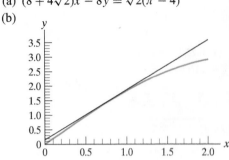

51. (a) $x + y = \ln 2 - 1$

(b)

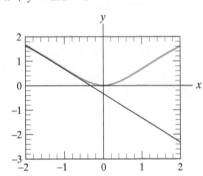

53. (a) $z = 11x - 15$

(b)

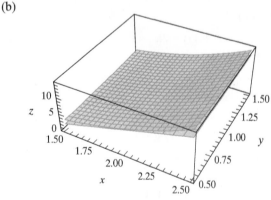

(c) Partial derivatives are polynomials—hence continuous—so f is differentiable at $(2, 1)$.

55. (a) $z = 0$

(b)

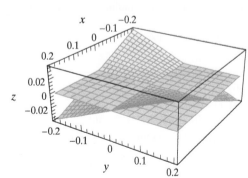

(c) Partial derivatives are rational functions defined on $\mathbf{R}^2$—hence, continuous—so f is differentiable at $(0, 0)$.

57. (a) $z = -\frac{\pi}{288}[(9\sqrt{3}\pi - 96\sqrt{2})x - (16\sqrt{2}\pi + 72)y + (4\sqrt{2} - 3\sqrt{3})\pi^2 + (16\sqrt{2} + 9)\pi]$

(b)

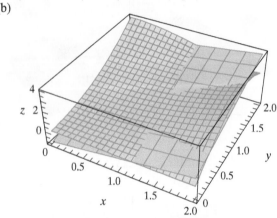

(c) Partial derivatives are products of polynomials and sine and cosine functions and, hence, are continuous. Thus, f is differentiable at $(\pi/3, \pi/4)$.

59. $D\mathbf{f}(\mathbf{x}) = A$. Note that $f'(x) = a$ in the one-variable case.

Section 2.4

1. $D(f + g)$
$= \begin{bmatrix} y - \sin x + y\cos(xy) & x + 3y^2 + x\cos(xy) \end{bmatrix}$

3. $D(\mathbf{f} + \mathbf{g})$
$= \begin{bmatrix} \sin y + 3x^2\cos x - x^3\sin x & x\cos y & 1 \\ -6x + yz & e^z + xz & ye^z + xy \end{bmatrix}$

5. $D(fg) = \begin{bmatrix} 3x^2 + y^2 & 2xy \end{bmatrix}$,

$D(f/g) = \begin{bmatrix} y^2 - y^4/x^2 & 2xy + 4y^3/x \end{bmatrix}$

7. $D(fg)$
$= \begin{bmatrix} 12x^3y + 3x^2y^5 - 12xy^3 - 2y^7 \\ 3x^4 + 5x^3y^4 - 18x^2y^2 - 14xy^6 \end{bmatrix}$,
$D(f/g)$
$= \begin{bmatrix} \dfrac{y(2y^6 - 6x^3 - 3x^2y^4)}{x^2(x^2 - 2y^2)^2} & \dfrac{3x^3 + 6xy^2 + 5x^2y^4 - 6y^6}{x(2y^2 - x^2)^2} \end{bmatrix}$

9. $f_{xx} = 6xy^7$, $f_{yy} = 42x^3y^5 + 6x$,
$f_{xy} = f_{yx} = 21x^2y^6 + 6y - 7$

11. $f_{xx} = -ye^{-x} + 2yx^{-3}e^{y/x} + y^2x^{-4}e^{y/x}$, $f_{yy} = x^{-2}e^{y/x}$,
$f_{xy} = f_{yx} = e^{-x} - x^{-2}e^{y/x} - yx^{-3}e^{y/x}$

13. $f_{xx} = \dfrac{2[\sin^2 2x - \cos 2x(\sin^2 x + 2e^y)]}{(\sin^2 x + 2e^y)^3}$,
$f_{yy} = \dfrac{2e^y(2e^y - \sin^2 x)}{(\sin^2 x + 2e^y)^3}$, $f_{xy} = f_{yx} = \dfrac{4e^y\sin 2x}{(\sin^2 x + 2e^y)^3}$

15. $f_{xx} = -y\sin x$, $f_{yy} = x\cos y$, $f_{xy} = f_{yx} = \cos x + \sin y$

17. $f_{xx} = 2e^y$, $f_{yy} = x^2 e^y$, $f_{zz} = 4e^{2z}$, $f_{xy} = f_{yx} = 2xe^y$, $f_{xz} = f_{zx} = 0$, $f_{yz} = f_{zy} = 0$

19. $f_{xx} = 2yz$, $f_{yy} = 2xz$, $f_{zz} = 2xy$, $f_{xy} = f_{yx} = 2xz + 2yz + z^2$, $f_{xz} = f_{zx} = 2xy + y^2 + 2yz$, $f_{yz} = f_{zy} = x^2 + 2xy + 2xz$

21. $f_{xx} = b^2 e^{bx} \cos z + a^2 e^{ax} \sin y$, $f_{yy} = -e^{ax} \sin y$, $f_{zz} = -e^{bx} \cos z$, $f_{xy} = f_{yx} = ae^{ax} \cos y$, $f_{xz} = f_{zx} = -be^{bx} \sin z$, $f_{yz} = f_{zy} = 0$

23. $\partial^n f/\partial x^n = 3^n y e^{3x}$, $\partial^n f/\partial y^n = 0$, for $n \geq 2$

25. $\partial^n f/\partial x^n = (-1)^{n-1}(n-1)!/x^n$, $\partial^n f/\partial y^n = (-1)^{n-1}(n-1)!/y^n$, $\partial^n f/\partial z^n = (-1)^n (n-1)!/z^n$. All mixed partials are zero.

27. (a) p_x and p_y have degree 16; p_{xx}, p_{yy}, and p_{xy} all have degree 15.
   (b) p_x and p_y have degree 3; p_{xx} has degree 2; p_{yy} has undefined degree; p_{xy} has degree 2.
   (c) The degree of $\partial^k p/\partial x_{i_1} \cdots \partial x_{i_k}$ is $d - k$, where d is the highest degree of a term of p of the form $x_1^{d_1} x_2^{d_2} \cdots x_n^{d_n}$ such that, for $j = 1, 2, \ldots, n$, d_j is at least the number of times x_j occurs in the partial derivative. If p has no such term, then the degree of $\partial^k p/\partial x_{i_1} \cdots \partial x_{i_k}$ is undefined.

29. (a)

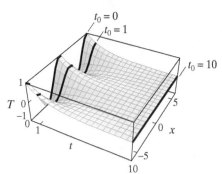

   (b)

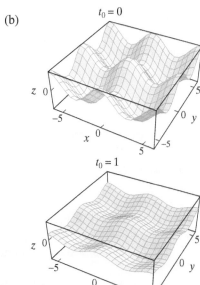

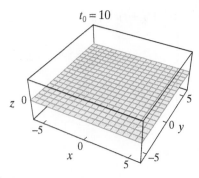

33. (a)

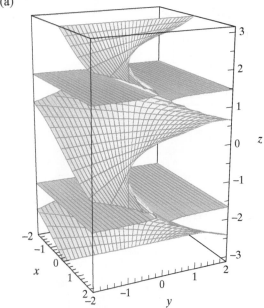

Section 2.5

1. $df/dt = (18t^2 + 14t) \sin 2t - 6 \cos 2t \sin^2 2t + (12t^3 + 14t^2) \cos 2t + 72t + 84$

2. $\partial f/\partial s = (3s^2 + t^2 + 2st) \cos((s+t)(s^2+t^2))$, $\partial f/\partial t = (s^2 + 3t^2 + 2st) \cos((s+t)(s^2+t^2))$

3. (a) $dP/dt = (36 - 27\pi)/\sqrt{2}$ atm/min
   (c) Approximately $(.36 + (9 - .27)\pi)/\sqrt{2} \approx 19.6477$ atm

5. -6 in^3/min. Decreasing.

7. 0.766 units/month

9. 0.2244 cm/min

13. Hint: $\partial w/\partial u = 2u(\partial w/\partial x) - 2u(\partial w/\partial y)$ from the chain rule.

15. Hint: $\partial w/\partial x = (dw/du)((y^3 - x^2 y)/(x^2 + y^2)^2)$ from the chain rule.

17. Hint: $\partial w/\partial x = -1/x^2(\partial w/\partial u + \partial w/\partial v)$ from the chain rule.

19. $D(\mathbf{f} \circ g) = \begin{bmatrix} 15(s - 7t)^4 & -105(s - 7t)^4 \\ 2e^{2s-14t} & -14e^{2s-14t} \end{bmatrix}$

21. $D(f \circ \mathbf{g}) = [(1 + s + t)e^{s-t} \quad (1 - s - t)e^{s-t}]$

23. $D(\mathbf{f} \circ \mathbf{g}) = \begin{bmatrix} 3s^2 - t^2 & -2st \\ 6s^5t^3 - s^{-2}t^{-2} & 3s^6t^2 - 2s^{-1}t^{-3} \end{bmatrix}$

25. $D(\mathbf{f} \circ \mathbf{g}) = \begin{bmatrix} e^{2t}(2\sin t + \cos t) \\ e^t(\sin^2 t + 2\sin t \cos t) \\ 3(\sin^2 t \cos t + e^{3t}) \end{bmatrix}$

27. $D(\mathbf{f} \circ \mathbf{g})$

$= \begin{bmatrix} t + u & s + u & s + t \\ 3s^2t^3 - tu^2e^{stu^2} & 3s^3t^2 - su^2e^{stu^2} & -2stue^{stu^2} \end{bmatrix}$

29. (a) $\begin{bmatrix} 7 & 10 \\ 31 & 44 \end{bmatrix}$

(b) $\begin{bmatrix} 1 & 13 \\ 2 & 31 \end{bmatrix}$

31. (a) $\dfrac{\partial^2}{\partial x^2} = \cos^2\theta \dfrac{\partial^2}{\partial r^2} + \dfrac{\sin^2\theta}{r}\dfrac{\partial}{\partial r} - \dfrac{2\sin\theta\cos\theta}{r}\dfrac{\partial^2}{\partial r\partial\theta}$

$+ \dfrac{2\sin\theta\cos\theta}{r^2}\dfrac{\partial}{\partial\theta} + \dfrac{\sin^2\theta}{r^2}\dfrac{\partial^2}{\partial\theta^2}$,

$\dfrac{\partial^2}{\partial y^2} = \sin^2\theta \dfrac{\partial^2}{\partial r^2} + \dfrac{\cos^2\theta}{r}\dfrac{\partial}{\partial r} + \dfrac{2\sin\theta\cos\theta}{r}\dfrac{\partial^2}{\partial r\partial\theta}$

$- \dfrac{2\sin\theta\cos\theta}{r^2}\dfrac{\partial}{\partial\theta} + \dfrac{\cos^2\theta}{r^2}\dfrac{\partial^2}{\partial\theta^2}$

33. (a) $\dfrac{\partial}{\partial r} = \sin\varphi\dfrac{\partial}{\partial\rho} + \dfrac{\cos\varphi}{\rho}\dfrac{\partial}{\partial\varphi}$

35. $dy/dx = (2xy^7 - y\cos xy)/(x\cos xy - 7x^2y^6 + e^y)$

37. $\partial z/\partial x = 3x^2z^3/(yz^2\sin z + \sin y - x^3z^2), \partial z/\partial y = (z^2\cos z + z\cos y)/(yz^2\sin z + \sin y - x^3z^2)$

39. (a) $\left(\dfrac{\partial w}{\partial x}\right)_{y,z} = 1, \left(\dfrac{\partial w}{\partial y}\right)_{x,z} = 7, \left(\dfrac{\partial w}{\partial z}\right)_{x,y}$

$= -10; \left(\dfrac{\partial w}{\partial x}\right)_y = 1 - 20x, \left(\dfrac{\partial w}{\partial y}\right)_x = 7 - 20y$

(b) $\left(\dfrac{\partial w}{\partial x}\right)_y = \left(\dfrac{\partial w}{\partial x}\right)_{y,z}\left(\dfrac{\partial x}{\partial x}\right)_y$

$+ \left(\dfrac{\partial w}{\partial y}\right)_{x,z}\left(\dfrac{\partial y}{\partial x}\right)_y + \left(\dfrac{\partial w}{\partial z}\right)_{x,y}\left(\dfrac{\partial z}{\partial x}\right)_y$

$= (1)(1) + (7)(0) + (-10)(2x)$

41. $\left(\dfrac{\partial s}{\partial z}\right)_{x,y,w} = xw - 2z;$

$\left(\dfrac{\partial s}{\partial z}\right)_{x,w} = xw - 2z + \dfrac{x^2y^3 - x^3}{xw - 3y^2z}$

Section 2.6

1. (a) The directional derivative of f at (x, y, z) in the negative z-direction.

(b) $\nabla f(x, y, z) \cdot (-\mathbf{k}) = -\partial f/\partial z$

3. $8\sqrt{5}/5$

5. $(2e - 9)\sqrt{5}/5$

7. $-4\sqrt{3}\,e^{-14}$

9. (a) $f_x(0, 0) = f_y(0, 0) = 0$

(b) $D_\mathbf{v} f(0, 0) = v|w|$ for all unit vectors $\mathbf{v} = v\,\mathbf{i} + w\,\mathbf{j}$.

(c)

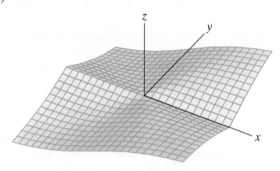

11. (a) $(-2\mathbf{i} + \mathbf{j})/\sqrt{5}$ direction

(b) $\pm(\mathbf{i} + 2\mathbf{j})/\sqrt{5}$ direction

13.

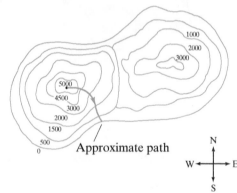

Approximate path

15. Travel along $y^3 = 27x$ (toward the origin)

17. $y - z = 1$ 19. $x - 2y - 2z = 2$

21. The tangent plane has equation $x - \pi z = 2$.

23. $\left(\frac{5}{4}, -\frac{5}{4}, -\frac{9}{2}\right)$ and $\left(-\frac{5}{4}, \frac{5}{4}, \frac{9}{2}\right)$

27. (a) $3x + 12y + 2z + 10 = 0$

(b) There is no tangent plane at $(0, 0, 0)$.

29. Tangent line is $5x - 3\sqrt[3]{4}\,y = -1$.

31. Parametric equations: $x = 5t + 5, y = 4t - 4$. Cartesian equation: $4x - 5y = 40$.

33. Parametric equations: $x = 14t + 2, y = t - 1$. Cartesian equation: $x - 14y = 16$.

35. $x = -2t - 1, y = t - 1, z = t - 1$

37. $x_5 - x_1 = \pi$

39. $x_1 + x_2 + \cdots + x_{n-1} - x_n = \sqrt{n}$

41. (a) Near all points of S such that $x \neq 0$. At such points
$f(x, y) = \ln(1 - \sin xy - x^3 y)/x$.
    (b) All points $(0, y, z)$ (i.e., the yz-plane).
    (c)

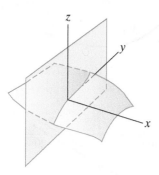

43. (b) Yes, $y = x^{2/3}$.

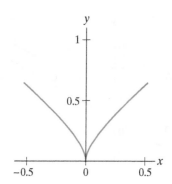

(c) The implicit function theorem suggests that we need not be able to solve for y in terms of x. Note that we can in this case, but that the function fails to be of class C^1 at $x = 0$.

45. (a) $G(-1, 1, 1) = F(-2, 1) = 0$
    (b) Hint: Use the chain rule to find $G_z(-1, 1, 1) = 30 \neq 0$.

47. (a) $\Delta(1, 0, -1, 1, 2) = -120 \neq 0$; apply the general implicit function theorem.
    (b) $\dfrac{\partial y_1}{\partial x_1}(1, 0) = -\dfrac{7}{5}, \dfrac{\partial y_2}{\partial x_1}(1, 0) = -\dfrac{1}{2}, \dfrac{\partial y_3}{\partial x_1}(1, 0) = -1$

49. (a) Anywhere except where $\varphi = 0$ or π.
    (b) We can solve anywhere except along the z-axis, which is where θ can have any value.

Section 2.7

1. $(1.302942538, -0.902880451)$

3. (a) Estimate intersection points near $(1, 1/2)$ and $(-1/2, -3/4)$.

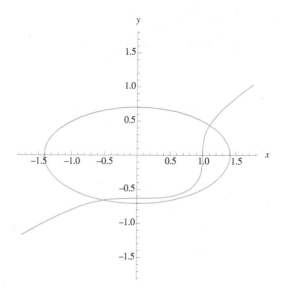

(b) $(1.103931711, 0.441965716)$ and $(-0.518214315, -0.657923613)$

5. (a) $\mathbf{x}_0 = (-1, 1)$ leads to $(-1.2649111, 1.54919334)$.
   (b) $\mathbf{x}_0 = (1, -1)$ leads to $(1.26491106, -1.5491933)$, while $\mathbf{x}_0 = (-1, -1)$ leads to $(-1.2649111, -1.5491933)$.
   (c) It appears that an initial vector leads to an intersection point that lies in the same quadrant.

9. $(-0.9070154, -0.9070154)$

True/False Exercises for Chapter 2

1. False

3. False. (The range also requires $v \neq 0$.)

5. True

7. False. (The graph of $x^2 + y^2 + z^2 = 0$ is a single point.)

9. False

11. False. ($\lim_{(x,y)\to(0,0)} f(x, y) = 0 \neq 2$.)

13. False

15. False. ($\nabla f(x, y, z) = (0, \cos y, 0)$.)

17. True

19. False. (The partial derivatives must be continuous.)

21. False. ($f_{xy} \neq f_{yx}$.)

23. True. (Write the chain rule for this situation.)

25. False. (The correct equation is $x + y + 2z = 2$.)

27. True   29. False

Miscellaneous Exercises for Chapter 2

1.(a) $f_1(\mathbf{x}) = -x_2$, $f_2(\mathbf{x}) = x_1 - x_3$, $f_3(\mathbf{x}) = x_2$
   (b) Domain is $\mathbf{R}^3$; range consists of all vectors in $\mathbf{R}^3$ of the form $a\,\mathbf{i} + b\,\mathbf{j} - a\,\mathbf{k}$.

3. (a) Domain: $\{(x, y) \mid x \geq 0,\ y \geq 0\} \cup \{(x, y) \mid x < 0,\ y < 0\}$
   Range: $[0, \infty)$

   (b) Domain is closed.

5.

$f(x, y) =$	Graph	Level curves
$\dfrac{1}{x^2 + y^2 + 1}$	D	d
$\sin\sqrt{x^2 + y^2}$	B	e
$(3y^2 - 2x^2)e^{-x^2 - 2y^2}$	A	b
$y^3 - 3x^2 y$	E	c
$x^2 y^2 e^{-x^2 - 2y^2}$	F	a
$ye^{-x^2 - y^2}$	C	f

7. 0

11. (a) 15°F
    (b) 5°F

13. 1.3

15. (a) 9.57°F; 16.87°F; 8.39 mph
    (b) Effect of windspeed is greater in the Siple formula than in the table.
    (c) If $t < 91.4°F$ or $s \geq 4$ mph, the Siple formula gives windchill values that are higher than the air temperature, which is unrealistic.

17. (a)

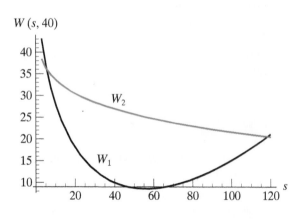

(b)

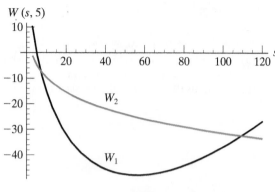

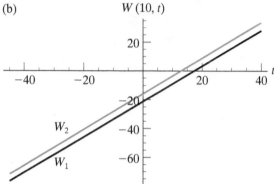

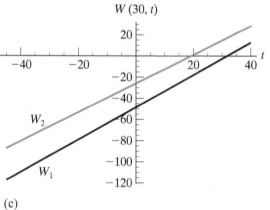

(c)

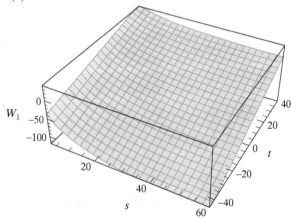

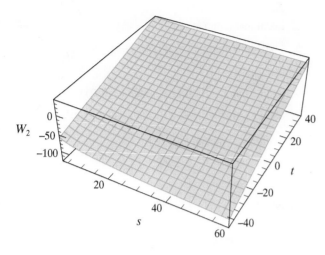

(c) $\partial f/\partial x = (x^4 + 6x^2y^2 - 3y^4)/(x^2 + y^2)^2,$
$\partial f/\partial y = -8x^3y/(x^2 + y^2)^2$ (if $(x, y) \neq (0, 0)$);
$f_x(0, 0) = 1$, $f_y(0, 0) = 0$

(d) $D_{\mathbf{u}}f(0, 0) = (\partial f/\partial r)|_{r=0} = \cos 3\theta$

(e) $f_y(0, 0) = 0$ from (c), but along $y = x$, $f_y(x, x) = -2$, which does not have a limit of 0.

(f)

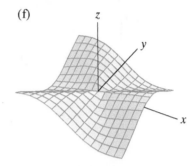

37. Homogeneous of degree 3
39. Homogeneous of degree 3
41. Homogeneous of degree 0

19. Hint: Compare the normal vector to the tangent plane with the vector $\overrightarrow{OP}$.

21. (a) $3x - 4y - 5z = 0$
    (b) $ax + by - cz = 0$

23. (a) $2x - 8y - z = 5$
    (b) $x = 1, y = t - 1, z = 5 - 8t$

25. 12, 201.4 units/month

27. (a) $\partial w/\partial \rho = 2\rho$, $\partial w/\partial \varphi = \partial w/\partial \theta = 0$

29. (a) $\partial z/\partial r = e^r(\cos\theta(\partial z/\partial x) + \sin\theta(\partial z/\partial y))$,
    $\partial z/\partial \theta = e^r(-\sin\theta(\partial z/\partial x) + \cos\theta(\partial z/\partial y))$;
    $\partial z/\partial x = e^{-r}(\cos\theta(\partial z/\partial r) - \sin\theta(\partial z/\partial\theta))$,
    $\partial z/\partial y = e^{-r}(\sin\theta(\partial z/\partial r) + \cos\theta(\partial z/\partial\theta))$

    (b) Hint: $\partial^2 z/\partial x^2 = e^{-2r}(\cos^2\theta(\partial^2 z/\partial r^2)$
    $+ (\sin^2\theta - \cos^2\theta)(\partial z/\partial r)$
    $+ 2\cos\theta\sin\theta(\partial z/\partial\theta)$
    $- 2\cos\theta\sin\theta(\partial^2 z/\partial r\partial\theta)$
    $+ \sin^2\theta(\partial^2 z/\partial\theta^2))$,

    $\partial^2 z/\partial y^2 = e^{-2r}(\sin^2\theta(\partial^2 z/\partial r^2)$
    $+ (\cos^2\theta - \sin^2\theta)(\partial z/\partial r)$
    $- 2\sin\theta\cos\theta(\partial z/\partial\theta)$
    $+ 2\sin\theta\cos\theta(\partial^2 z/\partial r\partial\theta)$
    $+ \cos^2\theta(\partial^2 z/\partial\theta^2))$

31. $u^u\left[u^{(u^u-1)} + u^{u^u}\ln u + u^{u^u}(\ln u)^2\right]$

35. (a) $z = f(x, y)$, where $f(x, y) = (x^3 - 3xy^2)/(x^2 + y^2)$ if $(x, y) \neq (0, 0)$; $f(x, y) = 0$ if $(x, y) = (0, 0)$
    (b) Yes

Chapter 4

Section 4.1

1. $p_4(x) = 1 + 2x + 2x^2 + 4x^3/3 + 2x^4/3$

3. $p_4(x) = 1 - 2(x - 1) + 3(x - 1)^2 - 4(x - 1)^3 + 5(x - 1)^4$

5. $p_3(x) = 3 + (x - 9)/6 - (x - 9)^2/216 + (x - 9)^3/3888$

7. $p_5(x) = 1 - (x - \pi/2)^2/2 + (x - \pi/2)^4/24$

9. $p_1(x, y) = \frac{1}{3} - 2(x - 1)/9 + 2(y + 1)/9$,
   $p_2(x, y) = \frac{1}{3} - 2(x - 1)/9 + 2(y + 1)/9 + (x - 1)^2/27 - 8(x - 1)(y + 1)/27 + (y + 1)^2/27$

11. $p_1(x, y) = -1 - 2x$,
    $p_2(x, y) = -1 - 2x - 2x^2 + 9(y - \pi)^2/2$

13. $p_1(x, y, z) = 1 + x + 8y + 4z$, $\quad p_2(x, y, z) = xy - 3y^2 + 2xz$

15. $p_1(x, y, z) = p_2(x, y, z) \equiv 0$

17. $\begin{bmatrix} -\frac{\sqrt{6}}{4} & -\frac{\sqrt{2}}{4} \\ -\frac{\sqrt{2}}{4} & -\frac{\sqrt{6}}{4} \end{bmatrix}$

19. $\begin{bmatrix} 6 & 2 & 0 \\ 2 & 0 & -2 \\ 0 & -2 & 12 \end{bmatrix}$

21. $p_2(x, y) = 1 + \begin{bmatrix} 0 & 0 \end{bmatrix} \begin{bmatrix} x \\ y \end{bmatrix}$

$+ \frac{1}{2} \begin{bmatrix} x & y \end{bmatrix} \begin{bmatrix} -2 & 0 \\ 0 & -2 \end{bmatrix} \begin{bmatrix} x \\ y \end{bmatrix}$

23. $p_2(x, y, z) = 2 + \begin{bmatrix} 0 & 5 & 1 \end{bmatrix} \begin{bmatrix} x \\ y \\ z - 2 \end{bmatrix}$

$+ \frac{1}{2} \begin{bmatrix} x & y & z-2 \end{bmatrix} \begin{bmatrix} 0 & 3 & 0 \\ 3 & 8 & 2 \\ 0 & 2 & 0 \end{bmatrix} \begin{bmatrix} x \\ y \\ z - 2 \end{bmatrix}$

25. (a) $Df(\mathbf{0}) = \begin{bmatrix} 1 & 2 & \cdots & n \end{bmatrix}$,

$Hf(\mathbf{0}) = \begin{bmatrix} 1 & 2 & 3 & \cdots & n \\ 2 & 4 & 6 & \cdots & 2n \\ 3 & 6 & 9 & \cdots & 3n \\ \vdots & \vdots & \vdots & \ddots & \vdots \\ n & 2n & 3n & \cdots & n^2 \end{bmatrix}$

(b) $p_1(x_1, \ldots, x_n) = 1 + x_1 + 2x_2 + \cdots + nx_n$

$p_2(x_1, \ldots, x_n) = 1 + \sum_{i=1}^{n} i x_i + \frac{1}{2} \sum_{i,j=1}^{n} i j x_i x_j$

27. (a) $2 - z + 3xy + x^2 y - xz^2 + 2y^3$
   (b) $-4 - 4(x - 1) + 11(y + 1) - z + \frac{1}{2}[4(x - 1)^2 +$
   $16(x - 1)(y + 1) - 12(y + 1)^2 - 2z^2] +$
   $\frac{1}{6}[18(x - 1)^3 + 24(x - 1)^2(y + 1) - 6(x - 1)z^2 +$
   $12(y + 1)^3]$

29. $2x\, dx + 6y\, dy - 6z^2 dz$

31. $e^x \cos y\, dx + (e^y \sin z - e^x \sin y)\, dy + e^y \cos z\, dz$

33. (a) 388.08   (b) 0.24625   (c) 1.1

35. The (1, 1)-entry (upper left)

37. 2.4 cm

39. 0.0068 m

41. (a) $p_2(x, y) = 1 - \frac{1}{2}[x^2 + (y - \frac{\pi}{2})^2]$
   (b) Accurate to at least 0.0360

43. (a) $p_2(x, y) = \frac{\pi}{2} - y - 2x(y - \frac{\pi}{2})$
   (b) Accurate to at least 0.0311

Section 4.2

1. (a) $(2, 3)$
   (b) $\Delta f = -h^2 - k^2$
   (c) There is a local maximum at $(2, 3)$.

3. Local maximum at $\left(\frac{2}{9}, \frac{4}{9}\right)$

5. Local minimum at $\left(\frac{27}{2}, 5\right)$; saddle point at $\left(\frac{3}{2}, 1\right)$

7. Minimum at $\left(4, \frac{1}{2}\right)$

9. Saddle point at $(0, 0)$; minimum at $(0, 2)$

11. Saddle point at $\left(0, \frac{1}{\sqrt{3}}\right)$; local minimum at $\left(0, -\frac{1}{\sqrt{3}}\right)$

13. Local maximum at $\left(-\frac{1}{2}, \frac{1}{3}\right)$

15. Saddle point at $(0, 6, -3)$

17. Local minimum at $(0, 0, 0)$

19. Saddle point at $\left(-1, \frac{1}{2}, \frac{1}{2}\right)$

21. (a) $(0, -2)$ and $(0, 3)$
   (b) Local maximum at $(0, -2)$;
       local minimum at $(0, 3)$

23. (a) Minimum if $a, b > 0$; maximum if $a, b < 0$; saddle point otherwise
   (b) Minimum if $a, b, c > 0$; maximum if $a, b, c < 0$; saddle point otherwise
   (c) Minimum if $a_1, \ldots, a_n > 0$; maximum if $a_1, \ldots, a_n < 0$; saddle point otherwise

25. Saddle points at $(0, 0)$, $\left(\pm\sqrt{\frac{3}{2}}, 0\right)$; local maxima at $\left(\frac{1}{\sqrt{2}}, -\frac{1}{\sqrt{2}}\right), \left(-\frac{1}{\sqrt{2}}, \frac{1}{\sqrt{2}}\right)$

27. Saddle points at $(0, 0, 0, 0)$, $(-\sqrt{2}, 2\sqrt{2}, 1, -\sqrt{2})$, $(\sqrt{2}, 2\sqrt{2}, -1, -\sqrt{2})$ $(-\sqrt{2}, -2\sqrt{2}, -1, \sqrt{2})$, $(\sqrt{2}, -2\sqrt{2}, 1, \sqrt{2})$

29. $\left(\frac{36}{13}, -\frac{48}{13}, -\frac{12}{13}\right)$

31. 1100 units of model X and 700 units of model Y

33. Maximum of 8 at $(0, 0, 2)$;
   minimum of $-\frac{191}{7}$ at $\left(-\frac{32}{7}, 3, \frac{8}{7}\right)$

35. Maximum of 1 at $(\pi/2, 0)$, $(\pi/2, 2\pi)$, $(3\pi/2, \pi)$;
   minimum of -1 at $(3\pi/2, 0)$, $(3\pi/2, 2\pi)$, $(\pi/2, \pi)$

37. Maximum of 11 at $(2, 0)$; minimum of $\frac{5}{2}$ at $\left(\frac{1}{2}, 1\right)$

39. Maximum of e^6 at $(0, 1, -2)$; minimum of e at all (x, y, z) such that $x^2 + y^2 - 2y + z^2 + 4z = 0$

41. (b) Maximum

43. (b) Neither

45. (b) Maximum

47. (a) Local maximum at $(0, 0, 0)$
   (b) $f(0, 0, 0) = e^2$ is a global maximum.

49. Global minimum of $2 + \ln 2$ at $\left(2, \frac{1}{2}\right)$. No global maximum.

51. (a) $\{(1, y)|y \in \mathbf{R}\} \cup \{(x, 2)|x \in \mathbf{R}\}$
   (b) Maxima of 3 along critical points in (a).

53. (b) Critical points are $(2, 1)$ and $(0, -1)$.

(c)

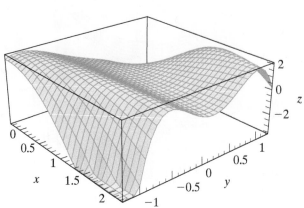

Section 4.3

1. (a) Minimize $f(x, y) = x^2 + y^2 + (2x - 3y - 4)^2$ to find that the closest point is $\left(\frac{4}{7}, -\frac{6}{7}, -\frac{2}{7}\right)$.

   (b) Minimize $f(x, y, z) = x^2 + y^2 + z^2$ subject to $2x - 3y - z = 4$.

3. $(\sqrt{2}, \sqrt{2})$ and $(-\sqrt{2}, -\sqrt{2})$

5. $\left(1, \frac{2}{3}, 2\right)$, $(3, 0, 0)$, $(0, 2, 0)$ and $(0, 0, 6)$

7. $\left(\frac{8}{11}, \frac{2}{11}, \frac{4}{11}\right)$

9. $\left(\frac{4}{3}, \frac{2}{3}, -\frac{4}{3}\right)$

11. $\left(\pm\frac{1}{\sqrt{2}}, \frac{1}{\sqrt{2}}, \sqrt{2}\right)$ and $\left(\pm\frac{1}{\sqrt{2}}, -\frac{1}{\sqrt{2}}, -\sqrt{2}\right)$

13. (a) $\left(\pm\sqrt{\frac{7}{8}}, \frac{1}{4}\right)$, $\left(0, \pm\frac{1}{\sqrt{2}}\right)$

    (b) $\left(\pm\sqrt{\frac{7}{8}}, \frac{1}{4}\right)$ give maxima; $\left(0, \pm\frac{1}{\sqrt{2}}\right)$ give minima.

15. $\left(\sqrt{\frac{2}{3}}, \frac{1}{2}, \frac{12-\sqrt{6}}{8}\right)$, $\left(-\sqrt{\frac{2}{3}}, \frac{1}{2}, \frac{12+\sqrt{6}}{8}\right)$

17. $(\pm 1, 0, 0)$, $(0, \pm 1, 0)$, $(0, 0, \pm 1)$, $\left(\frac{2}{3}, -\frac{2}{3}, \frac{1}{3}\right)$, $\left(-\frac{2}{3}, -\frac{2}{3}, -\frac{1}{3}\right)$,

    $\left(\frac{1}{8}\sqrt{\frac{11}{2}}, -\frac{3}{8}, -\frac{3}{8}\sqrt{\frac{11}{2}}\right)$, $\left(-\frac{1}{8}\sqrt{\frac{11}{2}}, -\frac{3}{8}, \frac{3}{8}\sqrt{\frac{11}{2}}\right)$

19. $\left(\frac{1}{\sqrt{2}}, \frac{1}{\sqrt{2}}, \frac{1-\sqrt{2}}{2}, \frac{1-\sqrt{2}}{2}\right)$, $\left(-\frac{1}{\sqrt{2}}, -\frac{1}{\sqrt{2}}, \frac{1+\sqrt{2}}{2}, \frac{1+\sqrt{2}}{2}\right)$

21. The numbers are 6, 6, 6.

23. Maximum value: 6. Minimum value: 0.

25. Height should be equal to diameter.

27. Locate at either $(-2, 2, 1)$ or $(-2, -2, 1)$.

29. Largest sphere has equation $x^2 + y^2 + z^2 = 2$.

31. $\left(\frac{9}{2}, 2, \frac{5}{2}\right)$

33. Highest point is $(-1, -1, 2)$; lowest point is $\left(\frac{1}{2}, \frac{1}{2}, \frac{1}{2}\right)$.

35. (a) $(\sqrt{6}, \sqrt{6})$ and $(-\sqrt{6}, -\sqrt{6})$

39. Nearest points are $(\sqrt{5}, -\sqrt{5})$ and $(-\sqrt{5}, \sqrt{5})$; farthest points are $(5, 5)$ and $(-5, -5)$.

41. (a) Critical point at $(1, 0)$

    (b) There is a minimum of 0 at $(0, 0)$ and a maximum of 1 at $(1, 0)$.

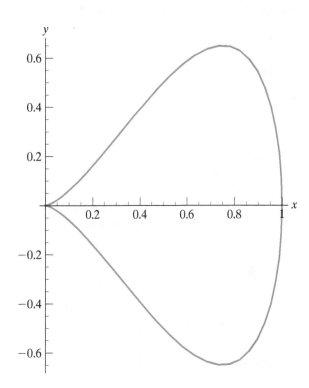

    (c) $\nabla g = \mathbf{0}$ at $(0, 0)$

43. (a) Hint: Check that $\partial L / \partial l_i = c_i - g_i(\mathbf{x})$ for $i = 1, \ldots, k$ and

$$\frac{\partial L}{\partial x_j} = \frac{\partial f}{\partial x_j} - \sum_{i=1}^{k} l_i \frac{\partial g_i}{\partial x_j}$$

    for $j = 1, \ldots, n$.

Section 4.4

1. $5x - 7y + 14 = 0$

3. (a) $D(a, b) = \sum_{i=1}^{n}(y_i - (a/x_i + b))^2$

   (b) Minimize D with respect to a and b.

5. Hint: Let $D(a, b, c) = \sum_{i=1}^{n}(y_i - (ax_i^2 + bx_i + c))^2$.

7. (b) There is a single, stable equilibrium point at $\left(-\frac{1}{4}, -\frac{1}{4}\right)$.

9. Single equilibrium point at $\left(-1, \frac{3}{2}, \frac{3}{2}\right)$. There are no stable equilibria.

11. Produce 50,000 each of both the standard and executive models and 100,000 deluxe models.

13. Irrigate only; Purchase $3333.\overline{3}$ gal of water.

15. (a) Invest $120,000 for capital equipment and $240,000 for labor.
    (b) Hint: Note that $L/K = 2$.

True/False Exercises for Chapter 4

1. True
3. True
5. True
7. False. (f is most sensitive to changes in y.)
9. False
11. True
13. False. (Consider the function $f(x, y) = x^2 + y^2$.)
15. True
17. False. (The point is not a critical point of the function.)
19. True
21. False. (The critical point is a saddle point.)
23. False. (Extrema may also occur at points where $g = c$ and $\nabla g = \mathbf{0}$.)
25. False. (You will have to solve a system of 7 equations in 7 unknowns.)
27. True
29. False. (The equilibrium points are the critical points of the potential function.)

Miscellaneous Exercises for Chapter 4

1. $r_0 = 2h_0$
3. Price the Mocha at $2.70 per pound and the Kona at $5 per pound.
5. Maximum value of 4 at $(1, -\sqrt{3}, 0)$. Minimum value of -4 at $(-1, \sqrt{3}, 0)$.
7. (e)

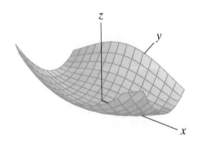

9. (a) $(0, 0, \pm 1)$, $\left(\frac{1}{\sqrt{2}}, \frac{1}{\sqrt{2}}, 0\right)$, $\left(\frac{1}{\sqrt{2}}, -\frac{1}{\sqrt{2}}, 0\right)$, $\left(-\frac{1}{\sqrt{2}}, \frac{1}{\sqrt{2}}, 0\right)$, $\left(-\frac{1}{\sqrt{2}}, -\frac{1}{\sqrt{2}}, 0\right)$

(b)

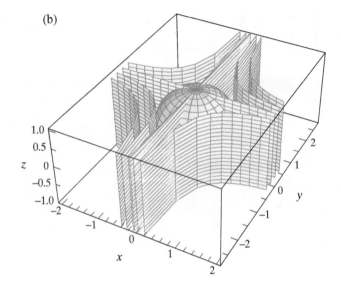

(c) Maxima at $\left(\frac{1}{\sqrt{2}}, \frac{1}{\sqrt{2}}, 0\right)$, $\left(-\frac{1}{\sqrt{2}}, -\frac{1}{\sqrt{2}}, 0\right)$; minima at $\left(\frac{1}{\sqrt{2}}, -\frac{1}{\sqrt{2}}, 0\right)$, $\left(-\frac{1}{\sqrt{2}}, \frac{1}{\sqrt{2}}, 0\right)$; saddle points at $(0, 0, \pm 1)$

11. $1/(a_1^2 + a_2^2 + \cdots + a_n^2)$

13. Dimensions are 4 (x-direction) by $2\sqrt{2}$ (y-direction) by 2 (z-direction).

15. 1

17. $a/3$ by $b/3$ by $c/3$

19. $3\sqrt{5}/8$

21. Hint: Minimize $D^2 = (x - x_0)^2 + (y - y_0)^2$, where (x, y) denotes a point on the line $ax + by = d$.

23. (a) Hint: Show that the maximum value occurs when $x^2 = y^2 = z^2 = a^2/3$.
    (b) Since $f(x, y, z) = x^2 y^2 z^2$ is maximized when $x^2 = y^2 = z^2 = a^2/3$, we must have $x^2 y^2 z^2 \leq (a^2/3)^3 = ((x^2 + y^2 + z^2)/3)^3$.
    (c) Hint: Since $x_1, x_2, \ldots, x_n$ are assumed to be positive, we can write $x_i = y_i^2$ for $i = 1, \ldots, n$. Maximize $f(y_1, y_2, \ldots, y_n) = y_1^2 y_2^2 \cdots y_n^2$ subject to $y_1^2 + y_2^2 + \cdots + y_n^2 = a^2$.

25. (a) $\lambda_1, \lambda_2 = \dfrac{(a + c) \pm \sqrt{(a + c)^2 - 4(ac - b^2)}}{2}$
    (b) Rewrite as $\lambda_1, \lambda_2 = \dfrac{(a + c) \pm \sqrt{(a - c)^2 + 4b^2}}{2}$.

Index